FERGUSON

CAREER RESOURCE GUIDE TO

APPRENTICESHIP

PROGRAMS

Third Edition

VOLUME 2

Edited by
Elizabeth H. Oakes

Ferguson
An imprint of Infobase Publishing

Ferguson Career Resource Guide to Apprenticeship Programs, Third Edition

Copyright © 2006 by Infobase Publishing

Ferguson
An imprint of Infobase Publishing
132 West 31st Street
New York NY 10001

Library of Congress Cataloging-in-Publication Data
Ferguson career resource guide to apprenticeship programs / edited by Elizabeth H. Oakes.— 3rd ed.
    p. cm.
   Rev. ed. of: Ferguson's guide to apprenticeship programs. 2nd ed. 1998
   Includes index.
   ISBN 0-8160-5573-4 (set) (hc : alk. paper)
   ISBN 0-8160-6203-X (vol. 1)— ISBN 0-8160-6204-8 (vol. 2)
1. Apprenticeship programs—United States—Directories. 2. Occupational training—United States—Directories. I. Oakes, Elizabeth H., 1964– II. Ferguson's Guide to apprenticeship programs.
   HD4885.U5F47 2006
   331.25'92202573—dc22

Text design by David Strelecky
Cover design by Salvatore Luongo

Printed in the United States of America

VB FOF 10 9 8 7 6 5 4 3 2 1

This book is printed on acid-free paper.

CONTENTS

APPRENTICESHIPS BY ELIGIBILITY

SCHOOLS, JOB CENTERS, AND ADMINISTRATIVE OFFICES

PART IV: FURTHER RESOURCES

PART III
DIRECTORY

APPRENTICESHIPS
BY CAREER FIELD

MEDICAL LABORATORY TECHNICIANS

RELATED SECTIONS: *health care workers, emergency services technicians, dispensing opticians*

Various specializations fall under the general umbrella of the *medical laboratory technician and technologist* field. Individuals may become *cytotechnologists, histotechnologists, medical technologists, histotechnicians,* and *phlebotomists,* to name the most common occupations. While the specific training and work responsibilities vary based on the specialization, all of these occupations are focused on the detection, diagnosis, and treatment of disease through laboratory testing. In general, medical laboratory technicians perform less complex tests and laboratory procedures than medical laboratory technologists. Technicians may prepare specimens and operate automated analyzers, for example, or they may perform manual tests in accordance with detailed instructions. Like technologists, they may work in several areas of the clinical laboratory or specialize in just one. Histotechnicians cut and stain tissue specimens for microscopic examination by pathologists, and phlebotomists collect blood samples. They usually work under the supervision of medical and clinical laboratory technologists or laboratory managers.

Medical laboratory technicians use a microscope to examine tissues, cells, and body fluids, such as blood, urine, and cerebro-spinal fluid. They search for bacteria, parasites, and other microorganisms; analyze the chemical content of fluids; match blood for transfusions; and test for drug levels in the blood to show how a patient is responding to treatment. Technicians may also prepare specimens for examination, count cells, and look for abnormal cells. They use automated equipment and instruments capable of performing a number of tests simultaneously, as well as microscopes, cell counters, and other sophisticated laboratory equipment. Then they analyze the results and report them to the physicians. With increasing automation and the use of computer technology, there is less actual hands-on work and more analysis involved in the technician's job.

Technicians are also responsible for establishing and monitoring programs to ensure the accuracy of tests and for modifying procedures as necessary in response to advances in medical research. Some medical technicians are responsible for supervising other technicians, which entails additional managerial work.

Medical laboratory technicians are employed in a variety of settings. Their hours and other working conditions vary accordingly. Some work in large hospitals or in independent laboratories that are based inside large hospitals. In these settings, the laboratory usually operates continuously, which means that technicians may work the day, evening, or night shifts. They may also work weekends and holidays. Those who work in small labs may work on rotating shifts instead of on regular shifts. In some situations, laboratory employees may be on call several nights a week or on weekends.

Medical laboratory technicians work with infectious specimens. They are well trained in proper methods of infection control and sterilization, so few hazards exist. But if proper procedures are not followed, such as wearing protective masks, gloves, and goggles, their safety is at risk.

Medical laboratories are clean and well-lighted, but the presence of specimens and solutions used in testing sometimes produces unpleasant fumes. In addition, medical laboratory technicians often spend a great deal of time on their feet.

The education requirements vary, depending upon the specific occupation, but in general there are fewer education requirements for medical laboratory technicians than there are for technologists. Many technicians have either an associate's degree from a community or junior college or a certificate from a hospital, a vocational or technical school, or one of the U.S. Armed Forces. A few technicians learn their skills on the job. Technologists generally have a bachelor's degree. Technicians who want to become technologists may do so through additional training and education.

The National Accrediting Agency for Clinical Laboratory Sciences (NAACLS) fully accredits 467 programs for medical and clinical laboratory technologists, medical and clinical laboratory technicians, histotechnologists and histotechnicians, cytogenetic technologists, and diagnostic molecular scientists. Other nationally recognized accrediting agencies that accredit specific areas for clinical laboratory workers include the Commission on Accreditation of Allied Health Education Programs and the Accrediting Bureau of Health Education Schools.

In some states, medical laboratory technicians must be licensed or registered. Specific requirements for licensure are available from the state department of health or the board of occupational licensing. In addition to possible licensing requirements, certification is a standard in the field and a prerequisite for most employment and advancement within the field. A voluntary process, certification is usually granted by a nongovernmental organization, such as a professional society or certifying agency, and is based on the individual meeting a set of prescribed standards that determine professional competence. Agencies that certify medical laboratory technicians include the Board of Registry of the American Society for Clinical Pathology, the American Medical Technologists, the National Credentialing Agency for Laboratory Personnel, and the Board of Registry of the American Association of Bioanalysts. Each agency has its own set of requirements for certification and different organizational sponsors.

In general an applicant should

- be a high school graduate or hold a GED certificate
- be good at working under pressure
- have good analytical skills
- be very precise and detail-oriented
- have excellent manual dexterity and normal color vision
- have good computer skills

Clinical laboratory technologists and technicians held about 297,000 jobs in 2002. More than half of jobs were in hospitals. Most of the remaining jobs were in offices of physicians and in medical and diagnostic laboratories. A small proportion was in educational services; other ambulatory healthcare services, including blood and organ banks; outpatient care centers; and scientific research and development services.

APPRENTICESHIP SALARIES

Salaries vary during training. Medical technicians who learn on the job while employed by a lab may earn as much 60 percent of the skilled worker's wage. The majority of medical technicians, however, learn their trade in a two-year associate's degree program in which the second year of study involves clinical rotations, or on-the-job training, but the student does not usually earn a salary at this time.

POSTAPPRENTICESHIP SALARIES

Medical laboratory technicians usually earn around $30,000 a year, with the lowest paid technicians earning just under $20,000 a year, and the highest paid technicians earning more than $44,000. Salaries vary for technicians depending upon the employer, the geographic area

in which they work, and the employee's experience and training. Hospitals generally pay technicians the highest wages, followed by colleges and universities, physicians' offices, medical laboratories, and other ambulatory health care services.

JOB OUTLOOK

This occupation is expected to grow about as fast as the average for all occupations through the year 2012.

For more information on training to become a medical laboratory technician, please contact the individual programs listed below.

For a list of accredited and approved educational programs for clinical laboratory personnel, contact
**National Accrediting Agency for Clinical
Laboratory Sciences**
8410 West Bryn Mawr Avenue, Suite 670
Chicago, IL 60631
773-714-8880
Fax: 773-714-8886
info@naacls.org
http://www.naacls.org

Information on certification is available from the following organizations:
American Association of Bioanalysts
Board of Registry
917 Locust Street, Suite 1100
St. Louis, MO 63101
314-241-1445
Fax: 314-241-1449
aab@aab.org
http://www.aab.org

American Association of Blood Banks
8101 Glenbrook Road
Bethesda, MD 20814-2749
http://www.aabb.org

American Medical Technologists
710 Higgins Road
Park Ridge, IL 60068
847-823-5169
Fax: 847-823-0458
http://www.amt1.com

American Society for Clinical Laboratory Science
6701 Democracy Boulevard, Suite 300
Bethesda, MD 20817

301-657-2768
Fax: 301-657-2909
ascls@ascls.org
http://www.ascls.org

American Society for Clinical Pathology
Board of Registry
2100 West Harrison Street
Chicago, IL 60612
312-738-1336
info@ascp.org
http://www.ascp.org/bor

American Society for Cytopathology
400 West 9th Street, Suite 201
Wilmington, DE 19801
302-429-8802
Fax: 302-429-8807
http://www.cytopathology.org

Clinical Laboratory Management Association
989 Old Eagle School Road
Wayne, PA 19087
610-995-9580
Fax: 610-995-9568
http://www.clma.org

National Credentialing Agency for Laboratory Personnel
PO Box 15945-289
Lenexa, KS 66285
913-438-5110, ext. 4647
Fax: 913-599-5340
nca-info@goamp.com
http://www.nca-info.org

Additional career information is available from the following sources:

CANADA
Alberta College of Medical Laboratory Technologists (ACMLT)
Whitemud Business Park, #105, Bldg. #1, 4245 - 97 Street
Edmonton, AB T6E 5Y7
780-435-5452
Fax: 780-437-1442
info@acmlt.org
http://www.acmlt.org

Canadian Society for Medical Laboratory Science (CSMLS)
PO Box 2830
Hamilton, ON L8N 3N8
905-528-8642
Fax: 905-528-4968
Alison@csmls.org
http://www.csmls.org/english/english.htm

College of Medical Laboratory Technologists of Ontario (CMLTO)
10 Bay Street, Suite 330
Toronto, ON M5J 2R8
416-861-9605
Fax: 416-861-0934
kwilkie@cmlto.com
http://www.cmlto.com

Manitoba Society of Medical Laboratory Technologists (MSMLT)
585 London Street
Winnipeg, MB R2K 2Z6
204-669-9050
Fax: 204-667-1747
msmlt@mb.sympatico.ca
http://www.msmlt.mb.ca

New Brunswick Society of Medical Laboratory Technologists (NBSMLT)
PO Box 20180
Fredericton NB E3B 7A2
506-455-9540
Fax: 506-455-7491
jkingst@nbsmlt.nb.ca
http://www.nbsmlt.nb.ca

Newfoundland and Labrador Society of Laboratory Technologists (NLSLT)
PO Box 39057, 430 Topsail Road
St. John's, NF A1E 5Y7
709-754-8324
http://students.northatlantic.nf.ca/~nlslt

Ontario Society of Medical Technologists (OSMT)
234 Eglinton Avenue East, Suite 402
Toronto, ON M4P 1K5
416-485-6768
Fax: 416-485-7660
osmt@osmt.org
http://www.osmt.org

Ordre professionnel des technologistes médicaux du Québec (OPTMQ)
1150, boul. St-Joseph Est, bureau 300
Montréal, QC H2J 1L5
514-527-9811
Fax: 514-527-7314
optmq@qc.aira.com
http://www.optmq.org

Prince Edward Island Society of Medical Technologists (PEISMT)
Prince County Hospital, 259 Beattie Avenue
Summerside, Prince EE C1N 2A9

Saskatchewan Society of Medical Laboratory Technologists (SSMLT)
Box 3837
Regina, SK S4P 3R8
306-352-6791
Fax: 306-352-6791
ssmlt@sk.sympatico.ca
http://www.ssmlt.sk.ca

APPRENTICESHIP PROFILE
Valdosta Technical College
4089 Val Tech Road
Valdosta, GA 31602-0929
229-259-5567
arobinson@valdostatech.edu
http://www.valdostatech.edu

General Nature of the Job
A student training to become a medical laboratory technician may learn their skills and gain the knowledge needed to succeed in this occupation through on-the-job training or some combination of education and on-the-job training, which usually takes the form of a two-year associate's degree program in medical laboratory technology at a technical or vocational school or a community college. According to Margaret Brown, a student in the medical laboratory technology program at Valdosta Technical College needs to enjoy detail-oriented activities and working in a clinical setting. "You need to be able to spend long hours monitoring automated equipment as it tests blood, for example, which can be tedious, but you also need to be able to deal compassionately with the public."

During the two-year program, the student must complete 122 credit hours, which has to include such courses as chemistry, algebra, technical communications, funda-

mentals of speech, and psychology. The occupational courses in the program include anatomy & physiology, serology/immunology, clinical chemistry, clinical microbiology, hematology/coagulation, and urinalysis/body fluids, among others. Instruction and clinical experience are conducted in labs at affiliated hospitals and private laboratories, so that students are exposed to the actual functioning of a laboratory and able to understand the challenges as well as the benefits of working in such a setting. Margaret says, "the clinical instruction is the fun part, when we actually get to try out the techniques and processes we've been reading about in the classroom." Clinical experience includes hands-on work in the areas of clinical chemistry, blood banking, microbiology, hematology, serology, and urinalysis/body fluids.

Typical Day
During the clinical phase of her training, Margaret works in a nearby medical laboratory, with which Valdosta Technical College is affiliated. Working with a licensed medical lab technician, she learns how to move freely and safely around the lab, following all the safety procedures required of employees and performing all the various activities of a medical lab technician. There is usually just one lab technician on-call overnight, and this person must carry a pager at all times and arrive at the hospital within 20 minutes of being paged. They are often called in for patients who have heart attacks, strokes, potential blood poisoning, or pain that the doctor is unable to diagnose. When Margaret works with the technician on-call, she must carry a pager and come in when called too. This way, she gets exposure to working under pressure in an emergency situation and also when there is little back-up from other laboratory staff. Although this work is inconvenient and often challenging, it is very rewarding, says Margaret. "It is when you understand how meaningful your work really is."

When the lab first opens in the morning, one of the first things Margaret must do is check all the instruments. She does daily maintenance and quality control to ensure that all automated systems are functioning properly. "I record the quality control data on graphs and check for statistical errors." In-patient blood work is also collected first thing in the morning by laboratory assistants or phlebotomists. "We spin the blood samples in a centrifuge to separate cells from serum, then load the spun test tubes onto an analyzer. When the analysis is finished, we check the results and report them to the doctor."

For the next six hours, the lab collects blood from out-patients. "We see between 50 and 70 patients a day," Margaret explains. "Some of the blood tests are sent out to a larger lab, but we do most of our own tests here. The work includes chemistry, hematology, and urinalysis. We spin, separate, or mix the test tubes of blood that are collected. If it's a hematology specimen, we might have to make a thin blood film on the slide. We then stain the blood cells and examine them under a microscope. We're looking for evidence of certain diseases, such as leukemia.

At any time during the day, we may have to stop what we're doing for an emergency. If there is an emergency patient, we go down to the Emergency Room and collect the patient's blood and perform whatever tests are needed quickly to assist the doctor in making a diagnosis. Once outpatient collecting hours are over, we finish any outstanding work and prepare to close the lab for the evening."

Path to Becoming an Apprentice

"I always wanted to work in a hospital," says Margaret. She volunteered in a hospital during the summers when she was in high school and gained some exposure to the various types of jobs available in the health care field. Her volunteer coordinator is the one who told her originally about the medical laboratory technology program at Valdosta Technical College.

To apply to the program, you need to have graduated from high school or have a GED certificate. You also need to be able to present acceptable ASSET, SAT, ACT or CPE scores. In addition, you must submit dental and medical records, an RPR blood test, a tuberculin skin test, and other medical information prior to beginning the clinical phase of training. The school also requires that each student receive the HB vaccination series or sign a waiver declining the vaccination prior to clinical experience. As with most degree-based programs, students working in the clinical part of their training continue to pay tuition and do not receive a salary.

Salary Range

Most medical laboratory technicians do not earn a wage during their training, although a small percentage of technicians may receive on-the-job training outside of a certified educational program.

For graduates of a certified program, starting wages are around $30,000 a year plus full benefits in a hospital or private laboratory setting. Technicians may advance within their field or move up to managerial positions or even to become medical laboratory technologists.

Advice

Margaret suggests that those interested in becoming medical laboratory technicians try to gain some experi-

ence working in a laboratory setting before committing themselves to a full two-year training program. "Some people thrive in this environment," she says, while others find the constant exposure to blood and other body fluids offputting" You also need to enjoy math and science. The classroom work is heavy on chemistry the first year. Flexibility in working with different kinds of people, as well as an ability to be self-directed and work alone when dealing with automated instruments or typing reports is very helpful.

Future Goals

Margaret likes the fast-paced and busy atmosphere of a big hospital laboratory. She hopes to move to Atlanta and work at such a lab. "I might decide to go on and finish the bachelor's degree in medical technology," Margaret says, "so that I have the ability to work as a medical laboratory technologist. This would give me more options when applying for jobs, as well as greater earning potential." She also explains that she looks forward to new developments in her field. There is always some new test to learn about, she says, and this makes the work challenging and rewarding.

ALASKA

University of Alaska—Anchorage
3211 Providence Avenue
Anchorage, AK 99508-4610
907-786-6924
http://www.uaa.alaska.edu
Occupational Fields: medical lab technician, medical lab technologist

ALABAMA

Gadsden State Community College
PO Box 227
1001 George Wallace Drive
Gadsden, AL 35902-0227
256-549-8470
http://www.gadsdenst.cc.al.us
Occupational Fields: medical lab technician, medical lab technologist

Jefferson State Community College
2601 Carson Road
Birmingham, AL 35215-3098
205-856-6031
chill@jeffstateonline.com

http://www.jeffstateonline.com
Occupational Fields: medical lab technician, medical lab technologist

Wallace State Community College
801 Main Street
PO Box 2000
Hanceville, AL 35077-2000
256-352-8347
Jhewes@aol.com
Occupational Fields: medical lab technician, medical lab technologist

ARKANSAS

Arkansas State University
College of Nursing and Health Professions
PO Box 910
Joesboro, AR 72467-0010
870-972-3073
wwilliam@astate.edu
http://www.astate.edu
Occupational Fields: medical lab technician, medical lab technologist

Arkansas State University–Beebe
PO Box 1000
Beebe, AR 72012
501-882-8214
jlboyd@asub.edu
Occupational Fields: medical lab technician, medical lab technologist

National Park Community College
101 College Drive
Hot Springs, AR 71913
501-60-4278
jwilborn@npcc.edu
http://www.npcc.edu
Occupational Fields: medical lab technician, medical lab technologist

North Arkansas College
1515 Pioneer Ridge Drive
Harrison, AR 72601
870-391-3288
sgibbany@northark.edu
http://www.northark.edu
Occupational Fields: medical lab technician, medical lab technologist

South Arkansas Community College
Attn: Mr. Oliver Borden
PO Box 7010
El Dorado, AR 71730
870-862-8131
oborden@southark.edu
http://www.southark.edu
Occupational Fields: medical lab technician, medical lab technologist

Phillips Community College of University of Arkansas
PO Box 785
Helena, AR 72342-0785
870-338-6474
mlocke@pccua.edu
http://www.pccua.edu
Occupational Fields: medical lab technician, medical lab technologist

CALIFORNIA

Hartnell College
156 Homestead Avenue
Salinas, CA 93901
831-775-6700
lindavpd@sbcglobal.net
http://www.hartnell.cc.ca.us
Occupational Fields: medical lab technician, medical lab technologist

COLORADO

Arapahoe Community College
5900 South Santa Fe Drive
PO Box 9002
Littleton, CO 80160-9002
303-797-5796
linda.comeaux@arapahoe.edu
http://arapahoe.edu
Occupational Fields: medical lab technician, medical lab technologist

CONNECTICUT

Housatonic Community College
900 Lafayette Boulevard
Bridgeport, CT 06604-4704
293-332-5106
pgutowski@hcc.commnet.edu

http://www.hcc.commnet.edu
Occupational Fields: medical lab technician, medical lab technologist

Manchester Community College
Great Path, M.S. #17
PO Box 1046
Manchester, CT 06045-1046
860-512-2703
http://www.mcc.commnet.edu
Occupational Fields: medical lab technician, medical lab technologist

DELAWARE
Delaware Technical & Community College
Jack F. Owens Campus
PO Box 610, Seashore Highway
Georgetown, DE 9947-0610
302-855-594
sshupe@dtcc.edu
http://www.dtcc.edu
Occupational Fields: medical lab technician, medical lab technologist

FLORIDA
Brevard Community College
Allied Health Division
1519 Clearlake Road
Cocoa, FL 32922-6597
321-632-7543
hulmem@brevardcc.edu
http://www.brevardcc.edu
Occupational Fields: medical lab technician, medical lab technologist

Erwin Technical Center
2010 East Hillsborough Avenue
Tampa, FL 33610-8299
813-231-1815
http://www.erwintech.org
Occupational Fields: medical lab technician, medical lab technologist

Florida Community College
North Campus
4501 Capper Road, A-271
Jacksonville, FL 32218-4499
904-766-680

rjost@fccj.edu
http://www.fccj.edu
Occupational Fields: medical lab technician, medical lab technologist

Indian River Community College
3209 Virginia Avenue
Fort Pierce, FL 34981-5599
772-462-7536
cdaniels@ircc.edu
http://www.ircc.edu
Occupational Fields: medical lab technician, medical lab technologist

Keiser College
1500 NW 49th Street
Fort Lauderdale, FL 33309
954-776-4456
lureens@keisercollege.edu
http://www.keisercollege.edu
Occupational Fields: medical lab technician, medical lab technologist

Lake City Community College
Route 19, Box 1030
Lake City, FL 32025
386-754-4221
kambackd@lakecitycc.edu
Occupational Fields: medical lab technician, medical lab technologist

Miami-Dade College
School of Allied Health Technologies
950 NW 20th St.
Miami, FL 33127-4693
305-237-4434
babatunde.amole@mdc.edu
http://www.mdc.edu
Occupational Fields: medical lab technician, medical lab technologist

St. Petersburg College
HEC, PO Box 13489
7200 66th Street, North
St. Petersburg, FL 33733-3489
727-341-3714
polanskyv@spjc.edu
http://www.spjc.edu
Occupational Fields: medical lab technician, medical lab technologist

GEORGIA

Central Georgia Technical College
3300 Macon Tech Drive
Macon, GA 31206
478-757-3571
lnorthup@centralgatech.edu
Occupational Fields: medical lab technician, medical lab technologist

Coastal Georgia Community College
Department of Allied Health
3700 Altama Avenue
Brunswick, GA 31520
912-264-7382
nzell@cgcc.edu
http://www.cgcc.edu
Occupational Fields: medical lab technician, medical lab technologist

Dalton State College
213 North College Drive
Dalton, GA 30720
706-272-4512
dshoemaker@em.daltonstate.edu
http://www.daltonstate.edu
Occupational Fields: medical lab technician, medical lab technologist

Darton College
2400 Gillionville Road
Albany, GA 31707-3098
229-430-846
beamonn@darton.edu
http://www.darton.edu
Occupational Fields: medical lab technician, medical lab technologist

DeKalb Technical College
495 North Indian Creek Drive
Clarkston, GA 30021-2397
404-297-9522
robertsg@dekalbtech.org
http://www.dekalbtech.org
Occupational Fields: medical lab technician, medical lab technologist

Lanier Technical College
2990 Landrum Education Drive
Oakwood, GA 30566

770-531-667
krandolph@laniertech.edu
http://www.laniertech.edu
Occupational Fields: medical lab technician, medical lab technologist

North Georgia Technical College
Highway 197 North, PO Box 65
Clarkesville, GA 30523-0065
706-754-7757
lstrader@ngtcollege.org
http://www.ngtcollege.org
Occupational Fields: medical lab technician, medical lab technologist

Okefenokee Technical College
1701 Carswell Avenue
Waycross, GA 31501-4016
912-287-5838
atuten@okefenokeetech.edu
http://www.okefenokeetech.edu
Occupational Fields: medical lab technician, medical lab technologist

Southeastern Technical College
3001 East First Street
Vidalia, GA 30474
912-538-3183
deward@southeasterntech.edu
http://www.southeasterntech.edu
Occupational Fields: medical lab technician, medical lab technologist

Southwest Georgia Technical College
15689 Highway 19 North
Thomasville, GA 31792
229-225-5203
rmiller@southwestgatech.edu
http://www.southwestgatech.edu
Occupational Fields: medical lab technician, medical lab technologist

Valdosta Technical College
4089 Val Tech Road
Valdosta, GA 31602-0929
229-259-5567
arobinson@valdostatech.edu
http://www.valdostatech.edu

Occupational Fields: medical lab technician, medical lab technologist

West Central Technical College
Murphy Campus
178 Murphy Campus Boulevard
Waco, GA 30182
770-5376043
jridley@westcentraltech.edu
http://westcentraltech.edu
Occupational Fields: medical lab technician, medical lab technologist

HAWAII
Kapiolani Community College
4303 Diamond Head Road
Honolulu, HI 96816-4496
808-734-9231
marciaa@hawaii.edu
http://www.hawaii.edu
Occupational Fields: medical lab technician, medical lab technologist

ILLINOIS
Blessing Hospital
1005 Broadway Street
Quincy, IL 6235
217-223-8400
hator@blessinghospital.com
http://www.blessinghospital.com
Occupational Fields: medical lab technician, medical lab technologist

Elgin Community College
1700 Spartan Drive
Elgin, IL 60123-7193
847-214-7308
wmiller@elgin.edu
http://www.elgin.edu
Occupational Fields: medical lab technician, medical lab technologist

Illinois Central College
Health Careers & Public Services
201 S.W. Adams Street
Peoria, IL 61635-0001
309-999-4661

astrow@icc.edu
http://www.icc.edu
Occupational Fields: medical lab technician, medical lab technologist

Kankakee Community College
River Road, PO Box 888
Kankakee, IL 60901-0888
815-802-8835
nsawalha@kankakee.edu
http://www.kankakee.edu
Occupational Fields: medical lab technician, medical lab technologist

Oakton Community College
Cluster One
1600 East Golf Road
Des Plaines, IL 60016-1268
847-635-1889
lynne@oakton.edu
http://www.oakton.edu
Occupational Fields: medical lab technician, medical lab technologist

Southern Illinois Collegiate Common Market
3213 South Park Avenue
Herrin, IL 62948
618-942-6902
pberry@siccm.com
http://www.siccm.com
Occupational Fields: medical lab technician, medical lab technologist

Southwestern Illinois College
2500 Carlyle Avenue
Belleville, IL 62221-5899
618-222-5386
Jean.Deitz@swic.edu
http://www.swic.edu
Occupational Fields: medical lab technician, medical lab technologist

INDIANA
Indiana University, Northwest
Allied Health Department
3400 Broadway
Gary, IN 46408
219-980-6923

sahiggin@iun.edu
http://www.iun.edu
Occupational Fields: medical lab technician, medical lab technologist

Ivy Tech State–North Central
220 Dean Johnson Boulevard
South Bend, IN 46619-3837
574-289-7001
pprimros@ivytech.edu
http://www.ivytech.edu
Occupational Fields: medical lab technician, medical lab technologist

Ivy Tech State–Terre Haute
7999 US Highway 41, South
Terre Haute, IN 47802-4898
812-298-2243
http://www.ivytech.edu
Occupational Fields: medical lab technician, medical lab technologist

IOWA
Des Moines Area Community College
2006 South Ankeny Boulevard, Building 9
Ankeny, IA 50021
515-964-6296
kjcampbell@dmacc.edu
http://www.dmacc.edu
Occupational Fields: medical lab technician, medical lab technologist

Iowa Central Community College
330 Avenue M
Fort Dodge, IA 50501
515-576-0099
EDWARDS@triton.iccc.cc.ia.us
http://www.iccc.cc.ia.us
Occupational Fields: medical lab technician, medical lab technologist

Hawkeye Community College
1501 East Orange Road
PO Box 8015
Waterloo, IA 50704-8015
309-296-2320
akapanka@hawkeye.cc.ia.us
http://www.hawkeye.cc.ia.us

Occupational Fields: medical lab technician, medical lab technologist

KANSAS
Barton County Community College
245 N.E. 30th Road
Great Bend, KS 67530-9803
620-792-9393
BunselmeyerL@bartonccc.edu
http://www.bartonccc.edu
Occupational Fields: medical lab technician, medical lab technologist

Seward County Community College
520 North Washington
Liberal, KS 67901-1137
620-626-3077
scampbel@sccc.edu
http://www.sccc.edu
Occupational Fields: medical lab technician, medical lab technologist

Wichita Area Technical College
324 North Emporia Street
Wichita, KS 67202
316-677-1378
bwenger@watc.edu
http://www.watc.edu
Occupational Fields: medical lab technician, medical lab technologist

KENTUCKY
Eastern Kentucky University
Dizney 220
521 Lancaster Avenue
Richmond, KY 40475-3102
859-622-3078
David.Hufford@eku.edu
http://www.eku.edu
Occupational Fields: medical lab technician, medical lab technologist

Henderson Community College
2660 South Green St.
Henderson, KY 42420
270-830-5318
Randa.Hawa@Kctcs.net

http://www.henderson.kctcs.edu
Occupational Fields: medical lab technician, medical lab technologist

Somerset Community College
808 Monticello Road
Somerset, KY 42501-2999
606-679-8501
nancy.powell@kctcs.edu
http://www.somcc.kctcs.net
Occupational Fields: medical lab technician, medical lab technologist

Southeast Kentucky Community and Technical College
3300 South Highway 25E
Pineville, KY 40977
606-242-2145
sheila.miracle@kctcs.edu
http://www.secc.kctcs.edu
Occupational Fields: medical lab technician, medical lab technologist

LOUISIANA
Delgado Community College
615 City Park Avenue
New Orleans, LA 70119
504-483-4198
shickm@dcc.edu
http://www.dcc.edu
Occupational Fields: medical lab technician, medical lab technologist

Louisiana State University–Alexandria
8100 Highway 71 South
Alexandria, LA 71302-9121
slienhop@lsua.edu
http://www.lsua.edu
Occupational Fields: medical lab technician, medical lab technologist

Louisiana Technical College, Lafayette Campus
1101 Bertrand Drive
Lafayette, LA 70502-4909
337-262-5962
http://www.lafayettecampus.net
Occupational Fields: medical lab technician, medical lab technologist

Our Lady of the Lake College
5345 Brittany Drive
Baton Rouge, LA 70808
225-768-1745
tcasanov@ololcollege.edu
http://www.ololcollege.edu
Occupational Fields: medical lab technician, medical lab technologist

Southern University at Shreveport
Bossier Campus
3050 Martin Luther King, Jr., Drive
Shreveport, LA 71107
318-674-3414
rrobinson@susla.edu
http://www.susla.edu
Occupational Fields: medical lab technician, medical lab technologist

MASSACHUSSETS
Bristol Community College
Division of Health Technology & Nursing
777 Elsbree Street
Fall River, MA 02720-7307
508-678-2811
scampos@bristol.mass.edu
http://www.bristol.mass.edu
Occupational Fields: medical lab technician, medical lab technologist

Springfield Technical Community College
PO Box 9000
Springfield, MA 01105-1204
413-755-4510
http://www.stcc.edu
Occupational Fields: medical lab technician, medical lab technologist

MARYLAND
Allegany College of Maryland
12401 Willowbrook Road, SE
Cumberland, MD 21502
301-784-5548
msaunders@allegany.edu
http://www.allegany.edu
Occupational Fields: medical lab technician, medical lab technologist

Villa Julie College
1525 Greenspring Valley Road
Stevenson, MD 21153-9999
443-334-2256
fac-grif@mail.vjc.edu
http://www.vjc.edu
Occupational Fields: medical lab technician, medical lab technologist

MAINE
Central Maine Community College
1250 Turner Street
Auburn, ME 04210-6498
207-755-5420
vferran@cmcc.edu
http://www.cmcc.edu
Occupational Fields: medical lab technician, medical lab technologist

Medical Laboratory Technology Program of Maine
181 Main Street
Presque Isle, ME 04769
207-768-9451
graves@umpi.maine.edu
http://www.umpi.maine.edu
Occupational Fields: medical lab technician, medical lab technologist

MICHIGAN
Baker College of Owosso
1020 South Washington Street
Owosso, MI 48867
989-729-3416
mary.vuckovich@baker.edu
http://www.baker.edu
Occupational Fields: medical lab technician, medical lab technologist

Ferris State University
200 Ferris Drive
Big Rapids, MI 49307-2740
231-591-2317
sossb@ferris.edu
http://www.ferris.edu
Occupational Fields: medical lab technician, medical lab technologist

Kellogg Community College
450 North Avenue
Battle Creek, MI 49017-3397
269-965-3931
paffk@kellogg.edu
http://www.kellogg.edu
Occupational Fields: medical lab technician, medical lab technologist

Northern Michigan University
School of Nursing & Allied Health
I-L Learning Resources Ctr, 201 Magers Hall
Marquette, MI 49855-5346
906-227-1660
lcontois@nmu.edu
http://www.nmu.edu
Occupational Fields: medical lab technician, medical lab technologist

MINNESOTA
Alexandria Technical College
1601 Jefferson Street
Alexandria, MN 56308
320-762-4524
wandah@alx.tec.mn.us
http://www.alextech.edu
Occupational Fields: medical lab technician, medical lab technologist

Argosy University
Twin Cities Campus
1515 Central Parkway
Eagan, MN 55121
952-252-1680
lcrispino@argosyu.edu
http://www.argosyu.edu
Occupational Fields: medical lab technician, medical lab technologist

Hibbing Community College
Hibbing Campus
1515 East 25th Street
Hibbing, MN 55746
218-262-7254
mitzimorris@hcc.mnscu.edu
http://www.hcc.mnscu.edu/programs/dept/medlab
Occupational Fields: medical lab technician, medical lab technologist

Lake Superior College
2101 Trinity Road
Duluth, MN 55811
218-733-7679
m.werner@lsc.mnscu.edu
http://www.lsc.edu
Occupational Fields: *medical lab technician, medical lab technologist*

Minnesota State Community & Technical College— Fergus Falls
1414 College Way
Fergus Falls, MN 56537
218-736-1592
pat.sjolie@minnesota.edu
http://www.minnesota.edu
Occupational Fields: *medical lab technician, medical lab technologist*

Minnesota West Community & Technical College
1450 Collegeway Drive
Worthington, MN 56187
507-372-3422
rmiller@wr.mnwest.mnscu.edu
Occupational Fields: *medical lab technician, medical lab technologist*

Northern Minnesota Consortium for CLT/MLT Education
905 Grant Avenue, SE
Bemidji, MN 56601
218-755-4270
paula.bowman@ntcmn.edu
Occupational Fields: *medical lab technician, medical lab technologist*

North Hennepin Community College
7411 85th Avenue North
Brooklyn Park, MN 55445
763-424-0768
nancy.denny@nhcc.edu
http://www.nhcc.mnscu.edu
Occupational Fields: *medical lab technician, medical lab technologist*

Saint Paul College
235 Marshall Avenue
St. Paul, MN 55102-1807
651-846-1421
michelle.briski@saintpaul.edu
http://www.saintpaul.edu
Occupational Fields: *medical lab technician, medical lab technologist*

South Central Technical College
1920 Lee Boulevard
North Mankato, MN 56003
507-332-5852
darla.petersen@southcentral.edu
http://southcentral.edu
Occupational Fields: *medical lab technician, medical lab technologist*

MISSISSIPPI

Copiah-Lincoln Community College
PO Box 457
Wesson, MS 39191-0457
601-643-8391
mary.shivers@colin.edu
http://www.colin.edu
Occupational Fields: *medical lab technician, medical lab technologist*

Hinds Community College
1750 Chadwick Drive
Jackson, MS 39204-3402
601-371-3515
tghenry@hindscc.edu
http://hindscc.edu
Occupational Fields: *medical lab technician, medical lab technologist*

Meridian Community College
910 Highway 19 North
Meridian, MS 39307
601-484-8755
kpoole@mcc.cc.ms.us
http://www.mcc.cc.ms.us
Occupational Fields: *medical lab technician, medical lab technologist*

Mississippi Delta Community College
PO Box 668
Moorhead, MS 38761
662-246-6501
pkelly@msdelta.edu
http://www.msdelta.edu

Occupational Fields: medical lab technician, medical lab technologist

Mississippi Gulf Coast Community College
2300 Highway 90
Gautier, MS 39553
228-497-7709
gretchen.cunningham@mgccc.edu
http://www2.mgccc.cc.ms.us/~medlabtech
Occupational Fields: medical lab technician, medical lab technologist

Northeast Mississippi Community College
Cunningham Boulvard, Box 1457
Booneville, MS 38829
662-720-7388
rcjones@nemcc.edu
http://www.necc.cc.ms.us
Occupational Fields: medical lab technician, medical lab technologist

Pearl River Community College
Forrest County Center
5448 US Highway 49, South
Hattiesburg, MS 39401
601-554-5523
ewallace@prcc.edu
Occupational Fields: medical lab technician, medical lab technologist

MISSOURI
St. Louis Community College
5600 Oakland Avenue
St. Louis, MO 63110
314-644-9645
kkiser@stlcc.edu
http://www.stlcc.cc.mo.us/fp/clt/index.html
Occupational Fields: medical lab technician, medical lab technologist

Three Rivers Community College
Riverside Campus
2080 Three Rivers Boulevard
Poplar Bluff, MO 63901
573-840-9677
deethomp@trcc.edu
http://www.trcc.edu/divisions/hhs/MLT.htm
Occupational Fields: medical lab technician, medical lab technologist

NEBRASKA
Central Community College
PO Box 1024
East Highway 6
Hastings, NE 68902-1024
402-437-2762
snoble@alltel.net
http://www.cccneb.edu
Occupational Fields: medical lab technician, medical lab technologist

Mid-Plains Community College
601 W State Farm Road
North Platte, NE 69101-9499
308-535-3754
steinbeckm@mpcc.edu
http://www.mpcc.cc.ne.us
Occupational Fields: medical lab technician, medical lab technologist

Southeast Community College
8800 "O" Street
Lincoln, NE 68520
402-437-2760
Jbible@southeast.edu
http://www.southeast.edu
Occupational Fields: medical lab technician, medical lab technologist

NEW HAMPSHIRE
New Hampshire Community Technical College
Allied Health and Human Services
One College Drive
Claremont, NH 03743-9707
603-542-7744
agordon@nhctc.edu
http://www.nhctc.edu
Occupational Fields: medical lab technician, medical lab technologist

NEW JERSEY
Camden County College
PO Box 200, College Drive
Blackwood, NJ 08012-0200
856-227-7200
pchappell@camdencc.edu
http://www.camdencc.edu
Occupational Fields: medical lab technician, medical lab technologist

Mercer County Community College
PO Box B
Trenton, NJ 08690-1099
609-586-4800
oreilly@mccc.edu
http://www.mccc.edu
Occupational Fields: medical lab technician, medical lab technologist

Middlesex County College
2600 Woodbridge Avenue
Edison, NJ 08818
732-906-2581
stephen_larkin@middlesexcc.edu
http://www.middlesexcc.edu
Occupational Fields: medical lab technician, medical lab technologist

Northern New Jersey Consortium for Medical Laboratory Technology Education
400 Paramus Road
Paramus, NJ 07869
201-612-5558
Bdavis@bergen.edu
http://www.bergen.edu
Occupational Fields: medical lab technician, medical lab technologist

NEW MEXICO
Albuquerque Technical Vocational Institute
525 Buena Vista, SE
Albuquerque, NM 87106
607-778-5211
http://www.tvi.cc.nm.us
Occupational Fields: medical lab technician, medical lab technologist

New Mexico State University–Alamogordo
2400 North Scenic Drive
Alamogordo, NM 88310
505-439-3761
jjobrien@nmsua.nmsu.edu
http://alamo.nmsu.edu
Occupational Fields: medical lab technician, medical lab technologist

NEW YORK
Clinton Community College
Lake Shore Rd, Route 9 South
136 Clinton Point Drive

Plattsburgh, NY 12901
518-562-4273
sharon.columbus@clinton.edu
http://www.clinton.edu
Occupational Fields: medical lab technician, medical lab technologist

Dutchess Community College
53 Pendell Road
Poughkeepsie, NY 12601
845-431-8321
ingham@sunydutchess.edu
http://www.sunydutchess.edu
Occupational Fields: medical lab technician, medical lab technologist

Erie Community College–North
6205 Main Street
Williamsville, NY 14221-7095
716-851-1553
bermel@ecc.edu
http://ecc.edu
Occupational Fields: medical lab technician, medical lab technologist

Orange County Community College
115 South Street
Middletown, NY 10940
845-341-4136
rcontari@sunyorange.edu
http://www.sunyorange.edu
Occupational Fields: medical lab technician, medical lab technologist

SUNY Farmingdale
Route 110, Gleeson Hall, Room 304
Farmingdale, NY 11735
631-420-2257
conforsl@Farmingdale.edu
http://www.farmingdale.edu
Occupational Fields: medical lab technician, medical lab technologist

NORTH CAROLINA
Alamance Community College
PO Box 8000
Graham, NC 27253-8000
336-506-4196
pam.hall@alamance.cc.nc.us

Occupational Fields: medical lab technician, medical lab technologist

Asheville–Buncombe Technical Community College
340 Victoria Road
Asheville, NC 28801
828-254-1921
mhyatt@abtech.edu
http://www.abtech.edu
Occupational Fields: medical lab technician, medical lab technologist

Bismarck State College
1500 Edwards Avenue
Bismarck, ND 58501-1299
701-224-569
Julie.Schroer@bsc.nodak.edu
http://www.bismarckstate.com
Occupational Fields: medical lab technician, medical lab technologist

Central Piedmont Community College
PO Box 35009
Charlotte, NC 28235-5009
704-330-5028
becky.sanders@cpcc.edu
http://www.cpcc.cc.nc.us/Health_Sciences/Medical_ Laboratory_Technology
Occupational Fields: medical lab technician, medical lab technologist

Coastal Carolina Community College
444 Western Boulevard
Jacksonville, NC 28546
910-938-6275
weaverc@coastal.cc.nc.us
Occupational Fields: medical lab technician, medical lab technologist

Davidson County Community College
PO Box 1287
Lexington, NC 27293-1287
336-249-8186
srohr@davidson.cc.nc.us
Occupational Fields: medical lab technician, medical lab technologist

Sandhills Community College
3395 Airport Road
Pinehurst, NC 28374
910-695-3839
mccormickc@sandhills.edu
http://www.sandhills.edu
Occupational Fields: medical lab technician, medical lab technologist

Southeastern Community College
4564 Chadbourn Highway
PO Box 151
Whiteville, NC 28472
910-642-7141
pwright@sccnc.edu
http://www.sccnc.edu
Occupational Fields: medical lab technician, medical lab technologist

Western Piedmont Community College
Health Sciences Department
1001 Burkemont Avenue
Morganton, NC 28655
828-438-6128
nshoaf@wpcc.edu
http://www.wpcc.edu
Occupational Fields: medical lab technician, medical lab technologist

OHIO
Clark State Community College
570 East Leffels Lane
Springfield, OH 45505-4749
937-328-8077
horns@clarkstate.edu
http://www.clarkstate.edu
Occupational Fields: medical lab technician, medical lab technologist

Columbus State Community College
550 East Spring Street, PO Box 1609
Columbus, OH 43216-1609
614-287-2518
Jdudas@cscc.edu
http://www.cscc.edu/DOCS/MedLab/index.html
Occupational Fields: medical lab technician, medical lab technologist

Jefferson Community College
4000 Sunset Boulevard
Steubenville, OH 43952-3594
740-264-5591

ssutherlan@jcc.edu
http://www.jcc.edu
Occupational Fields: medical lab technician, medical lab
technologist

Lakeland Community College
7700 Clocktower Drive
Kirtland, OH 44094-5198
440-525-7169
kertter@lakelandcc.edu
http://www.lakeland.cc.oh.us/ACADEMIC/SH/MLT/
INDEX.HTM
Occupational Fields: medical lab technician, medical lab
technologist

Lorain County Community College
1005 North Abbe Road
Elyria, OH 44035-1691
440-366-7194
jdaly@lorainccc.edu
http://www.lorainccc.edu
Occupational Fields: medical lab technician, medical lab
technologist

Marion Technical College
1467 Mount Vernon Avenue
Marion, OH 43302-5694
740-389-4636
batesd@mtc.edu
http://mtc.edu
Occupational Fields: medical lab technician, medical lab
technologist

Shawnee State University
940 Second Street
Portsmouth, OH 45662-0790
740-351-3388
mthoroughman@shawnee.edu
http://www.shawnee.edu
Occupational Fields: medical lab technician, medical lab
technologist

University of Rio Grande
MSC/F-39
218 North College Avenue
Rio Grande, OH 45674
740-245-7319
rcheadle@rio.edu
http://www.rio.edu

Occupational Fields: medical lab technician, medical lab
technologist

Washington State Community College
710 Colegate Drive
Marietta, OH 45750
740-374-8716
hkincaid@wscc.edu
http://www.wscc.edu
Occupational Fields: medical lab technician, medical lab
technologist

OKLAHOMA
Northeastern Oklahoma A&M College
200 I Street, NE
Miami, OK 74354-6497
918-540-6315
kharris@neoam.cc.ok.us
http://www.neoam.cc.ok.us
Occupational Fields: medical lab technician, medical lab
technologist

Rose State College
6420 Southeast Fifteenth Street
Midwest City, OK 73110-2704
405-733-7577
epaxton@rose.edu
http://www.rose.edu
Occupational Fields: medical lab technician, medical lab
technologist

Seminole State College
2701 Boren Boulevard, PO Box 351
Seminole, OK 74818
405-382-9214
latchaw_p@ssc.cc.ok.us
http://www.ssc.cc.ok.us
Occupational Fields: medical lab technician, medical lab
technologist

Tulsa Community College
909 South Boston Avenue
Tulsa, OK 74119
918-595-7008
kholmes@tulsacc.edu
http://www.tulsacc.edu
Occupational Fields: medical lab technician, medical lab
technologist

PENNSYLVANIA
Community College of Allegheny County
South Campus
1750 Clairton Road
West Mifflin, PA 15122-3097
412-469-6280
jcoughanour@ccac.edu
http://www.ccac.edu
Occupational Fields: medical lab technician, medical lab technologist

Community College of Philadelphia
1700 Spring Garden Street
Philadelphia, PA 19130-3991
215-751-8511
rkrefetz@ccp.edu
http://www.ccp.edu
Occupational Fields: medical lab technician, medical lab technologist

Reading Area Community College
10 South 2nd St, PO Box 1706
Reading, PA 19603-1706
610-372-4721
sneiman@racc.edu
http://www.racc.edu
Occupational Fields: medical lab technician, medical lab technologist

RHODE ISLAND
Community College of Rhode Island
Flanaghan Campus, CLT Program
1762 Louisquisset Pike
Lincoln, RI 02865-4585
401-333-7144
lmorgan@ccri.edu
http://www.ccri.edu
Occupational Fields: medical lab technician, medical lab technologist

SOUTH CAROLINA
Greenville Technical College
PO Box 5616
Greenville, SC 29606-5616
864-250-8292
Tommie.Whitt@gvltec.edu
http://www.greenvilletech.com
Occupational Fields: medical lab technician, medical lab technologist

Orangeburg-Calhoun Technical College
3250 St. Matthews Road
Orangeburg, SC 29118-8299
803-535-139
FanningB@octech.edu
http://www.octech.edu
Occupational Fields: medical lab technician, medical lab technologist

Spartanburg Technical College
Allied Health Division
PO Box 4386
Spartanburg, SC 29305-4386
864-591-3866
romanie@stcsc.edu
http://www.stcsc.edu
Occupational Fields: medical lab technician, medical lab technologist

Tri-County Technical College
PO Box 587
Pendleton, SC 29670-0587
864-646-1351
djones2@tctc.edu
http://www.tctc.edu
Occupational Fields: medical lab technician, medical lab technologist

York Technical College
452 South Anderson Road
Rock Hill, SC 29730
803-981-7082
Lfantry@yorktech.com
http://www.yorktech.com
Occupational Fields: medical lab technician, medical lab technologist

SOUTH DAKOTA
Mitchell Technical Institute
821 North Capital Street
Mitchell, SD 57301-2002
605-995-3024
feilmeierb@mti.tec.sd.us
http://mti.tec.sd.us
Occupational Fields: medical lab technician, medical lab technologist

TENNESSEE
Jackson State Community College
2046 North Parkway
Jackson, TN 38301-3797
731-425-2612
gjones@jscc.edu
http://www.jscc.edu
Occupational Fields: medical lab technician, medical lab technologist

MedVance Institute
1025 Hwy. 111
Cookeville, TN 38501
931-526-3660
laverne@multipro.com
http://www.medvance.edu
Occupational Fields: medical lab technician, medical lab technologist

Volunteer State Community College
1480 Nashville Pike
Gallatin, TN 37066
615-452-8600
http://www.volstate.edu
Occupational Fields: medical lab technician, medical lab technologist

TEXAS
Academy of Health Sciences
Dept of Clinical Support Services
3151 Scott Road
Fort Sam Houston, TX 78234-6137
210-221-7707
elaine.perry@amedd.army.mil
http://www.cs.amedd.army.mil
Occupational Fields: medical lab technician, medical lab technologist

El Centro College
Main at Lamar
Dallas, TX 75202-3604
214-860-2304
LaL5630@dcccd.edu
http://www.ecc.dcccd.edu
Occupational Fields: medical lab technician, medical lab technologist

El Paso Community College
PO Box 20500
El Paso, TX 79998-0500
915-831-4085
veronicad@epcc.edu
http://www.epcc.edu
Occupational Fields: medical lab technician, medical lab technologist

Houston Community College System
Coleman Health Science Center
1900 Galen Dr
Houston, TX 77030
713-718-5518
http://www.hccs.cc.tx.us
Occupational Fields: medical lab technician, medical lab technologist

McLennan Community College
1400 College Drive
Waco, TX 76708-1402
254-299-8406
dschmaus@mclennan.edu
http://www.mclennan.edu
Occupational Fields: medical lab technician, medical lab technologist

Navarro College
3200 West 7th Avenue
Corsicana, TX 75110
903-875-7516
evelyn.glass@navarrocollege.edu
http://www.navarrocollege.edu
Occupational Fields: medical lab technician, medical lab technologist

UTAH
Salt Lake Community College
Health Science Division
4600 South Redwood Road
Salt Lake City, UT 84130-0808
Karen.Brown@path.utah.edu
http://www.slcc.edu/pages/1285.asp
Occupational Fields: medical lab technician, medical lab technologist

Weber State University
3905 University Circle
Ogden, UT 84408-3905
801-626-780
ysimonian@weber.edu
http://departments.weber.edu/cls

Occupational Fields: medical lab technician, medical lab
technologist

VIRGINIA
Thomas Nelson Community College
99 Thomas Nelson Drive
PO Box 9407
Hampton, VA 23670-0407
757-825-2783
dezernl@tncc.vccs.edu
http://www.tncc.cc.va.us
Occupational Fields: medical lab technician, medical lab
technologist

Wytheville Community College
1000 East Main Street
Wytheville, VA 24382-3308
276-223-4828
wcreyna@wcc.vccs.edu
http://www.wcc.vccs.edu
Occupational Fields: medical lab technician, medical lab
technologist

WASHINGTON
Clover Park Technical College
4500 Steilacoom Boulevard, SW
Lakewood, WA 98499-4098
253-589-5625
anne.oneil@cptc.edu
http://www.cptc.ctc.edu/cptc/pages/MedicalLab.html
Occupational Fields: medical lab technician, medical lab
technologist

Shoreline Community College
16101 Greenwood Avenue North
Seattle, WA 98133-5667
206-546-6947
mmorse@shoreline.edu
http://www.shoreline.edu
Occupational Fields: medical lab technician, medical lab
technologist

Wenatchee Valley College
1300 Fifth Street
Wenatchee, WA 98801-1799
509-664-2522
dabbott@wvc.edu
http://www.wvc.edu

Occupational Fields: medical lab technician, medical lab
technologist

WEST VIRGINIA
Bluefield Regional Medical Center
500 Cherry Street
Bluefield, WV 24701-3306
304-327-1596
jgibberson@brmcwv.org
http://www.brmcwv.org
Occupational Fields: medical lab technician, medical lab
technologist

Fairmont State Community and Technical College
1201 Locust Avenue
211 Education Building
Fairmont, WV 26554-2491
304-367-4284
rromesburg@mail.fscwv.edu
http://www.fairmontstate.edu
Occupational Fields: medical lab technician, medical lab
technologist

Marshall University
Clinical Laboratory Science Department
1 John Marshall Drive
Huntington, WV 25755-2530
304-696-6596
fike@Marshall.edu
http://www.marshall.edu/clinical
Occupational Fields: medical lab technician, medical lab
technologist

**Southern West Virginia Community & Technical
College**
Logan Campus
PO Box 2900
Mount Gay, WV 25637
304-792-7098
Vernone@southern.wvnet.edu
http://www.southern.wvnet.edu
Occupational Fields: medical lab technician, medical lab
technologist

WISCONSIN
Chippewa Valley Technical College
Allied Health Division
620 West Clairemont Avenue

Eau Claire, WI 54701
715-833-6420
pgriffin@cvtc.edu
http://www.cvtc.edu/Programs/DeptPages/MLT/
    MLTHomePage.html
*Occupational Fields: medical lab technician, medical lab
    technologist*

Madison Area Technical College

3550 Anderson Street
Madison, WI 53704
608-246-6510
Manelson@matcmadison.edu
http://matcmadison.edu/matc
*Occupational Fields: medical lab technician, medical lab
    technologist*

Milwaukee Area Technical College

Health Occupations Division
700 West State Street
Milwaukee, WI 53233-1443
414-297-7142
schmidtd@matc.edu
http://www.matc.edu
*Occupational Fields: medical lab technician, medical lab
    technologist*

Moraine Park Technical College

235 North National Avenue
PO Box 1940
Fond du Lac, WI 54936-1940
920-924-6373
lbau@morainepark.edu
http://www.morainepark.edu/
*Occupational Fields: medical lab technician, medical lab
    technologist*

Northeast Wisconsin Technical College

2740 West Mason Street, PO Box 19042
Green Bay, WI 54307-9042
920-498-6374
patricia.cribb@nwtc.edu
http://www.nwtc.tec.wi.us
*Occupational Fields: medical lab technician, medical lab
    technologist*

Western Wisconsin Technical College

304 North Sixth Street
La Crosse, WI 54601-0908
608-789-6284
byomc@wwtc.edu

http://www.wwtc.edu
*Occupational Fields: medical lab technician, medical lab
    technologist*

CANADA

ALBERTA

Grant MacEwan College

PO Box 1796
Edmonton, AB T5J 2P2
780-497-5040
Fax: 780-497-5001
http://www.gmcc.ab.ca/web/home/DetailsPage.
    cfm?ID=239
*Occupational Fields: medical lab technician, medical lab
    technologist*

BRITISH COLUMBIA

Camosun College

4461 Interurban Rd
Victoria, BC V9E 2C1
250-370-3550
http://www.camosun.bc.ca
*Occupational Fields: medical lab technician, medical lab
    technologist*

Capilano College

2055 Purcell Way
North Vancouver, BC V7J 3H5
604-986-1911
TDD: 604-990-7848
Fax: 604-984-4985
http://www.capcollege.bc.ca
*Occupational Fields: medical lab technician, medical lab
    technologist*

Capilano College

Squamish Campus
PO Box 1538
1150 Carson Place
Squamish, BC V0N 3G0
604-892-5322
Fax: 604-892-9274
http://www.capcollege.bc.ca
*Occupational Fields: medical lab technician, medical lab
    technologist*

Capilano College

Sunshine Coast Campus
PO Box 1609

5627 Inlet Avenue
Sechelt, BC V0N 3A0
604-885-9310
Fax: 604-885-9350
http://www.capcollege.bc.ca
Occupational Fields: medical lab technician, medical lab
    technologist

MANITOBA
**Red River College of Applied Arts, Science &
    Technology**
2055 Notre Dame Avenue
Winnipeg, MB RH 0J9
204-632-2311
http://www.rrc.mb.ca
Occupational Fields: medical lab technician, medical lab
    technologist

SASKATCHEWAN
**Saskatchewan Institute of Applied Science &
    Technology**
400 119 4th Avenue South
Saskatoon, SK S7K 5X2
306-933-7331
http://www.siast.sk.ca/siast/contactus
Occupational Fields: medical lab technician, medical lab
    technologist

METALWORKERS

RELATED SECTIONS: *artists and artisans; auto body workers; boilermakers; crafts and trades workers at living historical sites and farms; elevator constructors; engineers and engineering technicians; farriers; ironworkers; machinists; mechanics; millwrights; operating engineers and stationary engineers; pipe trades workers; sheet metal workers; shipbuilding and ship maintenance workers; tool, die, mold, and pattern makers; welders*

Metalworkers shape metal into everything from wrought-iron railings to the lever that pops bread out of a toaster. Some, including goldsmiths, tinsmiths, coppersmiths, and silversmiths, specialize in working with one type of metal. Others design bronze sculptures and other artistic creations.

Metalworking and plastics-working machine operators set up and monitor machines that produce, cut, and form metal and plastic parts for most consumer products, such as toasters, toys, automobile parts, window frames, pop bottles, and wire. Some specialize in setting up the machines or operating a screw machine, plastics-molding machine, grinding machine, punch press, lathe, or other machine. Workers read blueprints, plan and set up the sequence of operations, adjust the machine's controls, choose lubricants and coolants, feed material into the machines, and select instruments or tools for each operation. These jobs usually involve repetitive operations that require little training. *Numerical-control machine-tool operators* tend machines that are electronically controlled, usually by computers. Metalworking and plastics-working machine operators who become skilled at their work may be promoted to more responsible positions within the department or receive advanced training to become machinists or tool and die makers.

Metalworkers often learn skills such as leather working or gem cutting to expand the scope of their craft. Many of these craftspeople are self-employed. *Blacksmiths* create furnishings such as chandeliers and coffee tables, stairway railings, and other architectural metalwork; some specialize in artistic creations such as sculptures. *Swordsmiths* fashion authentic or ornamental swords and leather sheaths, often decorated with jewels and precious metals. *Bladesmiths* fashion high-quality knives and other cutting tools. *Locksmiths* repair and open locks, make keys, change locks and safe combinations, and install and repair safes. *Jewelers* purchase, design, construct, repair, adjust, and appraise jewelry; their work often involves molding and shaping metal and setting gemstones.

Metalworking and plastics-working machine operators usually work indoors in clean, bright factories. They generally work 40 hours a week but sometimes put in overtime or work nights and weekends. To reduce the risk of injury from flying particles of metal and from operating powerful, high-speed machinery, metalworkers wear safety glasses, aprons, and other protective gear. They work with hammers, anvils, forges, soldering torches, welding equipment, saws, drills, pliers, jeweler's lathes, and various other hand tools and power tools, along with chemicals and polishing compounds, such as flux for soldering and tripoli and rouge for finishing.

Workers in the field sometimes belong to unions, such as the Manufacturing Jewelers and Silversmiths of America, or professional organizations, such as the Society of American Silversmiths or the Artist-Blacksmith's Association of North America (ABANA). These organizations often offer training workshops, seminars, and networking opportunities for aspiring metalworkers in search of apprenticeships.

Apprenticeship and on-the-job training are common ways of entering this field. Trainees learn under the supervision of experienced workers. The course of study may run from a few weeks to a year or more and typically includes instruction in welding, blueprint reading, and the properties of various metals. Apprenticeships at jewelry manufacturing plants typically last three to four years and include instruction in stone setting, casting, model making, and engraving.

In general an applicant should

- be at least 18 years old
- be a high school graduate or hold a GED certificate
- be able to do moderately heavy lifting
- have analytical or artistic ability
- have mechanical aptitude
- have manual dexterity
- have good hand-eye coordination
- have patience
- be able to work with precision and concentration

APPRENTICESHIP SALARIES

About 50 percent of what skilled workers earn. Some nontraditional programs in this field offer a stipend, room and board, or help with transportation costs.

POSTAPPRENTICESHIP SALARIES

About $12 an hour, up to about $25 an hour plus benefits. Earnings vary, depending on skill level, the employer, geographic location, and union membership.

JOB OUTLOOK

Generally good, because there will be a continued need for metal and plastic products. The demand for metalworking and plastics-working machine operators is expected to decline somewhat through the year 2012, however, due in part to increased use of computer-controlled equipment. The outlook for locksmiths is good, and the outlook for jewelers is fair.

For more information on apprenticeships for metalworkers, contact local job centers, your state bureau of apprenticeship training, or the individual programs listed below.

NATIONAL PROGRAMS

The Artist's Blacksmiths Association of North America (ABANA)
PO Box 816
Farmington, GA 30638-0816
706-310-1030
Fax: 706-769-7147
abana@abana.org
http://www.abana.org
Occupational Fields: blacksmith

Society of American Silversmiths
PO Box 72839
Providence, RI 02907
401-461-6840
Fax: 401-461-6841
Occupational Fields: silversmith

APPRENTICESHIP PROFILE

Angel Sword Corporation
Apprenticeship Program
350 Jennifer Lane
Driftwood, Texas 78619-9753
512-847-9679
a.sword@ccsi.com

General Nature of the Job

In 1979, Daniel Watson and his wife Olinca founded Angel Sword Forge. The name was chosen to convey their belief that the sword is not only a weapon but also an otherworldly work of art. That belief is reflected every day in the work done at this unique forge. Daniel and his apprentices use traditional, hands-on methods and the hammer, anvil, fire, and sweat to create edged weapons of the highest quality.

A bellows-driven charcoal kiln is used to heat the bar of steel that will eventually be a blade. At 1,600 degrees Fahrenheit, the molecular structure of the steel actually changes, allowing the metal to absorb carbon from the flame. The bar is then removed from the fire, placed on an anvil, and hammered into shape. When the blade is returned to the fire for another heating, it absorbs more carbon, making the metal harder and more durable. The core of the blade has the least amount of carbon, which allows the blade to bend and not break. Conversely, the sharp edge and tip of the blade, where the steel is the thinnest, has the highest carbon content.

Once the blade is created, it is tested for flexibility by being placed in a vise, bent up to 60 degrees, then bent back. If the blade is perfectly straight again (or "returned to true"), it passes inspection. The blades are finished using a high-mirror polish, an acid wash, or a bluing bath. As the final step, the blades are furnished with guards and unique handles made of bone, wood, brass, bronze, or horn. The swords' prices are indicative of this labor-intensive craftsmanship: swords made by Angel Sword cost upwards of $2,000. The new, more affordable line of Bright Knight swords is priced between $600 and $2,000.

The training of an apprentice at Angel Sword is rigorous and all consuming. Apprentices are provided with on-site housing and are asked to work approximately 10 hours a day, six days a week.

Typical Day

There are certain advantages to living at your job. Take the fact that head apprentice Gabriel Paavola wakes up at 7:45 A.M. and is at work just 15 minutes later. His first responsibility is to the milling machine that shapes steel bars into blades for the Bright Knight line. He's got to be sure it is in good working order by oiling it, cleaning it, and replenishing the steel bars. This can take as little as half an hour or—if there are problems—all day.

Then he "gets on the blade." Blades have already been ground to certain shapes by a journeyman and run through the kiln for hardening and tempering. Gabriel works on finishing a blade, sandblasting it to remove fire scale, and then bringing it up to a mirror polish or turning it black with an acidic bluing solution. Next, he tests the blade by bending it in a vise and straightening it. "It's a very arduous process to straighten a blade," he says. "You have to be able to see true ninety-degree angles. You learn how much pressure to apply and where to bend exactly." When the blade is ready, he consults with Daniel on what kind of guard and handle should be used. (A guard is the piece on a sword between the handle and the blade.) Each time that Gabriel does the finishing touches of fitting a guard and handle onto a blade, he's aware that he's creating a one-of-a-kind sword.

The workday at Angel Sword is a long one, often consuming 10 or 12 hours. Afterwards, Gabriel sometimes makes the twenty-minute drive into town to buy groceries or rent a movie. Other days, he'll read a book about edged weapons from Angel Sword's extensive library. In the early mornings, he sometimes joins Daniel and the others for Tai Chi Ch'uan. Gabriel readily admits that the downside to living on-site is its isolation. On occasion, apprentices are asked to travel to regional Renaissance and medieval festivals, where Angel Sword sells the bulk of its swords, knives, and daggers. Most apprentices enjoy this opportunity to dress in period costume and join in the festive revelry.

Path to Becoming an Apprentice

Gabriel describes his coming to work at Angel Sword as "a weird twist of fate." He was attending college in Michigan and—like many college seniors majoring in art—trying to figure out what to do with the rest of his life. But career decisions weren't really on his mind when he was surfing the Internet one day. He typed the word "sword" into a search engine, curious of what he might find about an object that's long fascinated him. "Ever since I was two years old, I've loved the sword," he says. He had even taken a blacksmithing course in college to learn more about blades.

But he credits the Internet with linking him to Angel Sword. After he clicked on Angel Sword's home page and discovered a description of the apprenticeship program, he sent a resume to Daniel. After a few conversations on the phone, he was convinced that Angel Sword had something to offer him and he to offer it. Soon after, he arrived in Texas to begin his journey as an apprentice swordsmith.

Salary Range

Gabriel is hesitant to give specifics on his salary as an apprentice. He came to Angel Sword debt-free (a requirement of the program) and is provided with living quarters and a small stipend. Of the stipend, he says, "It's enough for clothing and to put food in my belly. You don't do this for the money." Instead, he explains that his compensation comes from working on beautiful swords: "You spend all the energy you have on one piece, and finally, it's perfect."

Advice

"I would discourage anyone from doing this," Gabriel says emphatically when asked if he has advice for would-be swordsmiths. But then he backpedals, saying "What I mean is that I would welcome anyone who's willing. But if they can be discouraged so easily by me, then they won't make it." There have been, in fact, more dropout apprentices at Angel Sword than journeymen who've completed the program. "People think it's going to be all mystical and magical," he says. "But it's humbling, back-breaking work. If you don't have the heart and soul to do this for four to eight years, you won't stick with [swordsmithing] later on."

"Every day, I feel like I want to bolt," Gabriel admits. "I'll be working on a sword and something goes wrong. But then I find a creative way to make it better than when it began. That's the payoff."

Future Goals

In 10 years, Gabriel envisions himself starting his own company. His time at Angel Sword has given him the desire to forge his own swords, live on his own land, and eventually own his own gallery. He says that he's gradually uncovering his own ideas and opinions about swords. "I feel as though a lot more people could be reached than just the Renaissance crowd," he explains. "There are so many people who would like to experience swords."

Specifically, Gabriel is interested in researching and re-creating weaponry from different parts of the world, such as axes from China and Japan, or spears from Africa. In the future, he looks forward to creating "a worldwide spectrum of blades."

ALABAMA
Artist-Blacksmith's Association of America, Alabama Forge Council
889 County Road 1464
Cullman, AL 35058-0675
256-775-1575
akress@bellsouth.net
Occupational Fields: blacksmith

Artist-Blacksmith's Association of America, Alabama Forge Council
212 Park Place Way
Alabaster, AL 35007
205-824-0004

linnm@bellsouth.net
http://afc.abana-chapter.com
Occupational Fields: blacksmith, metalworker

ARIZONA
Arizona Artist-Blacksmith Association
840 East McKellips Road
Apache Junction, AZ 85219
480-983-2688
stonesmith@bigfoot.com
http://www.az-blacksmiths.org
Occupational Fields: blacksmith

Arizona Artist-Blacksmith Association
2522 West Loughlin Drive
Chandler, AZ 85224
480-839-6339
danshammer@cox.net
http://www.az-blacksmiths.org
Occupational Fields: blacksmith, metalworker

ARKANSAS
Blacksmith Organization of Arkansas
6829 Cottonwood Road
Harrison, AR 72601
870-743-1547
swordsmith2001@alltel.net
http://www.blacksmithsofarkansas.com
*Occupational Fields: blacksmith, metalworker,
   swordsmith*

Blacksmith Organization of Arkansas
4121 Homewoods Drive
Rogers, AR 72758
479-621-5238
http://www.blacksmithsofarkansas.com
Occupational Fields: blacksmith, metalworker

CALIFORNIA
California Blacksmith's Association
PO Box 997
San Jacinto, CA 92581
707-961-1246
http://www.calsmith.org/
Occupational Fields: blacksmith, metalworker

COLORADO
Rocky Mountain Smiths
2905 Aspen Drive
Durango, CO 81301
970-259-6553
forgingahead@sisna.com
http://www.rockymountainsmiths.org
Occupational Fields: blacksmith, metalworker

CONNECTICUT
Connecticut Blacksmith Guild
4 Haley Street
Mystic, CT 06355-2612
860-536-0679
mysticbs@aol.com
Occupational Fields: blacksmith, metalworker

DISTRICT OF COLUMBIA
National Rifle Association
1600 Rhode Island Avenue, Northwest
Washington, DC 20036
703-267-1000
Occupational Fields: gunsmith

FLORIDA
Florida Artist Blacksmith Association
Juan A Holbrook
6418 Nothwest 97 Court
Gainesville, FL 32653
applecrossforge@nettally.com
http://www.blacksmithing.org
Occupational Fields: blacksmith, metalworker

GEORGIA
Alex Bealer Blacksmith Association
c/o Jerry W. Green
PO Box 250 Emerson, GA 30137
706-635-7500
coe_wayne@ellijay.com
http://www.alexbealer.com
Occupational Fields: blacksmith, metalworker

Ocmulgee Blacksmith Guild
226 Fellowship Church Road
Fort Valley, GA 31030

478-397-4906
Occupational Fields: blacksmith, metalworker

Ocmulgee Blacksmith Guild
PO Box 1173
Pine Mountain, GA 31822
706-663-4896
pnmtnfrg@aol.com
Occupational Fields: blacksmith, metalworker

ILLINOIS
Illinois Valley Blacksmith Association
6710 South Grant Highway
Marengo, IL 60152
815-923-4370
info@illinoisblacksmith.org
http://www.illinoisblacksmith.org
Occupational Fields: blacksmith, metalworker

INDIANA
Conner Prairie Farm
13400 Allisonville Road, North
Fishers, IN 46038-4499
317-776-6000
http://www.connerprairie.org
Occupational Fields: blacksmith

**General Motors Corporation,
Allison Transmission Division**
4700 West 10th Street
PO Box 894
Indianapolis, IN 46206-0894
317-242-5321
Occupational Fields: tinsmith

Indiana Blacksmithing Association
Rural Route 1, Box 581
Dugger, IN 47848-9603
812-648-2557
hayden0911@ticz.com
http://www.indianablacksmithing.org
Occupational Fields: blacksmith, metalworker

Indiana Blacksmithing Association
3380 West 650, N
Middletown, IN 47356-9476
765-533-4153

http://www.indianablacksmithing.org
Occupational Fields: blacksmith, metalworker

IOWA
Iowa Operating Engineers
16299 Quebec Street
Indianola, IA 50125
641-942-7112
Occupational Fields: locksmith

University of Iowa
Physical Plant
165 CSSB, Facilities Management Staff Development
Iowa City, IA 52242
319-335-5115
Occupational Fields: locksmith

KANSAS
Great Plains Blacksmith Association
105 South Main Street
Haysville, KS 67060-1731
gpba@cox.net
http://gpba.abana-chapter.com
Occupational Fields: blacksmith, metalworker

KENTUCKY
Bluegrass Artist Blacksmith's Guild
6927 Oddville Sunrise Road
Cynthiana, KY 41031
859-234-6954
Occupational Fields: blacksmith, metalworker

Kentucky Blacksmiths' Association
PO Box 366
Brandenburg, KY 40108
207-422-3107
http://ky.abana-chapter.com
Occupational Fields: blacksmith, metalworker

LOUISIANA
Gulfcoast Blacksmiths Association
61 Hyacinth Drive
Covington, LA 70433
985-892-1137
budl1137@yahoo.com

http://www.GulfCoastBlacksmith.org
Occupational Fields: blacksmith, metalworker

Louisiana Metalsmiths Association
PO Box 305
Hammond, LA 70404
985-429-0575
dba-architect@worldnet.att.net
http://lametalsmiths.org
Occupational Fields: blacksmith, metalworker

MARYLAND

American Bladesmith Society
6612 Jefferson Boulevard
Braddock Heights, MD 21714
301-371-7543
Occupational Fields: bladesmith, knife maker

Blacksmith Guild of Central Maryland Inc.
PO Box 593
Randallstown, MD 21133
newky2@dejazzd.com
http://www.bgcmonline.com
Occupational Fields: blacksmith, metalworker

Chesapeake Forge Blacksmith Guild
74 Riverside Drive
Severna Park, MD 21146
410-647-6446
steel74@aol.com
Occupational Fields: blacksmith, metalworker

Furnace Town Blacksmith's Guild
6 Laport Court
Berlin, MD 21811
410-208-9098
skipjack394@mchsi.com
Occupational Fields: blacksmith, metalworker

Furnace Town Blacksmith's Guild
PO Box 7
Pocomoke City, MD 21851
410-957-2325
dmalloypcmd@aol.com
Occupational Fields: blacksmith, metalworker

Mid-Atlantic Smiths Association
Nathan's Forge
3476 Uniontown Road
Uniontown, MD 21158

410-848-7903
nickv@adelphia.net
Occupational Fields: blacksmith, metalworker

Mid-Atlantic Smiths Association
12800 Hammonton Road
Silver Spring, MD 20904
301-622-0897
nzastrow@erols.com
Occupational Fields: blacksmith, metalworker

MICHIGAN

Michigan Artist-Blacksmiths Association
3979 62nd Street
Holland, MI 49423
616-392-1514
mabaeditors@macatawa.com
http://www.miblacksmith.org
Occupational Fields: blacksmith, metalworker

Michigan Artist-Blacksmiths Association
121 Pleasant Street
Romeo, MI 48065
586-752-7016
http://www.miblacksmith.org
Occupational Fields: blacksmith, metalworker

MINNESOTA

**Artist-Blacksmith's Association of America,
  Guild of Metalsmiths**
PO Box 11423
St. Paul, MN 55111
http://www.metalsmith.org/inf/index.htm
*Occupational Fields: metalsmith, blacksmith, tinsmith,
  sculptor, coppersmith*

Central Minnesota Blacksmiths
13633 Ferman Avenue, Northwest
Clearwater, MN 55320
763-878-1694
rome.hutchings@theprairieismygarden.com
Occupational Fields: blacksmith, metalworker

Central Minnesota Blacksmiths
240 Division Street
Rice, MN 56367-8712
320-393-2713
tomcoalman@cs.com
Occupational Fields: blacksmith, metalworker

Guild of Metalsmiths
2153 Fox Place
Mendota Heights, MN 55120
651-683-0906
alan_olson@hotmail.com
Occupational Fields: *blacksmith, metalworker*

Guild of Metalsmiths
2526 California Ave, Northeast
Minneapolis, MN 55418
612-706-0198
mmceachron@earthlink.net
http://www.metalsmith.org
Occupational Fields: *blacksmith, metalworker*

Northern Minnesota Metal Smiths
9179 Beltrami Line Road, SW
Bemidji, MN 56601
keith@greatriverforge.com
Occupational Fields: *blacksmith, metalworker*

Northern Minnesota Metal Smiths
11170 County Road 25
Mizpah, MN 56660-9540
218-897-5067
Occupational Fields: *blacksmith, metalworker*

MISSISSIPPI
Mississippi Forge Council
1021 Pevey Lane
Crystal Springs, MS 39059
601-892-1867
wbpevey@aol.com
http://www.msforgecouncil.com
Occupational Fields: *blacksmith, metalworker*

Mississippi Forge Council
136 Munich Drive
Madison, MS 39110
601-982-1791
jpigott@vbaonline.com
http://www.msforgecouncil.com
Occupational Fields: *blacksmith, metalworker*

MISSOURI
Blacksmith Association of Missouri
2212 Ailewcik
St. Louis, MO 63129
http://www.bamsite.org
Occupational Fields: *blacksmith, metalworker*

Blacksmith Association of Missouri
6192 Highway 168
Shelbyville, MO 63469-2527
573-633-2010
eforge@marktwain.net
http://www.bamsite.org
Occupational Fields: *blacksmith, metalworker*

MONTANA
Northern Rockies Blacksmiths Association
PO Box 1445
Livingston, MT 59047
406-222-4770
morris@hallowellco.com
http://www.hallowellco.com/nrba.htm
Occupational Fields: *blacksmith, metalworker*

Prairie Blacksmiths Association
4020 West 13th Street
Grand Island, NE 68803-2912
308-382-5500
dstanley@cccusa.net
http://pba.abana-chapter.com
Occupational Fields: *blacksmith, metalworker*

Prairie Blacksmiths Association
3015 Orchard
Lincoln, NE 68503
402-477-4337
fvb@unl.edu
http://pba.abana-chapter.com
Occupational Fields: *blacksmith, metalworker*

NEW JERSEY
New Jersey Blacksmith Association
90 William Avenue
Staten Island, NY 10308
lp.brown@verizon.net
http://njba.abana-chapter.com
Occupational Fields: *blacksmith, metalworker*

NEW MEXICO
Southwest Artist-Blacksmiths Association
10427 San Gabriel Road, N.E.
Albuquerque, NM 87111
505-298-2280
lkernblacksmith@att.net
Occupational Fields: *blacksmith, metalworker*

Southwest Artist-Blacksmiths Association
506 Dartmouth, S.E.
Albuquerque, NM 87106
505-266-6991
Occupational Fields: blacksmith, metalworker

NEW YORK
Capital District Blacksmiths' Association
PO Box 156
Valley Falls, NY 12185
518-665-8308
contact@cdblacksmiths.org
http://www.cdblacksmiths.org
Occupational Fields: blacksmith, metalworker

Farmers' Museum
PO Box 800
Cooperstown, NY 13326-0800
607-547-1450
Occupational Fields: blacksmith

New York State Designer Blacksmiths
8500 Street Route 415
Campbell, NY 14821
607-527-3611
mydad@infoblvd.net
http://www.nysdb.org
Occupational Fields: blacksmith, metalworker

Northeastern Blacksmiths Association
496 Tow Path
High Falls, NY 12440
845-687-7130
jonned@hvc.rr.com
http://nba.abana-chapter.com
Occupational Fields: blacksmith, metalworker

Northeastern Blacksmiths Association
52 Black Road
Shokan, NY 12481
845-657-8212
spin-smythe@worldnet.att.net
http://nba.abana-chapter.com
Occupational Fields: blacksmith, metalworker

Northeastern Blacksmiths Association
112 North Putts Corner Road
New Paltz, NY 12561
845-255-8125

carlrd@worldnet.att.net
http://nba.abana-chapter.com
Occupational Fields: blacksmith, metalworker

NORTH CAROLINA
**Artist-Blacksmith's Association of America,
North Carolina Chapter**
2824 Regal Run Drive
Raleigh, NC 27603
919-661-0424
jalex@sunsite.unc.edu
Occupational Fields: blacksmith, metalworker

OHIO
Northwest Ohio Blacksmiths
3273 Angling Road
Collins, OH 44826
419-668-5327
Occupational Fields: blacksmith, metalworker

Northwest Ohio Blacksmiths
15784 Custar Road
Grand Rapids, OH 43522
419-832-5801
csheely@wcnet.org
Occupational Fields: blacksmith, metalworker

Oki Forgers
1340 High Street
Hamilton, OH 45011
513-844-1074
jgeisler@fuse.net
Occupational Fields: blacksmith, metalworker

Oki Forgers
1895 Howell Avenue
Hamilton, OH 45011
513-868-7769
habo_rs@swoca.net
Occupational Fields: blacksmith, metalworker

Southern Ohio Forge and Anvil
PO Box 24308
Huber Heights, OH 45424
937-335-6670
http://www.sofablacksmiths.org
Occupational Fields: blacksmith, metalworker

Steelworkers
Route 2, Box 232
Little Hocking, OH 45742-9704
Occupational Fields: tin smith

Western Reserve Artist Blacksmith Association
6374 Lake Road West
Madison, OH 44057
440-428-0822
mwyanko@hotmail.com
http://www.wraba.com
Occupational Fields: blacksmith, metalworker

Western Reserve Artist Blacksmith Association
17231 Messenger Road
Burton, OH 44021
440-543-8507
mlforge@aol.com
http://www.wraba.com
Occupational Fields: blacksmith, metalworker

OKLAHOMA
Saltfork Craftsmen Artist Blacksmiths Association
9501 Frontier
Perry, OK 73077
580-336-9213
colonel@fullnet.net
http://scaba.abana-chapter.com
Occupational Fields: blacksmith, metalworker

PENNSYLVANIA
Blacksmith Guild Of Central Maryland Inc.
PO Box 593
Randallstown, MD 21133
410-386-9150
http://www.bgcmonline.com
Occupational Fields: blacksmith, metalworker

Oil Valley Blacksmith's Association
21206 State Route 8
Centerville, PA 16404
814-671-1494
Occupational Fields: blacksmith, metalworker

Oil Valley Blacksmith's Association
9413 Millgrove Road
Springboro, PA 16435
814-756-0919

jspencer@velocity.net
Occupational Fields: blacksmith, metalworker

Pennsylvania Artist Blacksmith Association
5733 Cloverdale Road
Harrisburg, PA 17112
717-657-5795
Occupational Fields: blacksmith, metalworker

Pennsylvania Artist Blacksmith Association
1370 New Danville Pike
Lancaster, PA 17603
717-291-0214
redd1@ptd.net
Occupational Fields: blacksmith, metalworker

Pittsburgh Area Artist-Blacksmiths Association
2063 Lovi Road
Freedom, PA 15042
724-774-6757
steeljw@comcast.net
http://home.comcast.net/~paabasec
Occupational Fields: blacksmith, metalworker

Pittsburgh Area Artist-Blacksmiths Association
1630 Camp Meeting Road
Sewickley, PA 15143
412-741-6171
paabasec@comcast.net
http://home.comcast.net/~paabasec
Occupational Fields: blacksmith, metalworker

RHODE ISLAND
New England Blacksmiths
99 Chase Hill Road
Ashaway, RI 02804
410-377-2611
obostrom@cox.net
http://www.newenglandblacksmiths.org
Occupational Fields: blacksmith, metalworker

Society of American Silversmiths
PO Box 72839
Providence, RI 02907
401-461-6840
Fax: 401-461-6841
http://www.silversmithing.com
Occupational Fields: metalsmith, silversmith

SOUTH CAROLINA
Philip Simmons Artist-Blacksmith Guild of South Carolina
9744 Plantersville Road
Georgetown, SC 29440
843-546-5483
sharonmhill60@hotmail.com
Occupational Fields: blacksmith, metalworker

Philip Simmons Artist-Blacksmith Guild of South Carolina
1680 Laurel Street
Lexington, SC 29073
803-808-0802
tekoehler@earthlink.net
Occupational Fields: blacksmith, metalworker

SOUTH DAKOTA
Dakota Artist-Blacksmiths' Association
PO Box 394
Piedmont, SD 57769
jkhammer@rap.midco.net
Occupational Fields: blacksmith, metalworker

Dakota Artist-Blacksmiths' Association
14870 Jackie Lane
Rapid City, SD 57703
605-393-0232
Occupational Fields: blacksmith, metalworker

TENNESSEE
Artist-Blacksmith's Association of America, Appalachian Area Chapter
PO Box 838
Soddy Daisy, TN 37379
423-332-5463
http://aac.abana-chapter.com
Occupational Fields: blacksmith, metalworker

River Bluff Forge Council
1897 Crump
Memphis, TN 38107
901-278-7826
bobr@prodigy.net
http://rbfcmemphis.com
Occupational Fields: blacksmith, metalworker

River Bluff Forge Council
B 221 Meadowview
Millington, TN 38053
901-835-3095
tswirka@bnisp.com
http://rbfcmemphis.com
Occupational Fields: blacksmith, metalworker

TEXAS
American Bladesmith Society
PO Box 977
Cypress, TX 77410-1481
http://www.americanbladesmith.com
Occupational Fields: bladesmith, knife maker

Angel Sword Corporation
350 Jennifer Lane
Driftwood, TX 78619-9753
512-847-9679
Occupational Fields: swordsmith, knife maker

Balcones Forge
1906 Rampart Circle
Austin, TX 78727
512-328-4071
spotteddogforge@yahoo.com
http://www.balconesforge.org
Occupational Fields: blacksmith, metalworker

Balcones Forge
3318 Kirby Drive
San Antonio, TX 78219
210-661-3293
treefarm@swbell.net
Occupational Fields: blacksmith, metalworker

East Texas Blacksmith Alliance
320 Oak Ridge Drive
Onalaska, TX 77360
936-646-4985
tom@bluebirdforge.com
Occupational Fields: blacksmith, metalworker

East Texas Blacksmith Alliance
PO Box 888
Woodville, TX 75979
409-982-1500
Occupational Fields: blacksmith, metalworker

Four States Iron Munchers
612 South Lelia
Texarkana, TX 75501
903-792-1982

http://www.fourstatesironmunchers.com
Occupational Fields: blacksmith, metalworker

Houston Area Blacksmith's Association
10439 Rocky Hollow Road
Laporte, TX 77571
281-842-1294
dlhj66@yahoo.com
http://www.habairon.org
Occupational Fields: blacksmith, metalworker

Houston Area Blacksmith's Association
27923 FM 2978
Magnolia, TX 77345
281-356-5205
rsboswell@mindspring.com
http://www.habairon.org
Occupational Fields: blacksmith, metalworker

North Texas Blacksmiths Association
22 Citrus Way
Allen, TX 75002
972-727-7728
dwwilson@flash.net
http://home.flash.net/~dwwilson/ntba
Occupational Fields: blacksmith, metalworker

UTAH
Bonneville Forge Council
2288 North 1200 West
Clinton, UT 84015
801-773-3359
starforged@comcast.net
Occupational Fields: blacksmith, metalworker

Bonneville Forge Council
265 Valley View Drive
Tooele, UT 84074
435-882-2128
kennen03@netzero.net
Occupational Fields: blacksmith, metalworker

VIRGINIA
Blacksmiths' Guild of the Potomac
5436 21st Street North
Arlington, VA 22205-3023
703-534-3927
locustforge@cs.com
Occupational Fields: blacksmith, metalworker

Blacksmiths' Guild of the Potomac
3608 North Military Road
Arlington, VA 22207
703-620-6454
bgop.editor@verizon.net
http://www.bgop.org
Occupational Fields: blacksmith, metalworker

Central Virginia Blacksmith Guild
4790 Shady Grove Road
Glen Allen, VA 23059
804-360-2380
cattailforge@earthlink.net
http://www.cvbg.org
Occupational Fields: blacksmith, metalworker

Central Virginia Blacksmith Guild
408 Lakeside Boulevard
Richmond, VA 23227
804-264-4022
empireiron@aol.com
http://www.cvbg.org
Occupational Fields: blacksmith, metalworker

Colonial Williamsburg Foundation
PO Box 1776
Williamsburg, VA 23187-1776
757-229-1000
http://www.visitwilliamsburg.com
Occupational Fields: silversmith, blacksmith, gunsmith, cooper

Tidewater Blacksmith's Guild
601 Pembroke Ave, Suite 1005
Norfolk, VA 23507
757-627-1588
snoozp@aol.com
Occupational Fields: blacksmith, metalworker

Tidewater Blacksmith's Guild
4500 Drum Castle Court
Virginia Beach, VA 23455
757-363-0314
robjeniantim@sprynet.com
Occupational Fields: blacksmith, metalworker

WASHINGTON
Glaziers, Architectural Metal, and Glassworkers
6770 East Marginal Way, South
Seattle, WA 98108

206-762-7001
Occupational Fields: architectural metalworker

Inland Northwest Blacksmith Association
6001 West 4th Avenue
Kennewick, WA 99336-1856
Occupational Fields: blacksmith, metalworker

Inland Northwest Blacksmith Association
PO Box 4474
West Richland, WA 99353
509-308-1656
Occupational Fields: blacksmith, metalworker

Northwest Blacksmiths Association
7926-320th Street East
Eatonville, WA 98328
253-847-3235
tlcforge@aol.com
Occupational Fields: blacksmith, metalworker

Northwest Blacksmiths Association
8002 Northeast Highway 99, Suite 405
Spokane, WA 98665
509-624-0100
kagele@aol.com
http://www.blacksmith.org
Occupational Fields: blacksmith, metalworker

WEST VIRGINIA
Appalachian Blacksmith Association
640 Davisson Run Road
Clarksburg, WV 26301
304-242-2467
anvilwork@aol.com
http://www.appaltree.net
Occupational Fields: blacksmith, metalworker

WISCONSIN
Artist-Blacksmith's Association of America, Upper Midwest Blacksmiths Association
180 Cox Road
Edgerton, WI 53534
Occupational Fields: farrier, blacksmith

Upper Midwest Blacksmiths Association
1026 Tappan Street
Woodstock, IL 60098

608-362-3668
canoeman@ticon.net
http://www.umbaonline.org
Occupational Fields: blacksmith, metalworker

CANADA
ALBERTA
Kootenay Blacksmith's Association
Chinook Country Forge
Site 113, Box 12, RR 3
Sundre, AB T0M 1X0
403-638-3529
ironshop@telus.net
Occupational Fields: blacksmith, metalworker

Western Canadian Blacksmiths' Association
7115-4 Street, NW
Calgary, AB T2K 1C3
403-274-6486
giverhau@telusplanet.net
http://www.wcbg.org
Occupational Fields: blacksmith, metalworker

Western Canadian Blacksmiths' Association
14707-115th Street
Edmonton, AB T5X 1H7
780-456-0786
fwreyno@telusplanet.net
http://www.wcbg.org
Occupational Fields: blacksmith, metalworker

BRITISH COLUMBIA
Kootenay Forge
PO Box 119
Crawford Bay, BC V0B-1E0
250-225-3333
johnsmith2000@telus.net
Occupational Fields: blacksmith, metalworker

Vancouver Island Blacksmith's Association
1040 Marwood Avenue
Victoria, BC V9C-3C4
250-478-4095
viba@viblacksmiths.com
http://www.viblacksmiths.com
Occupational Fields: blacksmith, metalworker

NOVA SCOTIA

Maritime Blacksmiths Association
PO Box 46048 Novalea
Halifax, NS B3K 5V8
902-454-2266
allenbt@hfx.eastlink.ca
Occupational Fields: blacksmith, metalworker

ONTARIO

Ontario Artist-Blacksmiths Association
475 Columbus Road East
Brooklin, ON L1M 1Z6
905-471-3930
ontarioblacksmith@ncf.ca
ontarioblacksmith.ncf.ca
Occupational Fields: blacksmith, metalworker

SASKATCHEWAN

Western Canadian Blacksmiths' Association
618 Trent Crescent
Saskatoon, SK S7H 4T6
306-373-3159
bwilson@sk.sympatico.ca
http://www.wcbg.org
Occupational Fields: blacksmith, metalworker

MIDWIVES

RELATED SECTIONS: *emergency services technicians, health care workers, herbalists, social activists and human services workers*

Midwives are women who care for women and their babies before, during, and after childbirth. (The word "midwife" means "with woman.") Midwives strive to improve the health of women and infants, to lower the rate of death due to childbirth, and to help women take an active part in their own health care.

Midwifery provides an option for healthy women who expect an uncomplicated birth and wish to deliver their babies naturally, perhaps at home, with little intervention by a health care professional. This ancient profession has been practiced in the United States for centuries, most frequently in situations where the mother and baby were prevented by distance or other factors from receiving care from doctors and formally trained nurses. Midwives often collaborate with doctors and other health care professionals to ensure that their clients receive the best possible care. In 1995 nurse-midwives attended more than 200,000 births in this country; additional births were attended by lay midwives.

Certified nurse-midwives are registered nurses who specialize in women's health care and hold at least a bachelor's degree in nursing from a college or university. Nurses care for the "whole person," including physical, mental, and emotional needs. They may be employed by hospitals, clinics, physicians' offices, or they may be self-employed, often working in collaboration with physicians and other health-care professionals.

Certified midwives also hold at least a bachelor's degree and have taken certain college science courses, but they do not have the medical education of certified nurse-midwives. Certified professional midwives have passed a certification examination offered by a professional association called the Midwives Alliance of North America (MANA).

Lay midwives (also known as *direct entry, licensed, or professional midwives*) do not hold college or university credentials in nursing, but most of them have completed many of the same studies through some other avenue. *Doulas* are women who assist midwives.

Midwifery has been a source of controversy in recent decades as states have tried to establish standards and regulations to protect the health and safety of mothers and their babies. Every state and the District of Columbia have granted nurse-midwives the right to practice their profession. In contrast, the legal status of lay midwives

varies widely, depending on the state. In some states lay midwives are allowed to practice, generally with restrictions. In other states they can face criminal charges if they accept payment for their services. The legal status of lay midwives is in dispute in some states. Midwives whose practice is tied to their religious beliefs receive special consideration in certain states.

Lay midwives typically help mothers deliver babies at home or in birthing centers. Nurse-midwives sometimes attend births in homes or birthing centers but often have collaborative agreements with hospitals, allowing expectant mothers to schedule the birth there or to come to the hospital if unforeseen circumstances arise. Often nurse-midwives have the legal right to accompany expectant mothers through a hospital birth, but lay midwives may not.

All licensed midwives must complete training and pass an examination. Certified nurse-midwives earn a bachelor's degree in nursing from a college or university, complete clinical experiences in maternity and other subjects at a hospital or other health-care facility, and usually complete advanced studies in the special needs of women and children.

Lay midwives learn under the supervision of experienced midwives, usually through apprenticeship, and complete much of the same type of course work as nurse-midwives. Many mentors accept an apprentice only after the applicant has completed years of study and experience. Midwifery schools often help their students obtain apprenticeships with practicing midwives. In states such as California, where lay midwives were first granted the right to obtain licenses in 1993, apprenticeships have become increasingly common.

The course of study can run from several months to several years and typically includes instruction in such subjects as anatomy, embryology, microbiology, genetics, pharmacology, prenatal care, labor, delivery, and examinations of mother and baby after the birth.

In general an applicant should

- be caring and sympathetic
- have an aptitude for science
- be able to accept great responsibility
- be willing to accommodate expectant mothers' wishes as much as possible

APPRENTICESHIP SALARIES

Apprentices may or may not be paid for their services as they assist their mentors during births. In many programs, apprentices must pay tuition when they enroll.

POSTAPPRENTICESHIP SALARIES

About $15 an hour for nurse-midwives, up to $20 or more plus benefits. Lay midwives establish their own fees; their earnings vary widely, in part because some of them are not allowed by state law to charge for their services.

JOB OUTLOOK

Generally good, because many mothers prefer to experience childbirth in the company of other women and in the most natural way possible. The prospects are particularly good for nurse-midwives, due to a general shortage of nurses throughout the health-care professions. Because of legal issues, lay midwives should expect difficulties if they wish to practice their profession in states that have not sanctioned lay midwifery.

For more information on apprenticeships for midwives, contact the individual programs listed below, local job centers, your state bureau of apprenticeship training, or local midwives.

WEB SITES

Marilyn's Midwifery Page
midwife@heartoftn.net
http://www.midwifery2000.com
Occupational Fields: midwife

Midwifery Today
http://www.midwiferytoday.com
Occupational Fields: midwife

Online Birth Center
http://www.efn.org/~djz/birth/birthindex.html
Occupational Fields: midwife

Sabrina's Pregnancy Page
swnymph@fensende.com
http://www.fensende.com/Users/swnymph
Occupational Fields: midwife

APPRENTICESHIP PROFILE

Maternidad La Luz
1308 Magoffin Street
El Paso, TX 79901
915-532-5895
Fax: 915-532-7127
http://www.maternidadlaluz.com

General Nature of the Job

Maternidad La Luz is one of the largest midwifery teaching clinics in the country, offering training programs on many different levels. Some students are already midwives who want more on-the-job training; others come to observe for a short time. Some, like Ruth Leah Caussman, train for a full year to become certified professional midwives.

Apprentices work three 24-hour shifts a week. Once an apprentice learns certain techniques, she's right there taking vital signs, doing pap smears, and listening to a baby's heart. There's also laundry to do, equipment to sterilize and restock, and ringing phones to answer.

After six months of training, apprentices begin their internship. As an intern, Ruth has five of her own clients, women she follows through pregnancy. She is the primary staff on her clients' birth team, helping the woman through her labor and catching the baby when it comes. Birth teams consist of a staff midwife, who oversees the process, the primary, and three other people, often apprentices, who assist in the birth process.

Typical Day

"Maternidad is an intense combination of clinical and academic work," Ruth says. For her first two weeks in the program, Ruth attended classes all day. Once you begin working 24-hour shifts, classroom instruction is reduced to three-hour classes three times a week. "In class, you learn the basic skills," Ruth says, "like taking vital signs and the physiology of birth. You also learn about complications, such as diabetes and hypertension." Ruth and her classmates practiced certain procedures on each other. "When I was ready, I started on clients," she says.

When Ruth begins her shift, "the first thing we do is meet with the staff going off duty, to see where we're at, what births may be in progress, things like that." Clients come in for prenatal and postpartum checkups all day long from 8:00 A.M. to 8:00 P.M. "It's a busy clinic," Ruth explains. "One day we had twenty-three appointments, a woman dilated at nine centimeters in one birthing room, and another across the hall at seven."

By 8:00 at night, when appointments are over, Ruth may get a chance to slow down a little and eat some supper. If the rest of the night is quiet, she'll sterilize equipment, prepare rooms, and maybe catch a little sleep. "I also need to find time to study. There are three intense exams a year and lots of homework. "But if babies come, there's none of that," Ruth says.

Path to Becoming an Apprentice

Ruth's journey to Maternidad began years ago in West Africa while she was in the Peace Corps. "In my village, European and local midwives provided all the health care for the entire community. I knew if I wanted health care that reached the people, I should do midwifery." For years Ruth immersed herself in women's health issues, such as rape prevention and family planning, before she made her way back to midwifery.

At first Ruth enrolled in the University of Pennsylvania's nurse midwifery program. "The medical model there was difficult for me," Ruth said. "Our medical system treats pregnant women as sick patients and pregnancy as an illness. In midwifery, pregnancy is viewed as normal and healthy. Oh, there can be problems, but the whole idea is to teach women to get in touch with their own birth process." One major contrast in the two models involves fetal monitoring. "We do intermittent monitoring," Ruth said, "with a hand-held device called a dopler. Hospitals hook women up to a monitor, which restricts their movement. Our women are free to move around, take walks. It's natural to birthing to move around."

"It was important for me to come here," Ruth said about Maternidad. "One of my beliefs is the need to change the status quo. Midwifery helps to do that. Taking control of our birthing process is one way to get control of our lives."

Maternidad accepts people into their program every March and September. To receive a booklet with an application, call the clinic. Your background and what inspired you to become a midwife are a very important part of the application process. Six months of study costs apprentices about $2,150, and there is no pay for on-the-job training. Ruth provides her own room and board off campus.

Salary Range

Midwifery is for the dedicated, Ruth says. Midwives charge anywhere from $500 to $2,000 for complete pregnancy care, and, according to Ruth, many need second jobs to help support their families. At Maternidad, a full-time staff midwife who works two 24-hour shifts a week makes about $21,000 a year.

Midwifery is beginning to flourish as a profession, but complicated issues still surround it in many states. "Whether or not you can make a living at it depends on where you want to practice," Ruth says. "In New York, for instance, midwifery is illegal." Having a midwife deliver a baby is usually more economical than a traditional hospital birth. "Providing economical health care is part of midwifery," Ruth says. "It's not for people who want to be rich."

Advice

Ruth advises people who want to be midwives to read everything they can get their hands on. Take jobs at women's clinics, volunteer to be a support person to women in labor, or become a Lamaze instructor. "Being effective with women is the most important skill you can have," Ruth said. "You can learn the procedures, but if you can't empower women, you won't be able to do this job well."

Future Goals

Ruth plans to stay on at Maternidad as a staff-in-training, working closely with another staff member for pay. Ruth sees herself as a midwife for years to come, actively creating community health programs that support women and their families. Later on, she would love to do a combination of home births and center births.

ALABAMA

Alabama Midwives
c/o Mary Rutherford
1610 Douglas Street, SE
Cullman, AL 35055
http://www.alabamamidwives.com
Occupational Fields: midwife

ALASKA

Board of Certified Direct-Entry Midwives
Department of Commerce and Economic
    Development
PO Box 110806
Juneau, AK 99801
907-465-2534
Steve_Snyder@dced.state.ak.us
Occupational Fields: midwife

Midwives Association of Alaska
c/o Pam Weaver
PO Box 672169
Chugiak, AK 99567
907-688-2000
Fax: 907-688-2000
Occupational Fields: midwife

ARIZONA
Midwifery Education Accredidation Council (MEAC)
c/o Mary Ann Baul, LM
220 West Birch
Flagstaff, AZ 86001
520-214-0997
info@meacschools.org
http://www.meacschools.org
Occupational Fields: midwife

ARKANSAS

Arkansas Association of Midwives
c/o Ida Darragh
4322 County Club Boulevard
Little Rock, AR 72207-2030
501-663-6051
ivd@aol.com
Occupational Fields: midwife

CALIFORNIA
Association for Pre- & Perinatal Psychology and Health (APPPAH)
c/o Maureen Wolfe, C.N.M., Executive Director
340 Colony Road
Geyserville, CA 95441
707-857-4041
Fax: 707-857-4042
apppah@aol.com
http://www.birthpsychology.com
Occupational Fields: midwife

California Association of Midwives
PO Box 460606
San Francisco, CA 94146
800-829-5791
midwives@wenet.net
http://www.californiamidwives.org
Occupational Fields: midwife

Full Moon Childbirth Support Services
333 East Camino Real Avenue
Monrovia, CA 91016
626-358-2318
Fax: 626-358-9478
info@Support4Birth.com
http://www.Support4Birth.com
Occupational Fields: midwife

Informed Homebirth/Informed Birth and Parenting
PO Box 1733
Fair Oaks, CA 95628
916-961-6923
IHIBP@softcom.net
Occupational Fields: midwife

COLORADO
Birthing the Future/Suzanne Arms
PO Box 1040
Bayfield, CO 81122
303-884-4090
suzanne@birthingthefuture.com
http://www.birthingthefuture.com
Occupational Fields: midwife

Colorado Midwives Association
PO Box 1067
Boulder, CO 80306
800-829-5791
http://www.coloradomidwives.org
Occupational Fields: midwife

Rocky Mountain Midwives
4150 Darley Avenue, Suite 10
PO Box 1067
Boulder, CO 80306
303-494-9195
http://guide.boulder.net/Midwives
Occupational Fields: midwife

CONNECTICUT
Alliance of Connecticut Midwives
2 Alpine Drive
Sandy Hook, CT 06482-1203
203-426-4248
CTmidwife@aol.com
Occupational Fields: midwife

The Birth Institute, LLC
West Hartford, CT
860-280-5893
Occupational Fields: midwife

FLORIDA
Midwives Association of Florida
PO Box 4413
Hallandale, FL 33008
preciouspackages@earthlink.net
Occupational Fields: midwife

GEORGIA
Citizens for Midwifery
PO Box 82227
Athens, GA 30608-2227
888-236-4880
http://www.cfmidwifery.org
Occupational Fields: midwife

Georgia Midwives Association,
c/o Debbie Pulley
5257 Rosestone Drive
Lilburn, GA 30047
770-381-2339
manamw@aol.com
Occupational Fields: midwife

Midwives Alliance of North America
375 Rockbridge Road, Suite 172-313
Lilburn, GA 30047
888-923-6262
Fax: 417-777-6181
info@mana.org
http://www.mana.org
Occupational Fields: midwife

HAWAII
Hawaii Midwives Alliance
c/o Helen Green
808-965-7503
bayofp@1hawaii.net
Occupational Fields: midwife

IDAHO
Idaho Midwifery Council
c/o Kathleen McDonald
2115 N. 29th

Boise, ID 83703
208-343-8251
Occupational Fields: midwife

INDIANA
Doulas of North America
PO Box 626
Jasper, IN 47547
888-788-DONA
Fax: 812-634-1491
doula@dona.org
http://www.dona.com
Occupational Fields: midwife, doula

Indiana Midwives Association and Indiana Midwifery Taskforce
c/o Diane Holmes, CPM
832 N. State Road 15
Wabash, IN 46992
adholmes@netusa1.net
Occupational Fields: midwife, doula

IOWA
Iowa Midwives Association
c/o Beverly Francis
Rural Route 1 Box 172A
Mt. Sterling, IA 52573
319-494-5512
iowamama@aol.com
Occupational Fields: midwife

KANSAS
Kansas Midwives Association
c/o Signe Rogers
PO Box 175
Newton, KS 67114
Occupational Fields: midwife

KENTUCKY
Frontier School of Midwifery and Family Nursing
Hospital Hill
PO Box 528
Hyden, KY 41749
606-672-2312
http://www.midwives.org
Occupational Fields: nurse-midwife

LOUISIANA

Louisiana Midwives Association
c/o Misty Richard
1901 Carolyn
Denham Springs, LA 70726
225-667-1210 (home)
225-955-8262 (cellular)
rdrunr7@juno.com
Occupational Fields: midwife

MARYLAND

Chesapeake Midwifery Guild
c/o Gwen Peters
6741 Cedar Lane
Columbia, MD 21044
410-531-5839
Fax: 410-531-5839
havinbabies@home.com
Occupational Fields: midwife, doula

Maryland Friends of Midwives
c/o Sandra Loats
153 East Main Street
Westminster, MD 21157
Occupational Fields: midwife

MASSACHUSETTS

**Association of Labor Assistants and Childbirth
   Educators**
PO Box 390436
Cambridge, MA 02139
617-441-2500
Occupational Fields: midwife, doula

**Boston University School of Public Health Nurse-
   Midwifery Education Program**
715 Albany Street, TWS
Boston, MA 02118
617-638-5012
Occupational Fields: midwife

Massachusetts Friends of Midwives
c/o Jim Henderson, President
PO Box 81301
Wellesley, MA 02481-0003
781-237-9920
info@mfom.org
http://www.mfom.org
Occupational Fields: midwife, doula

MICHIGAN

Birthnetwork
c/o Shawn Spry
5704 Clinton River
Waterford, MI 48237
781-237-9920
Occupational Fields: midwife

Michigan Friends of Midwives
c/o Helen Lowe
13042 Michalek's Lane
South Lyon, MI 48178-9169
410-876-0551
Occupational Fields: midwife

Michigan Midwives Association
4220 East Loop Road
Hesperia, MI 49421
877-BIRTH-4U
pbobier@voyager.net
http://www.michiganmidwives.org
Occupational Fields: midwife

MINNESOTA

Minnesotans for Midwifery
c/o Kerry Dixon
769 Ashland Avenue
St. Paul, MN 55104
612-224-7480
kdmidwife@aol.com
Occupational Fields: midwife

MISSOURI

**National Association of Parents and Professionals
   for Safe Alternatives in Childbirth, Intl.
   (NAPSAC,Intl)**
PO Box 267
Marble Hill, MO 63764
573-238-2010
Occupational Fields: midwife

MONTANA

Dolly Ellen Browder
200 Woodworth Avenue
Missoula, MT 59801
406-543-6826
dbrowder@uswest.net
Occupational Fields: midwife

Montana Midwifery Association
c/o Stacey Haughland, CPM
508 North Third Street
Bozeman, MT 59715
406-585-0752
Occupational Fields: midwife

NEVADA
Nevada Midwives Association
c/o Marjorie Dacko
286 Merrick Way
Henderson, NV 89014
702-433-8533
dacko@lvcm.com
Occupational Fields: midwife

NEW HAMPSHIRE
New Hampshire Midwives Association
c/o Sherry Stevens
124 Winona Road
Meredith, NH 03253
http://www.nhmidwives.org
Occupational Fields: midwife

NEW JERSEY
New Jersey Friends of Midwives
c/o Joanne Gottschall
200 North Jasper Avenue
Margate, NJ 08402
609-487-0779
birthwise@webtv.net
Occupational Fields: midwife

NEW MEXICO
Julia Knight-Williamson
511 Wellesley, SE
Albuquerque, NM 87106
505-265-2782
abq2001@aol.com
Occupational Fields: midwife

New Mexico Midwives Association
PO Box 40647
Albuquerque, NM 87196-1647
Aural@swcp.com
Occupational Fields: midwife

NEW YORK
Midwives Alliance of New York State
223 Vienna Road
Newark, NY 14513
315-331-8482
swiss223@flare.net
Occupational Fields: midwife

New York Friends of Midwives
c/o Tisha Graham
69 Van Dam Street
Saratoga Springs, NY 12866
518-584-6619
tgnyfom@aol.com
Occupational Fields: midwife

Rochester Birth Network/Monthly Homebirth Circle
c/o Lauren Sample
173 Weldon Street
Rochester, NY 14611
716-527-0943
bullmoose@att.net
Occupational Fields: midwife

OHIO
Midwives Alliance of North America (MANA)
58 West Jefferson
West Jefferson, OH 3162
http://ohiomidwives.org
Occupational Fields: midwife

OKLAHOMA
Oklahoma Midwives Alliance
c/o Gail Brown, CPM
okmidwife@juno.com
Occupational Fields: midwife

OREGON
Birthingway College of Midwifery and Birthingway Midwifery Center
Contact: Cathy Warren, Operations Coordinator
12113 SE Foster Road
Portland, OR 97266
503-706-3131
birthing@teleport.com
Occupational Fields: midwife

International Center for Traditional Childbearing
PO Box 11923
Portland, OR 97217
503-460-9324
http://www.blackmidwives.org/index2.php
Occupational Fields: midwife

International School of Traditional Midwifery
3607 Highway 66
Ashland, OR 97520
541-488-8273
http://www.oregonmidwifery.org/ORschools.htm
Occupational Fields: midwife

Oregon Board of Direct Entry Midwifery
700 Summer Street, Northeast, Suite 100
Salem, OR 97301-1287
503-378-8667
http://www.oregon.gov/HLO/DEM/index.shtml
Occupational Fields: midwife

Oregon Midwifery Council
c/o Peggy Sawyer
10798 Yank Gulch Road
Talent, OR 97540
Peggy@Jeffnet.org
Occupational Fields: midwife, doula

Oregon School of Midwifery
Contact: Daphne Singingtree, LM,CPM, Executive
    Director
342 East 12th
Eugene, OR 97404
541-338-9778
info@orgeonmidwifery.org
http://www.oregonmidwifery.org
Occupational Fields: midwife

Waterbirth International/Global Maternal Child Health Association
c/o Barbara Harper, RN, Founder and Director
24285 SW Stafford Road
Tualatin, OR 97062
800-507-6103
waterbirth@aol.com
http://www.waterbirth.org
Occupational Fields: midwife

PENNSYLVANIA
Midwives Alliance of Pennsylvania
PO Box 54
Mercer, PA
Occupational Fields: midwife

Pennsylvania Midwives Association
c/o Judy Mentzer
4560 Orrstown Road
Orrstown, PA 17244
717-530-9366
Occupational Fields: midwife

RHODE ISLAND
Supporting Mother's Life Experiences in Rhode Island (SMILE)
c/o Laura Taylor
PO Box 1017
Chepachet, RI 02814
401-258-4507
smileinRI@juno.com
Occupational Fields: midwife

SOUTH CAROLINA
South Carolina Midwives Association
c/o Tavish Brinton
1644 Charles Town Road
Leesville, SC 29070
803-894-3829
Occupational Fields: midwife

SOUTH DAKOTA
South Dakota Safe Childbirth Options
c/o Elizabeth Avery
PO Box 424
Alcester, SD 57001
605-547-1020
burningbush@eastplains.net
sdsco@eastplains.net
http://www.vbfree.org/sdsco
Occupational Fields: midwife

TENNESSEE
The Farm Midwives
PO Box 217
Summertown, TN 38483

931-964-2472
midwives@themacisp.net
http://www.midwiferyworkshops.org
Occupational Fields: midwife

Tennessee Midwives Association
c/o Maggie Barry
725 Maryland Avenue
Bristol, TN 37620
423-764-2374
maggie@3wave.com
Occupational Fields: midwife

TEXAS
Association of Texas Midwives
401 East Front Street, Suite 143
Tyler, TX 75702
903-592-4220
http://www.texasmidwives.com
Occupational Fields: midwife

Center for Professional Midwifery Education
1517 East Missouri
El Paso, TX 79902
Occupational Fields: midwife

Maternidad La Luz
1308 Magoffin Avenue
El Paso, TX 79901
915-532-5895
http://www.maternidadlaluz.com
Occupational Fields: midwife

Texas Department of Health
Bureau of Women and Children
1100 West 49th Street
Austin, TX 78756-3183
512-458-7700
http://www.dshs.state.tx.us
Occupational Fields: midwife

UTAH
Utah Midwives Association
c/o Katherine Tarr
438 S. State Street
Mt. Pleasant, UT 84647
Occupational Fields: midwife

Utah Midwives Association
1168 S. Foothill Dr., Suite 636
Salt Lake City, UT 84108
801-581-9717
Occupational Fields: midwife

VIRGINIA
Commonwealth Midwives' Alliance
c/o Trinlie Wood
PO Box 339
Sperryville, VA 22740
etlan@summit.net
Occupational Fields: midwife

Virginia Families for Natural Birth and Health Care
c/o Julie Greene
1025 Chesapeake Avenue
Hampton, VA 23661
757-244-7657
Occupational Fields: midwife

VERMONT
Luce, Judith E., LM, CPM
30 Park Street
Barre, VT 05641
802-476-7056
MidwifeOne@aol.com
Occupational Fields: midwife

Vermont Midwives Alliance
c/o Barbara Darshan
PO Box 128
Hancock, VT 05748
Occupational Fields: midwife

WASHINGTON
Doulas of North America (DONA)
1100 23rd Avenue, East
Seattle, WA 98112
206- 325-0472
http://www.dona.com
Occupational Fields: midwife

Midwives Association of Washington State
PO Box 13136
Mill Creek, WA 98082-1136

888-422-4784
Occupational Fields: midwife

Seattle Midwifery School
4000 Northeast 41st, Building D, Suite 3
Seattle, Washington 98105
206-322-8834
Fax: 206-328-2840
info@seattlemidwifery.org
http://www.seattlemidwifery.org
Occupational Fields: midwife

WEST VIRGINIA
Midwives Alliance of West Virginia
c/o Martha Blizzard-White
PO Box 279
Arthurdale, WV 26520-0279
304-864-3845
ottrmoon@aol.com
Occupational Fields: midwife

WISCONSIN
Wisconsin Guild of Midwives
c/o Jane Peterson, CPM
E453 County Road B
Scandinavia, WI 54977
715-445-2277
wimidwife@usa.net
Occupational Fields: midwife

WYOMING
Wyoming Midwives
c/o Julie Buckles
2716 Warren Avenue
Cheyenne, WY 82001
Occupational Fields: midwife

CANADA
ALBERTA
Alberta Association of Midwives
Main Post Office Box 11957
Edmonton, AB T5J 3L1
780-425-5464
albertamidwives@shaw.ca
Occupational Fields: midwife

BRITISH COLUMBIA
Canadian Association of Midwives
#207-2051 McCallum Road
Abbotsford, BC V2S 3N5
Occupational Fields: midwife

Midwifery Program
University of British Columbia
B54-2194 Health Sciences Mall
Vancouver, BC CV6T1Z3
604-822-0352
Fax: 604-822-8030
midwifery@familymed.ubc.ca
http://www.midwifery.ubc.ca
Occupational Fields: midwife

Midwives Association of British Columbia
#336, 5740 Cambie Street
Vancouver, BC V5Z 3A6
604-736-5976
Fax: 604-736-5957
mabc@telus.net
Occupational Fields: midwife

MANITOBA
Midwives Association of Manitoba
LL-691 Woseley Avenue
Winnipeg, MB R3G 1C3
204-788-8141
Fax: 204-772-7998
infor@manitobamidwives.com
http://manitobamidwives.com
Occupational Fields: midwife

NEW BRUNSWICK
Midwives Association of New Brunswick
PO Box 25023
Moncton, NB E1C 9M9
506-536-0709
midwives@manb-asfnb.ca
Occupational Fields: midwife

NEWFOUNDLAND
Association of Midwives of Newfoundland and Labrador
Rm 107, Centre for Nursing Studies
Southcott Hall, 100 Forest Road

St. John's, NF A1A 1E5
709-777-8140
Occupational Fields: midwife

NOVA SCOTIA
Association of Nova Scotia Midwives
PO Box 968
Wolfville, NS B0P 1X0
902-582-7133
Occupational Fields: midwife

ONTARIO
Association of Ontario Midwives
789 Don Mills Road, Suite 201
Toronto, ON M3C 1T5
Fax: 416-425-6905
admin@aom.on.ca
Occupational Fields: midwife

Midwifery Education Program
Laurential University
935 Ramsey Lake Road
Sudbury, ON P3E2C6
705-675-4822
sjames@laurentian.ca
Occupational Fields: midwife

Midwifery Education Program
McMaster University
Michael G. DeGroote Centre for Learning & Discovery
Third Floor, 3103
1200 Main Street West
Hamilton, ON L8N 3Z5
905-525-9140 ext. 26654
Fax: 905-523-6459
Occupational Fields: midwife

Midwifery Education Program
Ryerson University
350 Victoria Street
Toronto, ON M5B 2K3
416-979-5000
http://www.ryerson.ca/midwife
Occupational Fields: midwife

PRINCE EDWARD ISLAND
Prince Edward Island Midwives Association
34 Russet Drive
Charlottetown, PE C1E 1B7
Occupational Fields: midwife

QUEBEC
Regroupement les Sages-Femmes du Quebec
Suite 442
6555 Chemin de la Cote-des-Neiges
Montreal, QC H3S 2A6
514-738-8090
Fax: 514-738-0370
sages.femmes.qc@sympatico.ca
Occupational Fields: midwife

SASKATCHEWAN
Midwives Association of Saskatchewan
226 7th Street East
Saskatoon, SK S7H 0X1
306-653-3755
Occupational Fields: midwife

MILLWRIGHTS

RELATED SECTIONS: *auto body workers; boilermakers; carpenters; elevator constructors; ironworkers; laborers; machinists; masons; mechanics; metalworkers; operating engineers and stationary engineers; pile drivers; railroad workers; sheet metal workers; shipbuilding and ship maintenance workers; tool, die, mold, and pattern makers; welders*

Millwrights install, repair, and replace industrial manufacturing equipment and machinery, such as electric turbines and generators, conveyor systems, and escalators. They also lubricate parts, perform routine maintenance, and pour concrete foundations for new equipment.

Millwrights position heavy, bulky machinery with pulleys, cables, and other hoisting devices. Sometimes operators of hydraulic lifts, trucks, and cranes help millwrights move extremely large machines. Millwrights use a wide variety of hand tools and power tools, including cutting torches, welding machines, soldering guns, lathes, grinders, squares, and calipers. They must know how to read blueprints, pour concrete, work with wood and steel, fit bearings, align gears and wheels, connect belts, measure angles and small distances, and solve various mechanical difficulties. They sometimes work with manufacturer's representatives or experts in electronics or computers when they install and service complex, automated machinery. The job requires physical strength and the ability to work well with other people.

Millwrights often work in shops at factories. They sometimes wear protective gear, such as shatterproof glasses, helmets, and safety belts, to reduce their risk of on-the-job injury. Typically, they work 40 hours a week, but overtime is sometimes required. They are often expected to work with little supervision and must possess good problem-solving skills. They occasionally are promoted to supervisory jobs, but in general they receive raises instead of advancement to other positions.

Most millwrights work for manufacturing companies, particularly in industries that produce automobiles, equipment, items made of steel, and other durable products. Others work on construction projects or for wholesalers that sell machines and equipment. Many are members of labor unions. There are more job openings in this trade in industrialized parts of the country.

Unions and other organizations in the building and construction trades offer apprenticeship training for millwrights. Apprenticeships and on-the-job training are common ways of entering this trade. Apprentices work under the supervision of experienced workers and receive at least 144 hours of classroom training each year. Typically, the course of study includes instruction in welding, sheet metal work, carpentry skills, mathematics, computers, electronics, blueprint reading, electricity, and hydraulics.

In general an applicant should

- apply in person
- be at least 18 years old
- be a high school graduate or hold a GED certificate
- have good mathematical skills
- be able to work with precision
- be able to work independently or as a member of a team
- be able to work swiftly and efficiently
- have a strong aptitude for mechanics
- be in good physical condition
- have good communication skills

APPRENTICESHIP SALARIES

About 30 to 40 percent of journeyman's wage, with incremental increases.

POSTAPPRENTICESHIP SALARIES

About $15 an hour, up to $28 an hour. Earnings vary, depending on the specific job and geographic location.

JOB OUTLOOK

Employment of millwrights is expected to grow more slowly than the average for all occupations through 2012. The development of new technologies such as hydraulic torque wrenches, ultrasonic measuring tools, and laser shaft alignment, which allow millwrights to work more efficiently, has slowed expansion in this field.

For more information on apprenticeships for millwrights, contact local job centers, your state bureau of apprenticeship training, or the national organizations and individual programs listed below.

NATIONAL PROGRAMS

United Brotherhood of Carpenters and Joiners of America
101 Constitution Avenue, NW
Washington, DC 20001

202-546-6206 ext. 300
Fax: 202-546-3054
http://www.carpenters.org
Occupational Fields: carpenter, cabinetmaker, millwright,
    pile driver, floor layer

APPRENTICESHIP PROFILE
Millwrights Union, Local #1607
Southern California-Nevada Regional Council of
    Carpenters
923 South Gerhart, Suite 200
Los Angeles, CA 90022
323-724-0178
http://users.adelphia.net/~mwron/1607.html

General Nature of the Job
You'll find millwrights like Faye Tolson working at brewer-
ies, waste water treatment plants, food processing plants,
refineries, and nuclear power plants—places where metal
machinery is used. Millwrights install, dismantle, disassemble, repair, and replace units in order to keep production
flowing smoothly. In a factory or nuclear plant, for example, a millwright might install and perform maintenance
on conveyor systems, escalators, and electrical generators.
Millwrights may also plan the layout of new machinery,
using tools such as engine lathes, metric sockets, drill
presses, planers, shapers, and hand tools. Millwrights can
become certified in specialized skills such as laser alignment, valve repair, compressor repair, and welding.

It's a job that requires excellent hand-eye coordination.
Millwrights have to look at a one-dimensional blueprint,
and then visualize it in order to create a three-dimen-
sional product. Considering that millwrights often work
to specifications of 1/1,000 of an inch, they need to be
perfectionists. Millwrights are responsible for purchasing
their own tools. With the average precision tool costing
upwards of $200, Faye estimates that she's invested over
$2,000 in tools so far.

Typical Day
Since she often has a long drive to a job site (which can
be anywhere in Southern California), Faye wakes up at
4:00 A.M. It is always pitch black outside when her alarm
goes off, even on the longest summer days. But she takes
pride in the fact that she has her tools on her cart, ready
to go, right at 6:00 A.M.

Early on in her apprenticeship, Faye performed an
assortment of tasks on the job. "You count parts and

deliver them to a journeyman, set up welders, carry ladders, and clean up. It's not glamorous, but you're exposed
to all sides of the trade," she says. During her first year, a
supervisor once dumped a large pile of hardware on the
floor and asked Faye to separate it by type and size. What
could have been an afternoon of drudgery was exciting
for her. "I learned so much that day," Faye enthuses. "I
learned the names of bolts, washers, and nuts, whether
they were plated or stainless, whether they were flathead,
beveled, or slotted. I learned the difference between castle
nuts and jack nuts. I just asked the journeymen a lot of
questions."

At this stage of her training, Faye is usually assigned
to repair or install pumps, compressors, and conveyors,
which she knows inside and out. She's shown an aptitude for certain manual skills, earning her the reputation as "a good hand." For instance, she's good at making
"twists," a conveyor device that allows a bottle or can to
be turned over, washed out, turned back up, filled, and
sealed. Faye uses her left hand almost as dexterously as her
right, thanks to a tip a journeyman gave her early in her
apprenticeship. "It's the key to getting into certain tight
spots," she explains.

Quitting time comes at 2:30 P.M. on most jobs. Faye,
who's been covered in grease and dirt since mid-morning,
gathers up her tools and has a quick chat with her supervisor. She heads out to her car, carefully placing a plastic sheet
over the driver's seat before making the drive home.

Path to Becoming an Apprentice
According to Faye, hers is not the typical path to apprenticeship. She volunteered in her church's publications and
administrative office for more than 17 years, receiving
food, clothing, and shelter in lieu of pay. "When I hit
forty, I knew I wanted something radically different,"
she says. "I saw a sign on the road saying workers were
needed to help build a new freeway, and I called." After
a six-week, pre-apprenticeship program in general construction, she heard about a millwright class that was
being offered.

In class, she quickly discovered that many of the skills
she'd acquired throughout her life were applicable. "Growing up, I was the girl who wanted a drill for Christmas,"
she recounts, laughing. "When my brother got a bike that
needed assembly, I put it together." Even skills like reading
a tape measure came easily to Faye because she'd made her
own patterns for sewing in the past.

Her apprenticeship program requires four years of on-
the-job training and six hundred hours of supplemental

classes. These classes are taught during a two-week block every six months, during which time most apprentices collect unemployment insurance. The first year of classes covered basic safety, basic hand tools and precision tools, layout and blueprint, lots of math, and basic physics for rigging. As the years go on, classes take on more sophisticated subjects such as repair of specific machinery and installation of conveyors.

Salary Range

In southern California, beginning apprentices are currently paid $9.30 an hour. Every six months, they receive standard pay increases, right up to the journeyman's rate of $25.25 an hour.

Advice

Gene VanWinckel, committee chairman for Faye's apprenticeship program, feels that a strong grounding in math—including algebra and geometry—can give incoming apprentices an advantage. "If you don't understand geometry," he explains, "You won't be able to lay out a conveyor section."

For her part, Faye offers some on-the-job advice: "You'll only gain from an apprenticeship if you go in with the right attitude. Don't come in cocky. Have a teach-me attitude." She also suggests that apprentices be physically fit so they can handle heavy and awkward materials.

As the only woman millwright at many job sites, Faye feels that she has to work doubly hard to prove herself sometimes. She recommends that women apprentices take advantage of women's support groups. Monthly get-togethers through an organization called Women in Non-Traditional Roles (WINTER) have provided Faye with moral support and good career information.

Future Goals

Faye has recently extended her apprenticeship for an additional year in order to gain exposure to some new areas. For instance, she is eager to work on a turbine—a large steam engine—at some point. She recognizes that, at 46 years old, her age might put some physical limits on her as she gets older. She'd like to begin focusing more on the welding aspect of being a millwright, since welding is less physically demanding.

"Hypothetically, I'd also like to have my own company, one that does smaller jobs. Maybe I'd have a two- or three-person crew," she muses. She also reveals that the artist in her would love to create and sell large metal sculptures someday. No matter what she ends up doing, Faye feels

that the millwright's apprenticeship has given her proficiencies that will apply to many jobs.

ARIZONA

Arizona State Carpenters
4547 West McDowell Road
Phoenix, AZ 85035
602-272-6547
Occupational Fields: millwright

Millwrights Union, Local #102
8400 Enterprise Way, Suite 201
Oakland, CA 94621
510-430-1463
Fax: 510-635-6965
Occupational Fields: millwright

COLORADO

Colorado Carpenters and Millcabinet Workers
4290 Holly Street
Denver, CO 80216-4531
303-393-6060
Occupational Fields: millwright

DISTRICT OF COLUMBIA

United Brotherhood of Carpenters and Joiners of America
101 Constitution Avenue, NW
Washington, DC 20001
202-546-6206
http://www.carpenters.org
Occupational Fields: carpenter, cabinetmaker, millwright, pile driver, floor layer

FLORIDA

Millwrights Union, Local #1000
9711 U.S. 92 East
Tampa, FL 33610
813-620-0175
Occupational Fields: millwright

South Florida Millwrights, Piledrivers, and Divers Highway Constructors
2727 South Park Road
Hallandale, FL 33009

954-981-1810
Occupational Fields: millwright

GEORGIA
Carpenters and Millwrights Union, Local #256
1526 Dean Forest Road
Savannah, GA 31408
912-966-0335
Occupational Fields: millwright

Carpenters and Millwrights Union, Local #283
1225 Gordon Park Road
Augusta, GA 30901
706-722-4445
Occupational Fields: millwright

Carpenters and Millwrights Union, Local #1723
Six East Ninth Street
Columbus, GA 31904
706-322-1452
Occupational Fields: millwright

Millwright Joint Apprenticeship and Training Program
4620-A South Atlanta Road
Smyrna, GA 30080
Occupational Fields: millwright

United Auto Workers, Local #10
5407 Buford Highway, Northeast
Doraville, GA 30340-1125
404-457-3128
Occupational Fields: millwright

ILLINOIS
Millwrights, Local #1693
930 North York Road, Suite 202
Hinsdale, IL 60521
630-325-6036
Fax: 630-325-6052
ray@millwright1693.com
http://www.millwright1693.com
Occupational Fields: millwright

INDIANA
Allison Engine Company
2355 South Tibbs Avenue
Indianapolis, IN 46206

317-230-5112
Occupational Fields: millwright

Budget Maintenance and Construction Inc.
4900 Railroad Avenue
East Chicago, IN 46312
219-398-2844
Occupational Fields: millwright

Central Indiana Carpenters
6125 East 38th Street
Indianapolis, IN 46226-5603
317-549-9417
Occupational Fields: millwright

Chrysler Corporation Foundry Plant
1100 South Tibbs Avenue
Indianapolis, IN 46241
317-240-4932
Occupational Fields: millwright

Dana Corporation
Spicer Axle Division
2100 West State Street
Fort Wayne, IN 46801
260-481-3017
Occupational Fields: millwright

Delphi Energy and Engine Management Systems
2401 Columbus Avenue
Anderson, IN 46018
317-646-3628
http://www.delphi.com
Occupational Fields: millwright

General Motors Corporation, Indianapolis
Metal Fabricating Division
PO Box 388
Indianapolis, IN 46206
317-269-5956
Occupational Fields: millwright

Northeast Indiana Carpenters Joint Apprenticeship Training Fund
1091 Mariner Drive
PO Box 1690
Warsaw, IN 47581-1690
574-269-4220
Occupational Fields: carpenter, floorlayer, millwright, pile driver

Whirlpool Corporation
Employment and Wage Administration
5401 U.S. Highway 41, North
Evansville, IN 47727
812-426-4496
Occupational Fields: millwright

IOWA
ADM Construction Division
1251 Beaver Channel Parkway
Clinton, IA 52732-5935
800-637-5843
info@admworld.com
http://www.admworld.com
Occupational Fields: millwright

Associated Builders and Contractors, Iowa
939 Office Park Road, Suite 123
Des Moines, IA 50265
515-224-9800
http://www.abciowa.org
Occupational Fields: millwright

Glacier Vandervell Inc.
West Highway 83
Atlantic, IA 50022
712-243-5060
Occupational Fields: millwright

Ralston Foods Company Inc.
601 16th Street, NE
Cedar Rapids, IA 52402
319-368-0237
Occupational Fields: millwright

KANSAS
Colgate-Palmolive Company
18010 Kansas Avenue
Kansas City, KS 66105
913-573-6464
Occupational Fields: millwright

MARYLAND
District Council of Carpenters
801 West Patapsco Avenue
Baltimore, MD 21230

410-355-5555
Occupational Fields: millwright

Joint Carpentry Apprenticeship Committee
9109 Westphalia Road
Upper Marlboro, MD 20774
301-736-1696
Occupational Fields: millwright

MASSACHUSETTS
Millwrights Union, Local #1121
New England Regional Council of Carpenters
90 Braintree Street
Allston, MA 02134
617-254-1655
Occupational Fields: millwright

MICHIGAN
United Auto Workers
3731 Covington Road
Kalamazoo, MI 49002
616-381-2703
Occupational Fields: millwright

MINNESOTA
Millwrights Union, Local #1348
307 First Street, North
Virginia, MN 55792-2539
218-741-6314
Occupational Fields: millwright

MISSOURI
Carpenters District Council
625 West 39th Street, Suite 201
Kansas City, MO 64111-2909
816-931-3414
http://cdckcmo.com
Occupational Fields: millwright

MONTANA
**United Brotherhood of Carpenters and Joiners
of America, Local #28**
208 East Main Street
Missoula, MT 59802
406-549-8067
Occupational Fields: millwright

NEBRASKA
**Carpenters and Millwrights Unions,
 Locals #444 and #1463**
1124 South 13th Street
Omaha, NE 68108
402-345-8658
Occupational Fields: millwright

NEW HAMPSHIRE
**District Council of Carpenters, Northern New
 England**
37 Dover Neck Road
Dover, NH 03820
603-749-2798
http://www.necarpenters.org
Occupational Fields: millwright

NEW YORK
Carpenters Union, Local #532
456 East Church Street
Elmira, NY 14901-2832
607-733-7542
Occupational Fields: millwright

District Council of Carpenters, New York
395 Hudson Street
New York, NY 10014
212-727-2224
http://www.nycdistrictcouncil.com
Occupational Fields: millwright

Millwright & Machinery Erectors, Local 740
89-07 Atlantic Avenue
Woodhaven, NY 11421
718-849-3636
Fax: 718-849-0070
http://www.millwright740.com
Occupational Fields: millwright

NORTH DAKOTA
**Bismarck-Mandan Carpenters Union,
 Local #1091**
217 South Mandan Street
Bismarck, ND 58504
701-255-3700
Occupational Fields: millwright

OHIO
District Council of Carpenters, Ohio
236 East Town Street
Columbus, OH 43215
614-461-4700
Occupational Fields: millwright

Millwrights Union
6475 Trenton Franklin Road
Middletown, OH 45042
513-422-0901
Occupational Fields: millwright

United Paperworkers Union, Local #1973
1630 Central Avenue
Middletown, OH 45055
513-423-7959
Occupational Fields: millwright

OKLAHOMA
**Eastern Oklahoma Building, Construction,
 and Trade Council**
4428 East Admiral Place
Tulsa, OK 74115
918-838-0311
Occupational Fields: millwright

PENNSYLVANIA
Central Pennsylvania Carpenters
1718 Heilmandale Road
Lebanon, PA 17404
717-273-5277
Occupational Fields: millwright

Millwrights Local 1906
1803 Spring Garden St.
Philadelphia, PA 19130
215-569-2558
Fax: 215-569-1077
http://www.philamillwrights.com/contact.html
Occupational Fields: millwright

TEXAS
Carpenters & Millwrights, Local 1266
400 Josephine
Austin, TX 78704
512-476-7354
Fax: 512-76-7360

http://www.unionmillwright.com
Occupational Fields: millwright

Carpenters, Millwrights, and Piledrivers Union
8505 Glen Vista
Houston, TX 77061
713-641-0275
Occupational Fields: millwright

Millwrights Union
3206 Pleasant Valley Lane
Arlington, TX 76015-2913
817-784-1421
Occupational Fields: millwright

North Texas Carpenters and Millwrights
1901 Susan Drive
Arlington, TX 76010-5333
817-640-8825
Occupational Fields: millwright

VIRGINIA
Newport News Shipbuilding
Admissions Office
4101 Washington Avenue
Newport News, VA 23607-2770
757-380-2000
Occupational Fields: millwright

WASHINGTON
Bellingham Carpenters
4054 Pacific Highway
Bellingham, WA 98226
360-734-7900
Occupational Fields: millwright

Boise Cascade
PO Box 500
Wallula, WA 99363
509-545-3326
Occupational Fields: millwright

Carpenters, Shipwrights, Millwrights, Drywallers, and Cabinet Makers
2201 South 78th Street, Building B-512
Tacoma, WA 98409
253-472-2629
Occupational Fields: millwright

Carpenters Union, Local #1715
612 East McLoughlin Boulevard
Vancouver, WA 98663-3393
360-693-0731
Occupational Fields: millwright

Everett Carpenters and Cabinet Makers
2810 Lombard Avenue, Suite 207
Everett, WA 98201
425-259-7235
Occupational Fields: millwright

INTALCO Aluminum Corporation
PO Box 937
Ferndale, WA 98248
360-384-7296
Occupational Fields: industrial millwright

James River Corporation and Association of Western Pulp and Paper Workers, Local #5
Camas Mill
Northeast Fourth and Adams
Camas, WA 98607
360-817-2157
Occupational Fields: millwright

King County Carpenters
3000 Northeast Fourth Street
Renton, WA 98056
425-235-2465
Occupational Fields: millwright

Longview-Kelso Carpenters, Millmen, Shipwrights and Millwrights
618 14th Avenue
Longview, WA 98632
360-423-5030
Occupational Fields: millwright

Pasco Millwrights
2819 West Sylvester
Pasco, WA 99301
509-545-1781
Occupational Fields: millwright

Port Townsend Paper Corporation
PO Box 3170
Port Townsend, WA 98368
360-379-2125
Occupational Fields: millwright

Sandvik Special Metals
PO Box 6027
Kennewick, WA 99336
509-586-4131
Occupational Fields: millwright

Simpson Timber Company
Woodworkers Lodge W38
PO Box 98
Shelton, WA 98584
360-426-5541
Occupational Fields: millwright

Skagit County Carpenters
927 East College Way
Mount Vernon, WA 98273
360-424-1532
Occupational Fields: millwright

Weyerhaeuser Company, Raymond
51 Ellis Street
Raymond, WA 98577
360-942-6317
Occupational Fields: millwright

Weyerhaeuser Company, Snoqualmie
7001 296th Avenue, Southeast
Snoqualmie, WA 98065
425-888-7570
Occupational Fields: millwright

WISCONSIN

Algoma Hardwoods Inc.
1001 Perry Street
Algoma, WI 54201-1698
920-487-5221
Occupational Fields: millwright

Appleton Papers Inc.
825 East Wisconsin Avenue
PO Box 359
Appleton, WI 54911-3873
920-734-9841
http://www.appletonideas.com
Occupational Fields: millwright

Associated General Contractors
4814 East Broadway
Madison, WI 53716

608-221-3821
Fax: 608-221-4446
http://www.agcwi.org
Occupational Fields: millwright

Friday Canning Corporation, Markesan
County Road As
Markesan, WI 53946
414-398-2344
Occupational Fields: millwright

Southeast Wisconsin Carpentry Training Center
9411 West Fond du Lac Avenue
Milwaukee, WI 53225
414-353-3000
http://www.sewctc.org
Occupational Fields: millwright

Wausaw Paper Company
515 West Davenport Street
Rhinelander, WI 54501
715-369-4100
Occupational Fields: millwright

CANADA

BRITISH COLUMBIA

British Columbia Millwrights, Local 2736
#202, 14625 - 108 Avenue
Surrey, BC V3R-1V9
603-585-2736
Occupational Fields: millwright

NEWFOUNDLAND

Carpenters Millwrights College, Local 1009
PO Box 3040
Paradise, NF A1L 3W2
709-364-5586
Occupational Fields: millwright

ONTARIO

Millwrights Regional Council of Ontario
79 Sunrise Avenue
Toronto, ON M4A 1A9
416-757-8754
Fax: 416-757-2225
http://www.millwrightsontario.com
Occupational Fields: millwright

MUSEUM AND GALLERY WORKERS

RELATED SECTIONS: *artists and artisans, book arts workers, carpenters, child care workers and educators, communications specialists, crafts and trades workers at living historical sites and farms, metalworkers*

Museum and art gallery workers search for, acquire, evaluate, study, document, restore, preserve, and display everything from fine paintings to preserved plants and animals. Professionals are expected to demonstrate a highly developed, philosophical commitment to the field and its ethics. The trade requires a broad understanding of history, the arts, and the sciences.

Archivists and *curators* plan, supervise, and help maintain collections of items to be preserved and displayed; conduct research; and organize public lectures, tours, and other educational efforts.

Curators, also known as collections managers, generally work with paintings, sculptures, plant and animal specimens, and other collections. They typically work in museums, zoos, historic sites, botanical gardens, aquariums, and nature centers. Many curators specialize in art, history, botany, or some other subject. Some curators travel a great deal to acquire objects, supervise exhibitions, and complete research. Curators develop exhibits highlighting their museum's collections and assembling objects from other museums and elsewhere. Together with museum educators, they work to interpret museum holdings and educate the public through writing and speaking.

Archivists typically maintain vast collections of documents and other records, along with any objects related to them, as permanent historical holdings. The records may be printed, on microfilm, on computer disks, on audiotapes, or in other media.

Conservators complete technical and scientific studies on objects, stabilize and refurbish cultural artifacts, and ensure that the artifacts are stored and displayed in surroundings that will protect them from deterioration. Many conservators specialize in a specific type of material, such as textiles or paper arts, or a type of object, such as historic documents or Renaissance paintings. Others are professionals in a wide variety of disciplines, such as archeologists and natural scientists.

Museum technicians help curators and conservators. *Archives technicians* help archivists. *Museum directors* handle administrative tasks at museums. *Preservation specialists, conservation scientists, conservation educators, conservation administrators,* and *preparators* are other professionals who work in museums and galleries.

Support workers are also needed. *Carpenters* and *cabinet builders* construct display cases, restore antique furniture or rare musical instruments, or perform other carpentry and construction projects. *Public relations specialists* and *tour guides* help visitors understand and appreciate the objects on display.

Museum and art gallery workers protect artifacts from potentially damaging light, moisture, pollution, insects, and many other threats. They keep detailed written and visual records of each project. They work with microscopes, special lights, X rays, and various types of laboratory equipment. Some spend a great deal of time interacting with the public in educational capacities. Others spend most of their time alone or with a few coworkers, conducting research, keeping records, and preparing exhibits. The job sometimes involves working with heavy exhibits and boxes of records; it may require lifting, stretching, climbing, and walking.

Workers are employed in a variety of settings, including museums, art galleries, libraries, universities, government agencies, corporate archives, conservation laboratories, historical societies, heritage institutions, religious organizations, and private conservation facilities. Many professionals in this field are self-employed, which provides them with great flexibility but generally less funding.

Apprenticeship or internship is the traditional way of entering this trade, often after the applicant has obtained a bachelor's or master's degree from a college or university. Advanced education is not required for some positions, however. Some students substitute a series of apprenticeships for a formal graduate program. Working part-time, as an intern or apprentice, or as a volunteer is a common way of gaining entry into the field. Some positions are paid, and others are not. Conservation interns working under the supervision of conservation professionals develop technical and scientific skills, esthetic sensibilities, and a strong sense of ethics. The course of study varies widely but typically includes course work, research, and readings, sometimes done independently by the student. Trainees typically study chemistry, art history, and studio art.

In general an applicant should

- be a high school graduate or hold a GED certificate
- have good eyesight
- not be color blind
- have manual dexterity

- be able to work with patience and great precision
- have an aptitude for science and technical fields
- have good communication skills
- appreciate and respect all types of cultural artifacts
- be extremely serious about pursuing a career in this field

APPRENTICESHIP SALARIES

Often include a stipend to cover room and board, transportation, and research expenses.

POSTAPPRENTICESHIP SALARIES

Vary widely, depending on geographic area, skill level, area of specialization, and employer. Large museums tend to pay more than smaller organizations. Median annual earnings of archivists, curators, and museum technicians in 2002 were $35,270.

JOB OUTLOOK

Generally fair, but there is keen competition for jobs and apprenticeships in this field. Employment opportunities in this field are expected to increase about as fast as the average profession for all occupations through 2012. Large galleries and museums often have a variety of programs available for volunteers, paid apprentices, and others interested in working there. State and local governments will also provide more openings as they expand their archives. Applicants with very specialized training are expected to have the best prospects.

For more information on apprenticeships for museum and art gallery workers, contact the individual programs listed below, local job centers, your state bureau of apprenticeship training, or local museums and galleries.

APPRENTICESHIP PROFILE

Harvard University Art Museum
Art Restoration Internship Program
Straus Center for Conservation and Technical Studies
Cambridge, MA 02138-3826
617-495-2392
Fax: 617-495-9936
http://www.artmuseums.harvard.edu/straus_pages

General Nature of the Job

Conservators like Penley Knipe are responsible for preserving, treating, and documenting works of art and artifacts for museums, galleries, private collectors, or historical societies. To become a conservator, you have to be a researcher, scientist, and artist all bundled into one. When a piece of art comes into a conservator's hands, he or she might need to conduct research on the piece's historical or archeological past. The conservator looks beneath the surface of a work of art—literally—by analyzing the piece's structural and chemical nature. Conservators use X rays, chemical testing, microscopes, special lights, and other laboratory equipment and techniques to examine and determine condition, the need for treatment or restoration, and the appropriate method of preservation.

Given the level of skill required to be a conservator, it's not surprising that extensive training and education is required. The Straus Center in Cambridge, Massachusetts, where Penley is an intern, was actually the first art conservation training program in the United States. Penley works in the paper laboratory on drawings, prints, watercolors, and photographs, and there are other interns who focus their conservation efforts on paintings, sculpture, decorative objects, and historic or archaeological artifacts. The overall goal of the program is to introduce graduate-level interns to sophisticated analytical and treatment techniques and introduce them to philosophical issues about the conservation of works of art.

Typical Day

Penley arrives at the paper lab a little before 9:00 A.M. She walks past several large tables before she gets to her own "bench," a working surface with flat files to store artwork horizontally. She keeps her tools, which include scalpels, spatulas, tweezers, brushes, and needles, nearby. As an intern, she works in collaboration with staff conservators, but how she allots her time each day is largely up to her. When she is assigned a new piece of artwork, for example, she begins by examining it and then writing a treatment plan. "I outline the steps I think are appropriate for treating a work of art, and then I show that to my supervisor for her thoughts and comments," she explains. The owner of the artwork must also approve the treatment plan before actual conservation work gets underway. She is currently working, for example, on a woodcut that was damaged and poorly mounted onto paper that was too thick and strong for the original print.

While she's fresh in the morning, she often does treatment, such as mending a torn print or removing old hinges from the back of a drawing. Then she turns her attention to her postgraduate research project, which is a requirement of the training program. Specifically, she's using analytical instruments to look at the pigments and binders that were applied to papers between the 15th and 17th centuries. This project also involves consulting with a conservation scientist to determine what materials were used.

After lunch, she heads to the library to look up and read an article on a particular artist. Then it's back to the lab to photograph artwork either before or after she works on it in order to record the object's condition. By late afternoon, she's tired and ready to spend time at the computer, writing treatment proposals or treatment reports. "Every day is different. Some days might be spent exclusively on treatment, especially if there is an exhibition deadline. Other days might be devoted completely to my research project."

Although she's only expected to stay until 5:00 P.M., she usually stays on much later. In fact, her biggest challenge is balancing tasks so that she does enough treatment but also has time to read recent publications, see exhibitions at the affiliated Harvard Art Museums, and work on her research project. "I find that it's so easy to get completely immersed in treatment and bench work," she admits. "The hands-on treatment is the part I like best, so it's hard to step back and do something else."

Path to Becoming an Apprentice

After earning her bachelor's degree in anthropology from St. Lawrence University, Penley went to work as a curatorial assistant in the Drawings Department of the Fogg Art Museum, one of Harvard University's art museums. This is where she got her first glimpse at the Straus Center and the field of conservation. "I used to bring new works of art on paper that we were acquiring to the paper lab to get the conservators' expert advice on the media and technique," she says. During these frequent interactions, Penley discovered that conservation was exactly what she was looking for. "I could stay involved with museum work and art history," she explains, "but I could also use my studio art skills. I was craving some kind of hands-on work."

Her next job was as a technician in the Straus Center's paper lab. Following that, she worked for a private paper conservator and two painting conservators in Connecticut for a year. Penley was then accepted into a master's program in fine arts and historic works at the University of Delaware/Wintertour Museum. During the three-

year program, she did two summer internships: one at the National Park Service's conservation lab and one at the British Museum in London. She spent her third year doing an 11-month internship at the Yale Center for British Art in New Haven, Connecticut.

Coming to the Straus Center was the logical next step for her. The program is designed specifically for postgraduate-level interns. In Penley's case, the reason for going through this training program was to gain more treatment skills and to get experience on types of art that she had not worked on before, such as objects made on parchment and non-Western objects. She hasn't been disappointed.

Salary Range

The Straus Center provides a stipend for interns that covers living expenses, health care, travel, and research activities. A beginning conservator can expect to earn approximately $23,000 to $28,000. Those with five or more years of experience make $35,000 to $40,000. Conservators can increase their earnings by establishing private practices; however, there are tremendous start-up expenses for the equipment, and it can take a few years to get established.

Advice

Penley thinks that people can do well in this field "if they have strong hand skills, are good artists, and have a real interest in art, archaeology, or a related field." But art is only part of the equation. She also notes that a sound background in science is critical because both inorganic and organic chemistry are required prior to a master's program, and there is more chemical and analytical science required in graduate school.

Like the handful of other conservation schools in the country, the Straus Center training program's eligibility requirements are rigorous. They include competence in one foreign language, a graduate degree in conservation, a bachelor's degree in applied arts or art history, and one or more college-level chemistry courses.

Future Goals

In the best-case scenario, Penley would love to work in a teaching museum's paper lab—someplace much like the Straus Center. She enjoys the constant interaction there between undergraduate and graduate students, conservators, and other interns. "A job in a situation like this would be ideal because the labs are so well equipped, well planned and laid out, and very up-to-date."

Realistically, however, Penley sees herself working with a partner as a private paper conservator. "I'd like to be in business with someone else for simple companion-ship, for another set of hands, and for someone to bounce ideas off of," she says.

CALIFORNIA
Western Association for Art Conservation
c/o Balboa Art Conservation Center
PO Box 3755
San Diego, CA 92163-1755
619-236-9702
Fax: 619-236-0141
http://palimpsest.stanford.edu/waac
Occupational Fields: museum conservator, art gallery conservator

CONNECTICUT
Mystic Seaport Museum
75 Greenmanville Avenue
Mystic, CT 06355-0990
860-572-5347
http://www.mysticseaport.org
Occupational Fields: museum curator

DELAWARE
University of Delaware
Museum Studies Program
207 Mechanical Hall
Newark, DE 19716-2558
302-831-1251
http://www.udel.edu/winterthurprogram/people.html
Occupational Fields: museum exhibition developer, researcher, collections manager, interpretive programmer, catalog producer

DISTRICT OF COLUMBIA
American Association of Museums
1575 I Street, NW, Suite 400
Washington, DC 20005
202-289-1818
http://www.aam-us.org
Occupational Fields: museum conservator, art gallery conservator

American Institute for Conservation of Historic and Artistic Works
1717 K Street, NW, Suite 200
Washington, DC 20006
202-452-9545
http://aic.stanford.edu
Occupational Fields: museum conservator, art gallery conservator

American Institute of Architects
1735 New York Avenue, NW
Washington, DC 20006
202-626-7300
infocentral@aia.org
http://www.aia.org
Occupational Fields: museum conservator, art gallery conservator

Heritage Preservation
Education Division
1012 14th Street, NW, Suite 1200
Washington, DC 20009
202-625-1495
Occupational Fields: museum conservator, art gallery conservator

International Council of Monuments and Sites, U.S. Committee
401 F Street, NW, Suite 331
Washington, DC 20001
202-842-1866
don.jones@usicomos.org
http://www.icomos.org/usicomos
Occupational Fields: museum conservator, art gallery conservator

National Gallery of Art
Office of Academic Programs
Washington, DC 20565
202-842-6399
http://www.nga.gov/programs/interned.htm
Occupational Fields: museum and gallery worker

National Trust for Historic Preservation
Office of Preservation Services
1784 Massachusetts Avenue, NW
Washington, DC 20036
202-588-6000
Fax: 202-588-6038

http://www.nationaltrust.org
*Occupational Fields: museum conservator, art gallery
    conservator*

Smithsonian Institution
Arts and Industries Building
900 Jefferson Drive
Washington, DC 20560
202-357-3049
http://www.si.edu
*Occupational Fields: historian, journalist, photographer,
    artist, teacher, environmental scientist, computer
    technician, carpenter*

Smithsonian Institution
Department of Conservation
Room 233, MRC 211
Washington, DC 20560
202-633-1000
info@si.edu
http://www.si.edu
Occupational Fields: art conservator

Smithsonian Institution
Education and Training Center
4210 Silverhill Road
Suitland, MD 20746
301-238-1240
Fax: 301-238-3709
http://palimpsest.stanford.edu/bytopic/education
Occupational Fields: museum conservator, archaeologist

U.S. National Park Service
Curatorial Services Division
800 North Capitol Street, #230
Mail Stop 408
Washington, DC 20013
202-343-8138
http://www.artcom.com/Museums/nv/mr/20013.htm
*Occupational Fields: museum conservator, art gallery
    conservator*

Washington Conservation Guild
PO Box 23364
Washington, DC 20026
wcg@washingtonconservationguild.org
http://palimpsest.stanford.edu/wcg/intro.html
*Occupational Fields: museum conservator, art gallery
    conservator*

ILLINOIS

American Library Association
Resources and Technical Services Division
50 East Huron Street
Chicago, IL 60611
800-545-2433
http://www.ala.org
*Occupational Fields: museum conservator, art gallery
    conservator*

Chicago Area Conservation Group
Chicago Historical Society
1601 North Clark Street
Chicago, IL 60614-6099
312-642-5035
http://palimpsest.stanford.edu/cacg
*Occupational Fields: museum conservator, art gallery
    conservator*

Museum of Contemporary Art
220 East Chicago Avenue
Chicago, IL 60611
312-280-2660
Fax: 312-397-4095
http://www.mcachicago.org
*Occupational Fields: museum and art gallery conservator,
    museum designer, editor*

Society of American Archivists
527 South Wells Street, Suite 500
Chicago, IL 60607
312-922-0140
Fax: 312-347-1452
http://www.archivists.org
*Occupational Fields: museum conservator, art gallery
    conservator*

MASSACHUSETTS

Harvard University Art Museum
Straus Center for Conservation and Technical
    Studies
Gund Hall, 32 Quincy Street
Cambridge, MA 02138-3826
617-495-2574
http://www.artmuseums.harvard.edu/straus
*Occupational Fields: art conservator, art restorer, art
    gallery conservator*

MINNESOTA
Saint John's University
Hill Museum & Manuscript Library
PO Box 7300
Collegeville, MN 56321
320-363-3514
Fax: 320-363-3222
hmml@csbsju.edu
http://www.hmml.org
Occupational Fields: manuscript researcher, cataloger, paleographer, codicologer, illuminator

NEW YORK
Guggenheim Museum
Education Department
1017 Fifth Avenue
New York, NY 10128
212-423-3500
http://www.guggenheim.org
Occupational Fields: museum curator

Metropolitan Museum of Art
Department of Education
1000 Fifth Avenue
New York, NY 10028-0198
212-535-7710
http://www.metmuseum.org
Occupational Fields: museum curator, art gallery curator

Mount Vernon Hotel Museum & Garden
421 East 61st Street
New York, NY 10021-8736
212-838-6878
Fax: 212-838-7390
http://www.mvhm.org
Occupational Fields: museum curator, administrator, museum preservator, researcher, tour guide

Smithsonian Institution
Cooper-Hewitt National Design Museum
2 East 91st Street
New York, NY 10128
212-849-8385
http://ndm.si.edu
Occupational Fields: museum curator, art gallery curator, museum designer, librarian

State University of New York
Faculty of Landscape Architecture
1 Forestry Drive
Syracuse, NY 13210
315-470-6500
http://fla.esf.edu
Occupational Fields: historic conservator, interpreter

Stoneyard Institute
Cathedral of Saint John the Divine
1047 Amsterdam Avenue
New York, NY 10025-1702
212-316-7493
Occupational Fields: historic conservator, interpreter, cultural resource manager

World Monuments Fund
95 Madison Avenue, 9th floor
New York, NY 10016
646-424-9594
http://www.wmf.org
Occupational Fields: museum curator, art gallery curator

OHIO
Midwest Regional Conservation Guild
Cleveland Museum of Art
11150 East Boulevard
Cleveland, OH 44106
216-421-7340
Occupational Fields: museum curator, art gallery curator

Ohio Historical Society
1982 Velma Avenue
Columbus, OH 43211
614-297-2340
http://www.ohiohistory.org
Occupational Fields: museum curator, art conservator, historian, exhibit designer

TENNESSEE
American Association for State and Local History
1717 Church Street
Nashville, TN 37203-2991
615-320-3203
Fax: 615-327-9013
http://www.aaslh.org/contact.htm
Occupational Fields: museum curator, art gallery curator

VIRGINIA

Association for Preservation Technology, International
PO Box 8178
Fredericksburg, VA 22404
703-373-1621
http://www.apti.org
Occupational Fields: museum curator, art gallery curator

College of William and Mary
Department of Modern Languages
Williamsburg, VA 23187
804-221-3676
http://www.wm.edu/modlang
Occupational Fields: manuscript researcher, cataloger,
codicologer, paleographer, illuminator

OPERATING ENGINEERS AND STATIONARY ENGINEERS

RELATED SECTIONS: *auto body workers; boilermakers; carpenters; elevator constructors; engineers and engineering technicians; ironworkers; machinists; mechanics; metalworkers; millwrights; pile drivers; pipe trades workers; railroad workers; sheet metal workers; shipbuilding and ship maintenance workers; tool, die, mold, and pattern makers; truck drivers; welders*

Operating engineers, often called *construction equipment operators,* drive bulldozers, cranes, trucks, tractors, backhoes, graders, front-end loaders, and other heavy duty equipment for projects such as construction, mining, and logging and in factories and similar settings. Because they move dirt, steel, manufactured goods, and other materials, they are also known as material moving equipment operators. They play an essential role in building bridges, highways, and dams, and they sometimes help dispose of hazardous materials.

Heavy duty mechanics are operating engineers who maintain and repair heavy duty equipment. Their job involves a great deal of preventive maintenance, usually done at a job site and sometimes performed at night after the workers who drive the machines have gone home.

Surveyors are operating engineers who precisely measure and define the geographical extent of a construction site or other project. This work requires advanced mathematical skills.

Most operating engineers are employed by construction companies, manufacturers, and state and local governments. The work is usually performed outdoors, often in bad weather, and workers are often dirty, dusty, muddy, and covered with grease. In some climates projects are shut down during the winter. Workers are often laid off after a project is completed; they are listed on rosters and may be called when other work is available. Overtime work is common.

Stationary engineers, sometimes called *boiler operators,* operate and maintain equipment that stays in one place (as opposed to vehicles that move, such as locomotives), including boilers, turbines, generators, air compressors, and engines. This equipment typically provides a building's heat, ventilation, air conditioning, electricity, or steam power. The work is usually done in settings such as factories, hospitals, schools, apartment buildings, power plants, airports, and shopping malls. Stationary engineers start the equipment and shut it down, monitor its operation, adjust it, and repair it as necessary. The job sometimes includes record-keeping duties.

Water and wastewater treatment plant managers treat water, primarily from sewer systems and industrial sources, to make it safe to drink and to avoid polluting the environment. They also treat drinking water that is pumped from rivers, wells, and other sources and distributed. The job requires knowledge of machinery, chemistry, tools, computers, and emergency management response procedures. The work is done both indoors and outdoors and involves reaching, climbing, walking, and bending.

Stationary engineers typically work a standard week of 40 hours, often at night, during the evenings or early mornings, on holidays, or on weekends. Employment tends to be steady throughout the year, and workers often stay with one employer for lengthy periods. The work is mostly performed indoors, often in dirty, dark, noisy, hot, or cold surroundings, but engine rooms and similar sites are bright and clean. There is risk of electric shock, burns, and other injuries from working around equipment. The job involves standing, crawling, kneeling, and bending, and workers are often in contact with grease, oil, fumes, and smoke.

Many workers in this field belong to labor organizations, primarily the International Union of Operating Engineers, which offers more than 100 apprenticeship and training programs through its locals.

Apprenticeships and on-the-job training are common ways of entering this field, and many unions and other organizations in the building and construction trades and other industries offer training. Apprentices learn under the supervision of experienced workers. Typically, the course of study runs for three to four years. For stationary engineers the apprenticeship includes classroom instruction in physics, chemistry, electricity, electronics, and blueprint reading. Stationary engineers usually must be licensed and may have to take an examination to obtain another license if they move to another state or city.

In general an applicant should

- apply in person
- be at least 18 years old
- be a high school graduate or hold a GED certificate
- be in good physical condition
- have excellent hand-eye coordination

- be able to work long hours with few breaks
- have mechanical aptitude
- have manual dexterity

APPRENTICESHIP SALARIES

Between $5 and $18 an hour, or about 40 percent to 60 percent of the rate paid to experienced workers, with periodic raises. Experienced apprentices earn between $10 and $24 an hour.

POSTAPPRENTICESHIP SALARIES

About $15 to $25 an hour, with some workers earning as much as $30 an hour plus benefits. Earnings vary widely, depending on the type of equipment being operated, the geographic area, and the weather. Stationary engineers tend to earn somewhat more than operating engineers.

JOB OUTLOOK

Growth in this field is expected to be fairly stagnant for the next decade. Employment prospects for stationary engineers are expected to be somewhat weaker than average through the year 2012, because automated systems and computerized controls are making newly installed equipment more efficient, thus reducing the number of jobs needed for its operation. Furthermore, relatively few job openings will arise from the need to replace experienced workers who transfer to other occupations or leave the labor force. The low replacement rate in this occupation reflects its high wages. There will be a significant number of openings in power-generating systems, because that machinery is becoming more complex and requires more maintenance. Prospects for water and wastewater treatment plant operators are expected to be good because of the continued need for clean water and the construction of new treatment plants.

For more information on apprenticeships for operating engineers and stationary engineers, contact the national organizations and individual programs listed below, local job centers, your state bureau of apprenticeship training, or water pollution control agencies.

NATIONAL PROGRAMS

Building Owners and Managers Institute International
1521 Ritchie Highway
Arnold, MD 21012
410-974-1410
Fax: 410-974-1935
service@bomi-edu.org
http://www.bomi-edu.org
Occupational Fields: stationary engineer, operating engineer

International Union of Operating Engineers
1125 17th Street, NW
Washington, DC 20036-4707
202-429-9100
Fax: 202-429-0316
http://www.iuoe.org
Occupational Fields: stationary engineer, operating engineer, heavy equipment operator, mechanic, surveyor

National Association of Power Engineers Inc.
1 Springfield Street
Chicopee, MA 01013
413-592-6273
napenatl@verizon.net
http://www.powerengineers.com
Occupational Fields: stationary engineer, operating engineer

APPRENTICESHIP PROFILE

International Union of Operating Engineers, Reno
Apprenticeship Program
1290 Corporate Boulevard
Reno, NV 89502
702-857-4440

General Nature of the Job

Operating engineers operate large construction machinery: backhoes (small bucket in front, large bucket in back), trackhoes (a backhoe with tank-like tracks instead of wheels), front-end loaders (a much larger version of a backhoe, but with a bucket in the front only), paddlewheel scrapers and push-pull scrapers (pushed by another vehicle), bulldozers, rollers, and compactors. Each of these requires excellent hand-eye coordination, "but the hardest part is keeping the order of operations straight," asserts Brian Prather, an operating engineer apprentice with Granite Construction, the third largest paving company in the world.

Operating engineers also descend from the driver's seat occasionally to help the general laborers shovel or to use hand-level rulers and grade setters. In fact, distinguishing between level and grade constitutes a key aspect of the job. Operating engineer apprentices must learn how to visualize high and low spots, look for drainage, read plans, and conceptualize the final outcome. At this point in his apprenticeship, Brian finds it easier to look for grade from the ground, for example, the standard two-percent grade of roads that is necessary to prevent hydroplaning. But he's training his eye to estimate grade from atop machinery, as most journeymen do.

Typical Day

"There's no such thing as a typical day," maintains Brian, though on the first day at all job sites he ascertains the same information: what's being built, who is fielding questions, and whether he should make decisions on his own or get clearance from the boss on every detail. Travel to job sites all over Nevada remains a constant for Brian. "Once, I had to work at Battle Mountain, six hours from my home in Reno. That crew got real friendly, because we'd work together all day and then go out together after work. When you're on the road, the union secures you subsistence pay of about $15 to $20 to cover out-of-pocket expenses, so you can stay in a cheap hotel. Sometimes there'll be extra room in a trailer, but I like to camp whenever I can since I enjoy the outdoors. You have to enjoy the outdoors on this job, because that's where you spend all your time, in all types of weather. Nevada's desert land, so in the summer it gets really warm, as you'd expect, but in the winter it can get downright cold. I appreciate battery-operated socks, insulated coveralls, and enclosed machinery. You have to have tough skin to work in the elements, hot and cold."

Path to Becoming an Apprentice

Brian's apprenticeship with Local Three of the International Union of Operating Engineers combines education with on-the-job training. The program requires 1,500 hours in heavy equipment school, studying topics such as grade setting and safety. Brian even studied the use of lasers, learning how to construct underground sewer drainages following a beam of light as the point of reference. Simultaneously, an apprentice works 6,000 hours (divided into four stages of 1,500 hours) before graduating to the status of journeyman.

Salary Range

Having invested more than 2,800 hours (almost two years) of hard work, Brian eagerly anticipates advancing to the third stage of his apprenticeship, when his pay rate will increase. Each stage is compensated at a percent-age of journeymen's wages, so that an apprentice's pay scale increases in conjunction with incremental gains in experience. Brian earns $14.75 an hour presently, or 70 percent of a journeyman's wage. A journeyman's wage depends upon the equipment operated, starting at $18 an hour for operating a roller, $23 an hour for operating a blade, and $25 an hour for vacation pay (an important consideration, since employment fluctuates with the seasons).

The apprenticeship requires membership in the union, which runs the program. Brian finds the union "extremely helpful, offering many resources: books, videos, journeymen." The union requires companies to hire apprentices in proportion to the number of journeymen employed on any job site, thus ensuring that apprentice and journeyman work side by side. Journeymen teach apprentices the tricks of the trade, as the saying goes. "Most journeymen keep a few tricks up their sleeves, though, and some won't even talk to apprentices," Brian maintains. "It's understandable. I mean, if journeymen teach apprentices all their tricks, those same apprentices will soon become journeymen who could take jobs away from their former mentors. There is extreme competition in this business, with ten thousand guys who can do your job. Still, most journeymen share their knowledge, because they know we can't compete with their experience."

Advice

"When you find a journeyman willing to teach you, you try to stick together from job to job," Brian continues. He met just such a person in Tony Hill, a journeyman blade operator. "Tony was incredibly generous. We would work a 12-hour day, and then he would stay three to four hours afterwards with me just to work on techniques outside the pressures of the workday. If I get a chance to learn more, I take it."

Before entering the program, Brian took a course in blueprint reading, which he's found extremely helpful. He also advises communication classes, since construction relies on understanding directions, as well as math classes in algebra, geometry, and trigonometry to establish a firm grasp on the Pythagorean theorem and other triangulation concepts, such as rise-over-run.

Future Goals

His father was an operator for 20 years, so Brian played around the equipment as a kid. Now, he's filling his dad's shoes, but he's still in the driver's seat for the same reason that he sat on his dad's lap years ago, operating the machinery—to have fun.

ALABAMA

International Union of Operating Engineers, Local #312
PO Box 26368
Birmingham, AL 35260
205-424-9670
Occupational Fields: operating engineer

**International Union of Operating Engineers,
Local #320**
405 Doctor Hicks Boulevard, East
Florence, AL 35630
205-764-6991
Occupational Fields: operating engineer

**International Union of Operating Engineers,
Local #653**
801 Springhill Avenue
Mobile, AL 36602
334-432-3328
*Occupational Fields: operating engineer, stationary
engineer*

**International Union of Operating Engineers,
Local #657**
640 Anderson Road
Gadsden, AL 35901
*Occupational Fields: stationary engineer, building
maintenance technician*

ALASKA

Alaska Operating Engineers
900 West Northern Lights Boulevard, Suite 200
Anchorage, AK 99503
907-561-5044
*Occupational Fields: operating engineer, heavy machinery
operator, heavy duty mechanic*

ARIZONA

Arizona Operating Engineers
PO Box 11249
Phoenix, AZ 85061-1249
602-252-1844
*Occupational Fields: operating engineer, plant operator,
construction equipment operator*

Central Arizona Water Conservation District
23636 North Seventh Street
Phoenix, AZ 85024

602-870-2384
*Occupational Fields: operating engineer, stationary
engineer*

Granite Construction Company
PO Box 27557
Tucson, AZ 85726
520-748-8000
*Occupational Fields: heavy equipment operator; truck
driver; rock, sand, and gravel operator*

Operating Engineers Union
10797 Randolph Road
Casa Grande, AZ 85222
520-836-1890
Occupational Fields: operating engineer

P-D Morenci Inc.
PO Box 187
Morenci, AZ 85540
520-865-4521
Occupational Fields: operating engineer

**Utility and Transportation Contractors Association
of Arizona**
725 West McDowell, Suite B
Phoenix, AZ 85007
602-252-4574
Occupational Fields: operating engineer, plant operator

ARKANSAS

International Union of Operating Engineers, Local #323
269 Vestal Loop
Strong, AR 71765
*Occupational Fields: stationary engineer, building
maintenance technician*

**International Union of Operating Engineers,
Local #381**
1210 1/2 Northwest Avenue
El Dorado, AR 71730
501-863-9545
*Occupational Fields: stationary engineer, building
maintenance technician*

**International Union of Operating Engineers,
Local #382**
5516 West 11th Street
Little Rock, AR 72204

501-663-6388
Occupational Fields: stationary engineer, operating engineer

International Union of Operating Engineers, Local #428
1426 North First Street
Phoenix, AR 85004
612-254-5266
Occupational Fields: stationary engineer, operating engineer

Marshall Construction Inc.
17739 Cartwright Mountain Road
Mountainburg, AR 72949
501-369-2268
Occupational Fields: operating engineer

CALIFORNIA

Cherrington Corporation
7398 San Joaquin Street
PO Box 254788
Sacramento, CA 95865
916-457-3040
Occupational Fields: operating engineer

International Union of Operating Engineers, Eureka
2806 Broadway
Eureka, CA 95501
707-433-7328
Occupational Fields: operating engineer

International Union of Operating Engineers, Fairfield
2540 North Watney Way
Fairfield, CA 94533
707-429-5008
Occupational Fields: operating engineer

International Union of Operating Engineers, Fresno
1745 North Fine Avenue
Fresno, CA 93727
209-252-8903
Occupational Fields: operating engineer

International Union of Operating Engineers, Local #3, Oakland
1620 South Loop Road
Alameda, CA 94502

510-748-7446
Occupational Fields: operating engineer

International Union of Operating Engineers, Local #3, Rancho Murieta
7388 Murieta Drive
Rancho Murieta, CA 95683
916-354-2029
Occupational Fields: operating engineer, construction equipment operator, heavy duty repairman, crane operator

International Union of Operating Engineers, Local #12
150 East Corson Street
Pasadena, CA 91103
818-792-8900
Occupational Fields: operating engineer

International Union of Operating Engineers, Local #39
337 Valencia Street
San Francisco, CA 94103
415-861-1135
Occupational Fields: stationary engineer, building maintenance technician

International Union of Operating Engineers, Local #82
7933 Hummingbird Lane, Apartment D
San Diego, CA 92123
Occupational Fields: stationary engineer, building maintenance technician

International Union of Operating Engineers, Local #501
2405 West Third Street
Los Angeles, CA 90057
213-385-1561
Occupational Fields: stationary engineer, building maintenance technician

International Union of Operating Engineers, Local #926
374 Maynard Terrace, SE, #202
Atlanta, CA 30316
404-370-0042
Occupational Fields: operating engineer

International Union of Operating Engineers, Marysville
1010 I Street
Marysville, CA 95901

916-743-7321
Occupational Fields: operating engineer

International Union of Operating Engineers, Redding
20308 Engineers Lane
Redding, CA 96002
916-222-6093
Occupational Fields: operating engineer

International Union of Operating Engineers, Sacramento
4044 North Freeway Boulevard, Suite 200
Sacramento, CA 95834
916-565-6190
Occupational Fields: operating engineer

International Union of Operating Engineers, San Francisco
Five Thomas Mellon Circle, Suite 266
San Francisco, CA 941334
415-468-6107
Occupational Fields: operating engineer

International Union of Operating Engineers, San Jose
760 Emory Street
San Jose, CA 95126
408-295-8788
Occupational Fields: operating engineer

International Union of Operating Engineers, Santa Rosa
6225 State Farm Drive
Rohnert Park, CA 94928
707-585-2487
Occupational Fields: operating engineer

International Union of Operating Engineers, Stockton
1916 North Broadway
Stockton, CA 95205
209-943-2332
Occupational Fields: operating engineer

Northern California/Northern Nevada Stationary Engineers
2280 Palou Avenue
San Francisco, CA 94124
415-285-3939
Occupational Fields: stationary engineer, waste water treatment plant operator

Operating Engineers Training Trust
2200 Pellissier Place
Whittier, CA 90601
562-695-0611
Occupational Fields: operating engineer

Operating Engineers Union, Local #12
120 Bernard Street
Bakersfield, CA 93305
805-325-9491
Occupational Fields: operating engineer

Operating Engineers Union, Local #39
2211 Royale Road
Sacramento, CA 95815
916-927-3399
Occupational Fields: operating engineer

COLORADO
International Union of Operating Engineers, Local #1
2701 Alcott Street, Suite 268
Denver, CO 80211
303-433-8482
Occupational Fields: stationary engineer, building maintenance technician

International Union of Operating Engineers, Local #9
990 Kalamath Street
PO Box 40008
Denver, CO 80204
303-623-3194
Occupational Fields: operating engineer, heavy duty equipment operator

CONNECTICUT
International Union of Operating Engineers, Local #478
1965 Dixwell Avenue
Hamden, CT 06514
203-288-9261
http://www.local478.org
Occupational Fields: operating engineer

DISTRICT OF COLUMBIA
International Union of Operating Engineers
1125 17th Street, NW
Washington, DC 20036-4707

202-429-9100
http://www.iuoe.org
Occupational Fields: stationary engineer, operating engineer, heavy equipment operator, mechanic, surveyor

International Union of Operating Engineers, Local #99
2461 Wisconsin Avenue, NW
Washington, DC 20007
202-337-0099
Occupational Fields: stationary engineer, building maintenance technician

Prince Construction Company Inc.
1111 Good Hope Road, SE
Washington, DC 20020
202-889-5050
Occupational Fields: operating engineer

FLORIDA
Arizona Chemical, Panama City
Caller Box 2447
Panama City, FL 32402
904-785-6700
Occupational Fields: operating engineer, stationary engineer

Arizona Chemical, Port St. Joe
Highway 98
PO Box 947
Port St. Joe, FL 32456
904-229-8271
Occupational Fields: operating engineer, stationary engineer

Broward County School Board
Maintenance Department
3810 Northwest 10th Avenue, Oakland Park
Fort Lauderdale, FL 33307
954-765-6000
Occupational Fields: building maintenance technician

Centerline Tool and Engineering
3107 29th Avenue, East
Bradenton, FL 34203
941-749-5519
Occupational Fields: stationary engineer

International Union of Operating Engineers, Local #478
South Florida Operating Engineers
1425 Northwest 36th Street
Miami, FL 33142
305-634-3419
Occupational Fields: operating engineer

International Union of Operating Engineers, Local #595
Box 2547 APO
Miami, FL 34002
Occupational Fields: operating engineer, stationary engineer

International Union of Operating Engineers, Local #673
Central Florida Operating Engineers
4510 North Orange Blossom Trail
Orlando, FL 32804
407-291-2210
Occupational Fields: operating engineer, stationary engineer

International Union of Operating Engineers, Local #675
2200 Park Central Boulevard, North, Suite 700
Pompano Beach, FL 33064
954-979-1700
Occupational Fields: operating engineer

International Union of Operating Engineers, Local #925
PO Box 398
Mango, FL 33550
813-626-4161
Occupational Fields: operating engineer, stationary engineer

North Florida Operating Engineers Union, Local #673
8366 Devoe Street
Jacksonville, FL 32202
904-783-6181
Occupational Fields: operating engineer

Operating Engineers Union
2201 Northwest Ninth Avenue
Fort Lauderdale, FL 33311
954-527-1078
Occupational Fields: operating engineer

Orange County Board of City Commissioners
Highway Maintenance Department
4200 South John Young Parkway
Orlando, FL 32809
407-836-7930
Occupational Fields: operating engineer

Pinellas County Schools
Maintenance Department
11111 Belcher Road, South
Largo, FL 33773
813-586-1818
Occupational Fields: building maintenance technician

Polk County Maintenance Program
7700 State Road 544, North
Winter Haven, FL 33881
941-299-5644
Occupational Fields: operating engineer

**South Florida Millwrights, Piledrivers, and Divers
Highway Constructors**
2727 South Park Road
Hallandale, FL 33009
954-981-1810
*Occupational Fields: operating engineer, highway
construction worker*

Tingen Hydraulic and Pneumatic Service
514 Edgewood Avenue, South
Jacksonville, FL 32205
904-384-4464
Occupational Fields: operating engineer

GEORGIA
**International Union of Operating Engineers,
Local #329**
1000 Victory Drive
Columbus, GA 31901
706-327-0453
*Occupational Fields: stationary engineer, building
maintenance technician*

**International Union of Operating Engineers,
Local #443**
PO Box 2215
Fort Benning, GA 31905
404-545-5750

*Occupational Fields: stationary engineer, building
maintenance technician*

**International Union of Operating Engineers, Local
#474**
3518 Ross Road
Savannah, GA 31405
912-232-0500
*Occupational Fields: operating engineer, stationary
engineer*

**International Union of Operating Engineers,
Local #926**
4179 Dunn Road
PO Box 130
Ellenwood, GA 30049-0130
404-363-2764
*Occupational Fields: operating engineer, heavy equipment
operator*

HAWAII
International Union of Operating Engineers, Hilo
50 Waianuenue Avenue, First Floor
Hilo, HI 96720
808-935-8709
*Occupational Fields: operating engineer, heavy duty
equipment operator, heavy duty welder, construction
equipment operator*

International Union of Operating Engineers, Maui
350 Hoohana Street, Bay C-5
Kahului, HI 96732
808-871-1193
Occupational Fields: operating engineer

Operating Engineers
1432 Middle Street, Room 103
Honolulu, HI 96819
808-847-5523
*Occupational Fields: construction equipment operator,
heavy duty equipment operator, heavy duty welder*

ILLINOIS
**International Union of Operating Engineers, Local
#143**
447 West 31st Street
Chicago, IL 60616

312-326-1430
Occupational Fields: stationary engineer, building maintenance technician

International Union of Operating Engineers, Local #148
148 Wilma Drive
Maryville, IL 62062
618-271-1807
Occupational Fields: stationary engineer, building maintenance technician

International Union of Operating Engineers, Local #150, Chicago District
6200 Joliet Road
Countryside, IL 60525
708-482-8800
http://www.crown.net/~ddurfee/150.html
Occupational Fields: operating engineer

International Union of Operating Engineers, Local #150, Joliet District
1050 North Interstate 55
East Frontage Road
Joliet, IL 60435
815-725-5561
http://www.crown.net/~ddurfee/150.html
Occupational Fields: operating engineer

International Union of Operating Engineers, Local #150, Lakemoor District
28872 Route 120
Lakemoor, IL 60050
815-363-0002
http://www.crown.net/~ddurfee/150.html
Occupational Fields: operating engineer

International Union of Operating Engineers, Local #150, Ottawa District
1411 Canal Street
Ottawa, IL 61350
815-434-6017
http://www.crown.net/~ddurfee/150.html
Occupational Fields: operating engineer

International Union of Operating Engineers, Local #150, Plainfield
20959 West Lockport Road
Plainfield, IL 60544
815-436-4150

http://www.crown.net/~ddurfee/150.html
Occupational Fields: operating engineer, heavy equipment operator

International Union of Operating Engineers, Local #150, Rockford
4477 Linden Road
Rockford, IL 61109
815-874-4166
http://www.crown.net/~ddurfee/150.html
Occupational Fields: operating engineer

International Union of Operating Engineers, Local #150, Rock Island
3511 78th Avenue
Rock Island, IL 61201
309-787-4646
http://www.crown.net/~ddurfee/150.html
Occupational Fields: operating engineer

International Union of Operating Engineers, Local #318
3310 Water Tower Road
Marion, IL 62959
618-993-0318
Occupational Fields: operating engineer

International Union of Operating Engineers, Local #399
763 West Jackson Boulevard
Chicago, IL 60661
312-372-9870
Occupational Fields: stationary engineer, building maintenance technician

International Union of Operating Engineers, Local #520
520 Engineer Road
Granite City, IL 62040
618-931-0500
Occupational Fields: operating engineer

International Union of Operating Engineers, Local #525
PO Box 397
Wood River, IL 62095
618-254-6441
Occupational Fields: stationary engineer, building maintenance technician

International Union of Operating Engineers, Local #553
1678 Zion Hill Road
Centralia, IL 62801
Occupational Fields: stationary engineer, building maintenance technician

International Union of Operating Engineers, Local #649
6408 West Plank Road
Peoria, IL 61604
309-697-0070
Occupational Fields: operating engineer

International Union of Operating Engineers, Local #965
PO Box 3025
Springfield, IL 62708
217-528-9659
Occupational Fields: operating engineer

Murphy Brothers Inc.
3150 Fifth Avenue
Moline, IL 61244
Occupational Fields: operating engineer

Operating Engineers Union
Buckhart Road
Mechanicsburg, IL 62545
217-498-7798
Occupational Fields: operating engineer

Operating Engineers Union
3520 East Cook Street
Springfield, IL 62703
217-528-3602
Occupational Fields: operating engineer

Operating Engineers Union, Local #148
Route 159
Collinsville, IL 62234
618-271-1807
Occupational Fields: operating engineer

INDIANA
Allison Engine Company
2355 South Tibbs Avenue
Indianapolis, IN 46206

317-230-5112
Occupational Fields: stationary engineer

Cummins Engine Company
PO Box 3005
Mail Code 11861
Columbus, IN 47202-3005
812-377-7174
Occupational Fields: mechanical engineer, chemical engineer, mechanical engineering technician

Delphi Energy and Engine Management Systems
2401 Columbus Avenue
Anderson, IN 46018
317-646-3628
Occupational Fields: stationary engineer

General Motors Corporation, Allison Transmission Division
4700 West 10th Street
PO Box 894
Indianapolis, IN 46206-0894
317-242-5321
Occupational Fields: stationary engineer

General Motors Corporation, Marion
Metal Fabricating Division
2400 West Second Street
Marion, IN 46952-3295
317-668-2080
Occupational Fields: stationary engineer

GM Powertrain
Training Programs
PO Box 271
Bedford, IN 47421
812-279-7261
Occupational Fields: mechanical engineer

International Union of Operating Engineers
PO Box 2204
Terre Haute, IN 47802
812-299-2184
Occupational Fields: grading and paving equipment operator, heavy duty mechanic, plant equipment operator, universal equipment operator

International Union of Operating Engineers, Local #19
1520 Profit Drive
Fort Wayne, IN 46808

219-482-5588
Occupational Fields: stationary engineer, building maintenance technician

International Union of Operating Engineers, Local #103
3707 East State Road Nine, North
Anderson, IN 46017
317-378-0013
Occupational Fields: grading and paving equipment operator, plant equipment operator, universal equipment operator, heavy duty mechanic

International Union of Operating Engineers, Local #103
9501 Corporation Drive
Indianapolis, IN 46256
317-849-0163
Occupational Fields: operating engineer

International Union of Operating Engineers, Local #103
514 West Superior Street
Kokomo, IN 46901-5285
317-459-4189
Occupational Fields: operating engineer

International Union of Operating Engineers, Local #150, Merrilville District
2193 JW 84th Place
Merrillville, IN 46410
219-736-7710
http://www.crown.net/~ddurfee/150.html
Occupational Fields: operating engineer

International Union of Operating Engineers, Local #150, South Bend District
1345 Northside Boulevard
South Bend, IN 46616
219-232-5985
http://www.crown.net/~ddurfee/150.html
Occupational Fields: operating engineer

International Union of Operating Engineers, Local #841
6801 South U.S. Highway 41
PO Box 2157
Terre Haute, IN 47802-4835

812-299-1177
Occupational Fields: operating engineer

Operating Engineers Union, Local #181
722 East State Road 68
Lynnville, IN 47619
812-922-5541
Occupational Fields: grading and paving equipment operator, plant equipment operator, universal equipment operator

Original Tractor Cab Company Inc.
6849 West Front Street
Arlington, IN 46104
317-663-2214
Occupational Fields: mechanical engineer

Zollner Company Unlimited Partnership
2425 Coliseum Boulevard, South
Fort Wayne, IN 46803
219-426-8081
Occupational Fields: stationary engineer

IOWA

Ace Construction Inc.
5095 NW 114th Street
Grimes, IA 50111
515-986-4479
Occupational Fields: operating engineer

A.H. Neumann Brothers Inc.
1435 Ohio Street
Box 1315
Des Moines, IA 50305
515-243-0156
Occupational Fields: operating engineer

Ahrens Laser Screed Company Inc.
1130 South Gilbert Street
PO Box 3132
Iowa City, IA 52244
319-358-5853
Occupational Fields: operating engineer

A.J. Allen Mechanical Contractor
25 Dunham Avenue
PO Box 931
Des Moines, IA 50304

515-244-6271
Occupational Fields: operating engineer

Allen Excavating
701 Marion Avenue
Des Moines, IA 50304
515-282-6719
Occupational Fields: operating engineer

Bailey Roofing Contractors
10110 Dennis Drive
Urbandale, IA 50322-3848
515-253-0191
Occupational Fields: operating engineer

Baker Electric Inc.
111 Southwest Jackson Avenue
Des Moines, IA 50315
515-288-6774
Occupational Fields: operating engineer

Baker Mechanical Inc.
2911 Hubbell Avenue
Des Moines, IA 50317
515-262-9327
Occupational Fields: operating engineer

Bowker Mechanical Contractors
1000 32nd Avenue, SW
Box 1273
Cedar Rapids, IA 52406
319-364-2403
Occupational Fields: operating engineer

Bries Construction Inc.
205 North Center Avenue
Epworth, IA 52045
Occupational Fields: operating engineer

Broeker Erection Company Inc.
3135 Sunnyside Avenue
PO Box 426
Burlington, IA 52601
319-753-6596
Occupational Fields: operating engineer

Brown Brothers Inc.
107 East Fifth Street
Des Moines, IA 50309

515-244-8433
Occupational Fields: operating engineer

Carl Schuler Masonry Construction
2130 Commercial Street
PO Box 1015
Waterloo, IA 50704
319-232-8113
Occupational Fields: operating engineer

Champion Crane Service Inc.
1136 Northeast 44th Avenue
Des Moines, IA 50313
515-266-1234
Occupational Fields: operating engineer

Coonrod Wrecker and Crane Service
4000 East Avenue, NW
Cedar Rapids, IA 52405
319-396-7600
Occupational Fields: operating engineer

Corell Contractor Inc.
501 Highway 28-2
Norwalk, IA 50211
Occupational Fields: operating engineer

Cramer and Associates Inc.
990 Northeast 44th Avenue
Des Moines, IA 50313
515-265-1447
Occupational Fields: operating engineer

Custom Steel Erectors
6220 Southwest 10th Street
Des Moines, IA 50315
515-287-3601
Occupational Fields: operating engineer

Dave Schmitt Construction Company
250 50th Avenue, SW
Cedar Rapids, IA 52404
319-365-8669
Occupational Fields: operating engineer

Davis NSE Company Inc.
5636 Northeast 17th Street, Suite One
Des Moines, IA 50312
Occupational Fields: operating engineer

Delaware Pumping
4000 Delaware Avenue
Des Moines, IA 50313
515-266-9796
Occupational Fields: operating engineer

De Phillips Excavating
9247 Aurora Avenue
Urbandale, IA 50322
515-278-6131
Occupational Fields: operating engineer

Des Moines Asphalt and Paving Company
903 Southeast 22nd Street
Des Moines, IA 50317
515-262-8296
Occupational Fields: operating engineer

**International Union of Operating Engineers,
    Local #150, West Burlington**
Rural Route Four, Box 306E1
Burlington, IA 52655
319-754-8135
http://www.crown.net/~ddurfee/150.html
Occupational Fields: operating engineer

**International Union of Operating Engineers,
    Local #234**
Iowa Operating Engineers
4880 Hubbell Avenue
Des Moines, IA 50317
515-265-7501
Occupational Fields: heavy equipment operator

**International Union of Operating Engineers,
    Local #275**
5101 Harbet Avenue
Cedar Rapids, IA 52405
319-396-7732
Occupational Fields: operating engineer

**International Union of Operating Engineers,
    Local #758**
3430 Dodge Street
Dubuque, IA 52003
319-582-0891
*Occupational Fields: stationary engineer, building
    maintenance technician*

Lee Crawford Quarry Company
Highway 94, NW
PO Box 1027
Cedar Rapids, IA 50313
319-396-5705
Occupational Fields: operating engineer

Longfellow Drilling
Rural Route One
Clearfield, IA 50840
515-336-2297
Occupational Fields: operating engineer

Loomis Brothers Inc.
1619 F Avenue, NE
PO Box 608
Cedar Rapids, IA 52406
319-366-7193
Occupational Fields: operating engineer

L.W. Matteson Inc.
One South Point
Burlington, IA 52601
319-754-6705
Occupational Fields: operating engineer

McAninch Corporation
3100 Dixon Street
PO Box 1486
Des Moines, IA 50306
515-265-2653
Occupational Fields: operating engineer

McDermott Excavating
12910 West Side Court
Dubuque, IA 52001
319-583-4633
Occupational Fields: operating engineer

McHan Construction Inc.
1700 Riverside Boulevard
Box 1289
Sioux City, IA 51102
712-233-1471
Occupational Fields: operating engineer

Melvin O. Smith and Son Ditching Company
5151 Northeast Third Street
Des Moines, IA 50313

515-282-3597
Occupational Fields: operating engineer

M. Harper, Limited
6800 Lake Drive, Suite 135
Des Moines, IA 50266
515-224-4876
Occupational Fields: operating engineer

Midwest Fly Ash and Materials
2220 Hawkeye Drive
PO Box 3557
Sioux City, IA 51102
712-252-4049
Occupational Fields: operating engineer

Miller the Driller
5125 East University Avenue
Des Moines, IA 50317
Occupational Fields: operating engineer

Modern Piping Inc.
210 33rd Street Drive, SE
Cedar Rapids, IA 52403
319-364-0131
Occupational Fields: operating engineer

National Concrete Services Inc.
1108 Southeast 30th Street, Suite A
Des Moines, IA 50317
515-246-8116
Occupational Fields: operating engineer

Neumann-Kiewit Constructors
717 Mulberry
Des Moines, IA 50305
Occupational Fields: operating engineer

Northwestern Development Inc.
PO Box 1174
Dubuque, IA 52001
Occupational Fields: operating engineer

Nuckrolls Concrete Services
5145 Northwest Beaver Drive, Suite A
Johnston, IA 50131
515-276-1228
Occupational Fields: operating engineer

Portzen Excavating and Concrete
205 Salina Street
PO Box 1426
Dubuque, IA 52001
319-557-7642
Occupational Fields: operating engineer

Renex Corporation
2390 Chaney, Suite 4
Dubuque, IA 52001
Occupational Fields: operating engineer

River City Stone
12567 English Mill Road
PO Box 1430
Dubuque, IA 52001
319-582-6764
Occupational Fields: operating engineer

R-MAC Contracting Inc.
PO Box 134
Eldon, IA 52554
Occupational Fields: operating engineer

Sandstone Management, Limited
525 North Ninth Street
PO Box 547
Carlisle, IA 50047
515-989-0557
Occupational Fields: operating engineer

Seedorff Masonry Inc.
408 West Mission Street
Strawberry Point, IA 52076
319-933-2296
Occupational Fields: operating engineer

Six Crane Service
284 Highway 65/69, South
Carlisle, IA 50047
515-285-2828
Occupational Fields: operating engineer

Skold Construction Services
5636 Northeast 17th Street, #2
Des Moines, IA 50316
515-264-8420
Occupational Fields: operating engineer

Young Radiator
PO Box 460
Centerville, IA 52544
515-856-8634
Occupational Fields: machine operator

KANSAS
Blackhawk Foundation Company Inc.
PO Box 335
Bonner Springs, KS 66012
Occupational Fields: operating engineer

Coffeyville, City of
Seventh and Walnut Streets
Coffeyville, KS 67337
316-252-6108
Occupational Fields: water treatment plant operator, wastewater plant operator

General Motors Corporation
3201 Fairfax
Kansas City, KS 66115-1399
913-573-7400
Occupational Fields: stationary engineer

International Union of Operating Engineers, Local #119
8405 West Central, Suite 502
Wichita, KS 67212
Occupational Fields: stationary engineer, building maintenance technician

International Union of Operating Engineers, Local #123
512 Westwood
Coffeyville, KS 67337
316-251-3037
Occupational Fields: stationary engineer, building maintenance technician

International Union of Operating Engineers, Local #126
1300 South 11th Street
Parsons, KS 67357
316-421-6329
Occupational Fields: stationary engineer, building maintenance technician

International Union of Operating Engineers, Local #418
1436 North King
Russell, KS 67665

913-483-4755
Occupational Fields: stationary engineer, building maintenance technician

International Union of Operating Engineers, Local #642
Route Two
Arkansas City, KS 67005
Occupational Fields: stationary engineer, building maintenance technician

International Union of Operating Engineers, Local #647
572 Road 390
Allen, KS 66833
316-443-5118
Occupational Fields: stationary engineer, building maintenance technician

L.G. Barcus and Sons
1430 State Avenue
Kansas City, KS 66102
913-621-1100
Occupational Fields: operating engineer

Operating Engineers Union, Local #101
3906 Northwest 16th Street
Topeka, KS 66618
913-233-3662
Occupational Fields: operating engineer

Piping and Equipment
3505 North Topeka
PO Box 1065
Wichita, KS 67201
316-838-7511
Occupational Fields: operating engineer

Sloan and Meier Surveyors
103 South Fourth Street
Manhattan, KS 66502-6165
800-776-0541
Occupational Fields: surveyor

KENTUCKY
International Union of Operating Engineers, Local #181
700 North Elm Street
PO Box 34
Henderson, KY 42420-2938

502-826-2704
Occupational Fields: operating engineer, stationary engineer

LOUISIANA

**International Union of Operating Engineers,
Local #214**
7438 Highway 157
Haughton, LA 71037
318-949-4577
*Occupational Fields: stationary engineer, building
maintenance technician*

**International Union of Operating Engineers,
Local #216**
6150 Hooper Road
Baton Rouge, LA 70811
504-355-5493
*Occupational Fields: stationary engineer, building
maintenance technician*

**International Union of Operating Engineers,
Local #225**
159 Davidson Lane
Monroe, LA 71203
318-329-2386
*Occupational Fields: stationary engineer, building
maintenance technician*

**International Union of Operating Engineers,
Local #406**
7370 Chef Menteur Highway
New Orleans, LA 70126
504-241-1311
Occupational Fields: operating engineer

**International Union of Operating Engineers,
Local #407**
PO Box 390
Lake Charles, LA 70602
318-433-8255
*Occupational Fields: stationary engineer, building
maintenance technician*

MARYLAND

Cianbro Corporation
711 Pittman Road
Baltimore, MD 21226
410-636-3000
Occupational Fields: operating engineer

Flippo Construction Company Inc.
3810 Penn-Belt Place
Forestville, MD 20747
301-967-6800
Occupational Fields: operating engineer

**International Union of Operating Engineers,
Local #37**
5901 Harford Road, Suite A
Baltimore, MD 21214
410-254-2030
Occupational Fields: operating engineer

**International Union of Operating Engineers,
Local #77**
4546 Brittania Way
Suitland, MD 20746
301-899-6900
Occupational Fields: operating engineer

Operating Engineers Union
5737 Allender Road
White Marsh, MD 21162-1306
410-256-2944
Occupational Fields: operating engineer

MASSACHUSETTS

**International Union of Operating Engineers,
Local #4**
120 Mount Hope Street
Roslindale, MA 02131
617-323-9300
Occupational Fields: operating engineer

**International Union of Operating Engineers,
Local #98**
Two Center Square
PO Box 217
Longmeadow, MA 01028
413-525-4291
Occupational Fields: operating engineer

**International Union of Operating Engineers,
Local #877**
89 Access Road, Unit Four
Norwood, MA 02062
617-769-1877
*Occupational Fields: stationary engineer, building
maintenance technician*

MICHIGAN

International Union of Operating Engineers, Local #324

37450 Schoolcraft Road, Suite 110
Livonia, MI 48150
313-462-3660
Occupational Fields: operating engineer

International Union of Operating Engineers, Local #547

Metro Detroit Area Stationary Engineers
24270 West Seven Mile Road
Detroit, MI 48219
313-532-2022
Occupational Fields: stationary engineer, building maintenance technician

United Auto Workers

3731 Covington Road
Kalamazoo, MI 49002
616-381-2703
Occupational Fields: stationary engineer

MINNESOTA

Aconite Corporation

3790 Dodd Road
Eagan, MN 55123
612-681-1900
Occupational Fields: operating engineer

American Underground Inc.

511 11th Avenue, South, #248
Minneapolis, MN 55415
612-339-5403
Occupational Fields: operating engineer

Barbarossa and Sons Inc.

11000 93rd Avenue, North
PO Box 367
Osseo, MN 55369
612-425-4146
Occupational Fields: operating engineer

International Union of Operating Engineers, Local #35

3470 Washington Drive, Suite 159
Eagan, MN 55122
612-686-6447
Occupational Fields: stationary engineer, building maintenance technician

International Union of Operating Engineers, Local #49

2829 Anthony Lane, South
Minneapolis, MN 55418
612-788-9441
Occupational Fields: operating engineer

International Union of Operating Engineers, Local #50

2564 Town Road 213
International Falls, MN 56649
Occupational Fields: stationary engineer, building maintenance technician

International Union of Operating Engineers, Local #70

2417 Larpenteur Avenue, West
St. Paul, MN 55113
612-646-4566
Occupational Fields: stationary engineer, building maintenance technician

International Union of Operating Engineers, Local #756

PO Box 101
Rochester, MN 55903
507-280-9743
Occupational Fields: stationary engineer, building maintenance technician

M. A. Mortenson Company

700 Meadow Lane, North
PO Box 710
Minneapolis, MN 55440
612-522-2100
Occupational Fields: operating engineer

Moorhead Machinery and Boiler Company

3477 University Avenue, NE
Minneapolis, MN 55418
612-789-3541
Occupational Fields: operating engineer

Northern Pipeline Construction Company

20000 Kenrick Avenue
Lakeville, MN 55044
612-469-2800
Occupational Fields: operating engineer

Operating Engineers Union

Rural Route Nine, Box 302
Mankato, MN 56001

507-625-3670
Occupational Fields: operating engineer

Park Construction Company
7900 Beach Street, NE
Minneapolis, MN 55432
Occupational Fields: operating engineer

S.J. Louis Construction Inc.
7284 County Road 138
PO Box 1373
St. Cloud, MN 56302
320-253-9291
Occupational Fields: operating engineer

MISSISSIPPI
International Union of Operating Engineers, Local #624
1328 Highway 80, West
Jackson, MS 39204-2501
601-353-3914
Occupational Fields: operating engineer

MISSOURI
Belger Cartage Service
1219 East 19th Street
Kansas City, MO 64108
816-472-0000
Occupational Fields: operating engineer

International Union of Operating Engineers, Local #2
2929 South Jefferson
St. Louis, MO 63118
314-865-1300
Occupational Fields: stationary engineer, building maintenance technician

International Union of Operating Engineers, Local #16
1833 North Broadway
Springfield, MO 65803
417-864-6889
Occupational Fields: operating engineer

International Union of Operating Engineers, Local #101, Kansas City
6301 Rockhill Road, #301
Kansas City, MO 64131

816-361-0880
Occupational Fields: operating engineer, heavy equipment operator

International Union of Operating Engineers, Local #513
3449 Hollenberg Drive
Bridgeton, MO 63044
314-739-3983
Occupational Fields: operating engineer

Operating Engineers Local #513, Silex
Rural Route One, Box 162A
Silex, MO 63377
314-485-2200
Occupational Fields: operating engineer

Operating Engineers Union, Local #513, Cape Girardeau
777 Enterprise Street
Cape Girardeau, MO 63703
573-334-5492
Occupational Fields: operating engineer

MONTANA
International Union of Operating Engineers, Local #375
58 West Quartz Street
Butte, MT 59701
406-723-7921
Occupational Fields: stationary engineer, building maintenance technician

International Union of Operating Engineers, Local #400
Montana Operating Engineers and Associated General Contractors
PO Box 5929
Helena, MT 59604
406-442-9597
Occupational Fields: operating engineer, heavy equipment operator

Montana Operating Engineers
3100 Canyon Ferry Road
Helena, MT 59635-3031
406-227-5600
Occupational Fields: operating engineer

Operating Engineers, Local #400
208 East Main Street
Missoula, MT 59802
406-728-2832
Occupational Fields: operating engineer

NEBRASKA

Anderson Excavating and Wrecking Company
1824 South 20th Street
Omaha, NE 68108
402-345-8811
Occupational Fields: operating engineer

Beaver Excavation Inc.
400 North Jackson Street
Papillion, NE 68046
402-339-1400
Occupational Fields: operating engineer

Davis Erection Company Inc.
5910 South 27th Street
Omaha, NE 68107
402-731-7484
Occupational Fields: operating engineer

International Union of Operating Engineers, Local #571
4660 South 60th Avenue
Omaha, NE 68117
402-733-1600
Occupational Fields: operating engineer

M and S Grading Inc.
8535 Irvington Road
Omaha, NE 68122
402-572-7161
Occupational Fields: operating engineer

NEVADA

Associated Builders and Contractors, Northern Nevada
593 Overmeyer Road
Sparks, NV 89431
702-358-7888
Occupational Fields: equipment operator

International Union of Operating Engineers
1720 Mountain City Highway
Elko, NV 89801-4495
702-753-8761
Occupational Fields: operating engineer, stationary engineer

International Union of Operating Engineers
1094 Lamoille Highway
Elko, NV 89801
702-753-8761
Occupational Fields: operating engineer

International Union of Operating Engineers, Local #3, Carson City
308 North Curry Street, #105
Carson City, NV 89703-4123
702-885-2323
Occupational Fields: operating engineer, stationary engineer

International Union of Operating Engineers, Local #3, Hawthorne
601 Fifth
Hawthorne, NV 89415
702-945-5595
Occupational Fields: operating engineer, stationary engineer

International Union of Operating Engineers, Reno
1290 Corporate Boulevard
Reno, NV 89502
702-857-4440
Occupational Fields: operating engineer

Operating and Maintenance Engineers Union
301 Deauville Street
Las Vegas, NV 89106-3912
702-382-8452
Occupational Fields: operating engineer, maintenance engineer

Southern Nevada Operating Engineers
2750 East Ann Road
Las Vegas, NV 89036
702-649-7888
Occupational Fields: operating engineer, equipment operator, heavy duty repairman, surveyor

NEW HAMPSHIRE

International Union of Operating Engineers, Local #156
PO Box 2052
Portsmouth, NH 03801

207-439-4281
Occupational Fields: stationary engineer, building
maintenance engineer

NEW JERSEY

**International Union of Operating Engineers,
Local #25**
166 West Kelly Street
Metuchen, NJ 08840
908-548-8118
Occupational Fields: operating engineer, dredge operator

International Union of Operating Engineers, Local #68
11 Fairfield Place
PO Box 534
Caldwell, NJ 07006
800-562-2568
http://www.iuoe-68.org
Occupational Fields: operating engineer, stationary
engineer, building maintenance technician

**International Union of Operating Engineers,
Local #716**
322 Jersey Avenue
Gloucester, NJ 08030
609-456-7607
Occupational Fields: stationary engineer, building
maintenance technician

**International Union of Operating Engineers,
Local #825**
U.S. Route 46, East
Little Falls, NJ 07424
201-785-0500
Occupational Fields: operating engineer

NEW MEXICO

**International Union of Operating Engineers,
Local #953**
PO Box 8533
Albuquerque, NM 87198
505-266-5757
Occupational Fields: operating engineer

NEW YORK

International Union of Operating Engineers, Local #14
14157 Northern Boulevard
Flushing, NY 11354

718-939-0600
Occupational Fields: operating engineer

International Union of Operating Engineers, Local #15
265 West 14th Street
New York, NY 10011
212-924-6740
Occupational Fields: operating engineer

International Union of Operating Engineers, Local #17
150 North America Drive, West
Seneca, NY 14224
716-675-4544
Occupational Fields: operating engineer

**International Union of Operating Engineers,
Local #30**
11506 Myrtle Avenue
Richmond Hill, NY 11418
718-847-8484
Occupational Fields: stationary engineer, building
maintenance technician

**International Union of Operating Engineers,
Local #71**
510 Lyell Avenue
Rochester, NY 14606
716-254-3590
Occupational Fields: stationary engineer, building
maintenance technician

**International Union of Operating Engineers,
Local #94**
331 West 44th Street
New York, NY 10036
212-245-7040
Occupational Fields: stationary engineer, building
maintenance technician

**International Union of Operating Engineers,
Local #106**
1284 Central Avenue
Albany, NY 12205
518-453-6518
Occupational Fields: stationary engineer, building
maintenance technician

**International Union of Operating Engineers,
Local #137**
1360 Pleasantville Road
Briarcliff Manor, NY 10510

914-762-0600
Occupational Fields: operating engineer

**International Union of Operating Engineers,
Local #138**
PO Box 206
Farmingdale, NY 11735
516-694-2480
Occupational Fields: operating engineer

**International Union of Operating Engineers,
Local #211**
225 Broadway, 43rd Floor
New York, NY 10007
212-233-2690
Occupational Fields: stationary engineer, building
maintenance technician

**International Union of Operating Engineers,
Local #295**
61-04 Maurice Avenue
Maspeth, NY 11378
718-672-1415
Occupational Fields: stationary engineer, building
maintenance technician

**International Union of Operating Engineers,
Local #409**
PO Box 366
Niagara Square Station
Buffalo, NY 14201
716-882-6353
Occupational Fields: stationary engineer, building
maintenance technician

**International Union of Operating Engineers,
Local #463**
3365 Ridge Road
Ransomville, NY 14131
716-434-3327
Occupational Fields: operating engineer

**International Union of Operating Engineers,
Local #545**
4325 South Salina Street
Box 0100
Syracuse, NY 13205
315-492-1752
Occupational Fields: operating engineer

International Union of Operating Engineers, Local #832
PO Box 93310
Rochester, NY 14692
716-272-9890
Occupational Fields: operating engineer

**International Union of Operating Engineers,
Local #891**
4600 Broadway
New York, NY 10040
212-567-2203
Occupational Fields: stationary engineer, building
maintenance technician

NORTH CAROLINA
**International Union of Operating Engineers,
Local #415**
1220 Cross Roads
Roper, NC 27970
919-793-5191
Occupational Fields: stationary engineer, building
maintenance technician

**International Union of Operating Engineers,
Local #465**
PO Box 15250
Durham, NC 27704
919-596-6869
Occupational Fields: operating engineer, stationary engineer

Martin Marietta
2710 Wycliff Road
PO Box 30013
Raleigh, NC 27622
919-781-4550
Occupational Fields: operating engineer

OHIO
International Union of Operating Engineers
6051 North Dixie Drive
Dayton, OH 45414
937-890-5914
Occupational Fields: operating engineer

International Union of Operating Engineers
2033 Oak Court
Swanton, OH 43558

419-825-5551
Occupational Fields: operating engineer

International Union of Operating Engineers, Locals #10 and #18
3515 Prospect Avenue
Cleveland, OH 44115
216-432-3138
Occupational Fields: operating engineer, stationary engineer, building maintenance technician

International Union of Operating Engineers, Local #20
1216 East McMillan Avenue, #202
Cincinnati, OH 45206
513-751-1671
Occupational Fields: stationary engineer, building maintenance technician

International Union of Operating Engineers, Local #603
943 South Horning Road
Mansfield, OH 44903
419-468-9503
Occupational Fields: stationary engineer, building maintenance technician

International Union of Operating Engineers, Local #943
746 Elm Road, NE
Warren, OH 44483
Occupational Fields: stationary engineer, building maintenance technician

Ohio Operating Engineers Training Center
30410 Strawn Road
Logan, OH 45215
614-385-2567
Occupational Fields: operating engineer

Ohio Operating Engineers Training Center
4250 Soldiers Home Miamisburg Road
Miamisburg, OH 45342
937-859-5211
Occupational Fields: operating engineer

Ohio Operating Engineers Training Center
9235 Waterville Swanton Road
Waterville, OH 43566-0182

419-878-8521
Occupational Fields: operating engineer

Operating Engineers Union, Local #66
291 McClurg Road
Youngstown, OH 44512
330-758-7536
Occupational Fields: operating engineer

OKLAHOMA
International Union of Operating Engineers, Local #627
12109 East Skelly Drive
Tulsa, OK 74128
918-437-0370
Occupational Fields: operating engineer

International Union of Operating Engineers, Local #641
203 Northwest Theodore
Bartlesville, OK 74003
918-336-7359
Occupational Fields: stationary engineer, building maintenance technician

International Union of Operating Engineers, Local #670
58 Broadlawn
PO Box 2418
Ardmore, OK 73402
405-223-8854
Occupational Fields: stationary engineer, building maintenance technician

OREGON
Associated General Contractors, International Union of Operating Engineers, Local #701
5001 Franklin Boulevard
Eugene, OR 97403-2709
541-741-7292
Occupational Fields: operating engineer

International Union of Operating Engineers, Local #701
555 East First Street
Gladstone, OR 97027
503-650-7701

Occupational Fields: stationary engineer, operating
    engineer

PENNSYLVANIA

International Union of Operating Engineers, Local #61
5000 Richmond Street, Building 24
Philadelphia, PA 19137
Occupational Fields: stationary engineer, building
    maintenance technician

International Union of Operating Engineers, Local #66
300 Seco Road
Monroeville, PA 15146
412-856-8662
Occupational Fields: operating engineer

International Union of Operating Engineers, Local #95
300 Saline Street
Pittsburgh, PA 15207
412-422-4702
Occupational Fields: stationary engineer, building
    maintenance technician

International Union of Operating Engineers, Local #367
28 West Germania
Ashley, PA 18706
Occupational Fields: stationary engineer, building
    maintenance technician

**International Union of Operating Engineers,
    Local #542**
1375 Virginia Drive, Suite 100
Fort Washington, PA 19034
215-542-7500
Occupational Fields: operating engineer

**International Union of Operating Engineers,
    Local #543**
Rural Delivery Two
Sugar Grove, PA 16350
814-489-3478
Occupational Fields: stationary engineer, building
    maintenance technician

**International Union of Operating Engineers,
    Local #835**
3031 Walton Road #100
Norristown, PA 19401

610-825-6595
Occupational Fields: stationary engineer, building
    maintenance technician

**International Union of Operating Engineers,
    Local #859**
3042 Marcella Drive
Erie, PA 16506
814-871-6472
Occupational Fields: stationary engineer, building
    maintenance technician

Operating Engineers Union
821 Font Road
Glenmoore, PA 19343
610-458-5369
Occupational Fields: operating engineer

**Operating Engineers Union, Local #66,
    Thompson Run Road**
611 Thompson Run Road
Monroeville, PA 15146
412-373-3661
Occupational Fields: operating engineer

Western Pennsylvania Operating Engineers
Route 22
New Alexandria, PA 15670
412-668-2244
Occupational Fields: operating engineer

RHODE ISLAND
**International Union of Operating Engineers,
    Local #57**
141 Gano Street
Providence, RI 02906
401-421-6678
Occupational Fields: operating engineer

SOUTH CAROLINA
**International Union of Operating Engineers,
    Local #470**
PO Box 2462
Aiken, SC 29802
803-648-0729
http://www.local470.net
Occupational Fields: operating engineer

TENNESSEE

International Union of Operating Engineers, Local #369

2369 Airways Boulevard
Memphis, TN 38114
901-743-1311
Occupational Fields: stationary engineer, operating engineer

International Union of Operating Engineers, Local #900

PO Box 4548
Oak Ridge, TN 37831
423-220-8518
Occupational Fields: stationary engineer, building maintenance technician

International Union of Operating Engineers, Local #912

111 Nashville Highway
Columbia, TN 38401
615-388-3107
Occupational Fields: stationary engineer, building maintenance technician

International Union of Operating Engineers, Local #917

1098 McCallie Avenue
Chattanooga, TN 37404
423-624-4412
Occupational Fields: operating engineer

TEXAS

International Union of Operating Engineers, Local #178

4025 Rufe Snow Drive
Fort Worth, TX 76180
817-284-1191
Occupational Fields: operating engineer

International Union of Operating Engineers, Local #260

2200 Lake Air Drive
Waco, TX 76710
254-840-4149
Occupational Fields: stationary engineer, petrochemical engineer

International Union of Operating Engineers, Local #340

702 South Madison
Amarillo, TX 79101
806-373-2273
Occupational Fields: stationary engineer, petrochemical engineer

International Union of Operating Engineers, Local #347

PO Box 1429
Texas City, TX 77592
409-948-2001
Occupational Fields: stationary engineer, petrochemical engineer

International Union of Operating Engineers, Local #351

111 East Coolidge
Borger, TX 79007
806-274-4501
Occupational Fields: stationary engineer, petrochemical engineer

International Union of Operating Engineers, Local #450

PO Box 9468
Houston, TX 77261
713-923-7681
Occupational Fields: operating engineer

International Union of Operating Engineers, Local #564

223 South Avenue C
PO Box 745
Freeport, TX 77542
409-233-5283
Occupational Fields: stationary engineer, petrochemical engineer

International Union of Operating Engineers, Local #826

PO Box 1590
Big Spring, TX 79721
915-267-2563
Occupational Fields: stationary engineer, petrochemical engineer

Operating Engineers

1301 Alabama, Room 101 H
Houston, TX 77004

713-528-4707
Occupational Fields: operating engineer

Operating Engineers Union, Local #450
PO Box 817
Nederland, TX 77627
409-727-2331
Occupational Fields: operating engineer

Texas Natural Resource Conservation Commission
Occupational Certification Section, MC 177
PO Box 13087
Austin, TX 78711-3087
512-239-0530
Occupational Fields: water well driller, pump installer

Texas Water Well Association
206 San Jacinto Building
Austin, TX 78701
512-472-7216
Occupational Fields: water well driller, pump installer

UTAH
International Union of Operating Engineers, Local #3
1958 West North Temple
Salt Lake City, UT 84116
801-596-2677
Occupational Fields: operating engineer

Lang Exploratory Drilling
2286 West 1500 South
Salt Lake City, UT 84104-4126
702-753-2119
Occupational Fields: drilling contractor, water well driller, mineral driller

VIRGINIA
International Union of Operating Engineers, Local #147
Three Koger Executive Center, Suite 123
Norfolk, VA 23502
757-461-4505
Occupational Fields: operating engineer

International Union of Operating Engineers, Local #710
One Crawford Parkway, #1804
Portsmouth, VA 23704
757-399-1058

Occupational Fields: stationary engineer, building maintenance technician

International Union of Operating Engineers, Local #724
5307 East Virginia Beach Boulevard, Suite 131
Norfolk, VA 23502
804-466-8022
Occupational Fields: stationary engineer, building maintenance technician

WASHINGTON
Amalgamated Transit Union, Local #587
Municipality of Metropolitan Seattle
1555 Airport Way, South
Seattle, WA 98134
206-684-2714
Occupational Fields: operating engineer

Amalgamated Transit Union, Local #1015
1230 West Boone Avenue
Spokane, WA 99201
509-325-6000
Occupational Fields: operating engineer

Associated General Contractors, Inland Northwest Chapter
East 4936 Trent Avenue
PO Box 3266
Spokane, WA 99220-3266
509-535-0391
Occupational Fields: operating engineer

Community Transit
IAM District #160
7000 Hardeson Road
Everett, WA 98203
425-348-2339
Occupational Fields: operating engineer

David Evans and Associates Inc.
West 110 Cataldo
Spokane, WA 99201
509-327-8697
Occupational Fields: operating engineer

Eastern Washington Machinists
North 2110 Fancher Street
Spokane, WA 99212
509-533-7181
Occupational Fields: operating engineer

Fluor Daniel Hanford
M/S R2-88
PO Box 1500
Richland, WA 99352-1505
509-376-1523
Occupational Fields: operating engineer

International Union of Operating Engineers, Bremerton
632 Fifth Street
Bremerton, WA 98337-1492
360-377-5084
Occupational Fields: operating engineer, stationary engineer

International Union of Operating Engineers, Local #280
1305 Knight Street
Richland, WA 99352
509-946-5101
Occupational Fields: stationary engineer, building maintenance technician

International Union of Operating Engineers, Local #280
PO Box 5401
Spokane, WA 99205-0401
509-326-0777
Occupational Fields: operating engineer, stationary engineer

International Union of Operating Engineers, Locals #286 and #609
Western Washington Stationary Engineers
830 North Riverside Drive
Renton, WA 98055
425-235-4670
Occupational Fields: heating, ventilation, and air-conditioning mechanic, stationary engineer, facilities custodian

International Union of Operating Engineers, Local #302
Western Washington Operating Engineers
18701 120th Avenue, NE, Suite 101
Bothell, WA 98011
425-486-2273
Occupational Fields: operating engineer, heavy equipment operator

International Union of Operating Engineers, Local #302
2716 Western Avenue
Seattle, WA 98121

206-448-6187
Occupational Fields: operating engineer, stationary engineer

International Union of Operating Engineers, Local #370
2015 West Yakima Street
Pasco, WA 99301
509-545-1811
Occupational Fields: operating engineer, stationary engineer

International Union of Operating Engineers, Local #370
PO Box 3386
Spokane, WA 99220
509-624-5365
Occupational Fields: operating engineer

International Union of Operating Engineers, Local #609
2800 First Avenue, Room 311
Seattle, WA 98121
206-441-8544
Occupational Fields: stationary engineer, building maintenance technician

International Union of Operating Engineers, Local #612
417 North Pearl Street
Centralia, WA 98531-4668
360-736-8028
Occupational Fields: operating engineer, stationary engineer

International Union of Operating Engineers, Local #612
Western Washington Operating Engineers
1555 South Fawcett Avenue
Tacoma, WA 98402-1803
206-572-9612
Occupational Fields: operating engineer, surveyor

Northwest Automotive Machinists
5631 Tacoma Mall Boulevard
Tacoma, WA 98408
253-472-9692
Occupational Fields: operating engineer

Olympia, City of
PO Box 1967
Olympia, WA 98507

360-753-8034
Occupational Fields: stationary engineer

Operating Engineers Union, Western Washington
2209 West Nob Hill Boulevard
Yakima, WA 98902-5235
509-453-2567
Occupational Fields: operating engineer, surveyor

Pierce Transit
Amalgamated Transit Union, Local #758
3701 96th Street, Southwest
Tacoma, WA 98499-4431
253-581-8080
Occupational Fields: operating engineer

Seattle Automotive Machinists
District Lodge #160
9135 15th Place, South
Seattle, WA 98108
206-762-7990
Occupational Fields: operating engineer

Vancouver Machinists and Automotive Machinists
5000 East 18th Street
Vancouver, WA 98661
360-693-9172
Occupational Fields: operating engineer

Western States Operating Engineers
23500 South Operating Engineers Lane
PO Box 210
Spangle, WA 99031-0210
509-235-9393
http://www.wsopen.org
Occupational Fields: operating engineer, heavy duty mechanic, construction equipment operator, technical engineer, hoisting engineer

Western Washington Operating Engineers
2701 First Avenue
Seattle, WA 98121-1123
206-448-9611
Occupational Fields: surveyor, heavy duty repairman, construction equipment operator

Yelm School District #2
PO Box 476
Yelm, WA 98597

360-458-6113
Occupational Fields: operating engineer

WEST VIRGINIA

Construction Trades Training Center
2307 Seventh Avenue
Charleston, WV 25312-1811
304-346-3863
Occupational Fields: operating engineer

International Union of Operating Engineers, Local #132
606 Tennessee Avenue
PO Box 6770
Charleston, WV 25362
304-343-7731
Occupational Fields: heavy equipment operator

International Union of Operating Engineers, Local #141
UAFT
PO Box 2356
Weirton, WV 26062
304-797-0207
Occupational Fields: operating engineer

WISCONSIN

Arby Construction Inc.
19705 West Lincoln Avenue
New Berlin, WI 53151
414-549-1919
Occupational Fields: operating engineer

Associated General Contractors
4814 East Broadway
Madison, WI 53716
608-221-3821
Occupational Fields: operating engineer

Dawes Rigging and Crane Rental
805 South 72nd Street
PO Box 44080
Milwaukee, WI 53214
404-453-5335
Occupational Fields: operating engineer

International Union of Operating Engineers
3231 Laura Lane
Middleton, WI 53562

608-836-0139
Occupational Fields: operating engineer

International Union of Operating Engineers, Local #139

N27 W23233 Roundy Drive
PO Box 130
Pewaukee, WI 53072
414-549-9190
Occupational Fields: operating engineer

International Union of Operating Engineers, Local #266

3607 Division Street
Manitowoc, WI 54220
Occupational Fields: stationary engineer, building maintenance technician

International Union of Operating Engineers, Local #300

107 North Raymond Street
Marinette, WI 54143
715-735-6097
Occupational Fields: stationary engineer, building maintenance technician

International Union of Operating Engineers, Local #305

910 East Seventh Street
Superior, WI 54880
715-392-4354
Occupational Fields: stationary engineer, building maintenance technician

International Union of Operating Engineers, Local #309

43332 Spring Street
Racine, WI 53405
414-633-1765
Occupational Fields: stationary engineer, building maintenance technician

International Union of Operating Engineers, Local #310

1250 Radisson Street
Box 8323
Green Bay, WI 54308
414-437-2750
Occupational Fields: stationary engineer, building maintenance technician

International Union of Operating Engineers, Local #317

3152 South 27th Street
Milwaukee, WI 53215
414-671-3258
Occupational Fields: stationary engineer, building maintenance technician

International Union of Operating Engineers, Local #504

840 North 11th Street
Manitowoc, WI 54220
414-682-6622
Occupational Fields: stationary engineer, building maintenance technician

International Union of Operating Engineers, Local #533

East 7681 County Highway C
Freedom, WI 53951
608-544-4571
Occupational Fields: stationary engineer, building maintenance technician

International Union of Operating Engineers, Local #950

4429 South Kentucky Avenue
Milwaukee, WI 53221
414-282-7350
Occupational Fields: stationary engineer, building maintenance technician

J. F. Brennan Company

820 Bainbridge Street
PO Box 255
La Crosse, WI 54603
608-784-7173
Occupational Fields: operating engineer

Labor Temple

1602 South Park Street
Madison, WI 53715
608-255-2065
Occupational Fields: operating engineer

Lunda Construction Company

620 Gebhardt Road
PO Box 669
Black River Falls, WI 52406
715-284-9491
Occupational Fields: operating engineer

Madsen Johnson Corporation
901 Industrial Street
PO Box 486
Hudson, WI 54016
715-386-8201
Occupational Fields: operating engineer

Marshall Erdman and Associates Inc.
5117 University Avenue
Madison, WI 53705
608-238-4230
Occupational Fields: operating engineer

Mathy Construction Company
920 10th Avenue, North
Onalaska, WI 54650
608-783-6411
Occupational Fields: operating engineer

Mueller Pipeliners Inc.
2936 South 166th Street
PO Box 51650
New Berlin, WI 53151
414-782-6160
Occupational Fields: operating engineer

Operating Engineers Union
1920 Ward Avenue
La Crosse, WI 54601
608-788-0972
Occupational Fields: operating engineer

Operating Engineers Union, Local #139
115 North Douglas Street
Appleton, WI 54914
414-739-6378
Occupational Fields: operating engineer

Operating Engineers Union, Local #139
2233 Birch Street
Eau Claire, WI 54703
715-838-0139
Occupational Fields: operating engineer

Wisconsin Operating Engineers Training Center
West 1584 State Highway 21
PO Box 60
Coloma, WI 54930
715-228-4911
Occupational Fields: operating engineer

WYOMING
International Union of Operating Engineers, Local #800
4925 Wardell Industrial Drive
PO Box 3479
Casper, WY 82602
307-265-1397
Occupational Fields: operating engineer, stationary engineer

CANADA
ALBERTA
International Union of Operating Engineers, Local #955
17603 114th Avenue
Edmonton, AB T5S 2R9
780-483-0955
Fax: 780-483-1998
http://www.iuoe955.com
Occupational Fields: operating engineer, stationary engineer

BRITISH COLUMBIA
International Union of Operating Engineers, Local #115
4333 Ledger Avenue
Burnaby, BC V5G 3T3
604-291-8831
Fax: 604-473-5235
http://www.iuoe115.com
Occupational Fields: operating engineer, stationary engineer

International Union of Operating Engineers, Local #882
4333 Ledger Avenue, Room 304
Burnaby, BC V5G 3T3
604-294-5266
Fax: 604-294-0694
http://www.iuoe882.com
Occupational Fields: operating engineer, stationary engineer

International Union of Operating Engineers, Local #959
PO Box 4766
Williams Lake, BC V0K 2E0
250-398-3357

Occupational Fields: operating engineer, stationary engineer

International Union of Operating Engineers, Local #963
707 Durward Avenue
Vancouver, BC V5V 2Y9
604-876-6287
Fax: 604-876-5687
http://www.iuoe963.ca
Occupational Fields: operating engineer, stationary engineer

MANITOBA
International Union of Operating Engineers, Local #828
68 Church Street
Flin Flon, MB R8A 1K7
204-687-3764
Fax: 204-687-7123
Occupational Fields: operating engineer, stationary engineer

International Union of Operating Engineers, Local #987
1008 Wall Street
Winnipeg, MB R3G 2V3
204-786-8658
Fax: 204-786-6578
http://www.oe987.mb.ca
Occupational Fields: operating engineer, stationary engineer

NEW BRUNSWICK
International Union of Operating Engineers, Local #894
PO Box 633
Bathurst, NB E2A 3Z6
506-548-3600
Fax: 506-548-3600
Occupational Fields: operating engineer, stationary engineer

International Union of Operating Engineers, Local #946
PO Box 955
Saint John, NB E2L 4E3
506-635-1110
Fax: 506-635-1656

Occupational Fields: operating engineer, stationary engineer

NEWFOUNDLAND
International Union of Operating Engineers, Local #904
62 Commonwealth Avenue
Mount Pearl, NF A1N 1W8
709-747-9040
Fax: 709-747-6760
http://www.iuoe904.com
Occupational Fields: operating engineer, stationary engineer

NOVA SCOTIA
International Union of Operating Engineers, Local #721
251 Brownlow Avenue
Dartmouth, NS B3B 2A9
902-865-8844
Fax: 902-864-0676
Occupational Fields: operating engineer, stationary engineer

International Union of Operating Engineers, Local #968
28 Aberdeen Street
Kentville, NS B4N 3X9
902-678-9950
Fax: 902-678-1838
http://www.iuoe968.com
Occupational Fields: operating engineer, stationary engineer

ONTARIO
International Union of Operating Engineers, Local #772
370 Main Street East, Suite 302
Hamilton, ON L8N 1J6
905-527-5250
Fax: 905-527-6336
http://www.iuoe772.org
Occupational Fields: operating engineer, stationary engineer

International Union of Operating Engineers, Local #793
30 Commercial Road
Toronto, ON M4G 1Z4

416-425-8710
Fax: 416-425-2597
Occupational Fields: operating engineer, stationary
engineer

**International Union of Operating Engineers,
Local #865**
100-250 Park Avenue
Thunder Bay, ON P7B 5L4
807-343-9493
Fax: 807-346-8120
http://www.iuoe865.org
Occupational Fields: operating engineer, stationary
engineer

**International Union of Operating Engineers,
Local #920**
Rural Route 7
Pembroke, ON K8A 6W8
613-687-4228
Occupational Fields: operating engineer, stationary
engineer

PRINCE EDWARD ISLAND
**International Union of Operating Engineers,
Local #942**
326 Patterson Drive
Charlottetown, PE C1A 8K4
902-566-3255
Fax: 902-368-2974
Occupational Fields: operating engineer, stationary
engineer

QUEBEC
**International Union of Operating Engineers,
Local #484**
4869 Jarry East, Suite 220
Montreal, QC H1R 1Y1
514-323-9684
Fax: 514-326-9417
Occupational Fields: operating engineer, stationary
engineer

**International Union of Operating Engineers,
Local #905**
4881 Jarry East, Suite 228
Montreal, QC H1R 1Y1
514-326-9412
Fax: 514-326-9417
Occupational Fields: operating engineer, stationary
engineer

SASKATCHEWAN
**International Union of Operating Engineers,
Local #870**
2175 Airport Drive
Saskatoon, SK S7L 7E1
306-665-7718
Fax: 306-665-0998
Occupational Fields: operating engineer, stationary
engineer

PAINTERS AND PAPERHANGERS

RELATED SECTIONS: *artists and artisans, auto body workers, carpenters, drywallers and lathers, floor layers, glaziers and glass makers, insulators and asbestos workers, masons, plasterers, tile setters*

Painters decorate and protect buildings, vehicles, furniture, and other structures with paint, stain, varnish, and other finishes. Paints and sealers protect exterior walls from damage caused by sun, wind, rain, and snow, and they make interior surfaces clean and bright. *Auto body painters* specialize in spray-painting cars, trucks, and other vehicles. Painters may also specialize in structures such as bridges and towers. *Spray-machine operators* use spray guns to coat manufactured articles with paint. Some workers do both wallpapering and painting.

Painters must know what type of paint to use for each project. They generally use premixed paint but sometimes mix the paint themselves. Surface preparation is a large part of the job; the worker must strip or wash off any old paint, wallpaper, oil, and dirt. This may involve sanding, wire brushing, burning, or blasting with water or abrasive substances. Holes, cracks, and other imperfections must be filled and sanded. Usually a coat of primer is applied to prevent resins and other substances from seeping through. Then coats of paint are applied with brushes, rollers, or paint sprayers. Manufactured articles are often dipped in paint.

Paperhangers install decorative wall coverings of paper, vinyl, fabric, or other material. They prepare the surface, apply a sealer to the wall, apply adhesive to the back of the wall covering, and smooth it into place with brushes or rollers. Sometimes the old covering must first be removed with water, steam, or solvents. Paperhangers must take care to make the covering fit with tight, closed seams and to ensure that the pattern of each strip of wall covering is precisely aligned.

Paperhangers work indoors, but painters may work indoors or outdoors, sometimes high above the ground. The work is seldom performed in bad weather. Workers must climb ladders and scaffolds, and they run the risk of falling. The job involves long periods of standing, kneeling, bending, and reaching. Workers tend to become spattered or covered with paint, and they sometimes must wear protective masks to filter out harmful fumes.

Some painters and paperhangers are employed by construction companies. Others do maintenance work in offices, housing complexes, schools, hospitals, and industrial settings. About half are self-employed, and many work part time. There are often periods of unemployment between projects.

Many construction painters belong to unions, such as the International Brotherhood of Painters and Allied Trades or the Associated Builders and Contractors, but others are nonunion. Auto body painters often belong to the International Association of Machinists and Aerospace Workers; the International Union of United Automobile, Aerospace and Agricultural Implement Workers of America; the Sheet Metal Workers' International Association; the International Brotherhood of Teamsters; or the International Brotherhood of Painters and Allied Trades.

Many unions and other organizations in the building and construction trades offer apprenticeship training for painters and paperhangers. Trainees work under the supervision of experienced workers and may start by erecting scaffolds and performing other simple tasks. They participate in on-the-job training and at least 144 hours of classroom work annually. Typically the course of study runs for two to four years and includes instruction in application techniques, color coordination, decorating concepts, blueprint reading, paint mixing and matching, wood finishing, and cost estimation. Skilled workers may advance to supervisory positions or become estimators.

In general an applicant should

- apply in person
- be at least 16 years old
- be a high school graduate or hold a GED certificate
- be in good physical condition
- have good eyesight
- have a keen sense of color
- have manual dexterity

APPRENTICESHIP SALARIES

Between $6 an hour and $12 an hour, or about 40 percent to 50 percent the rate paid to experienced workers. Experienced apprentices earn between $11 an hour and $24 an hour.

POSTAPPRENTICESHIP SALARIES

About $9 an hour, up to $24 an hour. Earnings vary, depending on union membership and geographic location. Paperhangers typically earn more than painters.

JOB OUTLOOK

Generally this field will grow about as fast the average job through 2012, as new construction is expected to increase and existing structures will continue to require maintenance and renovation. Many people with limited skills enter this trade, then leave because they dislike the work, creating numerous job openings each year. In addition, painting is labor-intensive and not subject to technological changes that increase efficiency and limit the number of laborers needed. Many fewer openings will arise for paperhangers because the number of these jobs is comparatively small.

Painters, however, must be prepared for periods of unemployment, especially until they gain experience. Many construction projects are of short duration, and construction activity is cyclical and seasonal in nature. Remodeling, restoration, and maintenance projects, however, often provide many jobs for painters and paperhangers even when new construction activity declines. The most versatile painters and skilled paperhangers generally are best able to keep working steadily during downturns in the economy.

NATIONAL PROGRAMS

International Union of Painters and Allied Trades, National Headquarters
1750 New York Avenue, NW
Washington, DC 20006-5301
202-637-0741
mail@ibpat.org
http://www.ibpat.org
Occupational Fields: painter, paperhanger, paint maker, theatrical scenic artist, drywaller, glazier, architectural metalworker, sign painter

Painting and Decorating Contractors of America
11960 Westline Industrial Drive, Suite 201
St. Louis, MO 63146-3209
800-332-7322
Fax: 314-514-9417
http://www.pdca.org
Occupational Fields: painter, paperhanger

APPRENTICESHIP PROFILE
Painters District Council #51
Joint Apprenticeship and Training Committee
3900 James Street
Suitland, MD 20746
301-420-1983
Fax: 301-420-1309
cramosdc51@verizon.net

General Nature of the Job

Patrick Parker is an apprentice with Painters District #51, working at a Giant Supermarket in Washington, D.C. Patrick's job mostly consists of assisting the men who operate the spray guns by preparing their next project on racks, storing new paint, or loading trailers with painting materials bound for a job site. "I mostly work with steel, wheeling it into the paint shop after the millwrights finish welding and assembling it in the steel shop. I prepare the surface for the spray-men by cleaning it with Simple Green and water or maybe with a lacquer thinner. The steel might go for construction projects or else for warehouse scaffolding, increasing the efficiency of space use by stacking shelf upon shelf of goods."

On more exciting days, he dresses in a snowsuit to paint areas in huge refrigeration units of warehouses. He has gained some experience with brushes, rollers, and spray guns, the main tools of the trade. He's also had a chance to use some of the newest technology: electrostatic spray guns. "I don't fully understand how they work, but basically, the machine charges the electrons in the paint so that when you point the spray gun and pull the trigger, the paint jumps at the metal and wraps around the surface with a smooth, clean coat. The paint goes on very easily—it's fun to use these new spray guns."

Typical Day

Now that he's on day shift, Patrick typically wakes up at 5:00 A.M. to be at work by 5:30, even though his shift doesn't begin officially until 6:00. "They're pretty strict here at Giant—they want you to be in half an hour before work starts to get in uniform and to make sure you won't be late." On the positive side, he only works until 2:30 in the afternoon.

After 13 months indoors, Patrick will spend the next four weeks on the road, traveling to stores from Germantown to Rockville to paint doorframes, rusting pipes, butchers' meat racks, and whatever else needs a new coat. "Most of our work orders respond to Health Department codes. Fresh paint makes for safer conditions." His apprenticeship program requires at least some of this hands-on experience, traveling to diverse work sites to practice painting as well as decision-making skills. "In the morning, I call the foreman and he lets me know the store number where we'll work that day. Giant operates about two thousand stores, so we go all over the place. Now that

I'm on the road, I'm spending more time actually painting. Also, we have to decide on our own how to approach the project, organizing a plan of action and gathering the proper tools and materials."

Path to Becoming an Apprentice

Patrick likens his role as apprentice to the rank of private in the army, where he spent five years. "Being in the military humbles you—you learn to take orders and do what needs to be done." So Patrick doesn't mind sweeping floors or fetching lunch; the hierarchy doesn't faze him, not only because of his military experience, but also because he realizes that, soon enough, he will be the journeyman giving orders. "If you're serious about this occupation, it's a commitment to doing grunt work at the start." Patrick understands, though, that this system makes sense: journeymen have accumulated their skills through experience, so it makes sense for them to use their skills, not sweep floors. Apprentices accumulate those same skills by observation and only then by direct experience. If Patrick hadn't served in the military, he might resent the hierarchy, as many of the "younger fellows" do, instead of understanding his role in the system as a whole.

Salary Range

Patrick started this apprenticeship in the middle of the other apprentices' first year, so he's just now becoming a second-stage apprentice. The painter's apprenticeship, run by Local 1773 of the International Brotherhood of Painters and Allied Trades, divides its program into three stages, each compensated at a percentage of journeymen's wages, starting at 50 percent in the first stage and increasing to 80 percent at the end of the third stage. Recently Patrick graduated into the second stage, in which he will earn 65 percent of journeymen's wages. Less than two years from now, Patrick will graduate from his apprenticeship to become a journeyman, earning full wages of $18 an hour. After that, the union grants a raise after every 1,000 hours, which is about six months of full-time work.

Advice

"Pick up techniques and skills from your journeymen," Patrick advises. He views the journeymen he works with as his primary resources. As an apprentice, he lacks full confidence in his work. "I know what I am, and that I don't always do things right. When I'm unsure of myself, I call on a journeyman to help me out." For Patrick, the apprenticeship represents a process of gaining confidence in himself, his skills, and his judgment.

Future Goals

Patrick's main goal is to become a journeyman, which will stabilize him in his career. He also contemplates the idea of returning to school on the GI Bill after his apprenticeship, when he has a profession to fall back on while furthering his education. For now, he's happy painting over graffiti on walls, though. "I'm enjoying what I'm doing—I like my job, and not many people can say that."

ALABAMA

Painters, Paperhangers, and Decorators Union, Local #571
5353 First Avenue, North
Birmingham, AL 35212-2401
205-592-7293
Occupational Fields: painter, paperhanger, decorator

Painters and Allied Trades Union
3381 Atlanta Highway
Montgomery, AL 36109
334-272-6268
Occupational Fields: painter

Painters and Allied Trades Union
109 Gusmus Boulevard
Muscle Shoals, AL 35661
205-383-1997
Occupational Fields: painter

Painters and Allied Trades Union, Local #779
659 Dauphin Street
Mobile, AL 36602
334-432-0133
Occupational Fields: painter

ALASKA

Painters and Allied Trades Union, Local #1555
PO Box 71428
800 30th Avenue, Building A
Fairbanks, AK 99701
907-457-4444
lu1555pb@mesquito.com
Occupational Fields: painter

ARIZONA

P-D Morenci Inc.
PO Box 187
Morenci, AZ 85540

520-865-4521
Occupational Fields: construction painter

Phoenix Painters and Decorators
1841 North 24th Street
Phoenix, AZ 85008
602-244-0768
Occupational Fields: painter

CALIFORNIA
Alameda-Contra Costa, San Francisco Counties
7717 Oakport Street, Suite 2
Oakland, CA 94621
501-569-8450
Occupational Fields: automotive painter

Associated General Contractors, San Diego
2231 Hotel Circle, South
San Diego, CA 92108
619-297-4001
Occupational Fields: painter

Construction Craft Training Center
26218 Industrial Boulevard
Hayward, CA 94545
510-785-2282
http://www.cctc.edu
Occupational Fields: painter

Los Angeles Housing Authority
Human Resources Department
2600 Wilshire Boulevard, Suite 5100
Los Angeles, CA 90057
213-252-5396
http://www.hacla.org
Occupational Fields: painter

Painters Union
26 Bernard Street
Bakersfield, CA 93305-3493
805-325-1825
Occupational Fields: painter

Painters Union, Local #294
Central Valley Painters, Decorators and
    Paperhangers
4831 East Shields
Fresno, CA 93726-6437
209-255-2113
Occupational Fields: painter, decorator, paperhanger

Painters Union, Local #376
404 Nebraska Street
Vallejo, CA 94590
707-644-2249
Occupational Fields: painter

Sign Painters Union, Local #831
5900 South Eastern Avenue
Los Angeles, CA 90040
213-727-7151
Occupational Fields: sign painter

Southern California Painters
2077 South Yates Avenue
Los Angeles, CA 90040
213-727-2811
Occupational Fields: painter, decorator

COLORADO
Colorado and Area Painting Committee
4290 Holly Street
Denver, CO 80216-4531
303-394-0033
Occupational Fields: painter

CONNECTICUT
General Dynamics
Electric Boat Division
75 Eastern Point Road
Groton, CT 06340-4989
860-433-3332
Fax: 860-433-4732
Occupational Fields: painter (marine)

DISTRICT OF COLUMBIA
**International Union of Painters and Allied Trades,
    National Headquarters**
1750 New York Avenue, NW
Washington, DC 20006-5301
202-637-0742
Fax: 202-637-0771
http://www.iupat.org
Occupational Fields: painter, paperhanger, paint maker,
    theatrical scenic artist, drywaller, glazier, architectural
    metalworker, sign painter

Smithsonian Institution
Office of Exhibits Central
Arts and Industries Building

Suite 2235, MRC 427
Washington, DC 20560
202-357-3101
http://www.si.edu/ofg/internopp.htm
Occupational Fields: painter

Tito Contractors Inc.
7308 Georgia Avenue, NW
Washington, DC 20012
202-291-2255
Occupational Fields: painter

FLORIDA
Brotherhood of Painters
162 Northwest 29th Street
Miami, FL 33127-3930
305-573-8440
Occupational Fields: painter

Central Florida Painters and Allied Tradesmen
8434 Avenue C, Building 126
McCoy Air Force Base
Orlando, FL 32827
407-843-0050
Occupational Fields: painter

Jacksonville Painters, Decorators and Allied Trades
4000 Union Hall Place
Jacksonville, FL 32205
Occupational Fields: painter, decorator

Painters Union
2152 Johnson Street
Hollywood, FL 33020-3969
Occupational Fields: painter

Painters Union, Local #88
3818 West Bay Vista Avenue
Tampa, FL 33611
813-835-5888
Occupational Fields: painter

Painters Union, Local #164
1236 East 18th Street
Jacksonville, FL 32206
Occupational Fields: painter

Sam Cook Painting Company
916 Pebble Drive
Sun City, FL 33570
Occupational Fields: painter

Tri-County Painters and Decorators
2070 CC Tigertail Road
Dania, FL 33004
305-891-2128
Occupational Fields: painter

United Painting and Decorating
5120 North 40th Street
Tampa, FL 33610
Occupational Fields: painter, decorator

West Palm Beach Painters Union, Local #452
1213 Omar Road
Palm Beach, FL 33405
407-833-6812
Occupational Fields: painter

GEORGIA
Painters and Allied Trades Union
4816 Impala Lane
Albany, GA 31705
912-438-7278
Occupational Fields: painter

Painters Union
PO Box 1722
Brunswick, GA 31521
912-265-7371
Occupational Fields: painter

Painters Union, Local #193
501 Pulliam Street SW, Suite 427
Atlanta, GA 30312
404-524-8859
Occupational Fields: painter, paperhanger

HAWAII
Associated Builders and Contractors, Hawaii
1001 Dillingham Boulevard, Room 304
Honolulu, HI 96817
808-845-4887
Occupational Fields: painter

Color Dynamics Inc.
816 Gulick Avenue
Honolulu, HI 96819
808-848-7000
Occupational Fields: painter

Honolulu, City and County of
Department of Civil Service
City Hall Annex
Honolulu, HI 96813
808-523-4233
Occupational Fields: painter, sign painter

Kawika's Painting
2147 Eluwene Street
Honolulu, HI 96819
808-848-0030
Occupational Fields: painter

Painters Union, Local #1791
2240 Young Street
Honolulu, HI 96826
808-947-6606
Occupational Fields: painter

ILLINOIS
Painters, Decorators, and Paperhangers Union, Local #157
400 Northeast Jefferson Avenue
Peoria, IL 61603-3739
309-674-9294
Occupational Fields: painter, decorator, paperhanger

Painters and Allied Trades Union, Local #607
212 South First Street
Rockford, IL 61104
815-963-1254
Occupational Fields: painter

Painters Union
520 12th Street
Rock Island, IL 61201
309-788-8081
Occupational Fields: painter

INDIANA
Lafayette Painters
2535 South 30th Street
Lafayette, IN 47905
317-477-7848
Occupational Fields: painter

North Central Indiana Painters
Joint Apprenticeship Council
1345 Northside Boulevard

South Bend, IN 46615
219-287-8200
Occupational Fields: painter

Painters Union, Local #47
6501 Massachusetts Avenue
Indianapolis, IN 46226-5645
317-546-5638
Fax: 317-546-5903
Occupational Fields: painter

Universal Stripping and Finish Shop
Second Chances
Rural Route One, Box 237
Whiteland, IN 46184
317-535-9070
Occupational Fields: furniture refinisher

IOWA
Cedar Rapids Painters
5000 J Street
Cedar Rapids, IA 52404
319-366-0509
Occupational Fields: painter, sign painter

Color Ad Signs Inc.
PO Drawer E
Burlington, IA 52655
319-752-5516
Occupational Fields: sign painter

Des Moines Painters
2121 Delaware
Des Moines, IA 50317
515-265-5303
Occupational Fields: painter

DMACC, Ankeny Campus
2006 South Ankeny Boulevard
Ankeny, IA 50021
515-964-6206
Occupational Fields: painter

Dubuque Painters
164 Main Street
Dubuque, IA 52001
319-582-4084
Occupational Fields: painter

Quad City Painters
PO Box 626
Bettendorf, IA 52722
309-355-7353
Occupational Fields: painter

KANSAS
Colgate-Palmolive Company
18010 Kansas Avenue
Kansas City, KS 66105
913-573-6464
Occupational Fields: painter

International Brotherhood of Painters and Allied Trades, Local Union
417 East English Street
Wichita, KS 67202-4400
316-264-3384
Occupational Fields: painter

Painters Union, Local #96
American Federation of Labor and Congress of Industrial Organizations
1231 Northwest Eugene Street
Topeka, KS 66608-1403
913-233-2035
Occupational Fields: painter

LOUISIANA
Painters and Allied Trades Union
1930 Beaumont Drive
Baton Rouge, LA 70806
504-927-2446
Occupational Fields: painter

Painters and Decorators Union, Local #1244
2669 Lexington Avenue
Kenner, LA 70062-5370
504-466-3294
Occupational Fields: painter, decorator

Painters Union, Local #783
533 11th Street
Lake Charles, LA 70601
318-436-5625
Occupational Fields: painter

MARYLAND
Bethlehem Steel Corporation, Sparrows Point
5111 North Point Boulevard
Baltimore, MD 21219
410-388-3000
Occupational Fields: painter

International Association of Machinists and Aerospace Workers
9000 Machinists Place
Upper Marlboro, MD 20772-2687
301-967-4586
Occupational Fields: automotive painter, truck painter

Painters District Council #51
3900 James Street
Suitland, MD 20746
301-420-1983
Fax: 301-420-1309
http://www.iupatdc51.com
Occupational Fields: painter

Painters Union, Local #1, American Federation of Labor and Congress of Industrial Organizations
518 South Broadway
Baltimore, MD 21231-2912
301-276-5960
Occupational Fields: painter

MICHIGAN
Flint Area Painters Union
2817 Corunna Road
Flint, MI 48503-3253
810-232-0005
Occupational Fields: painter

Painters Union
1191 East Ten Mile Road
Madison Heights, MI 48071
810-548-0090
Occupational Fields: painter

MINNESOTA
Painters Union, Local #106
2002 London Road
Duluth, MN 55812-2144
218-724-6466
Occupational Fields: painter, decorator, paperhanger

MISSISSIPPI
Painters Union, Local #1225
2941 Market Street
Pascagoula, MS 39547-5164
601-762-1806
Occupational Fields: painter

MISSOURI
**Builders' Association Education and Training
  Center**
105 West 12th Avenue
Kansas City, MO 64116
816-471-0880
http://www.buildersassociation.com/~education/body_
  index.html
Occupational Fields: painter

Painters District Council #2
2501 59th Street
St. Louis, Mo. 63110
314-647-3327
Fax: 314-647-3350
painters@paintersdc2.com
http://www.paintersdc2.com
Occupational Fields: painter, glazier

Painters District Council #3
9902 East 62nd Street
Raytown, MO 64133
816-358-2440
Fax: 816-358-5430
Occupational Fields: painter

MONTANA
Painters Union, Local #260
208 East Main Street
Missoula, MT 59802
Occupational Fields: painter

NEVADA
**Southern Nevada Painters and Decorators
  Union**
4150 East Bonanza Road
Las Vegas, NV 89110-2279
702-438-2611
Occupational Fields: painter, decorator

NEW YORK
Painters District Council
585 Aero Drive
Buffalo, NY 14225-1405
716-886-3984
Occupational Fields: painter

OKLAHOMA
**Eastern Oklahoma Building and Construction
  Trades Council**
2651 East 21st Street, #405
Tulsa, OK 74114
918-742-3305
Occupational Fields: painter

OREGON
**Western Oregon and Southwest Washington
  Industrial Painters**
6915 Northeast 42nd Street
Portland, OR 97218
503-287-4856
Occupational Fields: painter

RHODE ISLAND
District Council 11
1808 Elmwood Avenue
Warwick, RI 02888
401-467-7010
Fax: 401-467-7075

**Painters Union, Local #195, American Federation of
  Labor and Congress of Industrial Organizations**
14 Jefferson Park Road
Warwick, RI 02888
401-467-7010
Occupational Fields: painter

TENNESSEE
Painters and Decorators Union
1000 Buchanan Avenue
Knoxville, TN 37917
423-524-3966
Occupational Fields: painter

Painters and Glaziers Union, Local #456
1123 Third Avenue, North
Nashville, TN 37208-2701

615-255-7863
Occupational Fields: painter

Painters Union
3540 Summer Avenue
Memphis, TN 38122
901-452-6862
Occupational Fields: painter

Painters Union, Local #226
2715 Belle Arbor Avenue
Chattanooga, TN 37406
423-698-4163
Occupational Fields: painter

TEXAS

Painters
259 West Rittenhouse
Houston, TX 77076
Occupational Fields: painter

Painters and Glaziers
7940 Northaven, Suite Four
Dallas, TX 75230
214-363-6358
Occupational Fields: painter

Painters Union, Local #318
4200 South Freeway
Fort Worth, TX 76115-1400
817-924-8277
Occupational Fields: painter

UTAH

Painters and Drywall Finishers Apprenticeship Office
2261 South Redwood Road
Salt Lake City, UT 84119
801-977-0732
http://www.grand.k12.ut.us/cash/ao.htm
Occupational Fields: painter, drywaller

VIRGINIA

Newport News Shipbuilding
Apprentice School
4101 Washington Avenue
Newport News, VA 23607-2770
757-380-2000

Fax: 757-688-0305
Occupational Fields: painter

WASHINGTON

Associated Builders and Contractors,
   Inland Pacific Chapter
PO Box 3787
Spokane, WA 99220
509-534-0826
Occupational Fields: painter

Division of Capitol Building and Grounds
OB-2, M/S PA-11
Olympia, WA 98504-4848
360-902-6224
Occupational Fields: painter

Fluor Daniel Hanford
M/S R2-88
PO Box 1500
Richland, WA 99352-1505
509-376-1523
Occupational Fields: painter

Kaiser Aluminum and Chemical Corporation
Mead Works
2111 East Hawthorne Road
Mead, WA 99021
509-468-5483
Occupational Fields: painter

Northwest Automotive Machinists
5631 Tacoma Mall Boulevard
Tacoma, WA 98408
253-472-9692
Occupational Fields: painter

Northwest Washington Painters, Decorators, and
   Drywall Finishers
6770 East Marginal Way, South, Building D
Seattle, WA 98108
206-762-8332
Occupational Fields: painter, decorator

Olympic Painters, Decorators and Drywallers
1101 South Yakima Avenue
Tacoma, WA 98405
206-383-1330
Occupational Fields: painter, taper

Painters, Tapers and Glaziers
2110 North Fancher Road
Spokane, WA 99212-1331
509-533-8814
Occupational Fields: painter, taper, decorator

Painters Union, Local #64
1322 South Fawcett Avenue
Tacoma, WA 98402
206-272-2443
Occupational Fields: painter

Southeastern Washington Painter, Decorators &
   Drywall Apprenticeship Committee
6770 E. Marginal Way S.
Seattle, WA 98108-3400
206-762-8332
Fax: 206-762-6433
spencer.777@inetmail.att.net
Occupational Fields: painter, glazier

WEST VIRGINIA
Construction Trades Training Center
2307 Seventh Avenue
Charleston, WV 25312-1811
304-346-3863
Occupational Fields: painter

Painters and Decorators Union, Local #970
706 Virginia Street, East
Charleston, WV 25301-2706
304-344-9172
Occupational Fields: painter, decorator

Painters Union, Local #91
28th and Chapline Street
Wheeling, WV 26003
304-232-2540
Fax: 304-232-7241
Occupational Fields: painter

Painters Union, Local #813
2001 Pine Street
Kenova, WV 25530
304-453-2818
Occupational Fields: painter

Richard Hackney
115 Spring Street
Charleston, WV 25302
304-539-1903
Fax: 304-343-8260
rhac5059@aol.com
Occupational Fields: painter, glazier

WISCONSIN
Milwaukee Area Painters and Allied Trades
12300 West Center Street
Wauwatosa, WI 53222
414-475-1544
Occupational Fields: painter

Painters Union, Local #934
3030 39th Avenue
Kenosha, WI 53144-4210
414-657-1287
Occupational Fields: painter

CANADA
BRITISH COLUMBIA
District Council 38-British Columbia
Painters, Glaziers, Drywall Finishers & Allied Trades
7621 Kingsway
Burnaby, BC V3N 3C7
604-524-8334
Fax: 604-524-8011
Occupational Fields: painter, glazier, drywall finisher

NEW BRUNSWICK
Department of Training and Employment
   Development Apprenticeship and Occupational
   Certification
Chestnut Complex
Fredericton, NB E3B 5H1
506-453-2260
Fax: 506-453-5317
aoc-acp@gnb.ca
Occupational Fields: painter, glazier

PILE DRIVERS

RELATED SECTIONS: *boilermakers; carpenters; elevator constructors; engineers and engineering technicians; ironworkers; laborers; machinists; masons; metalworkers; millwrights; operating engineers and stationary engineers; railroad workers; roofers and waterproofers; sheet metal workers; shipbuilding and ship maintenance workers; tool, die, mold, and pattern makers; welders*

Pile drivers are frequently employed at the beginning stages of construction, but they also work on renovation projects. They operate giant, cranelike machines called pile-driving rigs. These machines drive long columns of timber, steel, or reinforced concrete (known as *piling*) into the ground. They also build the forms on pilings and bridges; drill holes to place pilings solidly in the earth; and do foundation work for welding, buildings, and assorted other projects. Many pile drivers are qualified carpenters.

Piling functions as a structural support in various projects, including bridges, docks, ferry landings, skyscrapers, and oil rigs. In general, concrete and metal piling is used for the construction of skyscraper foundations; wood and concrete piling is used for bridges, docks, and wharves. When a site is excavated, metal sheet piling is used to hold back dirt. Using welding equipment and torches, pile drivers also cut and put together metal construction materials.

Pile drivers use a variety of hand tools and power tools, including chain saws, burning torches, and air tools. Their work is extremely strenuous and requires walking, climbing, squatting, kneeling, and heavy lifting. They work indoors and outdoors, sometimes on boats or in other damp, cold surroundings. Pile drivers might work in a hole 100 feet below ground, or on a bridge or building 100 feet above the ground. They must travel to various job sites.

Apprenticeship training for pile drivers is offered by many unions and other organizations in the building and construction trades, particularly those that are largely composed of carpenters.

Apprentices to this trade work under the supervision of experienced pile drivers. Typically the course of study runs for about four years (8,000 hours of training) and includes on-the-job training and at least 144 hours a year of classroom instruction. Sometimes the classroom work is scheduled for two-week periods during the spring and fall.

In general an applicant should

- be at least 18 years old
- be a high school graduate or hold a GED certificate
- be physically capable of performing the work
- meet strength requirements
- be in good health
- possess required hand tools
- have good hand-eye coordination
- be agile

In 2002, median hourly earnings of pile driver operators were $21.84. The middle 50 percent earned between $14.89 and $29.24. The lowest 10 percent earned less than $11.73, and the highest 10 percent earned more than $33.97.

Pay scales generally are higher in large metropolitan areas. Annual earnings of some workers may be lower than hourly rates would indicate because work time may be limited by bad weather.

APPRENTICESHIP SALARIES

From about $12 an hour to $15, or about 50 percent of the wages paid to journeymen.

POSTAPPRENTICESHIP SALARIES

Median earnings fall between $15 and $30 an hour, with the lowest-paid workers receiving less than $12 an hour and the highest paid workers earning more than $33 an hour.

JOB OUTLOOK

Prospects for employment in this occupation are expected to be good through 2012, because the construction industry is likely to remain strong. The field is expected to grow about as fast as the average for all occupations.

For more information on apprenticeships for pile drivers, contact the national organizations and individual programs listed below, local job centers, or your state bureau of apprenticeship training.

NATIONAL PROGRAMS

United Brotherhood of Carpenters and Joiners of America
101 Constitution Avenue, NW
Washington, DC 20001

202-546-6206, x300
Fax: 202-546-3054
http://www.carpenters.org
Occupational Fields: carpenter, cabinetmaker, millwright, pile driver, floor layer

APPRENTICESHIP PROFILE
Eastern Washington and Northern Idaho Carpenters
    Employers
Joint Apprenticeship Training Trust Fund
127 East Augusta, Suite 102
Spokane, WA 99207
509-532-8833
Fax: 509-532-8811
wicat@netzero.net
http://www.lni.wa.gov/TradesLicensing/Apprenticeship/
    files/proginfo/0110aop.pdf

General Nature of the Job
Pile drivers use heavy equipment to drive piles, or supports, for bridges, buildings, docks, dams, and wharves. Piles are usually made of wood, concrete, or structural steel. Pile drivers also build forms and weld, welding together supports and work bridges. Basically, any span over water is considered pile driver work.

If you don't like heights or water, pile driving is probably not the best choice for a career, since pile drivers work over bodies of water from high places. A physically laborious trade, pile drivers work outdoors in all weather conditions. Basic math skills are necessary for reading measuring tapes and calculating formulas, and it helps to be physically coordinated—you don't want to fall in the water if you can avoid it.

The pile driver apprenticeship program through the Eastern Washington and Northern Idaho Carpenters Employers requires 8,000 hours of on-the-job training, which takes about three to four years, depending on how frequently the apprentice works. Apprentices also attend school four times a year for one week at a time.

Typical Day
Sherry Butler works 12-hour shifts during her stint at a dam. The pile drivers' goal is to build concrete shore anchors, but they must first set the wooden forms. Sherry begins work at 7:00 A.M. by placing forms in holes with a partner; they must make sure the forms are level and at the correct height out of the ground. Sherry holds the form in place while her partner nails it to another one.

They slog around in two feet of water for the first part of the day—the dam is opened at night, and the water hasn't drained completely by morning. The ground is extremely rocky, and they must excavate with shovels. This work continues throughout the day with breaks and lunch tossed in.

Sherry is the sole female pile driver in her union but doesn't find her gender to be a disadvantage. Her height, however, is another matter—at five feet and two inches, there are some things that are just too big for her to handle. Sherry says, "I have a really hard time carrying a full sheet of plywood. I usually drag it, and that's okay, too, as long as I get it there." While Sherry could do without working in the snow, there's not much she dislikes about the job. She states, "It's exciting, and I like big things, like when they're setting girders. They're just huge and awesome." Sherry also enjoys the variety of the job and says that each day is different. One day she may be welding and the next day hammering plywood together for forms.

Pile drivers are laid off between jobs, which can be exasperating. The weather conditions are often harsh, Sherry says. "It's all day, every day, outside freezing to death or sweating to death or soaking wet." Pile drivers frequently travel for jobs, especially in eastern Washington because there aren't many bodies of water. Sherry was away from home for a three-month duration once, which was difficult because she is a single mother of two. The job is also dangerous and dirty, but presents no challenges that safety equipment and a shower won't remedy.

Path to Becoming an Apprentice
Sherry had just started her first year as a carpentry apprentice when she learned about the pile driver program. Sherry's former brother-in-law, a carpenter, had told her about the apprenticeship program but was less than encouraging. Sherry recalls, "He pretty much told me I couldn't do it." Working outdoors with heavy equipment and building things with her hands, as well as the wages and benefits, appealed to Sherry, and she applied. Sherry decided to switch tracks when an opening for a pile driver apprentice cropped up. Although she knew little about pile driver work, the idea of welding and working over the water sounded fun and challenging to Sherry.

While Sherry cannot recall any school activities or classes that influenced her career choice, she believes growing up a tomboy may have prepared her for the trades. She climbed trees, rode motorcycles, and when her motorcycle broke down, she worked on it and gained mechanical know-how.

Salary Range

Beginning apprentices earn full benefits and 60 percent of the journeyman rate, which is $23.47 an hour in the Spokane, Washington, region where Sherry works. Foremen make $1 an hour more than the journeyman rate. Sherry gets a raise of $1.15 an hour for every 700 hours worked. These raises are tied to the completion of skill blocks at school as well as hours worked on the job.

Sherry is optimistic about the job outlook for pile drivers. Because she is the only woman in her union, she feels she will be in demand and the work will be steadily available. Some jobs may depend on government funding since bridges are under state and federal jurisdiction, but unless people start swimming or sailing across rivers, bridges will continue to be needed.

Advice

Sherry says that if you can handle being far from the ground in inclement weather conditions, pile driver work can be rewarding. She also asserts that you cannot be afraid of hard work, and you must do what you're told, even if you don't want to. Being a pile driver requires dedication, but Sherry claims, "I've never not wanted to do it. I've never wanted to give up on it." Physical stamina is important, but don't worry if you're not big and strong. Sherry says there's a lot of equipment to help lift and move things, and she manages just fine despite her petite size.

Future Goals

When Sherry finishes the apprenticeship program, she will receive her journeyman card and take the welding test to become certified. While additional school is not required, Sherry hopes to continue learning about new procedures and equipment through occasional classes. Sherry's motto is, "The more you know, the more you work."

Sherry has no goals to become a supervisor or foreman because she doesn't want the added responsibility or hours. She hopes to focus solely on welding at some point, stating, "I want to be certified in all facets of it, and I want to eventually just weld." If she ever tires of welding or pile driver work, however, there are many other opportunities. She can work out of the carpenters' union, do concrete form work, including shopping malls and parking garages, build foundations for houses or sidewalks, pour concrete slabs, or do framing. She can also become a certified diver and perform underwater welding, but although they are well compensated, diving is an extremely dangerous job. Sherry thinks she'll keep her head above the water for now.

ALASKA

Alaska Piledrivers and Divers Union, Local #2520
825 East Eighth Avenue
Anchorage, AK 99501-3877
907-272-7576
piledrivers2520@gci.net
http://local2520.org
Occupational Fields: pile driver, diver

CALIFORNIA

Pile Drivers Union, Local #34
55 Hegenberger Place
Oakland, CA 94621-1301
510-635-4227
Fax: 510-635-1234
pdl_34@pacbell.net
http://www.geocities.com/pdl_34/union.html
Occupational Fields: pile driver

Southern California Piledrivers Union, Local #2375
728 North Lagoon Avenue
Wilmington, CA 90744
310-830-5300
Occupational Fields: pile driver

DISTRICT OF COLUMBIA

United Brotherhood of Carpenters and Joiners of America
101 Constitution Avenue, NW
Washington, DC 20001
202-546-6206, x300
Fax: 202-546-3054
http://www.carpenters.org
Occupational Fields: carpenter, cabinetmaker, millwright, pile driver, floor layer

FLORIDA

South Florida Millwrights, Piledrivers, and Divers Highway Constructors
2727 South Park Road
Hallandale, FL 33009

954-981-1810
Occupational Fields: pile driver

INDIANA

Northeast Indiana Carpenters Joint Apprenticeship Training Fund
PO Box 1690
Warsaw, IN 47581-1690
219-269-4220
Occupational Fields: carpenter, floorlayer, millwright, pile driver

MARYLAND

Joint Carpentry Apprenticeship Committee
9109 Westphalia Road
Upper Marlboro, MD 20774
301-736-1696
Occupational Fields: pile driver

MASSACHUSETTS

New England Regional Council of Carpenters
Local Unions #51, #56, #67, and #2168
803 Summer Street, Fourth Floor
Boston, MA 02127
800-275-6200
http://www.necarpenters.org
Occupational Fields: pile driver

OKLAHOMA

Eastern Oklahoma Building, Construction, and Trade Council
2651 East 21st Street, Suite 405
Tulsa, OK 74114
918-742-3365
Occupational Fields: pile driver

WASHINGTON

Bellingham Carpenters
1500 West Bakerview Road
Bellingham, WA 98226
360-734-7900
Fax: 360-734-2462
Occupational Fields: pile driver

Carpenters, Shipwrights, Millwrights, Drywallers, and Cabinet Makers
2201 South 78th Street, Building B-512
Tacoma, WA 98409
253-472-2629
Fax: 253-475-2785
Occupational Fields: pile driver

Eastern Washington and Northern Idaho Carpenters Employers
5309 East Third Avenue
Spokane, WA 99212
509-533-8833
Fax: 509-533-8831
Occupational Fields: pile driver, millwright, carpenter

Southwest Washington Piledriver, Bridge, Dock and Wharf Builders
1316 Commerce Avenue
Longview, WA 98632
360-636-2350
Fax: 360-423-5529
Occupational Fields: pile driver

Western Washington Piledrivers, Bridge, Dock and Wharf Builders
315 Garden Avenue North, Room 100
Renton, WA 98055
425-227-4903
Fax: 425-227-8129
ksutphin@worldnet.att.com

Western Washington Piledrivers, Seattle
2512 Second Avenue, Room 214
Seattle, WA 98121
206-728-2396
Fax: 206-448-5063
Occupational Fields: pile driver

WISCONSIN

Southeast Wisconsin Carpentry Training Center
9411 West Fond du Lac Avenue
Milwaukee, WI 53225
414-353-3000
Fax: 414-353-6465
wwwinfo@sewctc.org

http://www.sewctc.org
Occupational Fields: pile driver

CANADA
BRITISH COLUMBIA
British Columbia Institute of Technology
3700 Willingdon Avenue
Burnaby, BC V5G 3H2
604-434-5734
http://www.bcit.ca
Occupational Fields: pile driver

NEW BRUNSWICK
**Department of Training and Employment
Development Apprenticeship and Occupational
Certification**
PO Box 6000
Chestnut Complex
Fredericton, NB E3B 5H1
506-453-2260
Fax: 506-453-5317
aoc-acp@gnb.ca
http://www.aoc-acp.gnb.ca/02/009eme.htm
Occupational Fields: pile driver

PIPE TRADES WORKERS

RELATED SECTIONS: *boilermakers, carpenters, electricians and line workers, electronics technicians, elevator constructors, engineers and engineering technicians, ironworkers, machinists, mechanics, metalworkers, millwrights, operating engineers and stationary engineers, sheet metal workers, shipbuilding and ship maintenance workers, welders*

Pipe trades workers install, maintain, and repair pipe systems that carry liquid, gas, and other materials. For example, pipes carry water to residences and offices, sewage to treatment plants, and steam to turbines that generate electricity in power plants. Pipes carry food in processing plants through various stages of production. They also deliver natural gas for heating and circulate fluorinated hydrocarbons in refrigeration units.

Plumbing and pipefitting are similar trades, but most pipe trades workers specialize in one or the other. *Plumbers* typically work in homes and commercial buildings, where they assemble, install, and repair water, drainage, and heating systems, including water pipes, bathtubs, water heaters, dishwashers, and heating and air-conditioning units. Some plumbers also work on septic tanks, cesspools, drains, and sewers.

Pipefitters usually design, install, and maintain complex pipe systems in large facilities, such as oil refineries, manufacturing plants, and defense plants. They typically work with systems that move water, gas, steam, air-conditioning materials, and other liquids and gases. *Steamfitters* specialize in systems that carry liquids or gases under high pressure. *Sprinkler fitters* work on systems used in buildings to extinguish fires.

Heating, air-conditioning, and refrigeration technicians, also known as *heating, ventilation, and air-conditioning (HVAC) mechanics* specialize in systems that control the temperature, humidity, and quality of air in places such as buildings and refrigeration units. Their work involves various mechanical, electrical, and electronic components, including fans, pumps, motors, thermostats, and switches. Technicians sometimes specialize in installation, maintenance and repair, or in a certain type of equipment, such as solar panels or oil burning appliances. *Furnace installers,* also known as *heating equipment technicians,* specialize in heating systems.

Pipe trades workers begin a project by reading blueprints or other instructions, measuring and marking the work site, checking for electrical wiring and other impediments, and preparing the area by cutting holes in walls or suspending supports from ceilings. Next, the system is assembled. Assembly may involve cutting and threading pipes, using hand tools or machines to bend the pipes where necessary, and fastening them together by means such as welding, soldering, or caulking. Pipe trades workers use an array of tools, including reamers, hammers, chisels, wrenches, drills, saws, torches, brazing equipment, and welding machines. They work with a variety of materials, such as copper, steel, plastic, and cast-iron pipes.

Pipe trades workers risk injury from accidents with tools, burns from hot pipes, and falls from ladders. The work is performed both indoors and outdoors, sometimes in inclement weather or in buildings that are too hot or too cold because the cooling or heating system is malfunctioning. The trade requires standing, heavy lifting, and working in awkward positions.

Most pipe trades workers are employed by plumbing and mechanical contractors, commercial and industrial companies, or government agencies. About 15 percent are self-employed. Typically they work 40 hours a week but may be on call for emergencies or have to put in overtime, evening, or weekend hours.

Many pipe trades workers belong to unions that sponsor apprenticeships, such as the National Association of Plumbing, Heating, and Cooling Contractors; the National Fire Sprinkler Association Inc.; the Mechanical Contractors Association; or the United Association of Journeymen and Apprentices of the Plumbing and Pipe Fitting Industry of the United States and Canada (UA). Nonunion apprenticeships are administered by the Associated Builders and Contractors, the National Association of Plumbing-Heating-Cooling Contractors, the American Fire Sprinkler Association, and the National Association of Home Builders-Home Builders Institute.

Apprenticeship is the traditional way of entering the pipe trades. Trainees learn on the job under the supervision of experienced workers. Typically, the course of study runs for four to five years and includes at least 144 hours of classroom instruction annually in mathematics, blueprint reading, drafting, plumbing codes, safety practices, and other subjects. In most parts of the country, plumbers are required to be licensed.

In general an applicant should

- apply in person
- be at least 18 years old

- be a high school graduate or hold a GED certificate
- be physically fit

APPRENTICESHIP SALARIES

Between $5 an hour and $16 an hour plus benefits, or about half the rate paid to skilled workers.

POSTAPPRENTICESHIP SALARIES

Between $10 and $32 an hour, with a median hourly wage between $16 and $19.

JOB OUTLOOK

Excellent because the demand for skilled workers in this field is expected to exceed the number of workers trained. In addition, employment in the occupation is expected to grow about as fast as the average. Construction is expected to continue at a strong pace, and pipe systems in existing buildings will need to be maintained and renovated. Improved efficiency, the increased use of plastic pipes, and other technological advances will reduce the need for some pipe trades workers, however. A substantial demand is expected for heating, air-conditioning, and refrigeration technicians, in part due to increased desire for energy-efficient heating and cooling systems.

For more information on apprenticeships for pipe trades workers, contact the national organizations and individual programs listed below; local job centers; your state bureau of apprenticeship training; or plumbing, pipefitting, and heating, air-conditioning, and refrigeration contractors.

NATIONAL PROGRAMS

Air Conditioning Contractors of America, National Capital Chapter

PO Box 4268
Silver Spring, MD 20914-4268
301-384-2222
Fax: 301-384-9623
plupson@acca-ncc.org
http://www.acca-ncc.org
Occupational Fields: heating, ventilation, and air conditioning technician

United Association of Journeymen and Apprentices of the Plumbing and Pipefitting Industry, National Headquarters

901 Massachusetts Avenue, NW
Washington, DC 20001-4397
202-628-5823
Fax: 202-628-5024
http://www.ua.org
Occupational Fields: plumber, pipefitter, sprinklerfitter, welder

APPRENTICESHIP PROFILE

Phoenix Pipefitting Trades

Joint Apprenticeship Council
2950 West Thomas Road
Phoenix, AZ 85017
602-269-8213
Fax: 602-269-1525
http://www.pipetrades.org

General Nature of the Job

Pipefitters install and repair all types of pipe, including black iron, stainless steel, copper, and plastic, in sizes ranging from half-inch to 36-inch pipe. Pipefitting and plumbing are often interchangeable skills, but plumbers deal mostly with domestic water pipes and drainage issues (think of kitchens and bathrooms). Pipefitters install pipe primarily for heating and cooling systems but also lay copper pipe for city drinking water. Steamfitters, a subgroup of pipefitters, specialize in high-pressure pipe systems that house gases or liquids. Pipefitters must be versatile; they must know how to weld, solder, and braze pipe underground or from extreme heights.

Common sense combined with cautious behavior is critical in this industry. When you're working with leaks in steam lines, you can't see the steam but you can hear it. If you're not alert and aware, the steam will burn you before you realize you've found the leak. You also need basic mechanical know-how, eye-hand coordination, and math skills to calculate formulas and pipe lengths. Pipefitters often work in pairs or on teams, so getting along with others is important as well. Work can range from one-day jobs to two-year-long projects, and you might find yourself driving one mile or 60 miles to the job site, so flexibility is mandatory.

The Phoenix Pipefitting Trades apprenticeship program takes five years to complete. Apprentices gain on-the-job training during the day and attend classes two nights a week. Apprentices are responsible for tuition and receive diplomas upon graduation. In addition, the classes are accredited and can be applied toward a bachelor's or associate's degree upon completion of the program.

Typical Day

Wayne Brown's workday begins at 6:00 A.M. as the pipefitters gather in a central area to perform stretching exercises for 30 minutes. Afterwards, they split into groups of 10 per foreman. Today Wayne pairs up with a journeyman pipefitter. The foreman indicates where a pipe should go, and Wayne sketches an isometric drawing of the best route for the pipe. After conferring with the journeyman and double-checking the measurements, Wayne takes a cutting torch and cuts pipe. He then holds the pieces together as the journeyman welds the lengths together. Wayne cleans and polishes the welded pipe with a grinder. They continue throughout the day, with breaks and lunch interspersed.

Wayne never gets bored because he does something different each day. He enjoys working with his hands and troubleshooting to figure out the best way to run pipes. Although the apprenticeship is rigorous and time consuming, Wayne finds the program effective. He says, "The apprenticeship teaches us in two different ways: we learn it through books and reading at school, and then we learn it out in the field by doing it with our hands."

The paperwork—applying for burn permits, filing SIPP (site incident protection plan) reports, requesting approval for every task—can be tedious, but Wayne knows that this process is necessary to ensure safety. Pipefitting can be a grimy, laborious job with long hours. Wayne recalls working 12-hour shifts, seven days a week for six months straight while also attending school. Wayne points to the overtime pay and considers the hours worthwhile, however. Pipefitters work on contract, which means layoffs occur between jobs. While some pipefitters have been laid off for months at a time, Wayne has been fortunate—he hasn't been out of work yet. In fact, he has been specifically requested for jobs several times.

Path to Becoming an Apprentice

Wayne found himself in the apprenticeship program immediately after graduating from high school. His uncle, a pipefitter, called Wayne and told him of some apprenticeship openings in the steamfitter program, so Wayne moved from Texas to Arizona three days after graduation. Wayne grew up working and building horse corrals and fences with his father, a sheet metal worker who also owned a blacksmith business, so working with his hands and using machinery were nothing new. Wayne believes that his background, in combination with high school shop classes, paved the way to pipefitting. Although Wayne had been offered a full college scholarship, the apprenticeship seemed the natural and practical path: "you actually work and get paid to work and also get a degree, unlike some colleges where you have to work for free, basically."

Besides the valuable experience Wayne is gaining through hands-on practice, Wayne's classes provide him with a broad knowledge base. Wayne is currently a fourth-year apprentice, and the classes he's taken include algebra, science (because pipefitters and steamfitters often work with dangerous chemicals and acids), rigging (to learn how to operate a crane and how to hand-signal a crane operator), first aid and CPR, and welding.

Salary Range

When Wayne began the apprenticeship program, he earned $9.50 an hour plus full benefits. Every six months he receives an average raise of $1 an hour. By the end of the five-year program, he will be earning $18.50 an hour. Upon completion of the program, he will have a mechanical license as a steamfitter and be eligible for the journeyman rate, which is $26.35 an hour in Phoenix. Foremen can earn one to three dollars an hour over scale.

As for the job outlook, things look promising for the next few years in Arizona, where the economy is growing rapidly and attracting major corporations. Wayne thinks work will taper off, but he's not worried. He says, "if you have a good reputation, you're going to stay employed." Currently, Wayne finds himself working more frequently on new buildings. New pipes are guaranteed for 20 to 30 years, and many don't show signs of decay for 45 years, so Wayne will probably be retired by the time those pipes need repair.

Advice

Wayne is happy with his choice of pipefitting and believes it's a great opportunity to make a good living and learn. He says, "if you get in and decide you don't like it, you can always get out, but you'll never know if you don't try it." You need to be willing to learn, get dirty, and pay your dues. Some journeymen don't like working with apprentices and will assign them unpleasant tasks that don't require much knowledge or skill. Wayne advises visiting a union in your area to ask about various jobs and trades to gain a better understanding of the job types and work conditions.

Future Goals

After completing the apprenticeship program, Wayne hopes to get a plumbing license. He would like to try supervising on jobs and may think about teaching—all of the instructors in the apprenticeship program are journeymen, and Wayne has already been asked about whether he is interested in teaching. Down the line, Wayne would like to have his own business, perhaps a blacksmith company like his father or a mechanical contracting company such as the one he currently works for.

Because of their skills in welding, soldering, designing, and brazing, pipefitters can branch into numerous careers. They can become plumbers, refrigeration hands, specialists in blueprints and drawing, managers, or business owners. Dedication and perseverance can open many doors, as Wayne has proven.

ALABAMA

United Association of Journeymen and Apprentices of the Plumbing and Pipefitting Industry, Local #52
PO Box 211105
Montgomery, AL 36121-1105
334-272-9500
Fax: 334-271-1647
http://www.ualocal52.org
Occupational Fields: plumber, pipefitter, sprinklerfitter, welder

United Association of Journeymen and Apprentices of the Plumbing and Pipefitting Industry, Local #91
3648 Ninth Avenue, North
Birmingham, AL 35222
205-591-2721
Fax: 205-591-2729
Occupational Fields: plumber, pipefitter, steamfitter

United Association of Journeymen and Apprentices of the Plumbing and Pipefitting Industry, Local #119
2458 Old Shell Road
Mobile, AL 36607
251-476-0035
Fax: 251-476-0606
Occupational Fields: plumber, pipefitter, sprinklerfitter, welder

United Association of Journeymen and Apprentices of the Plumbing and Pipefitting Industry, Local #372
3888 Greensboro Avenue
Tuscaloosa, AL 36505
205-758-6236

Fax: 205-349-4608
Occupational Fields: plumber, pipefitter, sprinklerfitter, welder

United Association of Journeymen and Apprentices of the Plumbing and Pipefitting Industry, Local #377
PO Box 6084
Huntsville, AL 35824
205-772-0616
Fax: 205-772-0617
Occupational Fields: plumber, pipefitter, sprinklerfitter, welder

United Association of Journeymen and Apprentices of the Plumbing and Pipefitting Industry, Local #498
PO Box E
Gadsden, AL 35904
205-546-6791
Fax: 205-547-6330
Occupational Fields: plumber, pipefitter, sprinklerfitter, welder

United Association of Journeymen and Apprentices of the Plumbing and Pipefitting Industry, Local #548
101 Oak Street
Wetumpka, AL 36092
Occupational Fields: plumber, pipefitter, sprinklerfitter, welder

ALASKA

United Association of Journeymen and Apprentices of the Plumbing and Pipefitting Industry, Local #262
723 West 10th Street
Juneau, AK 99801
907-586-2874
Fax: 907-463-5116
Occupational Fields: plumber, pipefitter, steamfitter

United Association of Journeymen and Apprentices of the Plumbing and Pipefitting Industry, Local #367
610 West 54th
Anchorage, AK 99518
907-562-2810
Fax: 907-562-2587
http://www.ualocal367.org
Occupational Fields: plumber, pipefitter, steamfitter

United Association of Journeymen and Apprentices of the Plumbing and Pipefitting Industry, Local #375
3568 Geraghty Street
Fairbanks, AK 99709
907-479-6221
Fax: 907-479-6227
Occupational Fields: plumber, pipefitter, steamfitter

ARIZONA

Aero Automatic Sprinkler Company
21605 North Central Avenue
Phoenix, AZ 85024
602-272-3237
Occupational Fields: pipefitter

Arizona Builder's Alliance, Phoenix
2702 North Third Street, Suite 2020
Phoenix, AZ 85004-4606
602-274-8222
Fax: 602-274-8999
mminter@azbuilders.org
http://www.azbuilders.org
Occupational Fields: plumber, pipefitter

Arizona Builder's Alliance, Tucson
1661 North Swan, Suite 144
Tucson, AZ 85712
520-881-7930
Fax: 520-327-1686
infotucson@azbuilders.org
http://www.azbuilders.org/
Occupational Fields: pipefitter, plumber

ASARCO USWA
PO Box 98
Hayden, AZ 85235
520-356-7811
Occupational Fields: construction pipefitter

BHP Copper, Pinto Valley Operation
PO Box 100
Miami, AZ 85539
520-473-6485
Occupational Fields: construction pipefitter

Grinnell Fire Protection Systems Inc.
3144 West Virginia Avenue
Phoenix, AZ 85009
602-269-2421
Occupational Fields: pipefitter

Interstate Mechanical Corporation (IMCOR)
1841 East Washington Street
Phoenix, AZ 85034
602-257-1319
Fax: 602-271-0674
info@imcor-az.com
http://www.imcor-az.com
Occupational Fields: pipefitter

Maricopa Community College District
Maintenance and Operations
2411 West 14th Street
Tempe, AZ 85281-6941
602-731-8121
Occupational Fields: heating and air conditioning installer, heating and air conditioning repairer

P-D Morenci Inc.
PO Box 187
Morenci, AZ 85540
520-865-4521
Occupational Fields: construction pipefitter

Phoenix Pipefitting Trades
2950 West Thomas Road
Phoenix, AZ 85017
602-269-8213
Fax: 602-269-1525
http://www.pipetrades.org
Occupational Fields: heating, ventilation, and air conditioning mechanic, plumber, pipefitter

Phoenix Sheetmetal
2534 East Adams Street
Phoenix, AZ 85034
602-275-6511
imaple@azsheetmetal.org
http://www.azsheetmetal.org
Occupational Fields: heating and air conditioning installer, heating and air conditioning servicer, air and hydronic balancing technician

Pipefitters Union, Local #741
ASARCO-Ray, IAM-H
PO Box Eight
Hayden, AZ 85235
520-356-3544
Occupational Fields: construction pipefitter

Plumbers and Pipefitters
601 West Rillito
Tucson, AZ 85705
520-620-0015
*Occupational Fields: construction pipefitter, plumber,
refrigeration mechanic*

**Southern Arizona Plumbing, Heating,
and Cooling Association**
3036 East Drachman
PO Box 40366
Tucson, AZ 85717
520-327-7422
Occupational Fields: plumber

Tucson Unified School District
530 South Norris Avenue
Tucson, AZ 85719
520-617-7000
Occupational Fields: refrigeration mechanic

**United Association of Journeymen and Apprentices of
the Plumbing and Pipefitting Industry, Local #469**
3109 North 24th Street
Phoenix, AZ 85016
602-956-9350
Fax: 602-956-9782
Occupational Fields: plumber, pipefitter, steamfitter

**United Association of Journeymen and Apprentices of
the Plumbing and Pipefitting Industry, Local #741**
2475 East Water Street
Tucson, AZ 85719
520-323-9476
Fax: 520-323-7069
Occupational Fields: plumber, pipefitter, steamfitter

Wolff Mechanical Inc.
1701 S. Indian Bend Road
Phoenix, AZ 85281
480-968-8208
http://www.wolffmechanical.com
*Occupational Fields: heating and air conditioning,
installer, heating and air conditioning servicer*

ARKANSAS
**United Association of Journeymen and Apprentices of
the Plumbing and Pipefitting Industry, Local #29**
2914 Midland Boulevard
Fort Smith, AR 72904

501-782-1255
Fax: 501-783-0512
Occupational Fields: plumber, pipefitter, steamfitter

**United Association of Journeymen and Apprentices of
the Plumbing and Pipefitting Industry, Local #155**
1223 West Markham
Little Rock, AR 72201
501-374-4943
Fax: 501-374-6349
Occupational Fields: plumber, pipefitter, steamfitter

**United Association of Journeymen and Apprentices of
the Plumbing and Pipefitting Industry, Local #706**
PO Box 30
El Dorado, AR 71731-0030
501-863-6169
Fax: 501-862-6408
Occupational Fields: plumber, pipefitter, steamfitter

CALIFORNIA
Associated Technical College
1670 Wilshire Boulevard
Los Angeles, CA 90017-1690
213-413-6808
Occupational Fields: plumber

California State Pipe Trades Council
1123 L Street
Sacramento, CA 95814
916-446-7311
Fax: 916-446-3520
tedreed@calpipes.org
http://calpipes.org/indexFlag.htm

Construction Craft Training Center
5750 Imhoff Drive
Concord, CA 94520
510-785-2282
Fax: 510-785-1798
http://www.cctc.edu
*Occupational Fields: heating, ventilation, and air
conditioning mechanic, plumber*

Construction Craft Training Center
26232 Industrial Boulevard
Hayward, CA 94545
510-785-2282
Fax: 510-785-9136

http://www.cctc.edu
Occupational Fields: heating, ventilation, and air conditioning mechanic, plumber

Los Angeles Housing Authority
Human Resources Department
2600 Wilshire Boulevard, Suite 5100
Los Angeles, CA 90057
213-252-5389
SANFORDR@hacla.org
http://www.hacla.org
Occupational Fields: plumber

Pipe Trades Training Center
780 Commercial Street
San Jose, CA 95112-1408
408-453-6330
http://www.sbaypipe.org/jlmtrain.htm
Occupational Fields: heating, ventilation, and air conditioning mechanic, steamfitter, plumber, pipefitter

United Association of Journeymen and Apprentices of the Plumbing and Pipefitting Industry, Local #38
1621 Market Street
San Francisco, CA 94103
415-626-2000
Fax: 415-626-2009
smazzola@ualocal38.org
http://www.ualocal38.org
Occupational Fields: plumber, pipefitter, steamfitter

United Association of Journeymen and Apprentices of the Plumbing and Pipefitting Industry, Local #62
11185 Commercial Parkway, Suite A
Castroville, CA 95012
408-633-6091
Fax: 408-633-1613
Occupational Fields: plumber, pipefitter, steamfitter

United Association of Journeymen and Apprentices of the Plumbing and Pipefitting Industry, Local #78
111 West Ninth Street
Los Angeles, CA 90015
213-688-9090
Fax: 213-627-4624
Occupational Fields: plumber, pipefitter, steamfitter

United Association of Journeymen and Apprentices of the Plumbing and Pipefitting Industry, Local #230
3909 Centre Street, #204
San Diego, CA 92103
619-297-1852
Fax: 619-297-9858
Occupational Fields: plumber, pipefitter, steamfitter

United Association of Journeymen and Apprentices of the Plumbing and Pipefitting Industry, Local #246
1303 North Rabe Avenue, #101
Fresno, CA 93727
209-252-7246
Fax: 209-252-1766
http://unionpipepros.org
Occupational Fields: plumber, pipefitter, steamfitter

United Association of Journeymen and Apprentices of the Plumbing and Pipefitting Industry, Local #250
18355 South Figueroa Street
Gardena, CA 90248
310-660-0042
Fax: 310-329-2465
Occupational Fields: steamfitter, pipefitter

United Association of Journeymen and Apprentices of the Plumbing and Pipefitting Industry, Local #342
Bay Area Pipe Trades Association
935 Detroit Avenue
Concord, CA 94518-2501
925-686-5880
Fax: 925-685-3710
UA342JAC@value.net
http://www.ua342.org
Occupational Fields: plumber, pipefitter, steamfitter

United Association of Journeymen and Apprentices of the Plumbing and Pipefitting Industry, Locals #343 and #355
Bay Area Pipe Trades Association
401 Nebraska Street
Vallejo, CA 94590
707-644-4071
Fax: 707-644-0314
Occupational Fields: plumber, pipefitter, steamfitter

United Association of Journeymen and Apprentices of the Plumbing and Pipefitting Industry, Local #364
223 South Rancho Avenue
Colton, CA 92324

909-825-0359
Fax: 909-824-0362
Occupational Fields: plumber, pipefitter, steamfitter

United Association of Journeymen and Apprentices of the Plumbing and Pipefitting Industry, Local #393
6150 Cottle Road
San Jose, CA 95123
408-225-3030
Fax: 408-225-3405
info@local393.org
http://www.sbaypipe.org/local393/index.htm
Occupational Fields: heating, ventilation, and air conditioning mechanic, pipefitter, steamfitter, plumber

United Association of Journeymen and Apprentices of the Plumbing and Pipefitting Industry, Local #398
170 West San Jose Avenue, Suite 303
Claremont, CA 91711
909-625-2493
Fax: 909-626-4620
Occupational Fields: plumber, pipefitter, steamfitter

United Association of Journeymen and Apprentices of the Plumbing and Pipefitting Industry, Local #403
3710 Broad Street
San Luis Obispo, CA 93401
805-543-2416
Fax: 805-541-0251
Occupational Fields: plumber, pipefitter, steamfitter

United Association of Journeymen and Apprentices of the Plumbing and Pipefitting Industry, Local #437, Stanislaus Plumbers, Pipe and Refrigeration
1314 Ninth Street
Modesto, CA 95354
209-526-0565
Occupational Fields: heating, ventilation, and air conditioning mechanic, pipefitter, plumber

United Association of Journeymen and Apprentices of the Plumbing and Pipefitting Industry, Local #447
5841 Newman Court
Sacramento, CA 95819
916-457-6595
Fax: 916-454-6151
Occupational Fields: plumber, pipefitter, steamfitter

United Association of Journeymen and Apprentices of the Plumbing and Pipefitting Industry, Local #460
6718 Meany Avenue
Bakersfield, CA 93308
805-589-4600
Fax: 805-589-3196
Occupational Fields: heating, ventilation, and air conditioning mechanic, pipefitter, steamfitter, plumber

United Association of Journeymen and Apprentices of the Plumbing and Pipefitting Industry, Local #467
Bay Area Pipe Trades Association
1519 Rollins Road
Burlingame, CA 94010
415-692-4730
Fax: 415-692-4730
Occupational Fields: plumber, pipefitter, steamfitter

United Association of Journeymen and Apprentices of the Plumbing and Pipefitting Industry, Local #483, Sprinkler Fitters
23314 Cabot Boulevard
Hayward, CA 94545
510-785-8483
Fax: 510-785-8508
http://www.sprinklerfitters483.org
Occupational Fields: sprinkler fitter, pipefitter

United Association of Journeymen and Apprentices of the Plumbing and Pipefitting Industry, Local #484
1955 North Ventura Avenue
Ventura, CA 93001
805-643-6345
Fax: 805-643-0425
Occupational Fields: plumber, pipefitter, steamfitter

United Association of Journeymen and Apprentices of the Plumbing and Pipefitting Industry, Local #492
3935 Coronado Avenue
Stockton, CA 95204
209-464-4559
Fax: 209-464-0522
Occupational Fields: plumber, pipefitter, steamfitter

United Association of Journeymen and Apprentices of the Plumbing and Pipefitting Industry, Local #494
1246 Locust Avenue
Long Beach, CA 90813
310-436-1082

Fax: 310-491-1875
Occupational Fields: plumber, pipefitter, steamfitter

**United Association of Journeymen and Apprentices of
    the Plumbing and Pipefitting Industry, Local #545**
8333 Airport Boulevard
Los Angeles, CA 90045
310-642-5900
Fax: 310-642-5954
Occupational Fields: plumber, pipefitter, steamfitter

**United Association of Journeymen and Apprentices of
    the Plumbing and Pipefitting Industry, Local #582**
3904 West First Street
Santa Ana, CA 92703
714-775-5563
Fax: 714-775-7976
http://www.ualocal582.com
Occupational Fields: plumber, pipefitter, steamfitter

**United Association of Journeymen and Apprentices of
    the Plumbing and Pipefitting Industry, Local #709**
12140 Rivera Road
Whittier, CA 90606
310-698-9909
Fax: 310-698-7255
Occupational Fields: plumber, pipefitter, steamfitter,
    sprinklerfitter

**United Association of Journeymen and Apprentices of
    the Plumbing and Pipefitting Industry, Local #761**
1305 North Niagara Street
Burbank, CA 91505
818-843-8670
Fax: 818-843-5209
Occupational Fields: plumber, pipefitter, steamfitter

**United Association of Journeymen and Apprentices of
    the Plumbing and Pipefitting Industry, Local #831**
PO Box 20310
Long Beach, CA 90801
310-435-1767
Fax: 310-436-1177
Occupational Fields: plumber, pipefitter, steamfitter

COLORADO
Associated General Contractors of Colorado
1114 West Seventh Avenue, Suite 200
Denver, CO 80204

303-388-2422
Fax: 303-388-0936
http://www.agccolorado.org
Occupational Fields: plumber, pipefitter

Plumbers Union, Local #3
565 East 70th Avenue, #1
Denver, CO 80229-6713
303-286-2575
Occupational Fields: plumber

**United Association of Journeymen and Apprentices
    of the Plumbing and Pipefitting Industry, Local #3**
140 Sheridan Boulevard
Denver, CO 80226-8101
303-935-2000
Fax: 303-935-6362
Occupational Fields: plumber, pipefitter, steamfitter

**United Association of Journeymen and Apprentices of
    the Plumbing and Pipefitting Industry, Local #20**
2901 Farabaugh Lane
Pueblo, CO 81005
719-560-9100
Fax: 719-560-9600
Occupational Fields: plumber, pipefitter, steamfitter

**United Association of Journeymen and Apprentices of
    the Plumbing and Pipefitting Industry, Local #58**
229 East Moreno Avenue
Colorado Springs, CO 80903
719-633-4052
Fax: 719-633-2561
Occupational Fields: plumber, pipefitter, steamfitter

**United Association of Journeymen and Apprentices of
    the Plumbing and Pipefitting Industry, Local #145**
2384 Highways Six and 50
Grand Junction, CO 81505
970-245-2012
Fax: 970-241-5950
Occupational Fields: plumber, pipefitter, steamfitter

**United Association of Journeymen and Apprentices of
    the Plumbing and Pipefitting Industry, Local #208**
6350 North Broadway
Denver, CO 80216-1035
303-428-4380
Fax: 303-428-2831
Occupational Fields: pipefitter

United Association of Journeymen and Apprentices of the Plumbing and Pipefitting Industry, Local #575
PO Box 426
Lafayette, CO 80026
303-665-9736
Fax: 303-665-5597
Occupational Fields: plumber, pipefitter, steamfitter

CONNECTICUT

General Dynamics
Electric Boat Division
75 Eastern Point Road
Groton, CT 06340-4905
860-433-3000
Fax: 860-433-1400
careers@gdeb.com
http://www.gdeb.com
Occupational Fields: maintenance pipefitter, pipefitter, pipecoverer, marine pipehanger

United Association of Journeymen and Apprentices of the Plumbing and Pipefitting Industry, Local #620
873 Poquonnock Road
Groton, CT 06340
860-445-8170
Fax: 860-445-8356
Occupational Fields: plumber, pipefitter, steamfitter

United Association of Journeymen and Apprentices of the Plumbing and Pipefitting Industry, Local #676, Sprinkler Fitters
81 Market Square, Room Two
Newington, CT 06111
860-666-4447
Fax: 860-666-4436
Occupational Fields: sprinkler fitter, pipefitter

DELAWARE

United Association of Journeymen and Apprentices of the Plumbing and Pipefitting Industry, Local #74
2111 West Newport Pike
Wilmington, DE 19804-3719
302-636-7400
Fax: 302-994-5474
Occupational Fields: plumber, pipefitter, steamfitter

United Association of Journeymen and Apprentices of the Plumbing and Pipefitting Industry, Local #782
2675 Sussex highway
Seaford, DE 19973
302-629-3521
Fax: 302-628-0782
Occupational Fields: plumber, pipefitter, steamfitter

DISTRICT OF COLUMBIA

EHI Construction Inc.
1017 Brentwood Road, NE
Washington, DC 20001
202-636-4585
Fax: 202-636-4587
Occupational Fields: plumber

Steamfitters Union, Local #602
809 Maryland Avenue, NE
Washington, DC 20002
301-333-2356
Occupational Fields: steamfitter, pipefitter

United Association of Journeymen and Apprentices of the Plumbing and Pipefitting Industry
National Headquarters
901 Massachusetts Avenue, NW
Washington, DC 20001-4307
202-628-5823
http://www.ua.org
Occupational Fields: plumber

FLORIDA

A. Gonzalez Plumbing
2119 West Columbus Drive
Tampa, FL 33607
813-251-0596
Fax: 813-254-6610
Occupational Fields: heating, ventilation, and air conditioning mechanic, plumber

Air Conditioning Contractors of America, Gold Coast Chapter
10251 West Sample Road
Coral Springs, FL 33065
954-340-8882
http://www.acca.org
Occupational Fields: heating, ventilation, and air conditioning mechanic

Brevard Air Conditioning Contractors Association Inc.
250 Grassland Road, SE
Palm Bay, FL 32900
Occupational Fields: heating, ventilation, and air conditioning mechanic

Brevard County Plumbers
700 North Wickham Road, Suite 108
Melbourne, FL 32935
Occupational Fields: plumber

Central Florida Air Conditioning and Refrigeration Contractors Inc.
7700 State Road, North
Winter Haven, FL 33881
Occupational Fields: heating, ventilation, and air conditioning mechanic

Central Florida Plumbing Contractors
Air Conditioning Association of Central Florida
PO Box 180458
Casselberry, FL 32718-0458
Occupational Fields: heating, ventilation, and air conditioning mechanic, plumber

Cox Fire Protection Inc.
2801 North 36th Street
Tampa, FL 33605
813-247-4777
Occupational Fields: sprinklerfitter

Dade County Air Conditioning, Refrigeration, and Pipefitting Education Committee
13201 Northwest 45th Avenue
Opa Locka, FL 33054
Occupational Fields: heating, ventilation, and air conditioning mechanic, pipefitter

Daniels Plumbing Company Inc.
1120 6th Street
Winter Haven, FL 32038
863-293-8653
http://www.danielsplumbing.com
Occupational Fields: plumber

Florida Association of Plumbing, Heating and Cooling Contractors
6801 Edgewater Drive
Orlando, FL 32810
407-578-7955

Fax: 407-578-7099
flphcc@flphcc.org
Occupational Fields: heating, ventilation, and air conditioning mechanic, plumber

Florida Plumbing Apprenticeship Association Inc.
2525 Old Okeechobee Road, Suite Nine
Palm Beach, FL 33409
561-697-2215
Occupational Fields: plumber

Martin County Plumbers Association Inc.
500 East Ocean Boulevard
Stuart, FL 34994
Occupational Fields: plumber

Palm Beach County Plumbing, Air Conditioning, and Pipefitting
1800 Longwood Road
Palm Beach, FL 33409
561-686-4233
Occupational Fields: heating, ventilation, and air conditioning mechanic, pipefitter, plumber

Panama City Plumbers and Steamfitters
3601 East 11th Street
Panama City, FL 32401
904-785-7663
Occupational Fields: plumber, steamfitter

Pinellas Mechanical Pipe Trades
7840 40th Street, North
Pinellas Park, FL 33781
813-544-9437
Occupational Fields: plumber

Plumbers Union, Local #519
14105 Northwest 58th Court
Hialeah, FL 33014
305-822-9411
Fax: 305-826-9792
Occupational Fields: plumber

Ridge Air Conditioning Inc.
2731 East Oak Island Road
Avon Park, FL 33825
863-453-3453
Occupational Fields: heating, ventilation, and air conditioning mechanic

Santa Rose Plumbers
4904 West Spencer Field Road
Pace, FL 32571
Occupational Fields: plumber

Slaughter and Sons Plumbing Inc.
2303 Ninth Street, East
Bradenton, FL 34208
941-748-6964
*Occupational Fields: heating, ventilation, and air
conditioning mechanic, plumber*

Suncoast Fire Sprinkler
4625 118th Avenue, North
PO Box 2280
Pinellas Park, FL 33780-2280
813-573-1556
Occupational Fields: sprinkler fitter

Traviss Technical Center
3225 Winter Lake Road
Lakeland, FL 33803
863-499-2700
Fax: 863-499-2703
http://www.travisstech.org
*Occupational Fields: heating, ventilation, and air
conditioning mechanic*

**United Association of Journeymen and Apprentices of
the Plumbing and Pipefitting Industry, Local #111**
4020 80th Avenue, North
Pinellas Park, FL 33781
813-541-1770
Fax: 813-546-0450
*Occupational Fields: heating, ventilation, and air
conditioning mechanic, pipefitter, plumber*

**United Association of Journeymen and Apprentices
of the Plumbing and Pipefitting Industry,
Locals #229 and #366**
2300 West Nine Mile Road
Pensacola, FL 32534-9417
Fax: 904-479-4571
Occupational Fields: plumber, pipefitter, steamfitter

**United Association of Journeymen and Apprentices
of the Plumbing and Pipefitting Industry,
Local #234**
5411 Cassidy Road
Jacksonville, FL 32254

904-786-0941
Fax: 904-786-8375
Occupational Fields: plumber, pipefitter

**United Association of Journeymen and Apprentices
of the Plumbing and Pipefitting Industry, Local
#295, Daytona Beach Plumbers and Pipefitters**
743 North Beach Street
Daytona Beach, FL 32114
Fax: 904-252-7171
info@ua295.org
http://www.ua295.org
Occupational Fields: plumber, pipefitter

**United Association of Journeymen and Apprentices
of the Plumbing and Pipefitting Industry,
Local #519, Dade County Plumbers**
14105 Northwest 58th Court
Miami Lakes, FL 33014
305-362-0519
Fax: 305-826-9792
Occupational Fields: plumber

**United Association of Journeymen and Apprentices
of the Plumbing and Pipefitting Industry,
Local #592**
1819 West Tennessee Street
Tallahassee, FL 32304
904-222-2818
Fax: 904-222-9019
*Occupational Fields: heating, ventilation, and air
conditioning mechanic, pipefitter, plumber*

**United Association of Journeymen and Apprentices
of the Plumbing and Pipefitting Industry,
Local #624**
Tampa Area Pipe Trades
3601 North McIntosh Road
Dover, FL 33527
813-659-0268
Fax: 813-659-2192
Occupational Fields: plumber, pipefitter, steamfitter

**United Association of Journeymen and Apprentices of
the Plumbing and Pipefitting Industry, Local #630**
1900 North Florida Mango Road
Palm Beach, FL 33409
407-689-8400
Fax: 407-687-7743
Occupational Fields: plumber, pipefitter, steamfitter

United Association of Journeymen and Apprentices of the Plumbing and Pipefitting Industry, Local #719, Broward County Plumbers and Pipefitters
2500 South Andrews Avenue
Fort Lauderdale, FL 33316
954-525-1830
Fax: 954-524-6234
Occupational Fields: plumber, pipefitter

United Association of Journeymen and Apprentices of the Plumbing and Pipefitting Industry, Local #725
13185 Northwest 45th Avenue
Opa Locka, FL 33054
305-681-8596
Fax: 305-688-1139
http://www.ua725.org
Occupational Fields: heating, ventilation, and air conditioning mechanic, pipefitter

United Association of Journeymen and Apprentices of the Plumbing and Pipefitting Industry, Local #803
2447 Orlando Central Parkway
Orlando, FL 32809
407-851-9240
Fax: 407-859-0053
Occupational Fields: plumber, pipefitter, steamfitter

GEORGIA

Albany Plumbers
PO Box 1151
Albany, GA 31702
912-436-3929
Occupational Fields: heating, ventilation, and air conditioning mechanic, pipefitter, plumber

Atlanta Plumbers and Pipefitters, JATC
5675 Tulane Drive, Southeast
Atlanta, GA 30336
404-696-7121
Occupational Fields: heating, ventilation, and air conditioning mechanic, pipefitter, plumber

Heating, Ventilation, Air Conditioning, and Refrigeration Training
PO Box 285
Morrow, GA 30260
Occupational Fields: heating, ventilation, and air conditioning mechanic

Mechanical Trades Institute
5675 Tulane Drive, SouthWest
Atlanta, GA 30336
404-696-7121
Fax: 404-696-0760
jatt@mindspring.org
http://www.mti-jatt.org
Occupational Fields: heating, ventilation, and air conditioning mechanic, pipefitter, plumber

Plumbers and Pipefitters
309 Main Street
Macon, GA 31201
Occupational Fields: heating, ventilation, and air conditioning mechanic, pipefitter, plumber

United Association of Journeymen and Apprentices of the Plumbing and Pipefitting Industry, Local #72, #368, and #766
374 Maynard Terrace, SE
Atlanta, GA 30316
404-373-5778
Fax: 404-373-2404
Occupational Fields: plumber, pipefitter, steamfitter

United Association of Journeymen and Apprentices of the Plumbing and Pipefitting Industry, Local #150
1211 Telfair Street
Augusta, GA 30901
706-724-8846
Fax: 706-722-6302
http://www.ua150.org
Occupational Fields: plumber, pipefitter, steamfitter

United Association of Journeymen and Apprentices of the Plumbing and Pipefitting Industry, Local #177
PO Box 246
Brunswick, GA 31521
912-265-1890
Fax: 912-267-1028
Occupational Fields: plumber

United Association of Journeymen and Apprentices of the Plumbing and Pipefitting Industry, Local #188
2337 East Victory Drive
Savannah, GA 31404
912-354-5520
Fax: 912-354-5090
http://www.local188.org
Occupational Fields: plumber, pipefitter, steamfitter

United Auto Workers, Local #10
5407 Buford Highway, NE
Doraville, GA 30340-1125
Occupational Fields: heating, ventilation, and air
conditioning mechanic, pipefitter, plumber

HAWAII

Del Monte Fresh Products Inc.
PO Box 200
Kunia, HI 96759
808-621-1208
Fax: 808-621-1262
Occupational Fields: plumber

Honolulu, City and County of
Department of Civil Service
City Hall Annex
Honolulu, HI 96813
808-523-4233
Occupational Fields: air conditioning mechanic, automatic
sprinkler system repairer, pipefitter, plumber, water
plant maintenance system repairer

Plumbers and Pipefitters Training Office
97-731-A Kamehameha Highway
Pearl City, HI 96782
808-456-0585
Occupational Fields: heating, ventilation, and
air conditioning mechanic, pipefitter, plumber,
sprinkler fitter

**United Association of Journeymen and Apprentices
of the Plumbing and Pipefitting Industry,
Local #675**
1109 Bethel Street, Basement Level
Honolulu, HI 96813
808-536-5454
Fax: 808-528-2629
Occupational Fields: plumber, pipefitter, steamfitter

**United Association of Journeymen and Apprentices
of the Plumbing and Pipefitting Industry,
Local #811**
PO Box 487
Aiea, HI 96701
808-471-3463
Fax: 808-422-4735
Occupational Fields: plumber, pipefitter, steamfitter

IDAHO

**United Association of Journeymen and Apprentices of
the Plumbing and Pipefitting Industry, Local #296**
8305 West State Street
Boise, ID 83703
208-853-3533
Fax: 208-853-3538
Occupational Fields: plumber, pipefitter, steamfitter

**United Association of Journeymen and Apprentices of
the Plumbing and Pipefitting Industry, Local #648**
456 North Arthur
Pocatello, ID 83204
208-232-6806
Fax: 208-232-6884
Occupational Fields: plumber, pipefitter, steamfitter

ILLINOIS

Sheet Metal Workers Union, Local #91
8124 42nd Street, West
Rock Island, IL 61201
309-787-0695
Fax: 309-787-0733
Smw91@gconline.com
Occupational Fields: heating, ventilation, and air
conditioning mechanic

**United Association of Journeymen and Apprentices of
the Plumbing and Pipefitting Industry, Local #23**
4623 Boeing Drive
Rockford, IL 61109
815-397-0350
Fax: 815-397-0466
Occupational Fields: plumber, pipefitter, steamfitter

**United Association of Journeymen and Apprentices
of the Plumbing and Pipefitting Industry,
Local #25, Rock Island Plumbers and Pipefitters**
1128 Third Avenue
Rock Island, IL 61201
309-788-4569
Fax: 309-788-3226
Occupational Fields: plumber, pipefitter

**United Association of Journeymen and Apprentices of
the Plumbing and Pipefitting Industry, Local #63**
116 Harvey Court
At Harmon Highway, Route 116
Peoria, IL 61611

309-699-3570
Fax: 309-699-6143
Occupational Fields: plumber, pipefitter, steamfitter

United Association of Journeymen and Apprentices of the Plumbing and Pipefitting Industry, Local #65
PO Box 3038
Decatur, IL 62524
217-877-3440
Fax: 217-877-3458
Occupational Fields: plumber, pipefitter, steamfitter

United Association of Journeymen and Apprentices of the Plumbing and Pipefitting Industry, Local #93
31855 North U.S. Highway, Route 12
Volo, IL 60073
815-759-5900
Fax: 815-759-5978
Occupational Fields: plumber, pipefitter, steamfitter

United Association of Journeymen and Apprentices of the Plumbing and Pipefitting Industry, Local #99
406 Eldorado Road
Bloomington, IL 61704
309-663-2337
Fax: 309-662-0254
Occupational Fields: plumber

United Association of Journeymen and Apprentices of the Plumbing and Pipefitting Industry, Local #101
137 Iowa Avenue
Belleville, IL 62220
618-234-5504
Fax: 618-234-3496
Occupational Fields: plumber, pipefitter, steamfitter

United Association of Journeymen and Apprentices of the Plumbing and Pipefitting Industry, Local #130
1340 West Washington Boulevard
Chicago, IL 60607-1936
312-421-1010
Fax: 312-421-9633
Occupational Fields: plumber

United Association of Journeymen and Apprentices of the Plumbing and Pipefitting Industry, Local #136
2300 Saint Joseph Industrial Park Drive
Evansville, IL 47720
812-423-8043
Fax: 812-423-5517

http://ualocal136.org
Occupational Fields: plumber, pipefitter, steamfitter

United Association of Journeymen and Apprentices of the Plumbing and Pipefitting Industry, Local #137
PO Box 3526
Springfield, IL 62708
217-544-2724
Fax: 217-744-6855
Occupational Fields: plumber, pipefitter, steamfitter

United Association of Journeymen and Apprentices of the Plumbing and Pipefitting Industry, Local #149
PO Box 725
Savoy, IL 61874
217-359-5201
Fax: 217-359-9875
Occupational Fields: plumber, pipefitter, steamfitter

United Association of Journeymen and Apprentices of the Plumbing and Pipefitting Industry, Local #160
PO Box 81
Murphysboro, IL 62966
618-684-4521
Fax: 618-687-1622
Occupational Fields: plumber, pipefitter, steamfitter

United Association of Journeymen and Apprentices of the Plumbing and Pipefitting Industry, Local #281
11900 South Laramie Avenue
Alsip, IL 60803
708-597-1800
Fax: 708-597-1894
Occupational Fields: plumber, pipefitter, steamfitter, sprinkler fitter

United Association of Journeymen and Apprentices of the Plumbing and Pipefitting Industry, Local #319
2175 Rochester Drive
Aurora, IL 60506
708-896-1806
Fax: 708-892-1898
Occupational Fields: plumber, pipefitter, steamfitter

United Association of Journeymen and Apprentices of the Plumbing and Pipefitting Industry, Local #353
6304 West Development Drive
Peoria, IL 61604
309-633-1353
Fax: 309-633-1201
Occupational Fields: plumber, pipefitter, steamfitter

United Association of Journeymen and Apprentices of the Plumbing and Pipefitting Industry, Local #360

Five Meadow Heights
Professional Park, IL 62234
618-346-2560
Fax: 618-346-9926
Occupational Fields: plumber, pipefitter, steamfitter

United Association of Journeymen and Apprentices of the Plumbing and Pipefitting Industry, Local #383

1390 Stanford Drive
Kankakee, IL 60901
815-933-7621
Fax: 815-933-3246
Occupational Fields: plumber, pipefitter, steamfitter

United Association of Journeymen and Apprentices of the Plumbing and Pipefitting Industry, Local #422

2114 South Interstate 80 Frontage Road
Joliet, IL 60436
815-725-0278
Fax: 815-725-0594
Occupational Fields: plumber, pipefitter, steamfitter

United Association of Journeymen and Apprentices of the Plumbing and Pipefitting Industry, Local #439

PO Box 887
East St. Louis, IL 62203
618-624-6096
Fax: 618-624-6159
Occupational Fields: plumber, pipefitter, steamfitter

United Association of Journeymen and Apprentices of the Plumbing and Pipefitting Industry, Local #507

1295 Butterfield Road
Aurora, IL 60504
630-978-4501
Fax: 630-978-9240
Occupational Fields: plumber, pipefitter, steamfitter

United Association of Journeymen and Apprentices of the Plumbing and Pipefitting Industry, Local #551

612 West Main
PO Box 156
West Frankfort, IL 62896
618-937-1363
Fax: 618-937-4401
Occupational Fields: plumber, pipefitter, steamfitter

United Association of Journeymen and Apprentices of the Plumbing and Pipefitting Industry, Local #553

995 East Airline Drive
Alton, IL 62024
618-259-6787
Fax: 618-259-7533
Occupational Fields: plumber, pipefitter, steamfitter

United Association of Journeymen and Apprentices of the Plumbing and Pipefitting Industry, Local #554

632 Schneider Drive
Elgin, IL 60177
Fax: 708-697-1090
Occupational Fields: plumber, pipefitter, steamfitter

United Association of Journeymen and Apprentices of the Plumbing and Pipefitting Industry, Local #555

PO Box 5188
Godfrey, IL 62035
618-372-8342
Occupational Fields: plumber, pipefitter, steamfitter

United Association of Journeymen and Apprentices of the Plumbing and Pipefitting Industry, Local #597

45 North Ogden Avenue
Chicago, IL 60607
312-829-4191
Fax: 312-829-0137
http://www.pf597.org
Occupational Fields: plumber, pipefitter, steamfitter

United Association of Journeymen and Apprentices of the Plumbing and Pipefitting Industry, Local #649

737 Veronica Avenue
PO Box 486
East St. Louis, IL 62202
618-874-7049
Occupational Fields: pipefitter

United Association of Journeymen and Apprentices of the Plumbing and Pipefitting Industry, Local #653

154 South Chestnut
Centralia, IL 62801
618-532-3351
Fax: 618-532-8007
Occupational Fields: plumber, pipefitter, steamfitter

INDIANA

ARS Service Express
25 Woodrow Avenue
Indianapolis, IN 46241
317-634-8690
Occupational Fields: plumber, pipefitter, steamfitter

Chrysler Corporation
Kokomo Casting Plant
PO Box 9007
Kokomo, IN 46902-9007
317-454-1632
Occupational Fields: plumber, pipefitter, steamfitter

Chrysler Corporation
Complex-Transmission
2401 South Reed Road
Kokomo, IN 46904
317-454-1457
Fax: 317-454-1967
Occupational Fields: pipefitter

Cummins Engine Company
PO Box 3005
Mail Code 11861
Columbus, IN 47202-3005
812-377-5784
Occupational Fields: heating, ventilation, and air
conditioning mechanic

Delphi Energy and Engine Management Systems
2401 Columbus Avenue
Anderson, IN 46018
317-646-3628
Occupational Fields: pipefitter

Earl's Heating and Air Conditioning Inc.
8621 Indiana Place
Merrilville, IN 46410
219-942-9023
Fax: 219-795-1946
Occupational Fields: heating, ventilation, and air
conditioning mechanic

Evansville Plumbers and Pipefitters Training
4301 North Saint Joseph
Evansville, IN 47720-1210
812-424-5212
Fax: 812-424-5249
Occupational Fields: plumber, pipefitter

General Motors Corporation
Allison Transmission Division
4700 West 10th Street
PO Box 894
Indianapolis, IN 46206-0894
317-242-5321
Fax: 317-242-6488
http://www.allisontransmission.com
Occupational Fields: heating, ventilation, and air
conditioning mechanic, pipefitter

General Motors Corporation, Marion
Metal Fabricating Division
2400 West Second Street
Marion, IN 46952-3295
317-242-5321
Occupational Fields: pipefitter

GM Powertrain
Training Programs
PO Box 271
Bedford, IN 47421
812-279-7261
Fax: 812-279-7334
Occupational Fields: plumber, pipefitter

Gordon Plumbing Inc.
PO Box 257
Fishers, IN 46038
317-845-1805
Fax: 317-842-8779
Occupational Fields: plumber

Hanzal Plumbing
725 East Goldsboro Street, Unit B
Crown Point, IN 46307
219-662-7310
Occupational Fields: plumber

Haynes International
1020 West Park Avenue
Kokomo, IN 46904-9013
317-456-6407
Fax: 317-456-6905
http://www.haynesintl.com
Occupational Fields: heating, ventilation, and air
conditioning mechanic

LD Mechanical
1051 Sloan Drive
Franklin, IN 46131

317-738-9449
Fax: 317-738-3295
http://www.ldmechanical.com
Occupational Fields: plumber

Midwest Mechanical and Climate Control
1730 South Ninth Street
Richmond, IN 47374
765-935-6462
Occupational Fields: heating, ventilation, and air conditioning mechanic

Paul E. Smith Company Inc.
PO Box 53377
Indianapolis, IN 46253
317-271-2222
Occupational Fields: plumber

Pipe Inc.
795 North Emerson Avenue
Greenwood, IN 46143
317-887-8770
Fax: 317-887-8776
Occupational Fields: plumber

The Plumber
813 West 129th Avenue
Crown Point, IN 46307
219-663-7608
Occupational Fields: plumber

R.T. Moore Company Inc.
6340 LaPas Trail
Indianapolis, IN 46268
317-291-1052
Fax: 317-298-2729
Occupational Fields: plumber

Trademaster Inc.
325 North Adams Street
Marion, IN 46952
765-664-3540
Occupational Fields: plumber

United Association of Journeymen and Apprentices of the Plumbing and Pipefitting Industry, Local #157
Terre Haute Plumbers and Steamfitters
8801 East Milner Avenue
Terre Haute, IN 47803-9796
812-877-1531

Fax: 812-877-4450
Occupational Fields: plumber, pipefitter, steamfitter

United Association of Journeymen and Apprentices of the Plumbing and Pipefitting Industry, Local #166
5515 Industrial Road
Fort Wayne, IN 46825
574-484-6905
Fax: 574-482-4756
Occupational Fields: heating, ventilation, and air conditioning mechanic, pipefitter, plumber, steamfitter

United Association of Journeymen and Apprentices of the Plumbing and Pipefitting Industry, Local #172
South Bend and Vicinity Plumbers and Pipefitters
4127 Ralph Jones Court
South Bend, IN 46628
574-273-0500
Fax: 574-273-1300
Occupational Fields: plumber, pipefitter

United Association of Journeymen and Apprentices of the Plumbing and Pipefitting Industry, Local #210
PO Box 11939
Hobart, IN 46342
219-942-7224
Fax: 219-942-6299
Occupational Fields: plumber, pipefitter, steamfitter

United Association of Journeymen and Apprentices of the Plumbing and Pipefitting Industry, Local #440
Indianapolis Steamfitters and Pipefitters
3747 South High School Road
Indianapolis, IN 46241
317-856-6426
Fax: 317-856-0591
webmaster@ualocal440.org
http://ualocal440.org
Occupational Fields: heating, ventilation, and air conditioning mechanic, steamfitter, pipefitter, plumber

United Association of Journeymen and Apprentices of the Plumbing and Pipefitting Industry, Local #661
4401 South Eaton Avenue
Muncie, IN 47302
765-282-7344
Fax: 765-282-5116
Occupational Fields: plumber, pipefitter, steamfitter

Whirlpool Corporation
Employment and Wage Administration
5401 U.S. Highway 41, North
Evansville, IN 47727
812-426-4496
Fax: 812-426-4957
Occupational Fields: plumber, pipefitter

IOWA

ACI Mechanical Corporation
3116 South Duff Avenue
Ames, IA 50010
515-232-1236
Fax: 515-232-0136
aci@acimech.com
http://www.acimech.com
Occupational Fields: plumber, pipefitter

Affordable Plumbing Service
816 First Avenue, NW
Cedar Rapids, IA 52405
319-364-3868
Fax: 319-369-0260
Occupational Fields: plumber, pipefitter

Angerer Plumbing and Heating
PO Box 447
Marion, IA 52302
319-377-5005
Occupational Fields: heating, ventilation, and air
conditioning mechanic, pipefitter, plumber

Beane Plumbing and Heating Company
3330 Gordon Drive
Sioux City, IA 51106-2994
Occupational Fields: plumber, pipefitter

Best Plumbing
5412 Center Point Road, NE
Cedar Rapids, IA 52402
319-393-0255
Fax: 319-393-0256
Occupational Fields: plumber, pipefitter

Brown Plumbing and Heating
1451 Linmar Drive, NE
Cedar Rapids, IA 52402
319-363-2034
Occupational Fields: plumber, pipefitter

Cedar Rapids Plumbers and Pipefitters, Local 125
205 50th Avenue, Southwest
Cedar Rapids, IA 52404
319-362-9259
Occupational Fields: plumber, pipefitter

Cedar Rapids Sheet Metal Workers, Local 263
1211 Wiley Boulevard, SW
Cedar Rapids, IA 52404
319-396-8045
Occupational Fields: heating, ventilation, and air
conditioning mechanic

Colony Heating and Air Conditioning
2224 16th Avenue, SW
Cedar Rapids, IA 52404
319-364-4755
Fax: 319-364-5935
Occupational Fields: heating, ventilation, and air
conditioning mechanic

Comfort Solutions
604 First Avenue
Springville, IA 52336
319-854-6945
Fax: 319-854-7475
Occupational Fields: heating, ventilation, and air
conditioning mechanic

Cunningham Inc.
112 Sixth Avenue, West
Oskaloosa, IA 52577-3744
515-673-8479
Occupational Fields: plumber, pipefitter

D and S Sheet Metal Inc.
5805 Locust Road, SW
Cedar Rapids, IA 52404
319-362-2472
Fax: 319-362-5269
Occupational Fields: heating, ventilation, and air
conditioning mechanic

Deere and Company
PO Box 1595
Des Moines, IA 50306
515-289-3208
Occupational Fields: plumber, pipefitter

Des Moines Plumbing/Lehman Com Service
63 College Avenue
Des Moines, IA 50314

515-243-5111
Occupational Fields: plumber, pipefitter

Emery Heating and Cooling
4202 Lewis Access Road
PO Box 909
Center Point, IA 52213
319-849-2554
Occupational Fields: heating, ventilation, and air
conditioning mechanic

Executive Plumbing
375 Collins Road, Suite Seven
Cedar Rapids, IA 52402
319-393-3725
Occupational Fields: plumber, pipefitter

Foster Heating and Air Conditioning Inc.
1040 East Post Road
Marion, IA 52302
319-377-6323
Occupational Fields: heating, ventilation, and air
conditioning mechanic

Gorsh Service Inc.
803 Fourth Street, SW
Cedar Rapids, IA 52404
319-363-9345
Occupational Fields: plumber, pipefitter

H and J Heating and Cooling Inc.
1130 Hawkeye Drive
Hiawatha, IA 52233
319-393-0523
Occupational Fields: heating, ventilation, and air
conditioning mechanic, pipefitter, plumber

Heating Service Company Inc.
923 F Avenue, NE
Cedar Rapids, IA 52405
319-362-3340
Occupational Fields: heating, ventilation, and air
conditioning mechanic

Hopkins Contracting Inc.
510 Brown Street
PO Box 13
Sloan, IA 51055-0013
712-428-6285
Occupational Fields: plumber, pipefitter

John's Plumbing and Heating
615 North Court Street
Ottumwa, IA 52501
515-683-1224
Occupational Fields: plumber, pipefitter

L.A. Fulton
3401 104th Street
Des Moines, IA 50322-3823
515-276-4265
Occupational Fields: plumber, pipefitter

Langan Plumbing Inc.
1401 Mount Vernon Road
Cedar Rapids, IA 52403
319-364-5044
Occupational Fields: plumber, pipefitter

Leo's Heating and Air Conditioning
245 Lynda Drive, NW
Cedar Rapids, IA 52405
319-396-2085
Occupational Fields: heating, ventilation, and air
conditioning mechanic

Lint Mechanical Inc.
PO Box 220
Dallas Center, IA 50063-0220
515-992-3970
Occupational Fields: plumber, pipefitter

M and D Plumbing and Heating Inc.
21713 County Road E-34
Anamosa, IA 52205
319-462-2268
Occupational Fields: heating, ventilation, and air
conditioning mechanic, pipefitter, plumber

Manning Seivert
PO Box 88
Granger, IA 50109-0088
515-999-2597
Fax: 515-999-2871
Occupational Fields: plumber, pipefitter

Master Plumbing Inc.
3111 First Avenue, SE
Cedar Rapids, IA 52403
319-363-7533
Occupational Fields: plumber, pipefitter

Parker Plumbing and Heating
780 West Main Street
Robins, IA 52328
319-378-9888
Occupational Fields: plumber, pipefitter

Proctor Mechanical Corporation
63 College Avenue
Des Moines, IA 50314
515-288-2251
Occupational Fields: plumber, pipefitter

Tri-Tech Construction
PO Box 1120
Keokuk, IA 52632-1120
319-524-9002
Occupational Fields: plumber, pipefitter

**United Association of Journeymen and Apprentices
of the Plumbing and Pipefitting Industry,
Local #33, Des Moines Plumbers and
Pipefitters**
2501 Bell Avenue
Des Moines, IA 50321
515-243-3244
Fax: 515-243-3243
Occupational Fields: plumber, pipefitter

**United Association of Journeymen and Apprentices
of the Plumbing and Pipefitting Industry,
Local #66, Dubuque Plumbers**
164 Main Street
PO 1176
Dubuque, IA 52004-1176
319-583-0150
Fax: 319-583-0150
Occupational Fields: plumber, pipefitter

**United Association of Journeymen and Apprentices
of the Plumbing and Pipefitting Industry,
Local #125**
PO Box 1091
Cedar Rapids, IA 52406
319-365-0413
Fax: 319-365-1136
Ua125org@aol.com
http://www.ua125.org
Occupational Fields: plumber, pipefitter, steamfitter

**United Association of Journeymen and Apprentices
of the Plumbing and Pipefitting Industry,
Local #212, Southeast Iowa Plumbers**
3203 Highway 61
PO Box 80
Burlington, IA 52601
319-752-5887
Occupational Fields: plumber, pipefitter

**United Association of Journeymen and Apprentices
of the Plumbing and Pipefitting Industry,
Local #387, Davenport Plumbers and Steamfitters**
702 West 35th Street
Davenport, IA 52806
319-386-2772
Fax: 319-386-2802
*Occupational Fields: heating, ventilation, and air
conditioning mechanic, pipefitter, steamfitter,
plumber*

**United Association of Journeymen and Apprentices of
the Plumbing and Pipefitting Industry, Local #405**
510 South Pennsylvania
Mason City, IA 50401
515-424-9675
Occupational Fields: plumber, pipefitter, steamfitter

Wykcoff Industries
PO Box 35070
Des Moines, IA 50315-0301
515-287-3725
Occupational Fields: plumber, pipefitter

KANSAS
**Associated Builders and Contractors,
Heart of America**
6950 Squibb Road, #418
Mission, KS 66202
913-831-2221
http://www.abcksmo.org
Occupational Fields: plumber

Colgate-Palmolive Company
18010 Kansas Avenue
Kansas City, KS 66105
913-573-6464
Fax: 913-573-6605
Occupational Fields: pipefitter

General Motors Corporation
3201 Fairfax Trafficway
Kansas City, KS 66115-1399
913-573-7400
Fax: 913-573-7109
Occupational Fields: pipefitter

Goss Service Company Inc.
7915 Hemlock Street
Shawnee Mission, KS 66204-3452
913-642-4616
Occupational Fields: pipefitter

Plumbers and Steamfitters Union, Local #664
103 Mendicki Road
Pittsburg, KS 66762-8549
316-231-4280
Occupational Fields: heating, ventilation, and air
    conditioning mechanic, plumber, pipefitter

**United Association of Journeymen and Apprentices
    of the Plumbing and Pipefitting Industry,
    Local #165, Plumbers, Pipefitters, and
    Steamfitters**
1231 Northwest Eugene Street
PO Box 8067
Topeka, KS 66608-1403
913-354-8539
Fax: 913-354-7090
Occupational Fields: plumber, pipefitter, steamfitter

**United Association of Journeymen and Apprentices
    of the Plumbing and Pipefitting Industry,
    Local #171, Plumbers and Steamfitters**
1330 East First Street, North, Suite 115
Wichita, KS 67214-4000
316-265-4291
Fax: 316-265-5731
Occupational Fields: heating, ventilation, and air
    conditioning mechanic, plumber, pipefitter

**United Association of Journeymen and Apprentices
    of the Plumbing and Pipefitting Industry,
    Local #664**
103 Mendicki Drive
Frontenac, KS 66763
316-231-4280
Occupational Fields: plumber, pipefitter, steamfitter

**United Association of Journeymen and Apprentices of
    the Plumbing and Pipefitting Industry, Local #763**
930 East 28th Street
PO Box 4041
Lawrence, KS 66046-1041
785-843-3151
Fax: 785-843-3421
Occupational Fields: plumber, pipefitter

KENTUCKY
Kentucky Pipe Trades Association
Marketing & Technology
2333 Alexandria Drive
Lexington, KY 40504
859-514-6704
Fax: (603) 909-1081
kpta@ua-ky.com
http://www.kypipetrades.com

**United Association of Journeymen and Apprentices of
    the Plumbing and Pipefitting Industry, Local #184**
1332 Broadway Street
Paducah, KY 42001
270-442-3213
Fax: 502-442-9209
Occupational Fields: plumber, pipefitter, steamfitter

**United Association of Journeymen and Apprentices of
    the Plumbing and Pipefitting Industry, Local #248**
PO Box 427
Ashland, KY 41105-0427
606-325-2544
Fax: 606-324-8401
Occupational Fields: plumber, pipefitter, steamfitter

**United Association of Journeymen and Apprentices of
    the Plumbing and Pipefitting Industry, Local #452**
525 DeRoode Street
Lexington, KY 40508
606-252-8337
Fax: 606-233-7119
Occupational Fields: plumber, pipefitter, steamfitter

**United Association of Journeymen and Apprentices of
    the Plumbing and Pipefitting Industry, Local #502**
PO Box 4429
Louisville, KY 40204
502-361-8492

Fax: 502-473-0694
Occupational Fields: plumber, pipefitter, steamfitter

United Association of Journeymen and Apprentices of the Plumbing and Pipefitting Industry, Local #522
1317 Berry Boulevard
Louisville, KY 40215
502-361-8492
Fax: 502-366-8459
Occupational Fields: plumber, pipefitter, steamfitter

United Association of Journeymen and Apprentices of the Plumbing and Pipefitting Industry, Local #633
3128 Alvey Park Drive, West
Owensboro, KY 42303
270-683-1587
Fax: 270-683-1588
Occupational Fields: plumber, pipefitter, steamfitter

LOUISIANA

American Federation of Unions, Local #102
17775 Airline Highway
Prairieville, LA 70769
225-927-6251
Occupational Fields: pipefitter

Sims Insulation and Air Conditioning Company
1960 Easy Street
Lake Charles, LA 70605
318-477-8700
Occupational Fields: pipefitter

United Association of Journeymen and Apprentices of the Plumbing and Pipefitting Industry, Local #60
PO Box 8428
Metairie, LA 70011
504-885-3062
Fax: 504-454-2584
http://www.local60.com
Occupational Fields: plumber, pipefitter, steamfitter

United Association of Journeymen and Apprentices of the Plumbing and Pipefitting Industry, Local #106
2013 Ryan Street
Lake Charles, LA 70601
318-436-4373
Fax: 318-433-2426
Occupational Fields: plumber, pipefitter, steamfitter

United Association of Journeymen and Apprentices of the Plumbing and Pipefitting Industry, Local #198
5888 Airline Highway
Baton Rouge, LA 70805
504-356-3333
Fax: 504-356-3336
Occupational Fields: plumber, pipefitter, steamfitter

United Association of Journeymen and Apprentices of the Plumbing and Pipefitting Industry, Local #247, Alexandria Pipe Trades
1211 Rapides Avenue
Alexandria, LA 71301
318-442-9923
Occupational Fields: pipefitter, plumber, welder

United Association of Journeymen and Apprentices of the Plumbing and Pipefitting Industry, Local #659
PO Drawer 2567
Monroe, LA 71207
318-322-4520
Fax: 318-324-1034
Occupational Fields: plumber, pipefitter, steamfitter

MAINE

Bath Iron Works
700 Washington Street
Bath, ME 04530-2574
207-442-1820
Fax: 207-442-1737
Occupational Fields: heating, ventilation, and air conditioning mechanic, pipefitter, pipe designer

United Association of Journeymen and Apprentices of the Plumbing and Pipefitting Industry, Local #217
Evergreen Drive
Portland, ME 04103
207-878-2231
Fax: 207-797-5762
Occupational Fields: plumber, pipefitter, steamfitter

United Association of Journeymen and Apprentices of the Plumbing and Pipefitting Industry, Local #321
40 Freedom Park
Bangor, ME 04401-5745
207-848-5381
Fax: 207-848-5589
Occupational Fields: plumber, pipefitter, steamfitter

United Association of Journeymen and Apprentices of the Plumbing and Pipefitting Industry, Local #485
150 Knox Street
Millinocket, ME 04462
207-723-5898
Occupational Fields: plumber, pipefitter, steamfitter

United Association of Journeymen and Apprentices of the Plumbing and Pipefitting Industry, Local #783
PO Box 292
Winthrop, ME 04364
207-377-8055
Fax: 207-377-6984
Occupational Fields: plumber, pipefitter, steamfitter

MARYLAND

Adrian L. Merton Inc.
9011 East Hampton Drive
Capitol Heights, MD 20743
301-336-2700
Occupational Fields: plumber, steamfitter

Air Conditioning Contractors of America, National Capital Chapter
12600 Laurie Drive
PO Box 4268
Silver Spring, MD 20914-4268
301-384-2222
Fax: 301-384-9623
plpupson@acca-nnc.org
http://www.acca-ncc.org
Occupational Fields: heating, ventilation, and air conditioning technician

Baltimore Plumbers Union, Local #48
Plumbers and Gasfitters Training School
5200 Westland Boulevard
Baltimore, MD 21227-2360
410-242-3348
Occupational Fields: plumber, gas fitter

Bethesda Sheet Metal Company
5511 Dorsey Lane
Bethesda, MD 20816
301-656-4300
Occupational Fields: plumber, pipefitter

Bethlehem Steel Corporation, Sparrows Point
5111 North Point Boulevard
Baltimore, MD 21219
410-388-3000
Occupational Fields: pipefitter

Capitol Sprinkler Contracting Inc.
6550 Dobbin Road
Columbia, MD 21045-4798
410-730-4711
Occupational Fields: sprinkler fitter, pipefitter

Hess Mechanical Corporation
7600 Fallard Court
Upper Marlboro, MD 20772
301-856-4700
Fax: 301-856-4720
Occupational Fields: plumber

Joint Plumbing Apprenticeship Inc.
8501 Rainswood Drive
Landover, MD 20785-2323
301-773-1199
Occupational Fields: plumber

Jones and Wood Inc.
3430 Hamilton Street
Hyattsville, MD 20782
301-779-8383
Fax: 301-779-6307
Occupational Fields: plumber

MC Company
4604 Largo Road
PO Box 830
Upper Marlboro, MD 20772
Occupational Fields: plumber, steamfitter

Sprinkler Fitters Union, Local #669
7676 New Hampshire Avenue, Suite 416
Langley Park, MD 50783
800-638-0592
Occupational Fields: sprinkler fitter, pipefitter

Steamfitters Union, Local #438
6650 Belair Road
Baltimore, MD 21206-1844
410-254-4800
Occupational Fields: steamfitter, pipefitter

United Association of Journeymen and Apprentices of the Plumbing and Pipefitting Industry
8421 Ardwick-Ardmore Road
Landover, MD 20785-2304
301-341-1555
Fax: 301-386-3271
Occupational Fields: plumber, steamfitter

United Association of Journeymen and Apprentices of the Plumbing and Pipefitting Industry, Local #486
1201 66th Street
Baltimore, MD 21237
410-866-5313
Fax: 410-866-1995
http://www.ualocal486.com
Occupational Fields: plumber, pipefitter, steamfitter

United Association of Journeymen and Apprentices of the Plumbing and Pipefitting Industry, Local #489
2 Park Street
Cumberland, MD 21502
301-722-8515
Fax: 301-759-4168
Occupational Fields: plumber, pipefitter, steamfitter

United Association of Journeymen and Apprentices of the Plumbing and Pipefitting Industry, Local #536, Sprinkler Fitters
6100 Baltimore National Pike, Lower Level, #7-9
Baltimore, MD 21228
Fax: 410-747-0669
Occupational Fields: sprinkler fitter, pipefitter

United Association of Journeymen and Apprentices of the Plumbing and Pipefitting Industry, Local #669
7050 Oakland Mills Road, Suite 200
Columbia, MD 21046
301-596-7669
Fax: 301-621-8045
http://www.sprinklerfitters669.org
Occupational Fields: pipefitter, spinklerfitter

MASSACHUSETTS

United Association of Journeymen and Apprentices of the Plumbing and Pipefitting Industry, Local #4
330 Soutwest Cutoff, Route 20
Worcester, MA 01607
508-799-7703
Fax: 508-752-0856

ua4@worldnet.att.net
http://www.ualocal4.org
Occupational Fields: plumber, pipefitter, steamfitter

United Association of Journeymen and Apprentices of the Plumbing and Pipefitting Industry, Local #12
1240 Massachusetts Avenue
Boston, MA 02125
617-288-6200
Fax: 617-288-3871
http://www.plumbersandgasfitterslocal12.org
Occupational Fields: plumber

United Association of Journeymen and Apprentices of the Plumbing and Pipefitting Industry, Local #138
40 Poplar Street
Danvers, MA 01923
Fax: 508-750-8254
Occupational Fields: plumber, pipefitter, steamfitter

United Association of Journeymen and Apprentices of the Plumbing and Pipefitting Industry, Local #537
35 Travis Street
Allston, MA 02134
617-787-5370
Fax: 617-787-5373
Occupational Fields: plumber, pipefitter, steamfitter

United Association of Journeymen and Apprentices of the Plumbing and Pipefitting Industry, Local #550
46 Rockland Street
Boston, MA 02132
617-323-0474
Fax: 617-323-1373
Occupational Fields: plumber, pipefitter, steamfitter

MICHIGAN

United Association of Journeymen and Apprentices of the Plumbing and Pipefitting Industry, Local #70
918 Benjamin, NE
Grand Rapids, MI 49503
616-458-1173
Fax: 616-458-6150
Occupational Fields: plumber, pipefitter, steamfitter

United Association of Journeymen and Apprentices of the Plumbing and Pipefitting Industry, Local #85
PO Box 6547
Saginaw, MI 48608

Fax: 517-791-3468
Occupational Fields: plumber, steamfitter

United Association of Journeymen and Apprentices of the Plumbing and Pipefitting Industry, Local #154, Plumbers and Steamfitters
1341 Getty Street
Muskegon, MI 49442-5126
616-722-9674
Occupational Fields: plumber, steamfitter

United Association of Journeymen and Apprentices of the Plumbing and Pipefitting Industry, Local #333
3101 Allied Drive, Suite A
Jackson, MI 49201
517-784-1106
Fax: 517-784-1147
Occupational Fields: plumber, pipefitter, steamfitter

United Association of Journeymen and Apprentices of the Plumbing and Pipefitting Industry, Local #335
5906 East Morgan Road
Battle Creek, MI 49017
616-968-0993
Fax: 616-968-0025
Occupational Fields: plumber, pipefitter, steamfitter

United Association of Journeymen and Apprentices of the Plumbing and Pipefitting Industry, Local #357
11847 Shaver Road
Schoolcraft, MI 49087
269-679-2570
Fax: 269-679-2571
Occupational Fields: plumber, pipefitter, steamfitter

United Association of Journeymen and Apprentices of the Plumbing and Pipefitting Industry, Local #388
5405 South Martin Luther King, Jr., Boulevard
Lansing, MI 48911-3593
517-393-5480
Fax: 517-393-0798
Occupational Fields: plumber, pipefitter, steamfitter

United Association of Journeymen and Apprentices of the Plumbing and Pipefitting Industry, Local #506
2601 North 30th Street
Escanaba, MI 49829
906-789-9784
Fax: 906-789-9799
Ua506rm@charterinternet.com

http://www.ua506.org
Occupational Fields: plumber

United Association of Journeymen and Apprentices of the Plumbing and Pipefitting Industry, Local #506
119 South Front Street
Marquette, MI 49855
906-226-6511
ua506marq@chartermi.net
http://www.ua506.org
Occupational Fields: plumber, pipefitter, steamfitter

United Association of Journeymen and Apprentices of the Plumbing and Pipefitting Industry, Local #513
PO Box 747
Benton Harbor, MI 49023
616-926-6557
Fax: 616-926-2212
Occupational Fields: plumber, pipefitter, steamfitter

United Association of Journeymen and Apprentices of the Plumbing and Pipefitting Industry, Local #728
205 East Fleshiem Street
Iron Mountain, MI 49801
906-774-6438
Fax: 906-774-0136
Occupational Fields: plumber, pipefitter, steamfitter

United Association of Journeymen and Apprentices of the Plumbing and Pipefitting Industry, Local #816
1300 West Thomas
Bay City, MI 48706
517-684-7981
Occupational Fields: plumber, pipefitter, steamfitter

MINNESOTA
United Association of Journeymen and Apprentices of the Plumbing and Pipefitting Industry, Local #11
4402 Airpark Boulevard
Duluth, MN 55811
218-727-2199
Fax: 218-727-2298
http://www.mnpipetrades.com/Local11maplink.htm
Occupational Fields: plumber, pipefitter, steamfitter

United Association of Journeymen and Apprentices of the Plumbing and Pipefitting Industry, Local #15
708 South Tenth Street
Minneapolis, MN 55404

612-333-8601
Fax: 612-341-0958
http://www.plumberslocal15.org
Occupational Fields: plumber, pipefitter, steamfitter

United Association of Journeymen and Apprentices of the Plumbing and Pipefitting Industry, Local #34
411 Main Street, Room 215
St. Paul, MN 55102
612-224-3828
http://www.mnpipetrades.com/Local34Maplink.htm
Occupational Fields: plumber, pipefitter, steamfitter

United Association of Journeymen and Apprentices of the Plumbing and Pipefitting Industry, Local #126
PO Box 14
Detroit Lakes, MN 56501
218-847-3222
Fax: 218-847-3020
Occupational Fields: plumber, pipefitter, steamfitter

United Association of Journeymen and Apprentices of the Plumbing and Pipefitting Industry, Local #308
1903 North Fourth Street
St. Cloud, MN 56303
320-251-5615
Occupational Fields: plumber, pipefitter

United Association of Journeymen and Apprentices of the Plumbing and Pipefitting Industry, Local #455
700 Transfer Road
St. Paul, MN 55114
612-647-9920
Fax: 612-647-1566
http://www.local455.com
Occupational Fields: plumber, pipefitter, steamfitter

United Association of Journeymen and Apprentices of the Plumbing and Pipefitting Industry, Local #561
310 McKinzie Street
Mankato, MN 56001
507-625-5126
Fax: 507-387-7768
Occupational Fields: plumber, pipefitter, steamfitter

United Association of Journeymen and Apprentices of the Plumbing and Pipefitting Industry, Local #589
107 South 15th Avenue, West
Virginia, MN 55792

218-741-2482
Fax: 218-741-2493
Occupational Fields: plumber, pipefitter, steamfitter

United Association of Journeymen and Apprentices of the Plumbing and Pipefitting Industry, Local #771
PO Box 430
International Falls, MN 56679
218-283-4159
Fax: 218-283-2803
Occupational Fields: plumber, pipefitter, steamfitter

MISSISSIPPI

United Association of Journeymen and Apprentices of the Plumbing and Pipefitting Industry, Local #568
939 West Capitol Street
Jackson, MS 39203-2691
601-352-7491
Occupational Fields: plumber, pipefitter

United Association of Journeymen and Apprentices of the Plumbing and Pipefitting Industry, Local #619
PO Box 261
Vicksburg, MS 39181
601-638-2546
Fax: 601-638-2692
Occupational Fields: plumber, pipefitter

United Association of Journeymen and Apprentices of the Plumbing and Pipefitting Industry, Local #714
PO Box 1042
Columbus, MS 39703
601-328-8287
Fax: 601-328-6692
Occupational Fields: plumber, pipefitter

MISSOURI

United Association of Journeymen and Apprentices of the Plumbing and Pipefitting Industry, Locals #8 and #533
United Association Building, Suite Two
8600 Hillcrest Road
Kansas City, MO 64138
816-363-8888
Fax: 816-363-8890
Occupational Fields: plumber, pipefitter

United Association of Journeymen and Apprentices of the Plumbing and Pipefitting Industry, Local #35
5735 Elizabeth Avenue
St. Louis, MO 63110
Fax: 314-781-7186
Occupational Fields: plumber, pipefitter

United Association of Journeymen and Apprentices of the Plumbing and Pipefitting Industry, Local #45
Fairleigh Station
PO Box 6272
St. Joseph, MO 64506-0272
816-279-5534
Fax: 816-364-5621
Occupational Fields: plumber, pipefitter

United Association of Journeymen and Apprentices of the Plumbing and Pipefitting Industry, Local #178
2501 West Grand
Springfield, MO 65802
417-869-0633
Occupational Fields: plumber, pipefitter

United Association of Journeymen and Apprentices of the Plumbing and Pipefitting Industry, Local #268
1710 South Broadway
St. Louis, MO 63104
314-241-8023
Fax: 314-436-0230
Occupational Fields: plumber, pipefitter, sprinklerfitter

United Association of Journeymen and Apprentices of the Plumbing and Pipefitting Industry, Local #314, Sprinkler Fitters
United Labor Building, Suite 312
6301 Rockhill Road
Kansas City, MO 64131
816-361-8585
Fax: 816-361-5156
Occupational Fields: sprinkler fitter, pipefitter

United Association of Journeymen and Apprentices of the Plumbing and Pipefitting Industry, Local #562
12385 Larimore Road
St. Louis, MO 63138
314-355-1000
Fax: 314-388-5467
Occupational Fields: plumber, pipefitter

United Association of Journeymen and Apprentices of the Plumbing and Pipefitting Industry, Local #781
PO Box 12918
Kansas City, MO 64124
816-931-6795
Fax: 913-362-3283
Occupational Fields: plumber, pipefitter

MONTANA

United Association of Journeymen and Apprentices of the Plumbing and Pipefitting Industry, Local #30
PO Box 30616
Billings, MT 59107
406-252-9371
Fax: 406-252-9373
http://www.cymt.net/uamt-wy/30/30home.asp
Occupational Fields: plumber, pipefitter

United Association of Journeymen and Apprentices of the Plumbing and Pipefitting Industry, Local #459
1026 South Fifth Street, West
Missoula, MT 59801
406-549-3479
Fax: 406-549-3479
http://www.cymt.net/uamt-wy/459/459home.asp
Occupational Fields: plumber, pipefitter

United Association of Journeymen and Apprentices of the Plumbing and Pipefitting Industry, Locals #41 and #139
3345 Harrison Avenue
Butte, MT 59701
406-494-3051
Fax: 406-494-5790
Occupational Fields: plumber, pipefitter

NEBRASKA

United Association of Journeymen and Apprentices of the Plumbing and Pipefitting Industry, Local #16
4801 F Street
Omaha, NE 68117
402-734-6274
Fax: 402-734-0180
Occupational Fields: plumber, pipefitter

United Association of Journeymen and Apprentices
of the Plumbing and Pipefitting Industry,
Local #464
PO Box 4717
Lincoln, NE 68504
402-466-5154
Fax: 402-466-6177
Occupational Fields: plumber, pipefitter

United Association of Journeymen and Apprentices
of the Plumbing and Pipefitting Industry,
Local #464
PO Box 45422
Omaha, NE 68145
402-333-5859
Fax: 402-333-0858
Occupational Fields: plumber, pipefitter

NEVADA

United Association of Journeymen and Apprentices
of the Plumbing and Pipefitting Industry,
Local #525
Southern Nevada Plumbers and Pipefitters
750 Legion Way
Las Vegas, NV 89110
702-452-1520
Fax: 702-452-2638
Local525@local525.org
http://local525.org
Occupational Fields: plumber, pipefitter

NEW HAMPSHIRE

United Association of Journeymen and Apprentices of
the Plumbing and Pipefitting Industry, Local #131
161 Londonderry Turnpike
Hookset, NH 03106
603-669-7307
Fax: 603-668-2037
http://www.newenglandpipe.com
Occupational Fields: plumber, pipefitter

United Association of Journeymen and Apprentices of
the Plumbing and Pipefitting Industry, Local #788
PO Box 2018
Portsmouth, NH 03804
http://www.newenglandpipe.com
Occupational Fields: plumber, pipefitter

NEW JERSEY

United Association of Journeymen and Apprentices
of the Plumbing and Pipefitting Industry, Local #9
Two Iron Ore Road at Route 33
Englishtown, NJ 07726
732-792-0999
Fax: 732-264-0566
info@uanj.org
http://www.uanj.org
Occupational Fields: plumber, pipefitter

United Association of Journeymen and Apprentices of
the Plumbing and Pipefitting Industry, Local #24
986 South Springfield Avenue
Springfield, NJ 07081-3508
973-912-0092
Fax: 973-912-0464
mmcmanus@ualocal24.org
http://www.ualocal24.org
Occupational Fields: plumber, pipefitter

United Association of Journeymen and Apprentices of
the Plumbing and Pipefitting Industry, Local #274
PO Box 459
Ridgefield, NJ 07657
201-943-4700
Fax: 201-943-0878
info@uanj.org
http://www.uanj.org/index.htm
Occupational Fields: plumber, pipefitter

United Association of Journeymen and Apprentices of
the Plumbing and Pipefitting Industry, Local #322
PO Box 73
Winslow, NJ 08095
609-567-3322
Fax: 609-567-9695
info@uanj.org
http://www.ua322.org
Occupational Fields: plumber, pipefitter

United Association of Journeymen and Apprentices
of the Plumbing and Pipefitting Industry,
Local #475
PO Box 4187
Warren, NJ 07059
908-754-1030
Fax: 908-769-7232
info@uanj.org

http://www.uanj.org.index.htm
Occupational Fields: plumber, pipefitter

United Association of Journeymen and Apprentices of the Plumbing and Pipefitting Industry, Local #696
41 East Willow Street
Milburn, NJ 07041
Fax: 201-379-4324
Occupational Fields: plumber, pipefitter

United Association of Journeymen and Apprentices of the Plumbing and Pipefitting Industry, Local #855
Unit 103, Building B
3840 Park Avenue
Edison, NJ 08820-2508
908-549-4290
Fax: 908-549-5653
Occupational Fields: plumber, pipefitter

NEW MEXICO
Plumbers Union
411 Arizona Street, SE
Albuquerque, NM 87108-3748
505-256-9257
Occupational Fields: plumber

United Association of Journeymen and Apprentices of the Plumbing and Pipefitting Industry, Local #412
510 San Pedro Drive, SE
Albuquerque, NM 87108
505-265-1513
Fax: 505-265-7127
http://www.ualocal412.org
Occupational Fields: plumber, pipefitter

NEW YORK
Steamfitters Industry Fund
Five Pennsylvania Plaza
New York, NY 10119
212-465-8888
Occupational Fields: steamfitter

Steamfitters Industry Training Center
4803 32nd Place
Long Island, NY 11101-2517
718-706-0218
Occupational Fields: steamfitter, pipefitter

United Association of Journeymen and Apprentices of the Plumbing and Pipefitting Industry, Locals #1, #2, and #371
158-29 George Meany Boulevard
Howard Beach, NY 11414
718-738-7500
Fax: 718-835-0896
Occupational Fields: plumber, pipefitter

United Association of Journeymen and Apprentices of the Plumbing and Pipefitting Industry, Locals #7 and #105
308 Wolf Road
Latham, NY 12110
518-785-9808
Fax: 518-785-9855
Occupational Fields: plumber, pipefitter

United Association of Journeymen and Apprentices of the Plumbing and Pipefitting Industry, Local #13
1645 Saint Paul Street
Rochester, NY 14621
585-338-2360
Fax: 585-544-0600
office@ualocal13.org
http://www.ua-local13.org
Occupational Fields: plumber, pipefitter

United Association of Journeymen and Apprentices of the Plumbing and Pipefitting Industry, Locals #21, #299, and #543
Five Westchester Plaza
Elmsford, NY 10523
914-347-2999
Fax: 914-345-2651
Occupational Fields: plumber, pipefitter

United Association of Journeymen and Apprentices of the Plumbing and Pipefitting Industry, Local #22
3651 California Road
Orchard Park, NY 14127
716-662-3952
Fax: 716-662-0819
Occupational Fields: plumber, pipefitter, steamfitter

United Association of Journeymen and Apprentices of the Plumbing and Pipefitting Industry, Local #73
PO Box 911
Oswego, NY 13126

315-343-4037
Fax: 315-343-5810
Occupational Fields: plumber, pipefitter

United Association of Journeymen and Apprentices of the Plumbing and Pipefitting Industry, Local #112
Binghamton Building & Construction Trades
PO Box 670
Binghamton, NY 13902
607-723-9593
Fax: 607-723-9467
Occupational Fields: plumber

United Association of Journeymen and Apprentices of the Plumbing and Pipefitting Industry, Local #128
105 Clinton Street
Schenectady, NY 12305
518-372-4341
Occupational Fields: plumber, pipefitter

United Association of Journeymen and Apprentices of the Plumbing and Pipefitting Industry, Local #129
3900 Packard Road
Niagara Falls, NY 14303
716-285-8449
Fax: 716-284-8766
Occupational Fields: plumber, pipefitter

United Association of Journeymen and Apprentices of the Plumbing and Pipefitting Industry, Local #200
PO Box 508
Mineola, NY 11501
631-981-2158
Fax: 631-747-6825
Occupational Fields: plumber, pipefitter

United Association of Journeymen and Apprentices of the Plumbing and Pipefitting Industry, Local #201
PO Box 3429
Poughkeepsie, NY 12603
914-229-0280
Occupational Fields: plumber, pipefitter

United Association of Journeymen and Apprentices of the Plumbing and Pipefitting Industry, Local #267
150 Midler Park Drive
Syracuse, NY 13206
315-437-7397
Fax: 315-437-2951
Occupational Fields: plumber, pipefitter

United Association of Journeymen and Apprentices of the Plumbing and Pipefitting Industry, Local #703
198 Tim Tam Terrace
Seneca, NY 14224
716-675-6931
Occupational Fields: plumber, pipefitter

United Association of Journeymen and Apprentices of the Plumbing and Pipefitting Industry, Local #773
30 Bluebird Road
South Glens Falls, NY 12803
518-792-9157
Fax: 518-792-4876
larryb@lu773.org
http://www.lu773.org
Occupational Fields: plumber, pipefitter

NORTH CAROLINA
American Tobacco Company
301 North Scales Street
Reidsville, NC 27320
910-349-6261
Occupational Fields: pipefitter

United Association of Journeymen and Apprentices of the Plumbing and Pipefitting Industry, Local #96
PO Box 560098
Charlotte, NC 28256
704-597-1615
Fax: 704-598-1788
Occupational Fields: plumber, pipefitter

Worsham Sprinkler Company Inc.
3380 Green Park Circle
Charlotte, NC 28217
704-319-5060
Fax: 704-319-5061
http://www.vasc.com/worsham.htm
Occupational Fields: sprinkler fitter, pipefitter

NORTH DAKOTA
United Association of Journeymen and Apprentices of the Plumbing and Pipefitting Industry, Local #300
3002 First Avenue, North
Fargo, ND 58102
701-237-5968
Fax: 701-235-2341
Occupational Fields: plumber, pipefitter

United Association of Journeymen and Apprentices of the Plumbing and Pipefitting Industry, Local #300
312 31st Avenue, Southwest
Minot, ND 58701
701-838-2654
Fax: 701-852-5570
Occupational Fields: plumber, pipefitter

United Association of Journeymen and Apprentices of the Plumbing and Pipefitting Industry, Local #795
2901 Twin City Drive, Suite 101
Mandan, ND 58554
701-663-0999
Fax: 701-663-7020
Occupational Fields: plumber, steamfitter

OHIO

APHC Plumbers
6200 Harbour Pointe, #302
Columbus, OH 43231-7718
614-891-0023
Occupational Fields: plumber

Jefferson Smurfit Corporation
407 Charles Street
Middletown, OH 45042
513-424-4200
Occupational Fields: pipefitter

United Association of Journeymen and Apprentices of the Plumbing and Pipefitting Industry, Local #42
187 Woodlawn Avenue
Norwalk, OH 44857
419-668-7305
Fax: 419-663-7301
Local42jatc@aol.com
http://pipetradeslu42.com
Occupational Fields: plumber, pipefitter

United Association of Journeymen and Apprentices of the Plumbing and Pipefitting Industry, Local #55
980 Keynote Circle
Brooklyn Heights, OH 44131
216-459-0099
Fax: 216-459-0085
Occupational Fields: plumber, pipefitter

United Association of Journeymen and Apprentices of the Plumbing and Pipefitting Industry, Local #59
19 Knollcrest Drive, Suite A
Cincinnati, OH 45237
Occupational Fields: plumber, pipefitter

United Association of Journeymen and Apprentices of the Plumbing and Pipefitting Industry, Local #94
PO Box 80567
Canton, OH 44708-0363
330-478-1864
Fax: 330-478-1866
Occupational Fields: plumber, pipefitter

United Association of Journeymen and Apprentices of the Plumbing and Pipefitting Industry, Local #120
6305 Halle Drive
Cleveland, OH 44125-4680
216-447-3408
Fax: 216-524-2385
Occupational Fields: plumber, pipefitter

United Association of Journeymen and Apprentices of the Plumbing and Pipefitting Industry, Local #162
1200 East Second Street
Dayton, OH 45403
937-222-8747
Fax: 937-461-3529
Occupational Fields: plumber, pipefitter

United Association of Journeymen and Apprentices of the Plumbing and Pipefitting Industry, Local #168
201 Front Street
Marietta, OH 45750
Occupational Fields: plumber, pipefitter

United Association of Journeymen and Apprentices of the Plumbing and Pipefitting Industry, Local #189
1250 Kinnear Road
Columbus, OH 43212
614-486-2497
Fax: 614-486-2533
Occupational Fields: plumber, pipefitter

United Association of Journeymen and Apprentices of the Plumbing and Pipefitting Industry, Local #392
Joint Apprenticeship Training Office
1300 Century Circle North
Springdale, OH 45246
513-671-5282

http://www.local392.com
Occupational Fields: plumber, pipefitter

United Association of Journeymen and Apprentices of the Plumbing and Pipefitting Industry, Local #396
493 Bev Road
Youngstown, OH 44512
330-758-4596
Fax: 330-758-4598
Occupational Fields: plumber, pipefitter

United Association of Journeymen and Apprentices of the Plumbing and Pipefitting Industry, Local #490
Plumbers Building
339 South Fifth Street
Steubenville, OH 43952
614-282-1112
Fax: 614-282-0721
Occupational Fields: plumber, pipefitter

United Association of Journeymen and Apprentices of the Plumbing and Pipefitting Industry, Local #776
1300 Bowman Road
Lima, OH 45804
419-229-5176
Fax: 419-224-7552
Occupational Fields: plumber, pipefitter

OKLAHOMA

Eastern Oklahoma Building and Construction Trades
2651 East 21st Street, #405
Tulsa, OK 74114
918-742-3305
Occupational Fields: plumber, pipefitter, sprinkler fitter

United Association of Journeymen and Apprentices of the Plumbing and Pipefitting Industry, Local #205
6558 East 40th Street
Tulsa, OK 74145
918-622-4243
Fax: 918-622-6438
Occupational Fields: plumber, pipefitter

United Association of Journeymen and Apprentices of the Plumbing and Pipefitting Industry, Local #344
4335 Southwest 44th Street
Oklahoma City, OK 73119

405-682-4571
Fax: 405-682-1327
Occupational Fields: heating, ventilation, and air conditioning mechanic, pipefitter, plumber

United Association of Journeymen and Apprentices of the Plumbing and Pipefitting Industry, Local #351
100 North York Street
Muskogee, OK 74403
918-682-5596
Fax: 918-682-0269
Occupational Fields: plumber, pipefitter

United Association of Journeymen and Apprentices of the Plumbing and Pipefitting Industry, Local #397
128 Northeast DeBell Street
Bartlesville, OK 74006
Fax: 918-335-3411
Occupational Fields: plumber, pipefitter

United Association of Journeymen and Apprentices of the Plumbing and Pipefitting Industry, Local #767
PO Box 1778
Ponca City, OK 74602
405-765-3628
Fax: 405-765-7778
Occupational Fields: plumber, pipefitter

United Association of Journeymen and Apprentices of the Plumbing and Pipefitting Industry, Local #798
PO Box 470798
Tulsa, OK 74147-0798
918-622-1900
Fax: 918-627-9327
http://www.local798.org
Occupational Fields: plumber, pipefitter

OREGON

United Association of Journeymen and Apprentices of the Plumbing and Pipefitting Industry, Local #290
Southwest Washington Plumbers, Metal Trades, and Steamfitters
20210 Southwest Teton Avenue
Tualatin, OR 97062-8810
503-691-1997
Fax: 503-691-0626

http://www.ua290.org
Occupational Fields: plumber, pipefitter, steamfitter

PENNSYLVANIA

United Association of Journeymen and Apprentices of the Plumbing and Pipefitting Industry, Local #27
104 Montour West Industrial Boulevard
Coraopolis, PA 15108
412-922-2217
Occupational Fields: plumber, pipefitter

United Association of Journeymen and Apprentices of the Plumbing and Pipefitting Industry, Local #354
PO Drawer I
Youngwood, PA 15697
412-925-7238
Fax: 412-925-6904
Occupational Fields: plumber, pipefitter

United Association of Journeymen and Apprentices of the Plumbing and Pipefitting Industry, Local #420
14420 Townsend Road, Suite C
Philadelphia, PA 19154
267-350-2610
http://lu420.org
Occupational Fields: plumber, pipefitter

United Association of Journeymen and Apprentices of the Plumbing and Pipefitting Industry, Local #449
1517 Woodruff Street
Pittsburgh, PA 15220
412-381-1133
Fax: 412-381-7875
http://www.ua449.com
Occupational Fields: plumber, pipefitter

United Association of Journeymen and Apprentices of the Plumbing and Pipefitting Industry, Local #520
PO Box 6596
Harrisburg, PA 17112
717-652-3135
Fax: 717-541-8908
local520@local520.com
http://www.local520.com
Occupational Fields: plumber, pipefitter

United Association of Journeymen and Apprentices of the Plumbing and Pipefitting Industry, Local #524
711 Corey Street
Scranton, PA 18505
Occupational Fields: plumber, pipefitter

United Association of Journeymen and Apprentices of the Plumbing and Pipefitting Industry, Local #542, Sprinkler Fitters
PO Box 58161
Pittsburgh, PA 15209
412-822-8040
Fax: 412-931-6189
Occupational Fields: sprinkler fitter, pipefitter

United Association of Journeymen and Apprentices of the Plumbing and Pipefitting Industry, Local #690
2791 Southampton Road
Philadelphia, PA 19154
215-677-6900
Fax: 215-677-7102
Occupational Fields: plumber, pipefitter

United Association of Journeymen and Apprentices of the Plumbing and Pipefitting Industry, Local #692, Sprinkler Fitters
14002 McNulty Road
Philadelphia, PA 19154-3023
215-671-1692
Fax: 215-673-7468
http://www.sprinklerfitters692.org
Occupational Fields: sprinkler fitter, pipefitter

RHODE ISLAND

Grinnel Fire Protection Systems Co.
Sprinker Fitters Union, Local #676
1467 Elmwood Avenue
Cranston, RI 02910-3849
401-781-8220
Occupational Fields: sprinkler fitter, pipefitter

United Association of Journeymen and Apprentices of the Plumbing and Pipefitting Industry, Locals #28, #51, and #476
11 Hemingway Drive
East Providence, RI 02915
401-943-3033
Fax: 401-943-1710

http://www.ualocal51.com
Occupational Fields: pipefitter, steamfitter

SOUTH CAROLINA

United Association of Journeymen and Apprentices of the Plumbing and Pipefitting Industry, Local #227
201 Plumbers Road
Columbia, SC 29203
803-754-3511
Occupational Fields: plumber, pipefitter

United Association of Journeymen and Apprentices of the Plumbing and Pipefitting Industry, Local #470
2556 Oscar Johnson Drive
Charleston, SC 29405
Occupational Fields: plumber, pipefitter

SOUTH DAKOTA

United Association of Journeymen and Apprentices of the Plumbing and Pipefitting Industry, Local #587
Labor Temple
612 East 4th Street
Sioux Falls, SD 57103
605-334-8351
Occupational Fields: plumber, pipefitter

TENNESSEE

United Association of Journeymen and Apprentices of the Plumbing and Pipefitting Industry, Local #43
3009 Riverside Drive
Chattanooga, TN 37406
423-698-6991
Fax: 423-624-6091
local43@bellsouth.net
http://uatn.org/43/43.htm
Occupational Fields: plumber, pipefitter

United Association of Journeymen and Apprentices of the Plumbing and Pipefitting Industry, Local #102
1216 Broadway, NE
Knoxville, TN 37917
865-523-7413
Fax: 865-522-1222
paulalu102@inetmail.att.net
http://uatn.org/102/102.htm
Occupational Fields: plumber, pipefitter

United Association of Journeymen and Apprentices of the Plumbing and Pipefitting Industry, Local #407
154 Hollywood Drive
Jackson, TN 38301
901-427-6398
Occupational Fields: plumber, pipefitter

United Association of Journeymen and Apprentices of the Plumbing and Pipefitting Industry, Local #538
121 Spring Street
Johnson City, TN 37604
423-928-5751
Fax: 423-928-8209
rdl538@charter.net
http://uatn.org/538/538.htm
Occupational Fields: plumber, pipefitter

United Association of Journeymen and Apprentices of the Plumbing and Pipefitting Industry, Local #572
225 Ben Allen Road
Nashville, TN 37207
615-254-1104
Fax: 615-226-3642
union572@aol.com
http://uatn.org/572/572.htm
Occupational Fields: plumber, pipefitter

United Association of Journeymen and Apprentices of the Plumbing and Pipefitting Industry, Local #614
3746 Jackson Avenue
Memphis, TN 38108
901-386-8166
Fax: 901-386-7514
local614@bellsouth.net
http://uatn.org/614/614.htm
Occupational Fields: plumber, pipefitter

United Association of Journeymen and Apprentices of the Plumbing and Pipefitting Industry, Local #702
PO Box 78487
Nashville, TN 37207
615-734-1772
Occupational Fields: plumber, pipefitter

United Association of Journeymen and Apprentices of the Plumbing and Pipefitting Industry, Local #718
1172 Swan Pond Circle
Harriman, TN 37748
423-590-1044
orglu614@bellsouth.net

http://uatn.org/718/718.htm
Occupational Fields: plumber, pipefitter

United Association of Journeymen and Apprentices of the Plumbing and Pipefitting Industry, Local #854
12501 Old Friendship Lane
Finger, TN 38334
Occupational Fields: plumber, pipefitter

TEXAS
Association of Plumbing, Heating and Cooling Contractors of Texas
505 East Huntland Drive, Suite 170
Austin, TX 78752
512-454-3445
Fax: 512-454-4191
http://www.phcc-tx.org/home.htm
Occupational Fields: plumber

Beaumont Area Pipefitters
PO Box 3430
Beaumont, TX 77704
409-727-1686
Occupational Fields: pipefitter

Plumbers and Pipefitters
6220 Anglin Drive
Fort Worth, TX 76119
817-534-9690
Occupational Fields: plumber, pipefitter

Plumbers Training Center
PO Box 8653
Houston, TX 77249-8653
713-861-3202
Occupational Fields: plumber

Plumbers Union, Local #68
PO Box 3042
Beaumont, TX 77704
409-842-3680
Occupational Fields: plumber

Texas Air Conditioning Contractors Association
13706 Research Boulevard, Suite 109
Austin, TX 78750
512-320-0616
Fax: 512-320-0952
http://www.tacca.org

Occupational Fields: heating, ventilation, and air conditioning mechanic

Texas Fire Sprinkler Contractors Association
PO Box 5186
Kingwood, TX 77325-5186
281-361-8069
Fax: 281-360-6732
info@txfsca.org
http://www.txfsca.org
Occupational Fields: sprinkler fitter, fire protection system contractor

United Association of Journeymen and Apprentices of the Plumbing and Pipefitting Industry, Local #68
PO Box 8746
Houston, TX 77249
713-869-3592
Fax: 713-869-3671
Occupational Fields: plumber, pipefitter

United Association of Journeymen and Apprentices of the Plumbing and Pipefitting Industry, Local #100
3629 West Miller Road
Garland, TX 75041
214-341-8606
Fax: 214-341-2223
Occupational Fields: plumber, pipefitter

United Association of Journeymen and Apprentices of the Plumbing and Pipefitting Industry, Local #142
231 North Center Street
San Antonio, TX 78202
210-226-1244
Fax: 210-226-2596
Occupational Fields: plumber, pipefitter

United Association of Journeymen and Apprentices of the Plumbing and Pipefitting Industry, Local #146
2640 East Lancaster Street
Fort Worth, TX 76103
817-536-1979
Fax: 817-536-1970
Occupational Fields: plumber, pipefitter

United Association of Journeymen and Apprentices of the Plumbing and Pipefitting Industry, Local #195
Route Four, Box 88
Beaumont, TX 77705
409-722-0434

Fax: 409-722-1970
Occupational Fields: plumber, pipefitter

United Association of Journeymen and Apprentices of the Plumbing and Pipefitting Industry, Local #196
1505 West Seventh Avenue
Amarillo, TX 79101
806-374-2895
Fax: 806-374-4437
Occupational Fields: plumber, pipefitter

United Association of Journeymen and Apprentices of the Plumbing and Pipefitting Industry, Local #211
2535 Old Galveston Road
PO Box 5026
Houston, TX 77017
713-644-5521
Fax: 713-644-3264
http://pflocal211.com
Occupational Fields: pipefitter

United Association of Journeymen and Apprentices of the Plumbing and Pipefitting Industry, Local #231
5519 East Paisano Drive
El Paso, TX 79905
915-772-5751
Occupational Fields: plumber, pipefitter

United Association of Journeymen and Apprentices of the Plumbing and Pipefitting Industry, Local #237
411 Spruce Street
Texarkana, TX 75501
903-792-1441
Occupational Fields: plumber, pipefitter

United Association of Journeymen and Apprentices of the Plumbing and Pipefitting Industry, Local #286
East Austin Station
PO Box 6357
Austin, TX 78762
512-385-0082
Fax: 512-385-0232
info@local286.org
http://www.local286.org
Occupational Fields: plumber, pipefitter

United Association of Journeymen and Apprentices of the Plumbing and Pipefitting Industry, Local #389
8832 Seymour Highway
Wichita Falls, TX 76308

817-692-9731
Occupational Fields: plumber, pipefitter

United Association of Journeymen and Apprentices of the Plumbing and Pipefitting Industry, Local #390
PO Box 696
Clute, TX 77531
409-238-4956
Occupational Fields: plumber, pipefitter

United Association of Journeymen and Apprentices of the Plumbing and Pipefitting Industry, Local #529
702 1/2 Franklin Avenue
Waco, TX 76701
817-754-3471
Occupational Fields: plumber, pipefitter

United Association of Journeymen and Apprentices of the Plumbing and Pipefitting Industry, Local #629
2002 Avenue J
Lubbock, TX 79405
806-744-3835
Occupational Fields: plumber, pipefitter

United Association of Journeymen and Apprentices of the Plumbing and Pipefitting Industry, Local #654
1717 Butternut Street
Abilene, TX 79602
915-673-5511
Fax: 915-677-0652
Occupational Fields: plumber, pipefitter

United Association of Journeymen and Apprentices of the Plumbing and Pipefitting Industry, Local #823
2809 South Highway 83
Harlingen, TX 78550-7613
800-442-5210
Fax: 210-428-2377
Occupational Fields: plumber, pipefitter

UTAH
United Association of Journeymen and Apprentices of the Plumbing and Pipefitting Industry
900 North 400 West, Building #4
Salt Lake City, UT 84054
801-295-6198
Occupational Fields: plumber, pipefitter

United Association of Journeymen and Apprentices of the Plumbing and Pipefitting Industry, Locals #19 and #57
2261 South Redwood Road, Suite 5
Salt Lake City, UT 84119
801-973-1183
Fax: 801-973-2327
info@UA19.com
http://www.ua19.com
Occupational Fields: plumber, pipefitter

United Association of Journeymen and Apprentices of the Plumbing and Pipefitting Industry, Local #348
1336 Washington Boulevard
Ogden, UT 84404
801-392-6185
Fax: 801-392-6188
Occupational Fields: plumber, pipefitter

VERMONT
United Association of Journeymen and Apprentices of the Plumbing and Pipefitting Industry, Local #693
Three Gregory Drive
South Burlington, VT 05403-6061
802-864-4042
Fax: 802-862-6379
http://www.ualocal693.org
Occupational Fields: plumber, pipefitter

VIRGINIA
District of Columbia Department of Corrections
PO Box 229
Lorton, VA 22199
202-673-2300, x115
Occupational Fields: plumber

Newport News Shipbuilding
Apprentice School Admissions Office
4101 Washington Avenue
Newport News, VA 23607-2770
757-380-3809
Fax: 757-688-0305
apprenticeschool@ngc.com
http://www.apprenticeschool.com/index.asp
Occupational Fields: heating, ventilation, and air conditioning mechanic, maintenance pipefitter, pipefitter

Sheet Metal Workers International Association and Sheet Metal and Air Conditioning Contractors' National Association
601 North Fairfax Street, Suite 240
Alexandria, VA 22314
703-739-7200
Fax: 703-683-7461
http://www.smwia.org
Occupational Fields: heating, ventilation, and air conditioning mechanic

United Association of Journeymen and Apprentices of the Plumbing and Pipefitting Industry, Local #110
520 Naval Base Road
Norfolk, VA 23505
804-587-4768
Fax: 804-588-7140
Occupational Fields: plumber, pipefitter

United Association of Journeymen and Apprentices of the Plumbing and Pipefitting Industry, Local #272
5304 South Palmyra Drive
Virginia Beach, VA 23462
804-490-2301
Occupational Fields: plumber, pipefitter

United Association of Journeymen and Apprentices of the Plumbing and Pipefitting Industry, Local #491
1606 Orange Avenue, NW
Roanoke, VA 24017
540-345-7611
Fax: 540-343-6090
Occupational Fields: plumber, pipefitter

United Association of Journeymen and Apprentices of the Plumbing and Pipefitting Industry, Local #540
7812 Warwick Boulevard
Newport News, VA 23607
757-247-9089
Fax: 757-247-5709
Occupational Fields: plumber, pipefitter

United Association of Journeymen and Apprentices of the Plumbing and Pipefitting Industry, Local #851
3014 Grace Street
Hopewell, VA 23860
804-541-5583
Occupational Fields: plumber, pipefitter

WASHINGTON

Associated Builders and Contractors, Inland Pacific Chapter

1404 North Thor Court
Spokane, WA 99220
509-534-0826
Fax: 509-535-9967
ipcabc@qwest.net
http://www.ipcabc.org
Occupational Fields: heating, ventilation, and air conditioning mechanic, pipefitter, steamfitter, plumber

Association of Western Pulp and Paper Workers, Local #5

514 Northeast Dallas
Camas, WA 98607
360-834-2232
Fax: 360-834-9783
http://www.awppw.com/portland.htm
Occupational Fields: plumber, pipefitter, steamfitter

Batelle-Northwest

Battelle PNNL, P7-08
PO Box 999
Richland, WA 99352
Occupational Fields: heating, ventilation, and air conditioning mechanic, pipefitter, steamfitter, plumber

Boise Cascade

PO Box 500
Wallula, WA 99363
509-545-3326
Fax: 509-545-3282
Occupational Fields: plumber, pipefitter, steamfitter

Ellensburg, City of

420 North Pearl Street
Ellensburg, WA 98926
509-962-7229
Fax: 509-248-3452
http://www.ci.ellensburg.wa.us
Occupational Fields: plumber, pipefitter, steamfitter

Fluor Daniel Hanford

M/S R2-88
PO Box 1500
Richland, WA 99352-1505
509-376-1523
Occupational Fields: plumber, pipefitter, steamfitter

Port Townsend Paper Corporation

PO Box 3170
Port Townsend, WA 98368
360-379-2125
Fax: 360-385-0355
human_resource@ptpc.com
http://www.ptpc.com
Occupational Fields: plumber, pipefitter, steamfitter

Seattle Area Pipe Trades

595 Monster Rd. SW, Suite 100
Renton, WA 98055-2937
425-271-5900
Fax: 425-271-4985
http://www.seattlepipetrades.org
Occupational Fields: plumber, pipefitter, steamfitter

Sprinkler Fitters of Advanced Fire Protection Inc.

PO Box 1543
Woodinville, WA 98072
425-483-5657
Fax: 425-483-5077
Occupational Fields: pipefitter, spinklerfitter

Tacoma, City of

Water Department
3628 South 35th Street
Tacoma, WA 98409-3115
253-502-8393
Fax: 253-502-8386
Occupational Fields: plumber, pipefitter, steamfitter

United Association of Journeymen and Apprentices of the Plumbing and Pipefitting Industry, Local #32

Seattle Area Plumbers, Housing Plumbers, Pipefitters, Marine Pipefitters, and Refrigeration Mechanics
595 Monster Road, SW, Suite 213
Renton, WA 98055
425-277-6680
Fax: 425-277-7370
http://www.ualocal32.com
Occupational Fields: heating, ventilation, and air conditioning mechanic, pipefitter, steamfitter, plumber

United Association of Journeymen and Apprentices of the Plumbing and Pipefitting Industry, Local #44

Inland Empire Plumbers, Residential Plumbers, Steamfitters, and Refrigeration Fitters
10 West Second Avenue
Spokane, WA 99204

509-624-5258
Fax: 509-624-5101
Occupational Fields: heating, ventilation, and air conditioning mechanic, residential plumber, steamfitter, plumber

United Association of Journeymen and Apprentices of the Plumbing and Pipefitting Industry, Local #82
Tacoma Area Plumbers and Steamfitters
2725 Pacific Avenue
Tacoma, WA 98402
253-272-7173
Fax: 253-572-1474
Occupational Fields: plumber, steamfitter

United Association of Journeymen and Apprentices of the Plumbing and Pipefitting Industry, Local #265, Plumbers and Steamfitters
5205 South Second Avenue
Everett, WA 98203
Occupational Fields: heating, ventilation, and air conditioning mechanic, pipefitter, steamfitter, plumber

United Association of Journeymen and Apprentices of the Plumbing and Pipefitting Industry, Local #598
Eastern Washington and Northeast Oregon Plumbers, Steamfitters, and Refrigeration Fitters
1328 Road 28
Pasco, WA 99301
509-547-6480
Fax: 509-545-3035
http://www.ua598.com/index.htm
Occupational Fields: heating, ventilation, and air conditioning mechanic, pipefitter, steamfitter, plumber

United Association of Journeymen and Apprentices of the Plumbing and Pipefitting Industry, Local #631, Plumbers and Steamfitters
1309 Highland Avenue
Bremerton, WA 98337-0114
360-377-1118
Fax: 360-373-2731
Occupational Fields: plumber, pipefitter, steamfitter

United Association of Journeymen and Apprentices of the Plumbing and Pipefitting Industry, Local #699, Sprinkler Fitters
2800 First Avenue, Room 111
Seattle, WA 98121

206-441-0737
Fax: 206-441-2939
Occupational Fields: sprinkler fitter, pipefitter

WEST VIRGINIA

United Association of Journeymen and Apprentices of the Plumbing and Pipefitting Industry, Local #83
177 29th Street
Wheeling, WV 26003
304-233-4445
Occupational Fields: plumber, pipefitter

United Association of Journeymen and Apprentices of the Plumbing and Pipefitting Industry, Local #152
100 Richard Avenue
Morgantown, WV 26505
304-292-8818
Fax: 304-292-7836
Occupational Fields: plumber, pipefitter

United Association of Journeymen and Apprentices of the Plumbing and Pipefitting Industry, Local #521
2584 Guyan Avenue
Huntington, WV 25703
304-523-8489
Fax: 304-529-3023
Occupational Fields: plumber, pipefitter

United Association of Journeymen and Apprentices of the Plumbing and Pipefitting Industry, Local #565
Cedar Grove Road
Route Five, Box 131
Parkersburg, WV 26101
304-485-5202
Fax: 304-485-5369
Occupational Fields: plumber, pipefitter

United Association of Journeymen and Apprentices of the Plumbing and Pipefitting Industry, Local #625
3601 James Street
Charleston, WV 25312
304-744-3881
Fax: 304-744-6313
http://ualocal625.com
Occupational Fields: plumber, pipefitter

WISCONSIN

Algoma Hardwoods Inc.
1001 Perry Street
Algoma, WI 54201-1698
920-487-5221
Fax: 920-487-3636
Occupational Fields: pipefitter, steamfitter

Appleton
825 East Wisconsin Avenue
Appleton, WI 54113-0129
920-734-9841
http://www.appletonideas.com
Occupational Fields: pipefitter

Bernie J. Buchner Inc.
20 Copeland Avenue
La Crosse, WI 54603
608-784-9000
Occupational Fields: plumber, steamfitter

Consolidated Papers Inc.
231 First Avenue, North
Wisconsin Rapids, WI 54495
715-442-3111
Occupational Fields: pipefitter

Fox River Paper Company
100 West Lawrence Street
Appleton, WI 54911
414-733-7341
Fax: 414-738-2975
http://www.foxriverpaper.com
Occupational Fields: pipefitter

Golden Books Publishing Company
1220 Mound Avenue
Racine, WI 53404
414-633-2431
Occupational Fields: pipefitter

James River Paper Company Inc.
2301 Lake Shore Drive, East
Ashland, WI 54806-2333
715-682-6666
Fax: 715-682-9284
Occupational Fields: pipefitter

P.H. Glatfelter Company
225 West Wisconsin Avenue
Neenah, WI 54956

414-727-2400
Occupational Fields: pipefitter

Southwest Wisconsin Technical College
Highway 18 East
Route 1, Box 500
Fennimore, WI 53809
608-822-3262
Fax: 608-822-6019
http://www.witechcolleges.com/swtc.htm
Occupational Fields: plumber

United Association of Journeymen and Apprentices of the Plumbing and Pipefitting Industry, Local #31
Labor Temple
1920 Ward Avenue, Suite Five
La Crosse, WI 54601
608-788-0970
Fax: 608-788-7353
Occupational Fields: plumber, pipefitter

United Association of Journeymen and Apprentices of the Plumbing and Pipefitting Industry, Local #75
11175 West Parkland Avenue
Milwaukee, WI 53224
414-359-1310
Fax: 414-359-1323
http://www.careernet.org/plumbing.htm
Occupational Fields: plumber

United Association of Journeymen and Apprentices of the Plumbing and Pipefitting Industry, Local #118
3030 39th Avenue
Kenosha, WI 53144
262-654-3815
Fax: 414-654-3199
http://www.wipipetrades.org/118.html
Occupational Fields: plumber, pipefitter

United Association of Journeymen and Apprentices of the Plumbing and Pipefitting Industry, Local #167
Labor Temple
1602 South Park Street
Madison, WI 53715
608-255-8111
Occupational Fields: plumber, pipefitter

United Association of Journeymen and Apprentices of the Plumbing and Pipefitting Industry, Local #183
633 South Hawley Road #103
Milwaukee, WI 53214

414-257-3159
Fax: 414-257-3168
http://www.wipipetrades.org/183.html
Occupational Fields: plumber, pipefitter, sprinkler fitter

United Association of Journeymen and Apprentices of the Plumbing and Pipefitting Industry, Local #206
460 West 11th Street
Fond Du Lac, WI 54935
414-921-6490
Occupational Fields: plumber, pipefitter

United Association of Journeymen and Apprentices of the Plumbing and Pipefitting Industry, Local #214
PO Box 799
Janesville, WI 53547
608-752-3738
Fax: 608-756-0244
Occupational Fields: plumber, pipefitter

United Association of Journeymen and Apprentices of the Plumbing and Pipefitting Industry, Local #298
1417 Cedar Street
Green Bay, WI 54302-1899
414-432-1015
Fax: 414-432-1153
Occupational Fields: plumber, pipefitter

United Association of Journeymen and Apprentices of the Plumbing and Pipefitting Industry, Local #385
2233 Birch Street
Eau Claire, WI 54703
715-832-1014
Fax: 715-835-7788
Occupational Fields: plumber, pipefitter

United Association of Journeymen and Apprentices of the Plumbing and Pipefitting Industry, Local #394
1214 Ann Street
Madison, WI 53713
608-256-6868
Fax: 608-256-6869
Occupational Fields: steamfitter, pipefitter, plumber

United Association of Journeymen and Apprentices of the Plumbing and Pipefitting Industry, Local #458
PO Box 1514
Appleton, WI 54913
414-739-2053
Fax: 414-739-1333
Occupational Fields: plumber, pipefitter

United Association of Journeymen and Apprentices of the Plumbing and Pipefitting Industry, Local #557
2307 Third Street
Wausau, WI 54403
715-842-3012
Fax: 715-842-8502
Occupational Fields: plumber, pipefitter

United Association of Journeymen and Apprentices of the Plumbing and Pipefitting Industry, Local #601
Milwaukee Area Steamfitter/Refrigeration Union
3300 South 103rd Street
Milwaukee, WI 53227
414-543-0601
Fax: 414-543-7721
http://www.wipipetrades.org/601.html
Occupational Fields: heating, ventilation, and air conditioning mechanic, steamfitter

United Association of Journeymen and Apprentices of the Plumbing and Pipefitting Industry, Local #778
6797 Highway 34
Rudolph, WI 54475-9301
715-435-3810
Fax: 715-435-3395
Occupational Fields: plumber, pipefitter

United Association of Journeymen and Apprentices of the Plumbing and Pipefitting Industry, Local #786
North 1802 Shore Drive
Marinette, WI 54143
715-735-6164
Fax: 715-735-6102
Occupational Fields: plumber, pipefitter

United Association of Journeymen and Apprentices of the Plumbing and Pipefitting Industry, Local #807
7020 Second Avenue, North
Rudolph, WI 54475
715-435-3586
Occupational Fields: pipefitter

U.S. Paper Mills Corporation
824 Fort Howard Avenue
De Pere, WI 54115
414-336-4229
Occupational Fields: pipefitter

Weyerhaeuser Company
118 South Palmetto Avenue
Marshfield, WI 54449

715-384-2141
Occupational Fields: pipefitter

Wisconsin Pipe Trades
Merrill, WI 54452-0827
715-539-1114
uajay@dwave.net
www.wipipetrades.org
Occupational Fields: pipefitter, plumber

WYOMING

United Association of Journeymen and Apprentices of the Plumbing and Pipefitting Industry, Locals #192, #193, and #199
PO Box 5040
Cheyenne, WY 82003
307-634-5837
Fax: 307-778-2718
Occupational Fields: plumber, pipefitter

Wyoming Contractors Association
McMurry Regional Training Center
2200 Bryan Stock Trail
Cheyenne, WY 82605
307-632-0573
http://www.wcagc.org
Occupational Fields: plumber

CANADA
ALBERTA
United Association, Local #488
United Association of Plumbers & Pipefitters
118 Avenue, Main Floor
Edmonton, AB T5V 1M6
780-452-7080
Fax: 780-452-1291
info@local488.com
http://www.local488.ca
Occupational Fields: plumber, pipefitter, steamfitter

United Association of Plumbers & Pipefitters, Local #496
5649 Burbank Road S.E.
Calgary, AB T2H 125
403-252-1166 ext. 225
Fax: 403-252-4591
kjones@local496.ca
http://local496.ca
Occupational Fields: plumber, pipefitter, steamfitter

BRITISH COLUMBIA
Pacific Vocational College
4064 McConnell Drive
Burnaby, BC V5A 3A8
604-421-5255
Fax: 604-421-7445
pvc@telus.net
http://www.pacificvocationalcollege.ca
Occupational Fields: plumber, pipefitter, steamfitter

United Association, Local Union #324
Plumbers & Steamfitters Union
919 Esquimalt
Victoria, BC V9A 3M7
250-382-0415
ualocal324@shaw.ca
http://www.ualocal324.com
Occupational Fields: plumber, pipefitter, steamfitter

MANITOBA
United Association, Local #254
Plumbers & Steamfitters Union
34 Higgins Avenue
Winnipeg, MB R3B 0A5
204-947-0497
Fax: 204-947-1512
http://www.ualocal254.ca
Occupational Fields: plumber, pipefitter, steamfitter

NEW BRUNSWICK
Department of Training and Employment Development
Apprenticeship and Occupational Certification
PO Box 6000
Chestnut Complex
Fredericton, NB E3B 5H1
506-453-2260
Fax: 506-453-5317
aoc-acp@gnb.ca
Occupational Fields: plumber, pipefitter

ONTARIO
St. Clair College
Windsor Campus
2000 Talbot Road West,
Windsor, ON N9A 6S4
519-966-1656
Fax: 519-972-3811

http://www.stclaircollege.ca/programs/apprenticeship/
   home_b.html
Occupational Fields: plumber, pipefitter, steamfitter

United Association, Local #46
Plumbers & Steamfitters Union
936 Warden Avenue
Scarborough, ON M1L 4C6
416-759-9351
Fax: 416-759-8658
office@ualocal46.org
http://www.ualocal46.org
Occupational Fields: plumber, pipefitter, steamfitter

United Association Local #787
United Association of Plumbers & Pipefitters
419 Deerhurst Drive
Brampton, ON L6T 5K3
905-790-1019
Fax: 905-790-1022
http://www.ualocal787.org
Occupational Fields: plumber, pipefitter, steamfitter

QUEBEC
United Association Plumbers & Pipefitters, Local #500
United Association of Plumbers & Pipefitters
1299, des Champs-Élysées, Bureau 207
Chicoutimi, QC G7H 6P3
418-543-9045
Fax: 418-543-9073
http://membres.lycos.fr/local500/
Occupational Fields: plumber, pipefitter, steamfitter

PLASTERERS

RELATED SECTIONS: *bricklayers, carpenters, drywallers and lathers, masons, painters and paperhangers, tile setters*

Plasterers finish walls, ceilings, and partitions with plaster, a pasty material that hardens as it dries. Plasterers also apply plaster veneer over drywall, apply stucco or insulation to exterior walls, and cast ornamental designs in plaster. Plaster finishes are particularly popular in the warmer climates of the Southwest, California, and Florida.

Plaster is fire resistant, helps soundproof rooms, and provides a smooth surface that can be painted or wallpapered. Sometimes the plaster is applied in swirls to create a decorative pattern. It can be applied to various surfaces, including wood, concrete, cinder blocks, and lath. For indoor projects, depending on the type of underlying material, the worker applies various base coats of gypsum plaster with a trowel or by spraying, then applies a finish mixture of lime, plaster of Paris, and water. For outdoor projects the worker applies stucco (a mixture of Portland cement, sand, and lime) over concrete, cement, masonry, or lath. Rock chips may be embedded in the finish for a decorative effect.

Ornamental plastering involves a great deal of skill and creativity. Complex designs for walls and ceilings are sometimes created by pouring or spraying plaster into molds, allowing the plaster to set, and applying it in accordance with blueprints drawn up by architects.

The work is usually done indoors, but some projects involve the application of stucco or insulation to exterior walls. The workers must sometimes climb ladders and scaffolds. The job requires physical stamina, standing, lifting, stretching, and bending. Workers are exposed to dust and dirt, which can irritate the lungs, eyes, and skin. Plasterers work with various tools, including trowels, straightedges, brushes, mixing machines, and pumps. Exterior projects are sometimes delayed because of cold or wet weather, but indoor projects offer steady employment.

Most plasterers are employed by construction companies, but about a third are self-employed. Many plasterers belong to unions, such as the Operative Plasterers and Cement Masons International Association of the United States and Canada or the International Union of Bricklayers and Allied Craftsmen.

Unions and other organizations in the building and construction trades offer apprenticeship training for plasterers. Apprenticeship is the recommended way to enter this trade, but less formal, on-the-job training is also available. Apprentices work under the supervision of experienced workers. They participate in on-the-job training and at least 144 hours of classroom studies annually.

Typically, the course of study runs for two to three years and includes instruction in mathematics, cost estimating, ornamental designs, drafting, and blueprint reading.

In general an applicant should

- apply in person
- be at least 17 years old
- be a high school graduate or hold a GED certificate
- be in good physical condition
- have manual dexterity

APPRENTICESHIP SALARIES

Between $7 and $15 an hour, or about half the rate paid to experienced workers. Experienced apprentices earn between $14 and $26 an hour.

POSTAPPRENTICESHIP SALARIES

About $15 an hour, up to $33 an hour. Earnings vary, depending on geographic location and union membership.

JOB OUTLOOK

Growth in the occupation will be about average through 2012 but job prospects are expected to be good, especially in the South and Southwest. The introduction of drywall, which is easier and cheaper to install, cut into the plastering trade for some years, but new plastering techniques and materials have begun to make plastering an attractive option again. Plaster is seen as a durable, attractive, affordable finish that provides some degree of fireproofing. Plasterers are also needed to repair plaster finishes in older buildings and to craft curved surfaces and other effects that are not possible with drywall.

For more information on apprenticeships for plasterers, contact local job centers, your state bureau of apprenticeship training, or the national organizations and individual programs listed below.

NATIONAL PROGRAMS
National Plastering Industry
1029 Vermont Avenue, NW, #1000
Washington, DC 20005-3517

202-347-2500
Occupational Fields: plasterer

APPRENTICESHIP PROFILE
Plasterers and Cement Masons Union
Apprenticeship Program
825 East Eighth Avenue
Anchorage, AK 99501
907-272-5113
opcm867@alaska.com

General Nature of the Job

Plasterers apply plaster to building exteriors and interior walls and ceilings for insulation, fireproofing, and durability. Exterior work consists primarily of stucco, a combination of cement and sand. Common tools of the plasterer include a trowel and a hawk—a flat, handled tool used to lay on plaster. Plasterers also mix plaster, or mud, hang insulating foam boards, and reinforce walls with wire mesh. Decorative plasterwork is growing in popularity, and some plasterers use their creativity for ornamental finishes.

Plasterers work on their feet all day, either on the ground or up on a scaffold, so it's important to have physical stamina. Count on having a sore neck at times from working overhead on ceilings. Hand coordination doesn't hurt, especially when you're troweling on a finish coat and it has to be perfect. Basic math skills come in handy when taking measurements and calculating plaster amounts. Finally, patience is critical—it takes a while to master the hand skills of using a trowel and hawk.

The apprenticeship program through the Plasterers and Cement Masons Union in Anchorage, Alaska, requires 1,000 work hours per year for a total of 4,000 hours, or four years. Apprentices attend school for three weeks each year to learn the basics, such as proper tool usage or techniques for mixing plaster.

Typical Day

Scott Kinneen's workday commences at 7:00 A.M. He mixes up a few buckets of mud and gets things set up. His partner takes wall measurements while Scott cuts foam. He applies plaster to the backside of the foam board, and then he and his partner hang it. If they are working on a new building, there is no stucco to adhere the foam to, so they use screws to attach the foam to the plywood. Scott and his partner cut and hang foam for the entire day.

When the task of hanging the foam is complete, Scott rasps, or scrapes, sharp edges to smooth out the surface.

He and his partner then apply plaster to the face of the foam, hang wire mesh on it, and then trowel plaster over the mesh. The following day, when the plaster is dry, Scott again rasps off the rough edges and is ready to apply the finish coat. Because he will trowel on the finish coat, he must first use a float—a rubber tool—to even out the surface. If they were to spray on the finish coat, they would need to paint the surface first. Then, using a handheld hopper, Scott would spray on the finish.

Scott finds finish work with hand tools the most challenging aspect of plasterwork. He says, "it takes a while to catch on, and when you're an apprentice, you don't know how to do it and you get really frustrated." Because some plastered exteriors are not painted, a botched job is easy to detect, even by an unskilled eye; there may be lumps or marks that don't belong on the smooth surface. Scott states, "it has to be perfect. All this work is mostly exterior, and that is the finish, so you have to do a good job."

Scott enjoys working as a plasterer, and now that he's acquired the hand skills, the only complaint he has is that plasterwork can sometimes be too hard on the body. On one project, Scott worked on a stucco ceiling and was always looking up while standing on a scaffold. Scott recalls, "stucco is cement and sand, so it's heavy. You just get worn out." There are layoffs between jobs, and you're not going to keep your clothes clean as a plasterer, but this doesn't bother Scott.

Path to Becoming an Apprentice

Scott knew nothing about plasterwork when he became an apprentice immediately after graduating from high school. Scott had worked during the summers as a commercial fisherman and wasn't looking forward to another summer on a boat, so when he heard nine Alaskan Native plasterer apprentices were needed to work on a new medical center, he thought he'd try it out. Scott has no regrets. "After doing that job for about two years and going to class, I figured that's what I wanted to do. I liked it."

Scott believes his carpentry class in high school taught him some fundamentals, such as taking measurements and working with tools, but because plasterwork is unique, he feels he has had to learn from the ground up. Scott enjoys working outdoors and can't imagine staying in an office all day, so that may have steered him toward plasterwork as well.

Salary Range

Plasterer apprentices in Anchorage start at 60 percent of journeyman rate. After logging 1000 on-the-job hours, the apprentice earns 70 percent of journeyman rate. The apprentice earns an additional 10 percent every 1000 hours until graduation, when the apprentice becomes a journeyman and receives 100 percent compensation, which is $30 an hour. Apprentices also receive full benefits.

Anchorage is currently experiencing growth, and Scott feels the job outlook is excellent. He says, "there's a lot of work coming up, but in the future, living in Alaska, I don't know what's going to happen." Scott's jobs have mostly been on new buildings, but there will always be remodel jobs or repair jobs on cracked stucco. If Scott decides to leave Alaska, there is plenty of plasterwork in the Southwest, where residential stucco buildings are abundant.

Advice

Scott emphasizes the importance of dedication when it comes to plasterwork. Scott is the sole plasterer apprentice in Alaska—the eight apprentices he began the program with dropped out, which Scott doesn't understand because he enjoys the work. He suggests, "I would say you could go talk to some contractors and find out what's going on around town and watch what they do. See if that's what you want to do. It's a big waste to get in the apprenticeship program and try it then drop out."

Future Goals

After Scott receives his journeyman card, he plans to work out of state for a few years, then return to Anchorage and start a plastering business. Scott asserts, "that's possible. I've talked about that with a partner, and we're going to do that." He hopes to work in all facets of plasterwork, including commercial and residential projects. If self-employment doesn't suit Scott, he can also advance into management or supervision for other contractors.

ALASKA
Plasterers and Cement Masons Union
Apprenticeship Program
825 East Eighth Avenue
Anchorage, AK 99501
907-272-5113
opcm867@alaska.com
Occupational Fields: plasterer

ARIZONA
Arizona Plasterers and Cement Masons
1437 East McDowell Road
Phoenix, AZ 85006
602-258-8148
Occupational Fields: plasterer, cement mason

Association of Wall and Ceiling Industries
PO Box 27693
Tempe, AZ 85285
602-802-0602
Occupational Fields: plasterer, drywaller, lather, taper, acoustical carpenter

CALIFORNIA
Northern California Plasterers
1555 Overland Court
West Sacramento, CA 95619
916-371-7640
Fax: 916-371-7251
Occupational Fields: plasterer

Plasterers and Cement Masons Union
818 Wall Street
Chico, CA 95928
916-342-7872
Occupational Fields: plasterer, cement mason

Plasterers and Cement Masons Union
26 Bernard Street
Bakersfield, CA 93305-3493
805-323-6018
Occupational Fields: plasterer

Plasterers Union, Local #188
4831 East Shields Avenue
Fresno, CA 93726-6437
209-251-8259
Occupational Fields: plasterer

Plasterers Union, Local #295
1555 Overland Court
Sacramento, CA 95691-3490
916-371-7640
Occupational Fields: plasterer

Southern California Plastering Institute
1610 West Holt Avenue, Suite B
Pomona, CA 91768
909-865-1773
Fax: 909-865-0873
Occupational Fields: plasterer

DISTRICT OF COLUMBIA
National Plastering Industry
1029 Vermont Avenue, NW, #1000
Washington, DC 20005
202-347-2500
Occupational Fields: plasterer

FLORIDA
Plasterers and Cement Masons Union, Local #401
1435 Naldo Avenue
Jacksonville, FL 32207
904-398-4233
Occupational Fields: plasterer

GEORGIA
Plasterers and Cement Masons
514 Flat Shoals Avenue
Atlanta, GA 30316
404-525-1233
Occupational Fields: plasterer

HAWAII
Hawaii Masons and Plasterers Training Office
2251 North School Street
Honolulu, HI 96819
808-845-5949
*Occupational Fields: plasterer, pointer caulker, ceramic tile
setter, cement finisher, mason*

Masons Training Office, Wailuku
1464 Lower Main Street
Wailuku, HI 96793
808-244-9504
*Occupational Fields: plasterer, pointer caulker, ceramic tile
setter, cement finisher, mason*

ILLINOIS
Operative Plasterers and Cement Masons
Rural Route Three
Bloomington, IL 61704-9803
309-828-3279
Occupational Fields: plasterer

Plasterers and Cement Masons Union
212 South First Street
Rockford, IL 61104-2073

815-965-9977
Occupational Fields: plasterer

Plasterers and Cement Masons Union
1808 10th Street
Waukegan, IL 60085-7638
815-363-6933
Occupational Fields: plasterer

**Plasterers and Cement Masons Union,
Local #12**
400 Northeast Jefferson Avenue
Peoria, IL 61603-3739
309-674-8742
Occupational Fields: plasterer

Plasterers Union, Local #5
6631 Stanley Avenue
Berwyn, IL 60402-3128
708-749-3660
Occupational Fields: plasterer

INDIANA
**Plasterers and Cement Masons Union,
Local #692**
1901 North Sherman Drive, Suite 201
Indianapolis, IN 46218
317-353-0397
Occupational Fields: plasterer, cement mason

IOWA
Cedar Rapids Cement Masons
965 West 10th Avenue
Marion, IA 52302
319-377-5061
Occupational Fields: plasterer, cement mason

Cement Masons and Plasterers Union
1501 East Aurora Avenue
Des Moines, IA 50317
515-266-1668
Occupational Fields: plasterer, cement mason

Quad City Plasterers, Local #18
201 South Eighth Street
Eldridge, IA 52748
319-285-8037
Occupational Fields: plasterer

KANSAS

Bricklayers and Allied Craftsmen
746 Osage Avenue
Kansas City, KS 66105-2040
913-321-7060
Occupational Fields: plasterer

MARYLAND

Plasterers Union
3702 Wells Avenue
Mount Rainier, MD 20712-2146
Occupational Fields: plasterer

MICHIGAN

Bricklayers and Allied Craftsmen
119 South Front Street
Marquette, MI 49855
906-226-3015
Occupational Fields: plasterer

Greater Detroit Cement Masons and Plasterers
15101 Wyoming Street
Detroit, MI 48238-1754
313-931-4200
Occupational Fields: plasterer

MINNESOTA

Plasterers Union, Local #65
312 Central Avenue, SE, Suite 386
Minneapolis, MN 55414
612-379-1515
Occupational Fields: plasterer

NEVADA

Plasterers and Cement Masons Union, Local #797
4150 East Bonanza Road
Las Vegas, NV 89110
702-452-8809
Occupational Fields: plasterer, cement mason

NEW YORK

Plasterers and Cement Masons Union, Local #60
15 East 15th Street
New York, NY 10003
212-924-8650
Occupational Fields: plasterer, cement mason

OHIO

Cement Masons and Plasterers
694 Bev Road
Youngstown, OH 44512-6422
330-726-1790
Occupational Fields: plasterer

Plasterers and Cement Masons Union, Local #109
2046 South Main Street
Akron, OH 44301-2868
330-724-1221
Occupational Fields: plasterer

Plasterers Union, Local #80
1651 East 24th Street
Cleveland, OH 44114-4211
216-771-5399
Occupational Fields: plasterer

OKLAHOMA

Eastern Oklahoma Building and Construction Trades Council
2651 East 21st Street, #405
Tulsa, OK 74114
918-742-3363
Occupational Fields: plasterer

OREGON

Plasterers Union, Local #82
Southwest Washington Plasterers
2215 Southeast Division Street
Portland, OR 97202
503-232-3257
Occupational Fields: plasterer

PENNSYLVANIA

Cement Masons and Plasterers Union, Local #592
2511 Snyder Avenue
Philadelphia, PA 19145
http://www.opcmia592.org

Plasterers Union, Local #31
2227 Jane Street
Pittsburgh, PA 15203
412-481-9888
Occupational Fields: plasterer

RHODE ISLAND
Plasterers and Cement Masons Union, Local #40
150 Ernest Street
Providence, RI 02905
401-785-2230
Occupational Fields: plasterer

TENNESSEE
Plasterers and Cement Masons Union, Local #521
3540 Summer Avenue
Memphis, TN 38122
901-327-6492
Occupational Fields: plasterer, cement mason

TEXAS
Triangle Plastering Systems Inc.
Highway 80, East
PO Box 38325
Mesquite, TX 75150
972-285-8976
http://www.triangleplastering.com/index.htm
Occupational Fields: plasterer

VIRGINIA
**Association of the Wall and Ceiling Industries,
    National Office**
307 East Annandale Road, Suite 200
Falls Church, VA 22042-2433
703-534-8300
http://www.awci.org
Occupational Fields: plasterer, drywaller, insulator, floor
    layer, ceiling installer, stucco contractor

WASHINGTON
Plasterers Union, Local #77
Renton Technical College
3000 Northeast Fourth Street, Box 28
Renton, WA 98056
425-235-7879
Occupational Fields: plasterer

**Spokane Area Cement Finishers and Plasterers,
    Local #72**
West 120 Mission Avenue
Spokane, WA 99201
Fax: 509-326-0574
Occupational Fields: plasterer, cement mason

WEST VIRGINIA
Construction Trades Training Center
2307 Seventh Avenue
Charleston, WV 25312-1811
304-346-3863
Occupational Fields: plasterer

WISCONSIN
Bricklayers Union, Local #1
2233 Birch Street
Eau Claire, WI 54703-3400
715-835-5164
Occupational Fields: plasterer

Plasterers and Cement Finishers
3030 39th Avenue
Kenosha, WI 53144-4210
414-654-1680
Occupational Fields: plasterer

Plasterers and Cement Masons Union
2025 Atwood Avenue
Madison, WI 53704-5324
608-249-7548
Occupational Fields: plasterer, cement mason

CANADA
NEW BRUNSWICK
**Department of Training and Employment
    Development Apprenticeship and Occupational
    Certification**
PO Box 6000
Chestnut Complex
Fredericton, NB E3B 5H1
506-453-2260
Fax: 506-453-5317
aoc-acp@gnb.ca
Occupational Fields: plasterer

PRINTING INDUSTRY WORKERS

RELATED SECTIONS: *artists and artisans, book arts workers, communications specialists, electronics technicians, machinists, mechanics, theater workers*

Printing industry workers design, print, and assemble books, magazines, newspapers, newsletters, menus, business forms, catalogs, brochures, calendars, coupon books, and other published products.

The first step is to design and compose pages and produce printing plates. Various *prepress workers* are involved in this stage of the project. *Typesetters*, also known as *compositors,* transform manuscript into type, following a house style or a designer's or publisher's layouts and specifications. The job requires excellent typing skills, attention to detail, and some knowledge of page design and type styles. *Electronic prepress technicians*, also known as *electronic pagination system operators*, use computers to design and lay out projects. Artistic ability is a helpful asset. *Paste-up artists* attach text, illustrations, and graphic elements to the layout board according to the design provided by electronic prepress technicians or graphic artists. This method of composition was formerly common but is now done mainly when some elements of the design cannot be generated by computer. *Photographers*, also called *camera operators*, then photograph the layout and make a photographic negative. A *scanner operator* can also make negatives, using computerized equipment. *Strippers* make last-minute corrections by "stripping" out and replacing type or other errors. *Etchers* and other workers transfer the film images to thin metal printing plates by a chemical process. *Finishers* touch up irregularities on the plates.

Next, *press workers* print the project on printing presses. Small shops most often have small presses that print one or two colors at a time and are run by one person. Book, newspaper, and magazine publishers often have enormous in-line web presses run by a team of operators and assistants. *Printing press operators* set up these machines and maintain them, often by pushing buttons on control panels. They install printing plates; adjust and lubricate the machines; add ink; load and align huge rolls of paper; and monitor the machine's operations to ensure that the printed pages are clear and straight. Their duties depend on what type of press they operate: offset, flexography, gravure, screen printing, letterpress, or plateless. Press operators need mechanical aptitude and mathematical skills.

Finally, *bindery workers* assemble the printed pages into finished publications. They collate, fold, sew, and glue pages together and attach covers. Specially trained workers, such as *folding-machine operators* and *book-sewing-machine operators*, run machines that perform all these steps for mass-produced publications. A few *bookbinders* still perform all the steps by hand. This expensive procedure is typically reserved for special editions and the repair of old or rare books.

Workers must handle the stress of meeting deadlines and may be required to work overtime, nights, and evenings. Prepress workers usually work in clean, comfortable, quiet surroundings. They risk eyestrain, backaches, and carpal tunnel syndrome from working on computers and focusing on small details. Platemakers sometimes experience skin irritations from exposure to chemicals. Press operators stand or walk a great deal of the time. Working with the moving parts of a high-speed press can be dangerous, but the newer, computerized presses are less hazardous. Because pressrooms can be noisy, workers sometimes wear earplugs. Bindery workers are exposed to fumes from glue and other substances, and they risk injury from working with cutters, staplers, and other equipment.

A few workers in the printing industry belong to unions, but most do not.

Apprentices to this trade learn under the supervision of experienced workers. Often the applicants accepted into a program are workers already employed by the sponsoring company. A typical program runs for two to four years and involves study via correspondence courses or in a classroom. Apprenticeships tend to provide a general background in various areas but focus on a specialization, such as stripping or platemaking. Periodic retraining is common in this industry.

In general an applicant should

- apply in person
- be at least 18 years old
- be a high school graduate or hold a GED certificate
- be physically capable of performing the work
- have manual dexterity
- have good eyesight
- be able to pay close attention to detail
- have good mathematical skills
- be able to work well as a member of a team
- be able to work quickly and efficiently

APPRENTICESHIP SALARIES
Between $6 an hour and $12 an hour. Experienced apprentices may earn as much as $18 an hour.

POSTAPPRENTICESHIP SALARIES
Between $11 an hour and $30 an hour. Earnings vary, depending on the job, the employer, and geographic location.

JOB OUTLOOK
These printing industry occupations are expected to grow more slowly than the average occupation due to a decreased demand for printed material and the increased use of new computer technology. Demand for typesetters, for example, has dropped in recent years, because many authors now deliver their manuscripts on computer disks. New technology has also somewhat reduced the demand for bindery workers. The demand for press operators is expected to be strong, however, because many press operators are expected to retire in the next decade.

For more information on apprenticeships for printing industry workers, contact the national organizations and individual programs listed below, local job centers, your state bureau of apprenticeship training, or local print shops and publishing companies.

NATIONAL PROGRAMS
Graphic Arts Technical Foundation
200 Deer Run Road
Sewickley, PA 15143
412-741-6860
Fax: 412-741-2311
info@gatf.org
http://www.gatf.org
Occupational Fields: printing trades worker

**Graphic Communications International Union
    Education Department**
1900 L Street, NW
Washington, DC 20036-5002
202-462-1400
http://www.gciu.org
Occupational Fields: printing trades worker

Printing Industries of America
100 Daingerfield Road
Alexandria, VA 22314

703-519-8100
Fax: 703-548-322
gain@printing.org
http://www.gain.net
Occupational Fields: printing trades worker

APPRENTICESHIP PROFILE
Indianapolis Newspapers Inc.
GI Bill Apprenticeships and On-the-Job Training
    Programs for Veterans
307 North Pennsylvania Street
Indianapolis, IN 46206
317-630-9593

General Nature of the Job
Pressmen, or press operators, handle all facets of pressroom production, including maintenance and repair, operation, and preparation of printing presses. A pressman working for a newspaper handles all steps necessary to produce a high-quality newspaper, including feeding newsprint through the press, readying the ink, and setting all mechanical adjustments on the press so the paper feeds through and folds correctly. While the newspaper is printing, the pressman must constantly make adjustments, feed more paper through, and watch the ink. Specific duties vary from shop to shop because of the different sizes and types of presses.

Apprentices at Indianapolis Newspapers Inc. spend four years in training to become pressmen. Plans to combine on-the-job training with classroom instruction are in the works, but for now the apprentices learn while working. Applicants must have a high school diploma and cannot be color blind.

While pressroom work is exciting, it is also extremely loud and dirty—it is guaranteed that ink will get on you. The machines can be more than six stories high, and when presses are running you can't hear much else. Morning newspapers are traditionally printed from midnight to 3:00 A.M., and there's no such thing as weekends or holidays off, so being a night person could work in your favor. It doesn't hurt to be mechanically inclined, but because pressrooms are becoming more computerized and automated, basic computer skills will help you more. Can you handle pressure? If not, pick another career—pressmen live on stress, and there are strict deadlines every day.

Typical Day
Richard Bales, pressroom superintendent for the day shift, makes sure all facets of the pressroom function efficiently.

He spends his days in meetings, planning, and scheduling while his apprentices work on the floor with journeymen pressmen. Richard brings in training videos, has vendors give seminars, and tries to instill good work habits and pride in his apprentices, but there is no formalized training—apprentices are out there in the pressroom, working as hard as everyone else.

Production apprentices at Indianapolis Newspapers Inc. typically work from 9:00 A.M. to 5:00 P.M. They spend up to three hours preparing the presses for the afternoon newspaper run, including hooking up the ink hoses to the press, webbing the press (feeding the paper through the units into the folder, which is a giant collator), washing the plates to erase the image from the previous run, and putting the new plates on. The run averages about four hours, and the apprentices constantly watch the press, making sure cut-offs are accurate (readers don't like it when they only get part of the front page), setting the ink and water, and replenishing the newsprint reels. Each reel holds three rolls of newsprint, and each roll, which is more than 50 inches wide, lasts about 15 minutes.

One of the greatest challenges in the pressroom is to use only as much newsprint as is necessary because paper equals money. In fact, newsprint waste of 1 percent adds up to a half-million dollars. Because of the deadlines, balancing the clock against quality calls for some tough decisions. Newspapers are, as Richard states, "the most perishable products there are—much worse than fruits or vegetables," so pressmen must be quick, efficient, and able to get the newspapers out while the news is still news.

While some may dislike the noise, grime, deadlines, and hours, Richard finds the newspaper business thrilling. He says, "I know it's not good for me, but I like the stress. I live on adrenaline, and I like the high pace." The immediate gratification that comes from printing a daily newspaper makes it all worthwhile for Richard.

Path to Becoming an Apprentice

Richard started in the newspaper business at age 17. His father had been in the paper business for 40 years, so Richard thinks presswork was in his blood. He says, "It's a very exciting business. You either love it or hate it." While most new hires start as paper handlers, handling the newsprint rolls and transporting them to the press area as well as cleaning the equipment and floors, Richard started as a pressman. The printing industry was mostly mechanical when Richard began, so he believes

his hobby of working on cars helped him succeed. Now that the industry is more automated, computer skills are a plus, but no prior experience is necessary to become a successful pressman.

Richard believes he became a superintendent because of his people skills, pressman capabilities, and assertiveness. He enjoys the teaching aspect of his job and notes that apprentices usually stick with the printing industry if they can handle the dirt and the night and weekend hours.

Salary Range

Apprentices earn 65 percent of journeyman scale when they begin the program, receiving incremental raises every six months. During the final six months of the apprenticeship, they make 95 percent of the journeyman rate, which is approximately $23 an hour at Indianapolis Newspapers Inc. Wages vary depending on region and company, and not all print shops require union membership. Apprentices receive full benefits during their tenure.

Richard believes the range of salaries in the printing industry starts at $11 an hour and tops out around $30. The pressman's job may change because of the computerization in the pressroom, but Richard feels the job outlook is stable. He says, "As long as we're putting ink on paper there's still going to be some pressmen around." Other printing industry jobs, however, will not survive automation. Printers, those responsible for composing and engraving the type onto the printing plates, will soon be obsolete, along with paper handlers.

Advice

For those interested in the printing industry, Richard advises, "get all the computer skills you can. The more computer literate and the more you can do with the computer, the more use you have in any department in the industry." Of course, you also need to be able to work well with others and tolerate the hours and the working conditions. Richard also suggests finding a newspaper that is hiring entry-level employees so you can spend some time learning the craft. He says, "once you get hired and show them you can do the job, it's pretty steady work." It might take some time finding shops that are hiring, though, so patience and persistence are crucial.

Future Goals

Richard is satisfied with his current position and employer and says it will take a really amazing offer to convince him to change jobs. Because of his responsibilities as superintendent, Richard does not believe his teaching responsibilities will increase when a more structured apprenticeship program is implemented.

Pressmen can diversify in a number of ways—pressmen in smaller shops with computer skills can work on color separations, prepress functions, manipulate photographs to enhance reproductive qualities, or work in desktop publishing. A large shop is more departmentalized so performing numerous tasks is less common. There is opportunity, however, to advance into management or supervision if you are responsible and proficient.

ARIZONA

Office Technologies
4320 East Cotton Center Drive, Suite 100
Phoenix, AZ 85040
602-248-7778
Fax: 602-277-0893
jschmidt@azofficetech.com
http://www.azofficetech.com
Occupational Fields: assembly technician

R.R. Donnelley
1145 West Gila Bend Highway, Box C-8
Casa Grande, AZ 85222
520-836-4418
Occupational Fields: photoengraver, bindery worker, print and publishing stripper, press operator, etcher, stripper

CALIFORNIA

Central Valley Opportunity Center, Madera
209 7th Street
Madera, CA 93638
559-662-4574
http://www.cvoc.org
Occupational Fields: lithographer, graphic artist (computer)

Central Valley Opportunity Center, Merced
6838 Bridget Court
PO Box 1389
Winton, CA 95388
209-357-0062
http://www.cvoc.org
Occupational Fields: lithographer, graphic artist (computer)

Central Valley Opportunity Center, Modesto
912 11th Street
Modesto, CA 95354
209-577-3210
http://www.cvoc.org
Occupational Fields: lithographer, graphic artist (computer)

Graphic Communications International Union
710 East Commonwealth Avenue
Fullerton, CA 92831
714-447-3382
Fax: 714-447-3385
Occupational Fields: press operator

Graphic Communications International Union
230 Grand Avenue
Oakland, CA 94610
510-451-0309
Fax: 714-447-3385
Occupational Fields: press operator

Graphic Communications International Union, Local 4N
433 Natoma Street
San Francisco, CA 94103
415-433-4012
Fax: 415-512-7986
tkimbala@yahoo.com
http://www.gciu4n.org
Occupational Fields: press operator

Graphic Communications International Union, Local 432M
10393 San Diego Mission Road
San Diego, CA 92108
619-283-6788
Fax: 714-447-3385
http://www.gciu432m.com
Occupational Fields: press operator

Graphic Communications International Union, Local 583
2301 Ocean Avenue
San Francisco, CA 94127
415-239-7700
gciu@igc.org
http://www.gciusf.org
Occupational Fields: press operator

CONNECTICUT
Graphic Communications International Union #434-C
308 Bristol Street
Southington, CT 06489
203-621-4237
Occupational Fields: press operator

DISTRICT OF COLUMBIA
Graphic Communications International Union
2310 Minnesota Avenue, SE
Washington, DC 20020
202-582-2800
http://www.gciu.org
Occupational Fields: press operator

Graphic Communications International Union Education Department
1900 L Street, NW
Washington, DC 20036-5002
202-462-1400
Fax: 202-721-0600
Occupational Fields: printing trades worker

ILLINOIS
Graphic Communications International Union
204 South Ashland Avenue
Chicago, IL 60607
312-738-4200
Occupational Fields: press operator

Graphic Communications International Union
5717 South Kedzie Avenue
Chicago, IL 60629
773-925-2877
Occupational Fields: press operator

Graphic Communications International Union
1204 West Washington Avenue, Suite 39B
Effingham, IL 62401
217-342-2364
Occupational Fields: press operator

Graphic Communications International Union
712 Indiana Avenue
Mendota, IL 61342
815-538-3617
Occupational Fields: press operator

Graphic Communications International Union
3416 Blackhawk Road, Suite 101
Rock Island, IL 61201
309-788-0389
Occupational Fields: press operator

Graphic Communications International Union
112 West Main Street
Salem, IL 62881
618-548-2094
Occupational Fields: press operator

Graphic Communications Limited
860 Rockbridge Drive
Naperville, IL 60540
630-369-8788
Occupational Fields: press operator

INDIANA
Graphic Communications International Union
516 North Fares Avenue
Evansville, IN 47711
812-422-6044
Occupational Fields: press operator

Graphic Communications International Union
7023 Kensington Drive
Indianapolis, IN 46226-5714
317-923-1558
Occupational Fields: printer

Graphic Communications International Union
800 West Seventh Street
Muncie, IN 47302
765-288-0994
Occupational Fields: press operator

Graphic Communications International Union, Local #19-M
704 West Jefferson Boulevard
Fort Wayne, IN 46802-4001
219-426-0995
Occupational Fields: press operator, prepress worker, bindery worker

Graphic Communications International Union, Local #303
1010 Main Street
Indianapolis, IN 46224-6941

317-244-1572
Occupational Fields: press operator, bookbinder

**Graphic Communications International Union,
Local #306C**
121 West Michigan Boulevard
Michigan City, IN 46360
219-874-7211
Occupational Fields: press operator

Indianapolis Newspapers Inc.
307 North Pennsylvania Street
Indianapolis, IN 46206
317-630-9593
Occupational Fields: press operator

IOWA
Graphic Communications International Union
2000 Walker Street, #D
Des Moines, IA 50317
515-265-1190
Occupational Fields: press operator

The Vernon Company
One Promotion Place
Newton, IA 50208
641-792-9000
Fax: 641-792-6901
http://www.vernoncompany.com
Occupational Fields: printer

KANSAS
Graphic Communications International Union #575-M
322 Laura Street
Wichita, KS 67211
316-267-3563
*Occupational Fields: bookbinder, prepress worker, press
operator*

Johnson County Industries
10501 Lackman Road
Lenexa, KS 66219-1223
913-492-6161
Fax: 913-492-5171
Occupational Fields: press operator

Service Business Forms Limited
815 East Second Street, North
PO Box 47068

Wichita, KS 67201-7068
316-264-4315
Fax: 316-268-1234
Occupational Fields: bindery worker

State Division of Printing
201 Northwest Macvicar Avenue
Topeka, KS 66606
913-296-3631
http://da.state.ks.us:9080/print
*Occupational Fields: printer, compositor, plate maker,
press operator, printer*

Topeka Capital-Journal
616 Southeast Jefferson Street
Topeka, KS 66607-1120
913-295-1111
Fax: 913-295-1230
http://www.cjonline.com
Occupational Fields: press operator

KENTUCKY
**Graphic Communications International Union
#395-C**
2241 Yewels Landing, Apartment A
Owensboro, KY 42303
502-926-4296
Occupational Fields: press operator

Graphic Communications International Union #619
659 South Eighth Street
Louisville, KY 40203
502-583-2709
Occupational Fields: press operator

MAINE
**Graphic Communications International Union,
Local #22-C**
112 Brachett Street
Portland, ME 04102
207-774-6461
Occupational Fields: press operator, platemaker

MARYLAND
Graphics Communications International, Local 72-C
6037 Baltimore Avenue
Riverdale, MD 20737

301-699-1202
Fax: 301-699-1203
local72c@msn.com
http://www.printing-union-local72c.com
Occupational Fields: press operator

MASSACHUSETTS
Graphic Communications International Union
856 Memorial Drive
Chicopee, MA 01020
413-593-1511
Occupational Fields: press operator

MICHIGAN
Detroit Graphic Arts Institute
22720 Woodward Avenue, Suite 110
Ferndale, MI 48220
detgraphicarts@sbcglobal.net
http://www.geocities.com/school289/GCIU_Training.html
Occupational Fields: press operator

Graphic Communications International Union
421 Eighth Street, NW
Grand Rapids, MI 49504
616-453-3303
Occupational Fields: press operator

Graphic Communications International Union
5070 East Main Street
Kalamazoo, MI 49004
616-344-3580
Occupational Fields: press operator

Graphic Communications International Union
1111 South Woodward Avenue, #100
Royal Oak, MI 48067
810-398-8533
Occupational Fields: press operator

MINNESOTA
**Graphic Communications International Union,
Local #1-M**
684 Transfer Road
St. Paul, MN 55114
612-645-0833
Fax: 612-645-8531

http://www.mtn.org/gciu1m/welcome.html
Occupational Fields: printer

MISSOURI
**Graphic Communications International Union,
Local #203-C**
3425 South Orin
Springfield, MO 65804
417-883-0874
Occupational Fields: press operator

**Graphic Communications International Union,
Local #235**
10221 East U.S. Highway 40
Independence, MO 64055-6124
816-358-4248
Occupational Fields: press operator

**Graphic Communications International Union,
Local #301-C**
1707 South Engineer
Scadalia, MO 65301
660-826-1083
Occupational Fields: press operator

MONTANA
Graphic Communications International Union
PO Box 2133
Missoula, MT 59806
406-543-8311
Occupational Fields: press operator

**United Paper Workers International,
Hellgate Local #885**
208 East Main Street
Missoula, MT 59802
406-543-7788
Occupational Fields: printer

NEW YORK
Amalgamated Lithographers of America, Local #1
113 University Place
New York, NY 10003
212-460-0800
Fax: 212-460-0859
Occupational Fields: printer

Graphic Communications International Union
22 Fourth Street
Rochester, NY 14609
716-454-2294
Occupational Fields: press operator

Graphic Communications International Union, Local #30
2495 Woodlawn Avenue
Niagara Falls, NY 14301
716-675-4661
Occupational Fields: press operator

Graphic Communications International Union, Local #164-C
856 Page Road
Frewsburg, NY 14738
716-569-4233
Occupational Fields: press operator

Graphic Communications International Union, Local #261
2185 Clinton Street
Buffalo, NY 14202
716-822-0734
Fax: 716-822-0734
Occupational Fields: bindery worker

NORTH CAROLINA
R.R. Donnelley Printing Company
1545 Saint James Church Road
Newton, NC 28658
704-464-8110
Occupational Fields: bookbinder, press operator, cylinder corrector, digital mechanical engraver

OHIO
Graphic Communications International Union
2105 South Hamilton Road
Columbus, OH 43232
614-759-9386
Occupational Fields: press operator

Graphic Communications International Union
30 Mohican Street
Shelby, OH 44875
419-347-2599
Occupational Fields: press operator

Graphic Communications International Union District Council 3
2351 West McMicken Avenue
Cincinnati, OH 45214
513-621-3974
Fax: 513-621-5283
dc3billie@cinci.rr.com
http://www.gciu2289m.com
Occupational Fields: press operator, prepress worker, bindery worker

OREGON
Graphic Communications International Union
2233 North Lombard Street
Portland, OR 97217
503-285-0529
Occupational Fields: press operator

Graphic Communications International Union
2705 Southeast Milwaukee Avenue
Portland, OR 97202
503-235-2135
Occupational Fields: press operator

PENNSYLVANIA
Graphic Communications International Union
143 North Walnut Street
Boyertown, PA 19512
610-367-7975
Occupational Fields: press operator

Graphic Communications International Union
83 East Essex Avenue
Lansdowne, PA 19050
610-622-3022
Occupational Fields: press operator

Graphic Communications International Union
27 South Fourth Street
Philadelphia, PA 19106
215-592-9900
Occupational Fields: press operator

Graphic Communications International Union
950 Weiser Street
Reading, PA 19601
610-373-8602
Occupational Fields: press operator

Graphic Communications International Union, Local #14-M
1310 East Sedgley Avenue
Philadelphia, PA 19134
215-533-9262
Fax: 215-744-4260
info@gciulocal14m.org
http://www.gciulocal14m.org
Occupational Fields: printer, press operator, graphic designer

Graphic Communications International Union, Local #24
1825 Boulevard of the Allies
Pittsburgh, PA 15219
412-391-1377
Occupational Fields: prepress worker, press operator

RHODE ISLAND
Graphic Communications International Union, Local #12N
845 Waterman Avenue
Providence, RI 02914
401-781-1007
Fax: 401-461-2121
http://members.aol.com/local239m/private/union.
html
Occupational Fields: press operator

TENNESSEE
Graphic Communications International Union
1418 Carroll Creek Road
Gray, TN 37615
615-283-4232
Occupational Fields: press operator

Graphic Communications International Union, Local #118-C
7601 Hawthorne Drive
Knoxville, TN 37919
615-691-1617
Occupational Fields: press operator

Graphic Communications International Union, Local #165-C
1162 West Boy Scout Road
Hixson, TN 37343

615-843-2630
Occupational Fields: press operator, press assistant, feeder operator

VIRGINIA
Graphic Communications International Union
7654 Elkhardt Road
Richmond, VA 23235
804-276-5224
Occupational Fields: press operator

WASHINGTON
Graphic Communications International Union, Local 767M
19309 West Valley Highway, Suite R-112
Kent, WA 98032
425-251-8585
Fax: 425-251-8015
office@gciu767m.org
http://www.gciu767m.org
Occupational Fields: press operator

WISCONSIN
Golden Books Publishing Company
1220 Mound Avenue
Racine, WI 53404
414-633-2431
Occupational Fields: press operator, prepress worker

Graphic Communications International, Local 577M
633 South Hawley Road, Suite 100
Milwaukee, WI 53214
414-476-1577
http://www.gciu577m.org
Occupational Fields: press operator

Graphic Communications International Union
512 Goold Street
Racine, WI 53402
414-633-3366
Occupational Fields: press operator

Sheboygan Paper Box Company
716 Clara Avenue
Sheboygan, WI 53081

920-458-8373
Fax: 920-458-2901
Occupational Fields: press operator

CANADA
ONTARIO
Ontario Graphic Communications Training Centre
80 Park Lawn Road, Suite 109
Toronto, ON M8Y 3H8
416-251-5449
Fax: 416-251-5449
http://www3.sympatico.ca/graph.comm/aboutus.html
Occupational Fields: press operator

RAILROAD WORKERS

RELATED SECTIONS: *auto body workers, boilermakers, electricians and line workers, electronics technicians, elevator constructors, engineers, ironworkers, machinists, mechanics, millwrights, operating engineers and stationary engineers, pile drivers, sheet metal workers, shipbuilding and ship maintenance workers, truck drivers, mechanics, welders*

Railroad workers provide an integral service for the nation's transportation system. They build, maintain, and repair railroad tracks, cars, bridges, and other equipment and structures; assemble, disassemble, and operate the huge trains that carry passengers and products from one station to another; load, unload, and route cargo; and assist customers.

Locomotive engineers operate trains transporting goods and people between stations. *Rail yard engineers* operate locomotives and move cars to assemble or disassemble trains within switching yards. *Dinkey operators* are engineers who operate small engines at mines or industrial sites, transporting ore, coal, supplies, and other materials. Most locomotives run on diesel, but some are powered by electricity.

Engineers regulate the train's speed, fuel, temperature, battery charge, and brake pressure, and they check for mechanical problems before and after each trip. They also note signals that warn of speed limits, other trains, and objects blocking the tracks. It is particularly important for engineers to be aware of the number of cars on the train, whether each is loaded or not, and how much slack is in the train; these factors significantly affect the train's response to braking, acceleration, and curves.

Conductors record the cargo on the train and make sure that it arrives at its intended destination. On passenger trains *road conductors* collect money and tickets and assist passengers in various ways. When the train is stopped they tell engineers when to leave the station, and during the trip they receive information from *dispatchers*, which they pass on to the engineers. They also communicate with brake operators and sometimes arrange for defective cars to be removed from the train. *Yard conductors* oversee the assembly and disassembly of trains in switching yards.

In recent years *brake operators* (also called *brakemen*) have taken over many of the duties of *assistant engineers* (also called *firers*), who watch instruments and signals and keep an eye out for obstructions on the tracks. Brake operators work under the direction of conductors, removing and adding cars to the train at stations and in switching yards. They examine trains before departure, watch for signs of mechanical problems during the trip,

uncouple cars, and sometimes run ahead to switch the train to another track.

Railroads also employ crews of *mechanics, boilermakers, carmen, car painters, electricians, computer operators and programmers*, and *machinists* to keep the trains mechanically sound and operating on time.

Employment in this industry often involves work at night, on weekends, and on holidays. Workers on freight trains seldom have scheduled assignments but place their names on waiting lists; they frequently are called to work with little notice. People who service trains typically travel hundreds of miles to perform their work and often spend several nights away from home each week. Brake operators and yard conductors spend a great deal of time outdoors, often in inclement weather; their work is strenuous and can be dangerous.

Railroad workers typically enter the profession as trainees under the supervision of engineers or brake operators, sometimes working part-time or irregularly for years until they gain sufficient seniority to be hired for regular work. From there they may advance to the position of engineer, which usually requires about six additional months of classroom instruction and on-the-job training in locomotive equipment, train handling, air brakes, fuel conservation, and regulations. Engineers must pass occasional evaluations of their physical fitness and general conduct to retain their positions. Brake operators may also advance to the position of conductor after passing examinations that evaluate their knowledge of operating rules, signals, and other topics.

Some railroads operate training centers that offer instruction for conductors, yard crews, locomotive engineers, dispatchers, maintenance-of-way crews, mechanics, signal systems technicians, telecommunications and system electrical technicians, and customer service personnel. These centers may operate in conjunction with community colleges so that students receive college credit for courses completed.

In general an applicant should

- be at least 21 years old
- be a high school graduate or hold a GED certificate

- have good eyesight
- not be color blind
- have good hearing
- have manual dexterity
- have mechanical aptitude
- be in good physical condition

APPRENTICESHIP SALARIES
Apprentices often start at 75 percent of the skilled worker's wage, but apprentices in this field often are required to pay tuition for their training program.

POSTAPPRENTICESHIP SALARIES
Median hourly wages range from about $20 to $24. Most railroad workers are paid based on miles traveled or hours worked, whichever leads to higher earnings.

JOB OUTLOOK
Employment in this field is expected to decline through the year 2012. Competition for available job opportunities will be keen. Many persons qualify for rail transportation occupations because education beyond high school generally is not required, and rail transportation occupations attract more applicants than the number of available job openings because the pay is good and the work is steady. The openings that do become available will be the result of retirements or transfers to other occupations.

Employment of subway and streetcar operators is expected to grow about as fast as the average occupation as a result of the increased demand for light-rail transportation systems around the country.

For more information on training opportunities for railroad workers, contact the national organizations and individual programs listed below, local job centers, your state bureau of apprenticeship training, employment offices of railroads and rail transit systems, or the U.S. Railroad Retirement Board, which posts a monthly list of job openings in the railroad industry.

NATIONAL PROGRAMS
International Brotherhood of Locomotive Engineers
1370 Ontario Street
Cleveland, OH 44113-1702
216-241-2630
Fax: 216-861-0932

james@ble.org
http://www.ble.org
Occupational Fields: railroad engineer, railroad worker

United States Railroad Retirement Board
844 North Rush Street
Chicago, IL 60611-2092
312-751-4701
http://www.rrb.gov
Occupational Fields: railroad engineer, railroad worker

APPRENTICESHIP PROFILE
Johnson County Community College
Railroad Operations Technology Program
National Academy of Railroad Sciences
Burlington Northern Santa Fe National Training Center
12345 College Boulevard
Overland Park, KS 66210-1299
913-469-8500
Fax: 913-469-2698
podrazik@johnco.cc.ks.us
http://www.johnco.cc.ks.us

General Nature of the Job
Conductors on freight trains ride in the locomotive with the engineer and are responsible for making sure their trains are operating properly. Conductors must understand the dynamics of how a string of heavy cars will move along the tracks. These highly skilled workers record the cargo being transported, know what railroad cars are in each train and in what order the cars were linked together, and write summaries of all trips. They inspect for hazardous materials, make sure the train meets safety and tonnage requirements, verify signals, and help pick up and set out locomotives from the train. Some conductors work in railroad yards, where they couple and uncouple cars, throw switches, and generally supervise the switching of cars from one train to another to ensure that all freight arrives at the correct destination. The work is sometimes dangerous and requires some physical strength, enough to lift about 40 pounds and carry it short distances.

About 300,000 miles of railroad tracks crisscross the nation, with trains that constantly move freight and passengers. Every day, thousands of cars must be loaded, hooked together, brought to their destinations, disconnected, and unloaded. Trains must depart and arrive on schedule, and since they often share the same rails, their journeys must be orchestrated to make optimum use of the tracks in the safest possible way. The roadbed and tracks must be maintained and monitored to prevent derailments. More than 500 companies in the industry need workers to service, maintain, and manage this complex network.

A railroad career offers great responsibility, constant challenges, and a high entry-level salary, but there's stiff competition for these jobs. "Say a person's number-one objective is to get a job on the railroad. My advice is to get a skill. Learn to be a conductor," says Bill Podrazik, who teaches railroad classes at Johnson County Community College in Overland Park, Kansas. The college houses the Burlington Northern Santa Fe National Training Center and has offered classes and on-the-job training in cooperation with the railroad for nearly 20 years.

Students in the railroad operations program can choose from five options: conductor, dispatcher, mechanic, maintenance-of-way welder, and general railroad worker. All students in the program take the same core classes for the first three semesters, then enter classes specific to the options they have chosen.

The conductor training program consists of six weeks of classes and laboratory work at the college, followed by 18 weeks of paid, on-the-job training with the railroad. The dispatcher program consists of seven weeks in field locations across the country; three weeks of study at the college; four weeks at the railroad dispatch center in Fort Worth, Texas; and 10 weeks of on-the-job training with a railroad. All students who complete the training earn 21 semester hours of college credit and may go on to earn an Associate of Science degree in railroad operations.

Typical Day

Conductors in training put in eight-hour days learning the basics of railroad work during the first part of the program. They start with five weeks of classroom studies, then complete one week of hands-on training at a nearby railroad yard. Next, the college helps them find employment with a railroad, and they begin 18 weeks of paid, on-the-job training. During these months, they are on call 24 hours a day, every day of the week.

A conductor's workday begins whenever a train is scheduled to depart. If the train is leaving at 3:00 A.M., the intern must be on board at that time or earlier, ride the train for perhaps 250 miles in nine hours, take a day of rest, show up for work on another train at 11:00 P.M., and ride it for nine hours back to the starting point.

No supervisor rides along to oversee the intern's work; the intern is alone in the locomotive with the engineer but maintains radio contact with supervisors throughout the

journey. The job is a highly responsible one, and interns are expected to exercise good judgment, maturity, and skill when they are on duty.

Path to Becoming an Apprentice

If you want to pursue a railroad career immediately after high school, Bill recommends taking some college classes, either at a local school or at one of the 16 community colleges in the United States that offer special courses in railroad studies. Courses taken at your local community college or vocational or technical school can be transferred later to an institution such as Johnson County Community College, where you can complete the special requirements for a railroad degree.

Many applicants to the railroad program are experienced workers, such as retired military personnel, who already have advanced skills and are changing careers. Often, these people must complete only a few classes to qualify for railroad jobs.

Bill says that students do better if they demonstrate an aptitude for and have completed studies in mathematics, physics, computers, writing and communication, and leadership. Applicants to the railroad program must be at least 18 years old and have completed at least 30 hours of college credit. They must take an aptitude test and a physical examination that includes a drug screening and color blindness test. Not all applicants are admitted to the program; that decision is made by representatives of the college and the railroad industry after the applicants are interviewed.

Salary Range

Salaries and benefits for skilled railroad employees are unusually high. Entry-level employees, including those who are completing on-the-job training, start at about 75 percent of a conductor's wage and receive periodic raises until they're promoted to conductors. Conductors and dispatchers start at about $35,000 a year. Locomotive engineers start at about $55,000 a year.

Students do incur some expenses during training, however. Tuition and fees for the Johnson County Community College program cost about $2,500 to $4,500, depending on residency and which training option the student chooses. Students receive a living stipend and intern wages during certain parts of the training but must pay for some of their rent and other living expenses. Students are also responsible for buying textbooks and arranging their own transportation to training sites, and those in the conductor training program must provide their own steel-toed work boots and work gloves.

Advice

A person considering a railroad career should realize that workers in this trade must make certain personal sacrifices. The schedule is unpredictable, and employees may be expected to accept positions far from home, although they are allowed to request the top three places where they would most like to be stationed. Many railroad employees work in less than ideal conditions for the first five or 10 years, earning a significant amount of money, then achieve seniority and bid for jobs that are more appealing to them.

Bill advises, "Ask yourself if you're willing to travel and be away from home periodically. Are you willing to move anywhere in the United States? And are you willing to work a shift that is unconventional, any day of the week, with no holidays?"

It's also important to realize how trying the on-the-job training can be. "It really has an impact on family life. Get ready for it. Adjust your eating habits and sleeping habits," he says. Above all, he adds, an appropriate education will all but guarantee that you'll be able to land a job in this extremely competitive field. "The placement rating for our graduates is high, near 100 percent," he notes.

Future Goals

Graduates of the conductor training program are not typically hired as conductors, but as brake operators, switch operators, or other entry-level workers. With solid skills and credentials earned through an internship, employees may be promoted in as little as two weeks. If they have not earned promotion to conductor within two years, they are usually dismissed. If they do advance to conductors, they have two more years to learn to operate a locomotive and be promoted to engineer or face dismissal.

"The railroads don't want people to be lifetime conductors," Bill explains. The job is only the first step toward more highly skilled positions, some of which require more college training. Ultimately, some of the most skilled conductors become railroad managers.

ALABAMA

U.S. Railroad Retirement Board
Medical Forum Building
950 22nd Street, North, Room 426
Birmingham, AL 35203-1126
205-731-0026
Occupational Fields: railroad worker

ARIZONA

U.S. Railroad Retirement Board
Financial Plaza, Suite 4850
1201 South Alma School Road
Mesa, AZ 85210-2097
480-610-5990
Fax: 480-610-5988
Occupational Fields: railroad worker

ARKANSAS

U.S. Railroad Retirement Board
1200 Cherry Brook Drive, Suite 500
Little Rock, AR 72211-4113
501-324-5241
Fax: 501-324-7159
Occupational Fields: railroad worker

CALIFORNIA

U.S. Railroad Retirement Board
Building B, Suite 360
1515 West Cameron Avenue
Covina, CA 91790-2726
626-339-9993
Fax: 626-814-1219
Occupational Fields: railroad worker

U.S. Railroad Retirement Board
Oakland Federal Building
1301 Clay Street, Suite 392, North
Oakland, CA 94612-5220
510-637-2973
Fax: 510-637-2978
Occupational Fields: railroad worker

U.S. Railroad Retirement Board
801 I Street, Room 205
Sacramento, CA 95814-2510
916-498-6654
Fax: 916-498-6659
Occupational Fields: railroad worker

COLORADO

U.S. Railroad Retirement Board
721 19th Street, Room 177
PO Box 8869
Denver, CO 80201-8869
303-844-4311

Fax: 303-391-5869
Occupational Fields: railroad worker

FLORIDA
CSX Transportation, Inc.
500 Water Street
Jacksonville, FL 32202
800-232-0144
http://www.csx.com
Occupational Fields: railroad worker

Florida Community College at Jacksonville, Downtown Campus
Engineering Technologies and Aviation
101 West State Street, Room A1025
Jacksonville, FL 32202
904-633-8289
Fax: 904-633-8105
http://www1.fccj.cc.fl.us
Occupational Fields: railroad worker

U.S. Railroad Retirement Board
400 West Bay Street, Room 315
Box 35026
Jacksonville, FL 32202-4412
904-232-2546
Fax: 904-232-2874
Occupational Fields: railroad worker

U.S. Railroad Retirement Board
Federal Annex Building, Room 100
501 Polk Street
Tampa, FL 33602-3953
813-228-2695
Fax: 813-228-2939
Occupational Fields: railroad worker

GEORGIA
Clayton State C
Technical Institute/Business Education
Morrow, GA 30260
770-960-2093
Fax: 770-961-3519
Occupational Fields: railroad worker

Norfolk Southern Railroad Corporation
101 Thoroughbred Drive
McDonough, GA 30253

404-914-3510
Fax: 404-914-3553
http://www.nscorp.com
Occupational Fields: railroad worker

U.S. Railroad Retirement Board
Peachtree Summit Building, Room 1702
401 West Peachtree Street
Atlanta, GA 30365-2550
404-331-2841
Fax: 404-331-7234
Occupational Fields: railroad worker

ILLINOIS
Brotherhood of Railroad Signalmen
601 West Golf Road
Mount Prospect, IL 60056-4276
847-439-3732
Occupational Fields: railroad worker

Burlington Northern Santa Fe Corporation
1700 East Golf Road
Schaumburg, IL 60173-5860
847-995-6000
http://www.bnsf.com
Occupational Fields: railroad worker

Carl Sandburg College
Community and Extension Services
2232 South Lake Storey Road
Galesburg, IL 61401
309-344-2518, ext. 250
Fax: 309-344-3526
http://www.sandburg.edu
Occupational Fields: railroad worker

National Railroad Hall of Fame
311 East Main Street, Suite 208
Galesburg, IL 61401
309-343-9261
Fax: 309-343-9261
http://www.nrhof.org
Occupational Fields: railroad worker

Richard J. Daley College
Workforce and Economic Development
7500 South Pulaski Road
Chicago, IL 60652
773-838-7500

http://daley.ccc.edu
Occupational Fields: railroad worker

U.S. Railroad Retirement Board
844 North Rush Street, Ninth Floor
Chicago, IL 60611-2092
312-751-4500
Fax: 312-751-7136
Occupational Fields: railroad worker

U.S. Railroad Retirement Board
Millikin Court
132 South Water Street, Suite 517
Decatur, IL 62523-1397
217-423-9747
Fax: 217-423-7872
Occupational Fields: railroad worker

U.S. Railroad Retirement Board
101 North Joliet Street, Room 120
PO Box 457
Joliet, IL 60434-0457
815-740-2101
Fax: 815-740-2139
Occupational Fields: railroad worker

INDIANA
U.S. Railroad Retirement Board
The Meridian Centre
50 South Meridian, Suite 303
Indianapolis, IN 46204-3530
317-226-6111
Fax: 317-226-5374
Occupational Fields: railroad worker

IOWA
U.S. Railroad Retirement Board
Federal Building
210 Walnut Street, Room 921
Des Moines, IA 50309-2182
515-284-4344
Fax: 515-284-4616
Occupational Fields: railroad worker

Western Iowa Tech Community College
Business and Applied Technology
4647 Stone Avenue, Box 265
Sioux City, IA 511106

712-274-6418
Fax: 712-274-6412
http://www.witcc.cc.ia.us
Occupational Fields: railroad worker

KANSAS
Johnson County Community College
National Academy of Railroad Sciences
12345 College Boulevard
Overland Park, KS 66210-1299
913-469-8500
Fax: 913-469-4409
http://www.johnco.cc.ks.us
Occupational Fields: conductor, dispatcher, railroad worker

Lindsay Group Limited
590 Lake Shore Drive, West
Lake Quivira, KS 66106
913-962-9881
Occupational Fields: railroad worker

U.S. Railroad Retirement Board
UNISYS Building, Suite 390
1861 North Rock Road
Wichita, KS 67206-1264
316-687-5973
Fax: 316-687-3572
Occupational Fields: railroad worker

KENTUCKY
U.S. Railroad Retirement Board
629 South Fourth Avenue, Suite 301
Box 3705
Louisville, KY 40201-3705
502-582-5208
Fax: 502-582-5518
Occupational Fields: railroad worker

LOUISIANA
U.S. Railroad Retirement Board
501 Magazine Street, Room 1045
New Orleans, LA 70130-3394
504-589-2597
Fax: 504-589-4899
Occupational Fields: railroad worker

MARYLAND

Transportation Communications International Union
Three Research Place
Rockville, MD 20850-3279
301-948-4910
Fax: 301-948-1369
http://www.tcunion.org
Occupational Fields: railroad worker

U.S. Railroad Retirement Board
300 West Pratt Street, Room 260
Baltimore, MD 21201-2803
410-962-2550
Occupational Fields: railroad worker

MASSACHUSETTS

U.S. Railroad Retirement Board
121 High Street, Room 301
PO Box 2448
Boston, MA 02208-2448
617-424-5790
Fax: 617-424-5795
Occupational Fields: railroad worker

MICHIGAN

Brotherhood of Locomotive Engineers
2450 Shawood Street
Novi, MI 48377-1970
810-926-0623
Occupational Fields: railroad engineer

Brotherhood of Locomotive Engineers
10874 Beech Daly Road
Taylor, MI 48180-3144
313-295-0690
Occupational Fields: railroad engineer

Brotherhood of Maintenance of Way Employees
360 River Street
Manistee, MI 49660-2708
616-723-3577
http://www.bmwe.org
Occupational Fields: railroad worker

Brotherhood of Maintenance of Way Employees
26555 Evergreen Road, #200
Southfield, MI 48076-4225

810-948-1010
Fax: 810-948-7150
http://www.bmwe.org
Occupational Fields: railroad worker

U.S. Railroad Retirement Board
McNamara Federal Building
477 West Michigan Avenue, Suite 1990
Detroit, MI 48226-2596
313-226-6221
Fax: 313-226-4233
Occupational Fields: railroad worker

MINNESOTA

Canadian Pacific Railroad
105 South Fifth Street, Suite 1110
PO Box 530
Minneapolis, MN 55440
612-347-8467
Fax: 612-337-8549
http://www8.cpr.ca
Occupational Fields: railroad worker

St. Paul Technical College
Business Division
235 Marshall Avenue
St. Paul, MN 55102
612-221-1316
Fax: 612-221-1416
http://www.saintpaul.edu
Occupational Fields: railroad worker

U.S. Railroad Retirement Board
Federal Building, Room 125
515 West First Street
Duluth, MN 55802-1392
218-720-5301
Fax: 218-720-5329
Occupational Fields: railroad worker

U.S. Railroad Retirement Board
First Trust Center, Suite 195, First Floor
180 East Fifth Street
St. Paul, MN 55101-1631
612-290-3491
Fax: 612-290-3076
Occupational Fields: railroad worker

MISSOURI

Brotherhood of Locomotive Engineers
3433 South Campbell Avenue
Springfield, MO 65807-5101
417-887-5267
Occupational Fields: railroad worker

Brotherhood of Railway Clerks
1139 Olive Street
St. Louis, MO 63101-1946
314-436-3310
Occupational Fields: railroad worker

Kansas City Southern Railway
Corporate Communications
114 West 11th Street
Kansas City, MO 64105
816-556-0303
Occupational Fields: railroad worker

U.S. Railroad Retirement Board
Federal Building, Room 258
601 East 12th Street
Kansas City, MO 64106-2882
816-426-5864
Fax: 816-426-5334
Occupational Fields: railroad worker

U.S. Railroad Retirement Board
Young Federal Building
1222 Spruce Street, Room 1213
St. Louis, MO 63103-2818
314-539-6220
Fax: 314-539-6229
Occupational Fields: railroad worker

MONTANA

Montana State University, Northern
Industrial and Engineering Technology
PO Box 7751
Havre, MT 59501-7751
800-662-6132
Fax: 406-265-3734
http://www.msun.edu
Occupational Fields: railroad worker

U.S. Railroad Retirement Board
Judge Jameson Federal Building
2900 Fourth Avenue, North, Room 101

Billings, MT 59101-1266
406-247-7375
Fax: 406-247-7379
Occupational Fields: railroad worker

NEBRASKA

U.S. Railroad Retirement Board
106 South 15th
PO Box 1415
Omaha, NE 68101-1415
402-221-4641
Fax: 402-221-4669
Occupational Fields: railroad worker

Union Pacific Railroad Company
Barkalow Building
1416 Dodge Street
Omaha, NE 68179
402-271-4872
Fax: 402-271-3493
http://www.up.com
Occupational Fields: railroad worker

Western Nebraska Community College
Power Technology
1601 East 27th Street
Scottsbluff, NE 69361-1899
308-635-3606
http://hannibal.wncc.cc.ne.us
Occupational Fields: railroad worker

NEW JERSEY

U.S. Railroad Retirement Board
Rodino Federal Building
970 Broad Street, Room 1435B
Newark, NJ 07102-2518
Occupational Fields: railroad worker

NEW MEXICO

U.S. Railroad Retirement Board
300 San Mateo, NE, Room 401
Albuquerque, NM 87108-1520
505-262-6405
Fax: 505-262-6407
Occupational Fields: railroad worker

NEW YORK
Long Island Rail Road, Hillside Support Facility
Metropolitan Transportation Authority
93-59 183rd Street, Department #3149
Hollis, NY 11423
718-558-3133
Fax: 718-558-3123
Occupational Fields: railroad worker

National Aviation and Transportation Center
Center for Intellectual Capital
Oakdale, NY 11769-1999
516-244-3391
Occupational Fields: railroad worker

U.S. Railroad Retirement Board
Clinton Avenue and Pearl Street
PO Box 529
Albany, NY 12201-0529
518-431-4004
Fax: 518-431-4000
Occupational Fields: railroad worker

U.S. Railroad Retirement Board
Dulski Federal Building
111 West Huron, Room 1106
Buffalo, NY 14202-2394
716-551-4141
Fax: 716-551-3802
Occupational Fields: railroad worker

U.S. Railroad Retirement Board
Federal Building
26 Federal Plaza, Room 3404
New York, NY 10278-0105
212-264-9820
Fax: 212-264-1687
Occupational Fields: railroad worker

U.S. Railroad Retirement Board
1400 Old Country Road, Suite 204
Westbury, NY 11590-5119
516-334-5940
Occupational Fields: railroad worker

NORTH CAROLINA
U.S. Railroad Retirement Board
Mart Office Building
800 Briar Creek Road, Room AA-405
Charlotte, NC 28205-6903
704-344-6118
Fax: 704-344-6429
Occupational Fields: railroad worker

NORTH DAKOTA
U.S. Railroad Retirement Board
657 Second Avenue, North
PO Box 383
Fargo, ND 58107-0383
701-239-5117
Fax: 701-239-5261
Occupational Fields: railroad worker

OHIO
Brotherhood of Locomotive Engineers
433 South Street
Wheelersburg, OH 45694-1716
614-574-5539
Occupational Fields: railroad engineer

Brotherhood of Maintenance of Way Employees
712 Second Street
Toledo, OH 43605-2113
419-693-3801
Occupational Fields: railroad worker

Brotherhood of Railroad Workers
12460 Christiansburg Jackson
Christiansburg, OH 45389
937-857-9302
Occupational Fields: railroad worker

International Brotherhood of Locomotive Engineers, Headquarters
Standard Building
1370 Ontario Street, Mezzanine
Cleveland, OH 44113-1702
216-241-2630, x218
Occupational Fields: railroad worker, railroad engineer

International Brotherhood of Locomotive Engineers, Local #13
1370 Ontario Street
Cleveland, OH 44113-1702
216-241-2630
Fax: 216-861-0932
http://ble13.tripod.com
Occupational Fields: railroad engineer, railroad worker

United Transportation Union
817 Kilbourne Street
Bellevue, OH 44811-9431
419-483-4476
Occupational Fields: railroad worker

United Transportation Union
6797 North High Street
Columbus, OH 43085-2533
614-846-7397
Occupational Fields: railroad worker

United Transportation Union
2021 East Dublin Granville Road
Columbus, OH 43229-3522
614-847-0011
Occupational Fields: railroad worker

United Transportation Union
14600 Detroit Avenue
Lakewood, OH 44107-4207
216-228-9400
Fax: 216-228-5755
Occupational Fields: railroad worker

United Transportation Union, Cleveland
27801 Euclid Avenue
Cleveland, OH 44132-3547
216-731-2031
Occupational Fields: railroad worker

United Transportation Union, Columbus
5918 Sharon Woods Boulevard
Columbus, OH 43229-2665
614-794-0009
Occupational Fields: railroad worker

United Transportation Union, National Headquarters
14600 Detroit Avenue
Cleveland, OH 44107-4207
216-228-9400
Fax: 216-228-5755
http://www.utu.org
Occupational Fields: railroad worker

United Transportation Union, Worthington
6797 North High Street
Worthington, OH 43085-2576

614-846-7397
Occupational Fields: railroad worker

U.S. Railroad Retirement Board
CBLD Center, Room 201
36 East Seventh Street
Cincinnati, OH 45202-4439
513-684-3188
Fax: 513-684-3182
Occupational Fields: railroad worker

U.S. Railroad Retirement Board
Celebrezze Federal Building
1240 East Ninth Street, Room 907
Cleveland, OH 44199-2093
216-522-4053
Fax: 216-522-2320
Occupational Fields: railroad worker

OREGON
U.S. Railroad Retirement Board
Green-Wyatt Federal Building, Room 377
1220 Southwest Third Avenue
Portland, OR 97204-2807
503-326-2143
Fax: 503-326-2157
Occupational Fields: railroad worker

PENNSYLVANIA
Amtrak
30th Street Station
Philadelphia, PA 19104
215-349-1069
Occupational Fields: railroad worker

Community College of Allegheny County
Airport West
1002 Church Hill Road
Pittsburgh, PA 15205
412-788-6464
Fax: 412-788-6468
http://www.ccac.edu
Occupational Fields: railroad worker

Community College of Philadelphia
Community Services and Continuing Education
1700 Spring Garden Street, Room S3-03J

Philadelphia, PA 19130-3991
215-751-8373
Fax: 215-751-8954
Occupational Fields: railroad worker

Consolidated Rail Corporation (Conrail)
2001 Market Street, #18-C
PO Box 41418
Philadelphia, PA 19101-1418
215-209-4000
http://www.conrail.com
Occupational Fields: railroad worker

U.S. Railroad Retirement Board
615 Howard Avenue, Room 209
PO Box 990
Altoona, PA 16603-0990
814-946-3601
Fax: 814-946-3620
Occupational Fields: railroad worker

U.S. Railroad Retirement Board
228 Walnut Street, Room 504
Box 576
Harrisburg, PA 17108-1697
717-221-4490
Fax: 717-221-3364
Occupational Fields: railroad worker

U.S. Railroad Retirement Board
1421 Cherry Street, Suite 660
Philadelphia, PA 19102-1493
330-656-6993
Fax: 330-656-6996
Occupational Fields: railroad worker

U.S. Railroad Retirement Board
Kossman Building, Room 1130
100 Forbes Avenue
Pittsburgh, PA 15222-1311
412-644-2696
Fax: 412-391-7689
Occupational Fields: railroad worker

U.S. Railroad Retirement Board
Siniawa Plaza II, Route Six
717 Scranton/Carbondale Highway
Scranton, PA 18508-1121

717-346-5774
Fax: 717-346-6042
Occupational Fields: railroad worker

TENNESSEE
Pellissippi State Technical Community College
10915 Hardin Valley Road
PO Box 22990
Knoxville, TN 37933-0990
423-694-6671
Fax: 423-694-6426
http://www.pstcc.edu
Occupational Fields: railroad worker

U.S. Railroad Retirement Board
233 Cumberland Bend Drive, Suite 206
Nashville, TN 37228-1813
615-736-5131
Fax: 615-736-7071
Occupational Fields: railroad worker

TEXAS
Burlington Northern Santa Fe Corporation
777 Main Street, #3800
Fort Worth, TX 76102-5384
817-333-2000
http://www.bnsf.com
Occupational Fields: railroad worker

Tarrant County Junior College
5301 Campus Drive
Fort Worth, TX 76119-5926
817-515-4100
http://www.tccd.edu
Occupational Fields: railroad worker

U.S. Railroad Retirement Board
819 Taylor Street, Room 10G02
PO Box 17420
Fort Worth, TX 76102-0420
817-978-2638
Fax: 817-978-2740
Occupational Fields: railroad worker

U.S. Railroad Retirement Board
Leland Federal Building, Suite 845
1919 Smith

Houston, TX 77002-8051
713-209-3045
Fax: 713-209-3044
Occupational Fields: railroad worker

UTAH
Union Pacific Railroad
400 West South Temple
Salt Lake City, UT 84101
801-532-4756
http://www.up.com
Occupational Fields: railroad worker, brakeman,
    conductor, train service engineer

U.S. Railroad Retirement Board
Bennett Federal Building, Room 1205
125 South State
Salt Lake City, UT 84138-1102
801-524-5725
Fax: 801-524-4313
Occupational Fields: railroad worker

VIRGINIA
Norfolk Southern Railroad
Manager of Employment
Three Commercial Place
Norfolk, VA 23510-9214
800-214-3609
http://www.nscorp.com
Occupational Fields: railroad worker

Roanoke Area Tech Prep Consortium
PO Box 14007
Roanoke, VA 24038
540-857-6917
Occupational Fields: railroad worker

Tidewater Community College
Norfolk Center
215 East City Hall Avenue
Norfolk, VA 23510
804-683-8303
http://www.tcc.edu
Occupational Fields: railroad worker

U.S. Railroad Retirement Board
704 East Franklin Street, Second Floor, Suite 232
Richmond, VA 23219-2313

804-771-2997
Fax: 804-771-8481
Occupational Fields: railroad worker

U.S. Railroad Retirement Board
210 First Street, SW
PO Box 270
Roanoke, VA 24002-0270
540-857-2335
Occupational Fields: railroad worker

Virginia Western Community College
Engineering/Industrial Technologies
PO Box 14007
Roanoke, VA 24038
540-857-7275
http://www.vw.vccs.edu
Occupational Fields: railroad worker

WASHINGTON
Burlington Northern-Santa Fe Railroad
Employee Relations-Carman
5302 Trent Road
Spokane, WA 99212
http://www.bnsf.com
Occupational Fields: railroad worker

U.S. Railroad Retirement Board
Pacific First Plaza, Suite 201
155 108th Avenue, NE
Bellevue, WA 98004-5901
206-553-5483
Occupational Fields: railroad worker

U.S. Railroad Retirement Board
U.S. Court House, Room 492
West 920 Riverside Avenue
Spokane, WA 99201-1081
509-353-2795
Occupational Fields: railroad worker

WEST VIRGINIA
U.S. Railroad Retirement Board
640 Fourth Avenue
PO Box 2153
Huntington, WV 25721-2153

304-529-5561
Occupational Fields: railroad worker

WISCONSIN
U.S. Railroad Retirement Board
Reuss Federal Plaza, Suite 1300
310 West Wisconsin Avenue
Milwaukee, WI 53203-2211
414-297-3961
Occupational Fields: railroad worker

WYOMING
**Northern Wyoming Community College District,
Gillette Campus**
Academic Affairs/Student Services
720 West Sinclair
Gillette, WY 82716
307-686-0254
Fax: 307-686-0339
http://www.sheridan.edu/gc
Occupational Fields: railroad worker

Sheridan College
3059 Coffeen Avenue
Sheridan, WY 82801-9133
307-674-6446
http://www.sheridan.edu
Occupational Fields: railroad worker

CANADA
QUEBEC
Teamsters Canada Railway Conference
PO Box 3008
Lapierre Branch Office
Lasalle, QC H8N 3H2
http://www.geocities.com/blediv89
Occupational Fields: railroad worker

ROOFERS AND WATERPROOFERS

RELATED SECTIONS: *bricklayers, carpenters, drywallers and lathers, floor layers, insulators and asbestos workers, laborers, masons, painters and paperhangers, plasterers, tile setters*

Roofers install and repair roofs, using shingles, tile, plastic, rubber, and other materials. *Waterproofers* use coating compounds or membranous materials to waterproof walls, floors, swimming pools, tanks, and other structures.

Roofers sometimes specialize in either pitched or flat roofs. A pitched roof has a slope and is commonly found on houses. Generally the first step in working on this type of roof is to tack strips of roofing felt (a fabric saturated with bitumen, a tarlike substance) lengthwise across the surface. Roofers then nail horizontal rows of asphalt or wood shingles, cedar shakes, or other roofing material on top of the felt. The shingles must be aligned carefully and cut to fit around chimneys, corners, and other objects. Strips of metal or shingles are positioned to seal the valleys where two sections of the roof meet. Nail heads and exposed joints are sealed with caulking or roofing cement. Pitched roofs may also be covered with tile, slate or fiberglass shingles, or large sheets of metal.

Flat roofs are commonly found on commercial, industrial, and apartment buildings. The workers cover the area with insulation, coat it with bitumen, and apply alternate layers of roofing felt and more bitumen. The top is then roughened with gravel or given a smooth finish.

Single layers of plastic or rubber roofing are becoming increasingly common for flat roofs. These sheets are rolled out on top of the layer of insulation and sealed, sometimes with a torch, a hot anvil, or bitumen. Some sheets are fastened with adhesives, stone weights, or mechanical fasteners.

During a roofing project, workers typically hammer thousands of nails, erect scaffolds, carry heavy materials and tools up ladders and across rooftops, and do a great deal of climbing, bending, and kneeling. There is the constant danger of slipping and falling in addition to the risk of being cut by tools, suffering scrapes and splinters from the building materials, and being burned by hot bitumen. Roofers have the highest accident rate of all the construction workers. Roofs become very hot during the summer and slick with frost in the mornings. Roofers work outdoors and must be available to make repairs even in bad weather. Most roofing projects are scheduled for spring and summer, when the weather is better. About three out of four roofing projects are not new construction but repair and re-roofing jobs, which creates a steady source of employment.

Most roofers are employed by roofing contractors. About a third are self-employed; they tend to work most often on houses. Most roofers and waterproofers belong to labor unions, such as the United Union of Roofers, Waterproofers & Allied Workers.

On-the-job training and apprenticeship are common ways of entering this trade. Many unions and other organizations in the building and construction trades offer apprenticeship training for roofers. Apprentices work under the supervision of experienced roofers and waterproofers. They participate in at least 2,000 hours of on-the-job training and at least 144 hours of classroom instruction each year. Typically, the course of study runs for three years and includes instruction in mathematics, the use of tools, and safety.

In general an applicant should

- apply in person
- be at least 18 years old
- be a high school graduate or hold a GED certificate
- be in good physical condition
- not be afraid of heights
- have a good sense of balance

APPRENTICESHIP SALARIES

Between $6 an hour and $15 an hour, or about 40 to 50 percent of the rate paid to skilled workers. Experienced apprentices may earn as much as $25 an hour.

POSTAPPRENTICESHIP SALARIES

About $8 an hour, up to $35 an hour. Earnings vary, depending on geographic location and skill level.

JOB OUTLOOK

Generally good, because roofs deteriorate and need to be repaired frequently. In addition, this trade has a high rate of turnover, which leaves numerous job openings every year. Employment for roofers is expected to grow about as fast as the average for all occupations through the year 2012. Downturns in the building industry do not affect roofers as much as other construction industry workers because roofing has a much higher proportion of repair and replacement work than most other construction occupations.

For more information on apprenticeships for roofers and waterproofers, contact the national organizations and individual programs listed below, local job centers, your state bureau of apprenticeship training, or local roofing contractors.

NATIONAL PROGRAMS

National Roofing Contractors Association
10255 W. Higgins Road, Suite 600
Rosemont, IL 60018-5607
847-299-9070
Fax: 847-299-1183
nrca@nrca.net
http://www.nrca.net
Occupational Fields: roofer

United Union of Roofers, Waterproofers, and Allied Workers
1660 L Street, NW, Suite 800
Washington, DC 20036-5603
202-463-7663
Fax: 202-463-6906
http://www.unionroofers.com
Occupational Fields: roofer, waterproofer

APPRENTICESHIP PROFILE

United Union of Roofers, Waterproofers, and Allied Workers, Local #162
Nevada Roofers Joint Apprenticeship and Training Committee
4200 East Bonanza Road
Las Vegas, NV 89115
702-453-5801
nvrooferjatc@rooferslocal162.org

General Nature of the Job

Roofing is a physically demanding, outdoor trade that generally offers employment and a good income anywhere in the country. "I always liked roofing, because everything is a challenge every day. It's always something different. Some projects are a day long, some are two days, some are a week," says Bill Penrose, coordinator of the Nevada Roofers Joint Apprenticeship and Training Committee. "And you're out in the fresh air, out in the open, not within four walls." He recalls one apprentice who had completed college, worked as a nuclear scientist,

joined the Peace Corps, and ended up becoming a roofer, like his father: "He didn't like those four walls. A lot of people don't."

This is a trade that requires strength, and it's guaranteed to keep you in shape. "You're exercising all the time. There's a lot of walking," Bill notes. Roofers also do a great deal of bending, kneeling, and carrying 100-pound kegs of asphalt and 80-pound rolls of roofing materials. They drive forklifts and trucks, and they use an assortment of tools for their trade: hammers, nail bags, hatchets, utility knives, tin snips, trowels, wrenches, nail bars, saws, hoists, kettles, compressors, generators, wheelbarrows, tile saws, nail guns, conveyors, and vacuums for removing rock chips from roofs.

Apprentices learn to install and maintain various types of roofs. Some materials are applied with a spray gun, shingles are nailed down, asphalt is heated and mopped on or applied with a felt machine, and modified bitumen comes in a roll that's spread across the roof and fused in place with a torch. When removing old asbestos on a roof, workers use safety gear, such as respirators. Many roofers also apply waterproofing compounds to basement floors and other areas where dampness is a problem.

Because of the heights involved, roofing is a dangerous job. One slip, and you can fall off a roof or through a hole and be seriously injured or killed. This training program continually emphasizes safety procedures, such as using safety harnesses and tying ladders securely so they won't skid to the side as the worker steps onto the roof.

Apprentices complete 432 hours of classes and hands-on experience and at least 3,600 hours of on-the-job training during their three years in the program. The apprenticeship committee has agreements with 16 local roofing and waterproofing contractors who provide jobs for trainees, instruct classes, give demonstrations, and participate in other ways. The class schedule varies, depending on when a professional is available to give a demonstration.

Typical Day

Apprentices attend class one night per week throughout the autumn, winter, and spring, usually after work, from 5:00 P.M. to 8:00 P.M. Some classes, demonstrations, and hands-on experiences are scheduled on Saturdays. Classes cover basic subjects related to the trade, including mathematics and blueprint reading. After hearing a lecture in a classroom, students go outside for hands-on practice and demonstrations on a variety of topics. They might observe a manufacturer showing how to install a product or watch a crane in operation, for example.

During the day, apprentices typically arrive at their job sites by about 5:00 A.M. to 6:00 A.M., but occasionally they work at night under lights, because sometimes it's too hot in Nevada to work during the day. They stop for a 10- or 15-minute break in the morning and afternoon and have half an hour for lunch.

Most work crews consist of about five people, including one apprentice, but sometimes an apprentice works with just one journeyman supervisor. Most job sites are within about 50 miles of the city, but they can be up to 200 miles away. In that case the employer would most likely pay for overnight lodging near the site.

Path to Becoming an Apprentice

People who know what to expect in the roofing trade are more apt to stay with it than someone who knows little about the occupation, according to Bill. Many successful apprentices are friends with roofers or have relatives in the trade. Some people learn roofing with the idea that it will be a temporary job, but then they realize they enjoy it, and they stay with it for years.

There's no waiting list for this program; you can get into the training quickly and will probably be put to work with a contractor right away. Applicants must be at least 18 years old. Instead of subjecting applicants to a selective admission process, the apprenticeship committee likes to let students prove their worth. Usually the union arranges a job for new applicants, who work as helpers in a pre-apprenticeship trial period for six months. Those who show promise are indentured as apprentices; they work on probation for another six months. As they see what the trade involves, some people quit because they realize they're afraid of heights, or that the work is too dirty or too heavy for them, or prefer work that is not seasonal. Those who continue the training then work as apprentices for several years.

Salary Range

Helpers who are not yet in the apprentice program are paid about $9 an hour. Apprentices start at $16.13 an hour and have a pension plan and medical, dental, and vision insurance for themselves and their families. They receive raises every six months as long as they attend classes regularly, put in the required number of hours at work, and perform well on the job. Graduates are paid journeyman wages of $25.18 an hour. Most roofers average about $40,000 to $50,000 a year. Part of the income paid to both apprentices and journeymen is in the form of union benefits and is not taxable.

Advice

Bill wishes more high school students, in particular, realized that apprenticeships are available and that they're very important for succeeding in certain careers: "Training is the name of the game. Anyone who's trained has more chance of going somewhere than the untrained. I wish the high schools understood that. If you're a skilled craftsman, you'll never be out of work."

For those who want to pursue roofing as a career, it's important to be in good physical shape and maintain a conscientious attitude. Bill says, "The thing about roofing is you're doing a service that I would say is a priority. Without a good roof, you don't have much. You have people underneath depending on you for their safety and health. You're helping a lot of people, even if you don't realize it."

Future Goals

Most apprentices work with just one company during their training and are employed by that company afterward. "Especially if he's a good person, they want to keep him and train him their own way," Bill explains. About 65 percent of the graduates from this program have advanced to positions as superintendent, foreman, general manager, or owner of a roofing company. "Most roofing businesses are owned by an ex-roofer," Bill notes. "I had an apprentice who is now general manager of a large roofing company in California. It makes you feel good when you see these guys getting up to the top. Whenever he's got a problem, he still calls me. They think I'm a miracle worker." Bill adds that most apprentices find satisfaction in the roofing trade. "Usually when they get into roofing, they stay. Ten years down the road, he's still there."

ALABAMA
United Union of Roofers, Waterproofers, and Allied Workers, Local #110
659 1/2 Dauphin Street
Mobile, AL 36602
Occupational Fields: roofer, waterproofer

ALASKA
United Union of Roofers, Waterproofers, and Allied Workers, Local #190
626 Cordova Street
Anchorage, AK 99501
907-272-4311

Fax: 907-277-4311
Occupational Fields: roofer, waterproofer

ARIZONA

United Union of Roofers, Waterproofers, and Allied Workers, Local #135
1917 East Washington Street
Phoenix, AZ 85034
602-254-7059
Fax: 602-254-4201
terrilynn34@aol.com
Occupational Fields: roofer, waterproofer

ARKANSAS

Bricklayers and Allied Crafts, Local #1
504 South Victory Street
Little Rock, AR 72201
501-372-3532
Occupational Fields: waterproofer

CALIFORNIA

Associated Roofing Contractors
8301 Edgewater Drive
Oakland, CA 94621
510-635-8800
Occupational Fields: roofer, waterproofer

Roofers and Waterproofers Union
4831 East Shields Avenue, Room 27
Fresno, CA 93726-6437
559-255-0933
Fax: 559-255-0983
Occupational Fields: roofer, waterproofer

United Union of Roofers, Waterproofers, and Allied Workers
150 Executive Park Boulevard, Suite 3625
San Francisco, CA 94117
415-508-0261
Fax: 415-508-0321
www.rooferslocal40.org
Occupational Fields: roofer, waterproofer

United Union of Roofers, Waterproofers, and Allied Workers, Local #36
5380 Poplar Boulevard
Los Angeles, CA 90032

323-222-0251
Fax: 323-222-3585
Occupational Fields: roofer, waterproofer

United Union of Roofers, Waterproofers, and Allied Workers, Local #40
293 Brokaw Road
Santa Clara, CA 95050
408-987-0440
Fax: 408-988-6180
Occupational Fields: roofer, waterproofer

United Union of Roofers, Waterproofers, and Allied Workers, Local #45
3737 Camino del Rio South, Suite 202
San Diego, CA 92108
619-516-0192
Fax: 619-516-0194
Occupational Fields: roofer, waterproofer

United Union of Roofers, Waterproofers, and Allied Workers, Local #56
3180 North Ad Art Road, #C-3
Stockton, CA 95215-2218
209-931-5571
Occupational Fields: roofer, waterproofer

United Union of Roofers, Waterproofers, and Allied Workers, Local #81
8400 Enterprise Way, Suite 122
Oakland, CA 94621
510-632-0505
Fax: 510-632-5469
roofers@pacbell.net
Occupational Fields: roofer, waterproofer

United Union of Roofers, Waterproofers, and Allied Workers, Local #220
1074 East LaCadena Drive, Suite 9
Riverside, CA 92501
909-684-3645
Occupational Fields: roofer, waterproofer

United Union of Roofers, Waterproofers, and Allied Workers, Local #220
283 North Rampart Street, Suite F
Orange, CA 92868
714-939-0220
Fax: 714-939-0246
Occupational Fields: roofer, waterproofer

United Union of Roofers, Waterproofers, and Allied Workers, Local #220
3222 West First Street
Santa Ana, CA 92703
Occupational Fields: roofer, waterproofer

COLORADO
United Union of Roofers, Waterproofers, and Allied Workers, Local #41
4515 West 41st Avenue
Denver, CO 80212
303-455-5514
Fax: 303-455-9575
lun41@gwest.net
Occupational Fields: roofer, waterproofer

United Union of Roofers, Waterproofers, and Allied Workers, Local #58
404 North Spruce Street
Colorado Springs, CO 80905
719-632-5889
Fax: 719-632-1261
Occupational Fields: roofer, waterproofer

CONNECTICUT
United Union of Roofers, Waterproofers, and Allied Workers, Local #9
114 Old Forge Road
Rocky Hill, CT 06067
860-721-1174
Fax: 860-721-6182
rooferlocal9@aol.com
Occupational Fields: roofer, waterproofer

United Union of Roofers, Waterproofers, and Allied Workers, Local #12
45 Water Street, Room 14
New Haven, CT 06511
203-772-2565
Fax: 203-772-2574
rooferslocal12@juno.com
Occupational Fields: roofer, waterproofer

DISTRICT OF COLUMBIA
HR General Maintenance Corporation
2021 Shannon Place, SE
Washington, DC 20020
202-889-8400
Occupational Fields: roofer

United Union of Roofers, Waterproofers, and Allied Workers
1660 L Street, NW, Suite 800
Washington, DC 20036-5603
202-463-7663
Fax: 202-463-6906
roofers@unionroofers.com
http://www.unionroofers.com
Occupational Fields: roofer, waterproofer

FLORIDA
Murton Roofing Corporation
7860 Northwest 67th Street
Miami, FL 33166
305-592-5385
Occupational Fields: roofer

United Union of Roofers, Waterproofers, and Allied Workers, Local #57
4349 Northwest 36th Street, Suite 101
Miami Springs, FL 33166
305-885-9759
Fax: 305-885-8788
Occupational Fields: roofer, waterproofer

United Union of Roofers, Waterproofers, and Allied Workers, Local #77
3057 West Broward Boulevard
Fort Lauderdale, FL 33312
954-792-4270
Fax: 954-797-7824
Occupational Fields: roofer, waterproofer

United Union of Roofers, Waterproofers, and Allied Workers, Local #179
5619 50th Street
Tampa, FL 33610
813-620-1399
Occupational Fields: roofer, waterproofer

United Union of Roofers, Waterproofers, and Allied Workers, Local #181
4000 Union Hall Place
Jacksonville, FL 32205
904-384-7692
Occupational Fields: roofer, waterproofer

United Union of Roofers, Waterproofers, and Allied Workers, Local #254
1003 Belvedere Road
Palm Beach, FL 33405
877-467-6637
Fax: 561-832-3454
Occupational Fields: roofer, waterproofer

GEORGIA
United Union of Roofers, Waterproofers, and Allied Workers, Local #136
374 Maynard Terrace, Southeast, Room 208
Atlanta, GA 30316
404-373-7081
Fax: 404-373-0926
rooferslocal136@bellsouth.net
Occupational Fields: roofer, waterproofer

HAWAII
Associated Builders and Contractors, Hawaii
1001 Dillingham Boulevard, Room 304
Honolulu, HI 96817
808-845-4887
Fax: 808-847-7876
Occupational Fields: roofer

United Union of Roofers, Waterproofers, and Allied Workers, Local #221
2045 Kamehameha IV Road, Room 203
PO Box 17250
Honolulu, HI 96817-0250
808-847-5757
Fax: 808-848-8707
Occupational Fields: roofer, waterproofer

IDAHO
United Union of Roofers, Waterproofers, and Allied Workers, Local #200
915 Berryman Road
Pocatello, ID 83201
208-237-5758
Fax: 208-234-2541
Occupational Fields: roofer, waterproofer

United Union of Roofers, Waterproofers, and Allied Workers, Local #209
204 C 29th Street
Nampa, ID 83687
208-466-0132
Occupational Fields: roofer, waterproofer

ILLINOIS
Quad City Roofers, Local #32
PO Box 4925
Rock Island, IL 61204
309-788-7406
Fax: 309-786-7490
Occupational Fields: roofer

United Union of Roofers, Waterproofers, and Allied Workers, Local #11
9838 West Roosevelt Road
Westchester, IL 60154
708-345-0970
Fax: 708-345-0981
Occupational Fields: roofer, waterproofer

United Union of Roofers, Waterproofers, and Allied Workers, Local #32
2827 Seventh Avenue
Rock Island, IL 61201
309-786-2117
Fax: 309-786-7490
Occupational Fields: roofer, waterproofer

United Union of Roofers, Waterproofers, and Allied Workers, Local #55
1219 West Main Street
Ottawa, IL 61350
815-433-4510
Occupational Fields: roofer, waterproofer

United Union of Roofers, Waterproofers, and Allied Workers, Local #69
400 Northeast Jefferson Street
Peoria, IL 61603
309-673-8033
Fax: 309-673-8036
Occupational Fields: roofer, waterproofer

United Union of Roofers, Waterproofers, and Allied Workers, Local #92
PO Box 1634
Decatur, IL 62525-1634
217-422-8953
Fax: 217-422-8955
Occupational Fields: roofer, waterproofer

United Union of Roofers, Waterproofers, and Allied Workers, Local #97
1401 North Prospect Avenue
PO Box 6569
Champaign, IL 61826
217-359-3922
Fax: 217-356-9934
Occupational Fields: roofer, waterproofer

United Union of Roofers, Waterproofers, and Allied Workers, Local #112
2725 East Old Ash Street
Springfield, IL 62703
217-544-7882
Fax: 217-525-1004
Occupational Fields: roofer, waterproofer

INDIANA

United Union of Roofers, Waterproofers, and Allied Workers, Local #23
1345 Northside Boulevard
South Bend, IN 46615
219-288-6506
Fax: 219-288-6511
Occupational Fields: roofer, waterproofer

United Union of Roofers, Waterproofers, and Allied Workers, Local #26
503 Conkey Street
Hammond, IN 46324
219-932-3338
Fax: 219-932-3443
Occupational Fields: roofer, waterproofer

United Union of Roofers, Waterproofers, and Allied Workers, Local #106
210 North Fulton Avenue, Box 8
Evansville, IN 47710
812-424-8641
Fax: 812-425-6376
Occupational Fields: roofer, waterproofer

United Union of Roofers, Waterproofers, and Allied Workers, Local #119
2702 South Foltz Street
Indianapolis, IN 46241
317-484-8990
Fax: 317-484-8993
Roofer119@juno.com

http://www.indyroofers.com
Occupational Fields: roofer, waterproofer

United Union of Roofers, Waterproofers, and Allied Workers, Local #150
31 1/2 South 13th Street, Suite 5
Terre Haute, IN 47807
812-232-7010
Occupational Fields: roofer, waterproofer

United Union of Roofers, Waterproofers, and Allied Workers, Local #205
111 Bing Street
Chesterfield, IN 46017
765-378-0556
Fax: 765-378-7566
uur205@aol.com
Occupational Fields: roofer, waterproofer

United Union of Roofers, Waterproofers, and Allied Workers, Local #233
2335 South 30th Street
PO Box 4721
Lafayette, IN 47903
317-477-7892
Occupational Fields: roofer, waterproofer

IOWA

Cedar Rapids Roofers, Local #182
750 49th Street
Marion, IA 52305
319-373-2575
Fax: 319-373-2575
http://www.rooferslocal182.com
Occupational Fields: roofer, waterproofer

Winters Architectural Roofing
1035 Lincoln Road
Bettendorf, IA 52722
319-355-0441
Occupational Fields: roofer

KANSAS

Roof-Techs
502 West Lincoln Street
PO Box 2307
Wichita, KS 67201-2307

316-262-7200
Occupational Fields: roofer

Roofers Union, Local #20
6321 Blue Ridge Boulevard, Suite 202
Raytown, MO 64133
816-313-9420
roofer20@attglobal.net
Occupational Fields: roofer

KENTUCKY
**United Union of Roofers, Waterproofers, and Allied
    Workers, Local #147**
7711 Beulah Church Road
PO Box 91696
Louisville, KY 40291
502-231-3344
Occupational Fields: roofer, waterproofer

LOUISIANA
**United Union of Roofers, Waterproofers, and Allied
    Workers, Local #76**
819 Holly Street
Lake Charles, LA 70601
318-478-0754
Occupational Fields: roofer, waterproofer

**United Union of Roofers, Waterproofers, and Allied
    Workers, Local #317**
3260 Winbourne Avenue
Baton Rouge, LA 70805
225-355-8502
Occupational Fields: roofer, waterproofer

MARYLAND
**United Union of Roofers, Waterproofers, and Allied
    Workers, Local #34**
729 Shawnee Avenue
Cumberland, MD 21502
301-777-7051
roofers34@hotmail.com
Occupational Fields: roofer, waterproofer

**United Union of Roofers, Waterproofers, and Allied
    Workers, Local #90**
5200 Westland Boulevard
Baltimore, MD 21227
410-288-4401

Fax: 215-331-8325
Occupational Fields: roofer, waterproofer

MASSACHUSETTS
**United Union of Roofers, Waterproofers, and Allied
    Workers, Local #33**
51 Neponset Avenue
Dorchester, MA 02122
617-288-7410
Fax: 617-288-3928
Occupational Fields: roofer, waterproofer

**United Union of Roofers, Waterproofers, and Allied
    Workers, Local #248**
63 ½ Main Street
Chicopee, MA 01020
413-594-5291
Fax: 413-594-5391
Occupational Fields: roofer, waterproofer

MICHIGAN
**United Union of Roofers, Waterproofers, and Allied
    Workers, Local #149**
1640 Porter Street
Detroit, MI 48216
313-561-6093
Fax: 313-561-7009
Occupational Fields: roofer, waterproofer

MINNESOTA
**United Union of Roofers, Waterproofers, and Allied
    Workers, Local #96**
312 Central Avenue, Room 456
Minneapolis, MN 55414
612-379-2918
Fax: 612-379-0932
http://www.rooferslocal.com
Occupational Fields: roofer, waterproofer

MISSOURI
**United Union of Roofers, Waterproofers, and Allied
    Workers, Local #2**
2920 Locust Street
St. Louis, MO 63103
314-535-9683
Fax: 314-535-6404
Occupational Fields: roofer, waterproofer

United Union of Roofers, Waterproofers, and Allied Workers, Local #20
6301 Rockhill Road, #420
Kansas City, MO 64131
816-333-9420
Fax: 816-333-9422
Occupational Fields: roofer, waterproofer

MONTANA
United Union of Roofers, Waterproofers, and Allied Workers, Local #229
PO Box 31866
Billings, MT 59107
406-668-7532
Fax: 406-668-7532
Occupational Fields: roofer, waterproofer

NEBRASKA
United Union of Roofers, Waterproofers, and Allied Workers
6202 South 33rd Street
Omaha, NE 68117
402-731-8130
Occupational Fields: roofer, waterproofer

NEVADA
United Union of Roofers, Waterproofers, and Allied Workers, Local #162
4125 Arctic Spings Avenue, Suite 5
Las Vegas, NV 89115
702-453-5801
Fax: 702-453-0426
union@rooferslocal162.org
Occupational Fields: roofer, waterproofer

United Union of Roofers, Waterproofers, and Allied Workers, Local #162
1110 Greg Street
Sparks, NV 89431
702-331-8666
Fax: 702-359-2144
Occupational Fields: roofer, waterproofer

NEW JERSEY
Roofers Union
172 Main Street
Orange, NJ 07052-5605

201-669-8677
Occupational Fields: roofer

United Union of Roofers, Waterproofers, and Allied Workers
305 South Main Street
Pleasantville, NJ 08232
609-646-7888
Occupational Fields: roofer, waterproofer

United Union of Roofers, Waterproofers, and Allied Workers, Local #10
321 Mason Avenue
Haledon, NJ 07508
201-595-5562
Fax: 201-595-5266
Occupational Fields: roofer, waterproofer

United Union of Roofers, Waterproofers, and Allied Workers, Local #30
1400 Genesee Street
Trenton, NJ 08610
609-394-2700
Occupational Fields: roofer, waterproofer

NEW YORK
United Union of Roofers, Waterproofers, and Allied Workers, Local #8
467 Dean Street
Brooklyn, NY 11217
718-789-8700
Fax: 718-398-8359
Occupational Fields: roofer, waterproofer

United Union of Roofers, Waterproofers, and Allied Workers, Local #74
2800 Clinton Street
West Seneca, NY 14224
716-824-7488
Fax: 716-824-7490
Occupational Fields: roofer, waterproofer

United Union of Roofers, Waterproofers, and Allied Workers, Local #154
370 Vanderbilt Motor Parkway, Suite 1
Hauppauge, NY 11788-8833
516-435-0655
Fax: 516-435-0262
Occupational Fields: roofer, waterproofer

United Union of Roofers, Waterproofers, and Allied Workers, Local #203
30 West State Street, Second Floor
Colonial Plaza
Binghamton, NY 13901
607-722-4073
roofers203@hotmail.com
Occupational Fields: roofer, waterproofer

United Union of Roofers, Waterproofers, and Allied Workers, Local #241
890 Third Street
Albany, NY 12206
518-489-7646
Fax: 518-489-5857
Occupational Fields: roofer, waterproofer

OHIO

United Union of Roofers, Waterproofers, and Allied Workers
PO Box 124
Colerain, OH 43916
304-232-2496
Occupational Fields: roofer, waterproofer

United Union of Roofers, Waterproofers, and Allied Workers, Local #42
1579 Summit Road
Cincinnati, OH 45237
513-821-3689
Fax: 513-761-3721
Occupational Fields: roofer, waterproofer

United Union of Roofers, Waterproofers, and Allied Workers, Local #44
1651 East 24th Street
Cleveland, OH 44114
216-781-4844
Fax: 216-781-7663
roofers44@sbcglobal.net
Occupational Fields: roofer, waterproofer

United Union of Roofers, Waterproofers, and Allied Workers, Local #71
2714 Martin Luther King
Youngstown, OH 44510
330-746-3020

Fax: 330-746-6020
Occupational Fields: roofer, waterproofer

United Union of Roofers, Waterproofers, and Allied Workers, Local #75
1200 East Second Street
Dayton, OH 45403
937-228-2464
Fax: 937-228-1233
Occupational Fields: roofer, waterproofer

United Union of Roofers, Waterproofers, and Allied Workers, Local #86
23 West Second Avenue
Columbus, OH 43201
614-299-6404
Occupational Fields: roofer, waterproofer

United Union of Roofers, Waterproofers, and Allied Workers, Local #88
6221 Promler Road, Northwest
North Canton, OH 44720
330-497-2848
Fax: 330-497-2037
Roofers88@aol.com
Occupational Fields: roofer, waterproofer

United Union of Roofers, Waterproofers, and Allied Workers, Local #134
4652 Lewis Avenue
Toledo, OH 43612
419-478-3785
Occupational Fields: roofer, waterproofer

OKLAHOMA

Eastern Oklahoma Building and Construction
2651 East 21st Street
Tulsa, OK 74114
918-742-3305
Occupational Fields: roofer, waterproofer

United Union of Roofers, Waterproofers, and Allied Workers, Local #143
111 Northeast 26th Street
Oklahoma City, OK 73105
405-524-4243
Fax: 405-524-5859
Occupational Fields: roofer, waterproofer

OREGON

United Union of Roofers, Waterproofers, and Allied Workers, Local #49
Southwest Washington Roofers
5032 Southeast 26th Street
Portland, OR 97202
503-232-4807
Fax: 503-232-1769
local49roof@msn.com
Occupational Fields: roofer

United Union of Roofers, Waterproofers, and Allied Workers, Local #156
1174 Gateway Loop, Suite 106
Springfield, OR 97477
541-744-1771
Fax: 541-736-3491
rul156@qwest.net
Occupational Fields: roofer, waterproofer

PENNSYLVANIA

United Union of Roofers, Waterproofers, and Allied Workers, Local #30
6447 Torresdale Avenue
Philadelphia, PA 19135
215-331-8770
Fax: 215-331-8320
Occupational Fields: roofer, waterproofer

United Union of Roofers, Waterproofers, and Allied Workers, Local #37
206 Federal Street
Pittsburgh, PA 15212
412-322-2166
Fax: 412-322-2167
local37@earthlink.net
Occupational Fields: roofer, waterproofer

United Union of Roofers, Waterproofers, and Allied Workers, Local #210
1701 State Street
Eerie, PA 16501
814-453-4503
Fax: 814-455-4340
Occupational Fields: roofer, waterproofer

RHODE ISLAND

United Union of Roofers, Waterproofers, and Allied Workers, Local #169
150 Ernest Street
Providence, RI 02905
401-467-6090
Occupational Fields: roofer, waterproofer

TENNESSEE

United Union of Roofers, Waterproofers, and Allied Workers, Local #115
3540 Summer Avenue, Suite 311
Memphis, TN 38122
901-327-6581
Occupational Fields: roofer, waterproofer

United Union of Roofers, Waterproofers, and Allied Workers, Local #176
5105 Alabama Avenue
PO Box 90996
Nashville, TN 37209
615-298-5215
Fax: 615-383-7767
Occupational Fields: roofer, waterproofer

TEXAS

United Union of Roofers, Waterproofers, and Allied Workers Local #116
PO Box 14188
Houston, TX 77221-4188
713-748-6111
Occupational Fields: roofer, waterproofer

United Union of Roofers, Waterproofers, and Allied Workers, Local #123
4025 Rufe Snow Drive
Fort Worth, TX 76180
817-589-2351
Occupational Fields: roofer, waterproofer

UTAH

United Union of Roofers, Waterproofers, and Allied Workers
2261 South Redwood Road
Salt Lake City, UT 84119
801-972-6830

Fax: 801-972-6830
Occupational Fields: *roofer, waterproofer*

WASHINGTON

United Union of Roofers, Waterproofers, and Allied Workers, Locals #54 and #78
2800 First Avenue, Room 320
Seattle, WA 98121-1114
206-728-2777
Fax: 206-728-7654
roofers54@qwest.net
Occupational Fields: *roofer, waterproofer*

United Union of Roofers, Waterproofers, and Allied Workers, Local #153
3049 South 36th Street, Suite 210A
Tacoma, WA 98409-5701
253-474-0528
Fax: 253-474-6877
rooferslocal153@earthlink.net
Occupational Fields: *roofer*

United Union of Roofers, Waterproofers, and Allied Workers, Local #189
East 102 Boone Avenue
Spokane, WA 99202
509-327-2322
Fax: 509-327-6451
Occupational Fields: *roofer*

WEST VIRGINIA

United Union of Roofers, Waterproofers, and Allied Workers, Local #185
PO Box 770
Elkview, WV 25071
304-346-9234
Fax: 304-346-9623
Occupational Fields: *roofer, waterproofer*

United Union of Roofers, Waterproofers, and Allied Workers, Local #242
1406 1/2 13th Street
Parkersburg, WV 26101
304-485-5099
Fax: 304-424-0446
roofers242mg@aol.com
Occupational Fields: *roofer, waterproofer*

WISCONSIN

United Union of Roofers, Waterproofers, and Allied Workers, Local #65
16601 West Dakota Street
New Berlin, WI 53151
414-771-3900
Fax: 414-771-4101
Occupational Fields: *roofer, waterproofer*

CANADA

BRITISH COLUMBIA

Roofing Contractors Association of British Columbia
9734 201st Street
Langley, BC V1M 3E8
604-882-9734
Fax: 604-882-1744
http://www.rcabc.org/index2.htm
Occupational Fields: *roofer*

NEW BRUNSWICK

Department of Training and Employment Development Apprenticeship and Occupational Certification
PO Box 6000
Chestnut Complex
Fredericton, NB E3B 5H1
506-453-2260
Fax: 506-453-5317
aoc-acp@gnb.ca
Occupational Fields: *roofer*

SHEET METAL WORKERS

RELATED SECTIONS: *auto body workers; boilermakers; carpenters; elevator constructors; ironworkers; machinists; mechanics; metalworkers; millwrights; operating engineers and stationary engineers; pipe trades workers; shipbuilding and ship maintenance workers; tool, die, mold, and pattern makers; welders*

Sheet metal workers fabricate, install, and repair ventilating, heating, and air-conditioning systems; gutters; metal roofing; skylights; storefronts; outdoor signs; stainless-steel kitchen and beverage equipment; and other products made of sheets of metal. They also work with plastics, fiberglass, and other materials. Some workers specialize in air-conditioning and ventilation systems. Sheet metal workers sometimes also remove asbestos and other hazardous substances.

The project typically begins in a shop, where the worker reads a blueprint or other specifications. The worker selects appropriate materials, then measures and cuts the metal with shears, saws, presses, or other machinery. Sometimes the pieces are assembled on site, perhaps with bolts, rivets, welding, or cement. Usually further assembly is completed at the construction site; some projects, such as metal roofs, are done entirely at the job site.

The worker often uses computerized equipment but must also be skilled with hand calculators, tapes, rulers, hacksaws, various types of shears, welding equipment, hammers, drills, and other tools. The worker must take care to cut the most possible number of pieces from each sheet of metal. This requires skill in layout and measuring.

Sheet metal workers tend to lose less time to inclement weather than do other construction workers, because much of their work is done indoors, but some of their time is spent on gutters, roofs and other outdoor projects. They typically work 40 hours per week in bright, well-ventilated shops. The work requires standing, climbing, bending, squatting, and some heavy lifting. There is danger of injury from machinery, cuts from sharp metal, soldering and welding burns, and falls from ladders and stages.

About three out of four sheet metal workers are employed by the heating, air-conditioning, and plumbing industries. Others work for roofing and sheet metal contractors, shipbuilders, railroads, and aircraft manufacturers. Few sheet metal workers are self-employed.

Many sheet metal workers belong to unions, such as the Sheet Metal Workers International Association, the Sheet Metal and Air-Conditioning Contractors National Association, or the Associated Builders and Contractors.

There is an increasing demand for apprentices in this field as employers seek qualified workers. Apprenticeship is the recommended way of entering this occupation. Trainees participate in on-the-job training under the supervision of experienced sheet metal workers and complete at least 144 hours of course work each year. Typically the course of study runs for four to five years and includes instruction in computers, drafting, trigonometry, geometry, mathematics, blueprint reading, and welding.

In general an applicant should

- apply in person
- be at least 18 years old
- be a high school graduate or hold a GED certificate
- be physically capable of performing the work
- have mechanical and mathematical aptitude
- have good hand-eye coordination
- have good spatial form perception
- have manual dexterity

APPRENTICESHIP SALARIES

Apprentices earn about 40 percent of the rate paid to skilled workers. This can range from $6 an hour up to $14 an hour or more, with periodic raises. Experienced apprentices may earn up to $32 an hour.

POSTAPPRENTICESHIP SALARIES

Earnings range from about $9 an hour up to $42 an hour, depending on geographic location, experience, and the specific industry in which the worker is employed. The median hourly wage is around $16.

JOB OUTLOOK

Employment of sheet metal workers is expected to grow about as fast as the average for all occupations through the year 2012. Job opportunities should be good in this occupation because of the pace of residential, commercial, and industrial construction. There is a particularly high demand for energy-efficient buildings, heating and air-conditioning units, and ventilation systems. Maintenance and renovation of existing equipment and structures will provide continued work as well.

NATIONAL PROGRAMS
National Training Fund for the Sheet Metal and Air Conditioning Industry
601 North Fairfax Street, #240
Alexandria, VA 22314-2054
703-739-7200
Occupational Fields: sheet metal worker, air conditioning technician

Sheet Metal Workers International Association, National Headquarters
1750 New York Avenue, NW, Sixth Floor
Washington, DC 20006-5301
202-783-5880
Fax: 202-662-0891
http://www.smwia.org
Occupational Fields: sheet metal worker

APPRENTICESHIP PROFILE
Lake County Sheet Metal Workers
Joint Apprenticeship and Training Committee
6450 Ameriplex Drive
Portage, IN 46383
219-764-1900
Fax: 219-764-1941

General Nature of the Job
Sheet metal workers fabricate and install all sorts of products made from flat sheets of metal, indoors and outdoors, under all sorts of conditions. "It's construction work. It can be very cold, dirty, and hot. You can be 200 feet in the air or 20 feet underground. You never know what you're going to do next. It takes a special breed. You have to really enjoy working with your hands," says Dale Hensen, Director of Training for the Joint Apprenticeship Committee sponsored by the Sheet Metal Workers Local Union 20-G in Gary, Indiana.

The trade requires knowledge of algebra, geometry, trigonometry, computers, drafting, and mechanical drawing. Dale recommends that prospective sheet metal workers also study general science and take wood or metal shop classes in high school. Most of these subjects are taught through the union's apprentice program, but applicants with a good education have a better chance of being accepted.

Local 20-G, which is affiliated with the Sheet Metal Workers International Association's national training fund, has operated an apprenticeship program for more than 40 years. "I went through it thirty-seven years ago. It's changed considerably, keeping up with the times," Dale notes. The program is mid-size for the industry, with about 90 apprentices from seven local counties currently enrolled. Their training runs for five years and features 320 hours a year of classroom work and 1,650 hours a year of on-the-job training.

The union's training facility includes classrooms, a hands-on area where apprentices learn roofing and other skills, and a large shop. "They do a lot of hands-on fabrication of fittings and that kind of thing. We give them a little of everything we can think of. Hopefully it makes them more employable," says Dale.

Typical Day
Some apprentices travel up to 40 miles to attend class or work for eight hours each day, from 7:00 A.M. to 3:30 P.M., with two coffee breaks and 45 minutes for lunch. They spend one day a week in classes for 40 weeks each year, and they receive half a day's pay for each day in class. This is not a program for loafers; students who fail to maintain a 78 percent average on their written examinations are eliminated from the training.

During their time working in the shop, most apprentices form and assemble material such as heating ducts, which will be sold or installed at job sites. A project might take anywhere from a day to three weeks. Whether in the shop or on a job site, apprentices are closely supervised, since the work can be dangerous and must be done properly. Because apprentices are indentured to the apprenticeship committee, not to the contractors who provide their on-the-job training, the committee arranges jobs for them instead of requiring them to find contractors who will serve as mentors.

The work varies widely, depending on the contractor's specialty and what jobs happen to be on the agenda, but a typical project might involve fabricating ducts to move air from a heating or cooling unit throughout the rooms of a building. The apprentice starts with a sheet of metal, decides how to cut it into the necessary pieces with the least amount of waste, cuts the pieces out, assembles them, and sometimes installs them. Most projects require the use of assorted equipment, such as seaming machines, power tools, drills, electric sanders, or power forming-roll machines. The contractors provide safety glasses, gloves, welding helmets, and ear plugs. Apprentices must supply their own steel-toed shoes.

Path to Becoming an Apprentice

"We have a lot of people that want these positions, but we try desperately to attract female applicants. Most of our applicants have already had some trade-related experience. It's pretty tough for an individual to come right out of high school and walk into these positions, but it does happen," Dale says.

The apprenticeship committee accepts about 25 students each year. Applications are accepted during the first two weeks of June, school starts in August, and apprentices report for work on the second day of training. Applicants must be at least 18 years old, have a high school diploma or GED and birth certificate, and pass a physical and drug test administered by their own physicians.

The eight-member apprenticeship committee interviews each applicant, making note of attitude and personal traits, interest in the work, aptitude, work experience, and education. "They get about five minutes to make an impression. If they've taken the more difficult path through school, we give them more credit for effort," says Dale.

Applicants who are not accepted into the apprenticeship program can enroll in the committee's preapprenticeship program, where they work with contractors to decide if they want to enter the trade, to determine if they're capable of succeeding at it, and to prepare for the apprenticeship program. Students can begin preapprenticeship training at any time during the year.

Salary Range

Students in the preapprenticeship program earn $10.44 an hour. Apprentices start at about $11.93 an hour and receive raises every six months if they perform well. During their five years in training they earn a total income that exceeds $100,000.

Journeymen sheet metal workers earn $29.83 an hour. They also receive health insurance, a pension plan, and other benefits. They must belong to a union and pay dues. "If you're willing to work overtime and become a superintendent, you can make up to $80,000 a year," Dale says.

Advice

To prepare for a career in this field, Dale advises, "Take all the math you can, and take computer training and any kind of shop classes." He reminds high school students that their conduct, including school attendance and other data, is a matter of record that will be considered before the apprenticeship committee invests the time and money to train them. "The biggest thing we need is reliability. We can't afford to take a chance. You need commitment, some way to show us that this is what you want to do."

Future Goals

Dale says it's possible to become a sheet metal worker without formal training, but it's not likely, and it would take years longer than an apprenticeship. Indiana does not require a license or certification for sheet metal workers in general, but certification is required for welding and other areas of specialization. A large percentage of people who have graduated from the program have been promoted to foreman or higher on the job. Apprentices who take the training seriously will find employment, Dale says.

ALABAMA

Sheet Metal Workers Union
Highway 72
Athens, AL 35611
205-729-1470
Occupational Fields: sheet metal worker

Sheet Metal Workers Union, Local #48
1108 29th Street, North
Birmingham, AL 35234
205-322-9016
Fax: 205-324-4129
Occupational Fields: sheet metal worker

Sheet Metal Workers Union, Local #441
PO Box 6708
Mobile, AL 36606
251-476-1900
Fax: 251-473-0378
Occupational Fields: sheet metal worker

ALASKA

Sheet Metal Union, Local #23
4141 B Street, Suite 209
Anchorage, AK 99503
907-277-5313
Fax: 907-277-2457
smwak@alaska.net
Occupational Fields: sheet metal worker

Sheet Metal Union, Local #23
3650 Braddock Street
Fairbanks, AK 99701-7617
907-452-3864
Fax: 907-456-3413
Occupational Fields: sheet metal worker

ARIZONA

Arizona Precision Sheet Metal
2140 West Pinnacle Peak Road
Phoenix, AZ 85027
602-516-3700
Occupational Fields: *fabricator, sheet metal worker*

Associated Builders and Contractors and Associated General Contractors, Phoenix
2702 North Third Street, Suite 2020
Phoenix, AZ 85004-4606
602-274-8222
Fax: 602-274-8999
http://www.azbuilders.org
Occupational Fields: *sheet metal worker*

Associated Builders and Contractors and Associated General Contractors, Tucson
1661 North Swan, Suite 144
Tucson, AZ 85712
520-881-7930
Fax: 520-327-1686
http://www.azbuilders.org
Occupational Fields: *sheet metal worker*

Interstate Mechanical Corporation (IMCOR)
1841 East Washington Street
Phoenix, AZ 85034
602-257-1319
Fax: 602-271-0674
Occupational Fields: *sheet metal worker*

P-D Morenci Inc.
PO Box 187
Morenci, AZ 85540
520-865-4521
Occupational Fields: *sheet metal worker*

Phoenix Sheet Metal
2534 East Adams Street
Phoenix, AZ 85034
602-275-6511
Occupational Fields: *sheet metal worker, air and hydronic balancing technician*

Salt River Project
Personnel Department
PO Box 52025 STC001
Phoenix, AZ 85072-2025

602-236-2182
Occupational Fields: *fabricator, sheet metal worker*

Tucson Sheet Metal Joint Apprenticeship Council
606 South Plumer
Tucson, AZ 85719
520-622-3593
Occupational Fields: *sheet metal worker*

CALIFORNIA

Construction Craft Training Center
5750 Imhoff Drive
Concord, CA 94520
510-785-2282
Fax: 510-785-9136
http://www.cctc.edu
Occupational Fields: *sheet metal worker*

Construction Craft Training Center
26232 Industrial Boulevard
Hayward, CA 94545
510-785-2282
Fax: 510-785-9136
http://www.cctc.edu
Occupational Fields: *sheet metal worker*

Sheet Metal Workers
415 Chapala Street, Room 103
Santa Barbara, CA 93101
805-962-1232
Occupational Fields: *sheet metal worker*

Sheet Metal Workers School
1624 Silica Avenue
Sacramento, CA 95815
916-922-9381
Occupational Fields: *sheet metal worker*

Sheet Metal Workers Union
10357 Merritt Street
Castroville, CA 95012-3306
408-633-6151
Occupational Fields: *sheet metal worker*

Sheet Metal Workers Union
1307 Seventh Street
Modesto, CA 95354
209-523-1138
Occupational Fields: *sheet metal worker*

Sheet Metal Workers Union
1700 Marina Boulevard
San Leandro, CA 94577-4203
510-483-9035
Occupational Fields: sheet metal worker

Sheet Metal Workers Union, Local #104
1939 Market Street
San Francisco, CA 94103
415-431-1676
Occupational Fields: sheet metal worker

Sheet Metal Workers Union, Local #108
464 Lucas Avenue
Los Angeles, CA 90017
213-481-2088
Occupational Fields: sheet metal worker

Sheet Metal Workers Union, Local #162
2840 El Centro Road, #110
Sacramento, CA 95833
916-922-1133
Fax: 916-922-2969
http://www.smwia162.com
Occupational Fields: sheet metal worker

Sheet Metal Workers Union, Local #162
4585 East Floradora Avenue
Fresno, CA 93703-4419
209-255-0454
Occupational Fields: sheet metal worker

COLORADO
Associated General Contractors
Colorado Building
1114 West Seventh Avenue, Suite 200
Denver, CO 80204
303-388-2422
Fax: 303-388-0936
dick@agccolorado.org
http://www.agccolorado.org
Occupational Fields: sheet metal worker

Sheet Metal Workers Union, Local #9
PO Box 27910
Denver, CO 80227-0910
303-922-1213

Fax: 303-922-1398
http://www.smw9.org
Occupational Fields: sheet metal worker

CONNECTICUT
General Dynamics
Electric Boat Division
75 Eastern Point Road
Groton, CT 06340-4905
860-433-3000
Fax: 860-433-1400
Occupational Fields: marine sheet metal worker

DISTRICT OF COLUMBIA
Sheet Metal Workers International Association,
** National Headquarters**
1750 New York Avenue, NW, Sixth Floor
Washington, DC 20006-5301
202-783-5880
http://www.smwia.org
Occupational Fields: sheet metal worker

FLORIDA
Associated General Contractors, Florida East Coast
** Chapter**
2617 North Australian Avenue
West Palm Beach, FL 33407-5697
561-833-3609
Fax: 561-833-6024
http://www.agcfla.com
Occupational Fields: sheet metal worker

East Central Florida Sheet Metal Workers Union
2688 South Design Court
Sanford, FL 32773
407-322-8601
Occupational Fields: sheet metal worker

Florida West Coast Sheet Metal, Local #15
5619 North 50th Street
Tampa, FL 33610
813-628-0021
Fax: 813-628-0222
MjeskeLU15@Verizon.net
Occupational Fields: sheet metal worker

Jacksonville Sheet Metal Workers, Local #435
1435 Naldo Avenue
Jacksonville, FL 32207
904-398-1838
Fax: 904-396-8657
http://www.jaxsheetmetal.org
Occupational Fields: sheet metal worker

Sheet Metal Workers Union, Local #32
20375 Northeast 15th Court
North Miami, FL 33179
305-651-8692
Fax: 305-654-0010
Occupational Fields: sheet metal worker

West Palm Beach Sheet Metal
1003 Belvedere Road, Room Five
Palm Beach, FL 33405
561-659-6093
Occupational Fields: sheet metal worker

GEORGIA
Georgia Sheet Metal
575 Fair Drive, SW
Atlanta, GA 30315
404-753-6466
Fax: 404-758-0881
Occupational Fields: sheet metal worker

HAWAII
Sheet Metal Workers Training Office
1405 North King Street, Room 404
Honolulu, HI 96817
808-841-6106
Fax: 808-841-1842
hwbsmwialocal.293@hawaii.rr.com
Occupational Fields: sheet metal worker

ILLINOIS
ILLOWA Sheet Metal Workers, Local #91
8124 42nd Street
Rock Island, IL 61201
309-787-0695
Fax: 609-787-0733
smw91@qconline.com
Occupational Fields: sheet metal worker

Sheet Metal Workers, Local #1
4220 North Boulevard Avenue
Peoria Heights, IL 61614
309-682-5677
Fax: 309-682-4164
smwone@sbcglobal.net
Occupational Fields: sheet metal worker

Sheet Metal Workers Union, Local #115
6643 North Avenue
Oak Park, IL 60302
708-383-8789
Occupational Fields: sheet metal worker

Sheet Metal Workers Union, Local #218
2855 Via Verde Street
Springfield, IL 62703
217-529-0161
Fax: 217-529-6005
Occupational Fields: sheet metal worker

INDIANA
Associated Builders and Contractors of Indiana
6825 Hillsdale Court
Indianapolis, IN 46250
317-596-4950
Fax: 317-596-4957
http://www.abc-indy.org
Occupational Fields: sheet metal worker

General Motors Powertrain
Training Programs
105 GM Drive
Bedford, IN 47421
812-279-7261
Fax: 812-279-7084
Occupational Fields: sheet metal worker

Generex Inc.
PO Box 15310
3403 East Washington Boulevard
Fort Wayne, IN 46885
260-424-1965
Fax: 260-424-1851
Occupational Fields: sheet metal worker

Lake County Sheet Metal Workers
Joint Apprenticeship and Training Committee
6450 Ameriplex Drive

Portage, IN 46368
219-764-1900
Fax: 219-887-9550
Occupational Fields: *sheet metal worker*

Sheet Metal Workers International Association
707 Main Street
Indianapolis, IN 46220-3531
317-786-5373
Occupational Fields: *sheet metal worker*

Sheet Metal Workers Union, Local #20
2828 East 45th Street
Indianapolis, IN 46205-2403
317-541-0050
Fax: 317-549-6001
Occupational Fields: *sheet metal worker*

Sheet Metal Workers Union, Local #20
PO Box 20530
Indianapolis, IN 46220
219-478-1614
http://www.smw20.com
Occupational Fields: *sheet metal worker*

Sheet Metal Workers Union, Local #20
608 North 13th Street
Terre Haute, IN 47807
812-234-0751
Occupational Fields: *sheet metal worker*

Whirlpool Corporation
Employment and Wage Administration
5401 U.S. Highway 41, North
Evansville, IN 47727
812-426-4496
Fax: 812-426-4957
Occupational Fields: *sheeetmetal worker*

IOWA

A-C Contractors Inc.
1495 Keo Way
Des Moines, IA 50314-1222
515-244-0606
Fax: 515-244-0735
Occupational Fields: *sheet metal worker*

ACI Mechanical Corporation
3116 South Duff Avenue
Ames, IA 50010-8460

515-232-1236
Fax: 515-232-0136
Occupational Fields: *sheet metal worker*

Central Iowa Sheet Metal Workers, Local #45
2425 Delaware Avenue
Des Moines, IA 50317-3581
515-262-7421
Fax: 515-266-3328
smw45@qwest.net
Occupational Fields: *sheet metal worker*

Cunningham Inc.
1112 Sixth Avenue
Oskaloosa, IA 52577
515-673-8479
Occupational Fields: *sheet metal worker*

Dahl Air Conditioning and Heating Company
PO Box 253
Van Meter, IA 50261-0253
515-996-2216
Occupational Fields: *sheet metal worker*

Kapaun and Brown Inc.
PO Box 1746
Ames, IA 50010-6569
515-232-0955
Occupational Fields: *sheet metal worker*

Maytag Company
One Dependability Square
Newton, IA 50208
515-792-7000
Occupational Fields: *sheet metal worker*

Sheet Metal Workers, Local #263
1211 Wiley Boulevard, SW
Cedar Rapids, IA 52404
319-396-8045
Fax: 319-396-4964
smwia263@ia.net
Occupational Fields: *sheet metal worker*

Sioux City Sheet Metal Workers
321 Fifth Street
Sioux City, IA 51101
712-255-9953
Occupational Fields: *sheet metal worker*

KANSAS

**Associated Builders and Contractors,
Heart of America**
6950 Squibb Road, #418
Mission, KS 66202
913-831-2221
Fax: 913-831-0808
http://www.abcksmo.org
Occupational Fields: sheet metal worker

General Motors Corporation
3201 Fairfax Trafficway
Kansas City, KS 66115-1399
913-573-7400
Fax: 913-573-7109
Occupational Fields: sheet metal worker

Sheet Metal Workers Union
555 Northwest Broad Street
Topeka, KS 66608-1841
785-233-4014
Fax: 785-233-7782
tinmanlu77@aol.com
Occupational Fields: sheet metal worker

Sheet Metal Workers Union, Local #29
1723 Southwest Boulevard
Wichita, KS 67213-1433
316-941-4311
Fax: 316-941-4313
sheetmetal29@sbcglobal.net
Occupational Fields: sheet metal worker

LOUISIANA

Sims Insulation and Air Conditioning Company
1960 Easy Street
Lake Charles, LA 70605
318-477-8700
Occupational Fields: sheet metal worker

MAINE

Bath Iron Works
700 Washington Street
Bath, ME 04530-2574
207-442-1820
Fax: 207-442-1737
Occupational Fields: sheet metal worker

MARYLAND

Bethlehem Steel Corporation, Sparrows Point
5111 North Point Boulevard
Baltimore, MD 21219
410-388-3000
Occupational Fields: sheet metal worker

Hess Mechanical Corporation
9600 Fallard Court
Upper Marlboro, MD 20772
301-856-4700
Fax: 301-856-4720
Occupational Fields: sheet metal worker

Sheet Metal Workers Union, Local #100
4725 Silver Hill Road
Suitland, MD 20746
301-568-8655
Fax: 301-967-1683
SMWIA100@AOL.COM
Occupational Fields: sheet metal worker

MASSACHUSETTS

Sheet Metal Workers Union, Local #17
1147 Adams Street
Dorchester, MA 02124-5710
617-298-0850
Fax: 617-296-1295
FJOYCE@SMW17BOSTON.ORG
Occupational Fields: sheet metal worker

MISSISSIPPI

Sheet Metal Workers Union, Local #406
510 Guidici Street
Jackson, MS 39204-3103
601-352-4182
Fax: 601-352-9848
Smwlu406@bellsouth.net
Occupational Fields: sheet metal worker

MISSOURI

Stadium Sheet Metal
11820 East 83rd Street
PO Box 37145
Raytown, MO 64138
816-356-7620
Occupational Fields: sheet metal worker

NEVADA
Associated Builders and Contractors,
Sierra Nevada Chapter
740 Freeport, Unit 101
Sparks, NV 89431
775-358-7888
Fax: 775-358-7893
http://www.abcsierranv.org
Occupational Fields: sheet metal worker

NEW JERSEY
Sheet Metal Workers Union, Local #27
PO Box 847
Farmingdale, NJ 07727-0847
732-9191-1999
732-938-7901
Occupational Fields: sheet metal worker

NEW MEXICO
Sheet Metal Workers Union, Local #49
2300 Buena Vista SE, Suite 110
Albuquerque, NM 87106
505-266-5878
Fax: 505-266-5879
tfarmer@spinn.net
Occupational Fields: sheet metal worker

NEW YORK
Dynabill Industries Inc.
Flint Mine Road
Coxsackie, NY 12051
518-731-2791
Occupational Fields: sheet metal worker

Sheet Metal Workers Union, Local #1A
4104 56th Street
Flushing, NY 11377-4744
Occupational Fields: sheet metal worker

Sheet Metal Workers Union, Local #28
500 Greenwich Street, 5th Floor
New York, NY 10013
212-941-7700
Fax: 212-226-0304
http://www.smwialu28.org
Occupational Fields: sheet metal worker

Sheet Metal Workers Union, Local #46
40 Rutter Street
Rochester, NY 14606-1806
585-254-9151
585-254-8584
http://www.smw46.com
Occupational Fields: sheet metal worker

Sheet Metal Workers Union,
Local #58
301 Sheet Metal Street
Syracuse, NY 13204-1132
315-472-4411
Fax: 315-472-4413
Occupational Fields: sheet metal worker

Sheet Metal Workers Union,
Local #71
24 Liberty Avenue
Buffalo, NY 14215-2112
716-835-8836
716-835-8496
agentloc71@aol.com
Occupational Fields: sheet metal worker

Sheet Metal Workers Union,
Local #83
718 Third Street
Albany, NY 12206-2007
518-489-1377
Fax: 518-453-9284
smwia83org@aol.com
Occupational Fields: sheet metal worker

Sheet Metal Workers Union,
Local #112
PO Box 1146
Elmira, NY 14902
607-733-9621
Fax: 607-732-3120
smw112@workingfamilies.com
Occupational Fields: sheet metal worker

NORTH DAKOTA
Sheet Metal Workers Union, Local #10
3906-155 R Avenue, SE
Dubin, ND 58059
701-347-5057
Occupational Fields: sheet metal worker

OHIO

Sheet Metal Workers, Local #24
4949 Northcutt Place
Dayton, OH 45414
937-277-7578
Fax: 937-277-2898
smwlu24day@voyager.net
Occupational Fields: sheet metal worker

OKLAHOMA

Sheet Metal Workers School
2439 East Admiral Place
Tulsa, OK 74110
918-834-2808
Occupational Fields: sheet metal worker

Sheet Metal Workers Union, Local #124
1404 Northwest First Street
Oklahoma City, OK 73106
405-232-1453
Fax: 405-232-1455
SMWIA124@aol.com
Occupational Fields: sheet metal worker

Sheet Metal Workers Union, Local #270
632 East Third Street
Tulsa, OK 74120
918-587-2388
Fax: 918-587-2442
http://www.smw270.org
Occupational Fields: sheet metal worker

OREGON

Clark and Skamania Washington Sheet Metal Workers, Local #16
2379 Northeast 178th Avenue
Portland, OR 97230
503-257-1022
http://www.sheetmetal-16.org
Occupational Fields: sheet metal worker

Sheet Metal Workers Union
2659 Commercial Street, SE
Salem, OR 97302
503-363-4306
Occupational Fields: sheet metal worker

Sheet Metal Workers Union, Local #16
825 Northeast 20th Avenue
Portland, OR 97232
Occupational Fields: sheet metal worker

Sheet Metal Workers Union, Local #16
1174 Gateway Loop, #107
Springfield, OR 97477
541-746-7626
Occupational Fields: sheet metal worker

PENNSYLVANIA

Sheet Metal Workers Training Center
539 Main Street
Shoemakersville, PA 19555
610-562-5306
Fax: 610-562-2166
Occupational Fields: sheet metal worker

Sheet Metal Workers Union
248 Parrish Street
Wilkes-Barre, PA 18702
570-822-4781
Fax: 570-822-6615
SM44@epix.net
Occupational Fields: sheet metal worker

Sheet Metal Workers Union, Local #12
1701 State Street
Erie, PA 16501
814-452-6563
Occupational Fields: sheet metal worker

Sheet Metal Workers Union, Local #12
1200 Gulf Lab Road
Pittsburgh, PA 15238
412-828-5300
Fax: 412-828-9363
cholt@smlocal12.org
Occupational Fields: sheet metal worker

Sheet Metal Workers Union, Local #520
7728 Farmdale Avenue
Harrisburg, PA 17104
717-564-1997
Occupational Fields: sheet metal worker

RHODE ISLAND

Sheet Metal Workers Union, Local #17
150 Ernest Street
Providence, RI 02905
401-941-8202
Occupational Fields: sheet metal worker

TENNESSEE

**Sheet Metal Workers Union,
    Local #4**
663 South Cooper Street, Suite 5-A
Memphis, TN 38104
901-278-7288
Fax: 901-278-7289
Occupational Fields: sheet metal worker

**Sheet Metal Workers,
    Local #5**
112 Hillcrest Drive
Knoxville, TN 37918
865-689-2928
Fax: 865-689-9959
Smwlu5@bellsouth.net
Occupational Fields: sheet metal worker

Sheet Metal Workers Union, Local #177
4709 Alabama Avenue
Nashville, TN 37209
615-292-0587
Fax: 615-383-4417
Smwia177@attglobal.net
Occupational Fields: sheet metal worker

Sheet Metal Workers Union, Local #483
541 School Street
Morrison, TN 37357
931-635-2696
Fax: 931-635-3336
Smw483@blomand.net
Occupational Fields: sheet metal worker

TEXAS

Sabine Area Sheet Metal Workers
8311 Old Highway 90
Orange, TX 77630
409-745-1096
Occupational Fields: sheet metal worker

Sheet Metal Workers, Local #54
900 West 34th Street
Houston, TX 77292
713-869-5843
Fax: 713-864-4598
tinnerlocal54@aol.com
Occupational Fields: sheet metal worker

**Sheet Metal Workers Union,
    Local #67**
130 Avenue Del Ray
San Antonio, TX 78216
210-349-3350
Fax: 210-349-6557
bwilson@sbcglobal.net
Occupational Fields: sheet metal worker

Sheet Metal Workers Union, Local #68
1020 South Industrial Boulevard
Euless, TX 76040-5841
817-267-9213
Fax: 817-571-1023
Occupational Fields: sheet metal worker

UTAH

Sheet Metal Workers, Local Union #312
2480 South 3400 West
Salt Lake City, UT 84119
801-973-4804
Fax: 801-973-4830
Occupational Fields: sheet metal worker

VIRGINIA

**National Training Fund for the Sheet Metal and Air
    Conditioning Industry**
601 North Fairfax Street, #240
Alexandria, VA 22314-2054
703-739-7200
Occupational Fields: sheet metal worker, air conditioning
    technician

Newport News Shipbuilding
Admissions Office
4101 Washington Avenue
Newport News, VA 23607-2770
757-380-2000
Occupational Fields: sheet metal worker

Sheet Metal Workers,
   Local #100
3204 Cutshaw Avenue
Richmond, VA 23230
804-353-2425
Occupational Fields: sheet metal worker

Sheet Metal Workers International Association and
   Sheet Metal and Air Conditioning Contractors'
   National Association
601 North Fairfax Street, Suite 240
Alexandria, VA 22314
703-739-7200
Occupational Fields: heating, ventilation, and air
   conditioning mechanic, sheet metal worker

WASHINGTON
Associated Builders and Contractors,
   Inland Pacific Chapter
PO Box 3787
Spokane, WA 99220
509-534-0826
Fax: 509-535-9967
ipcabc@qwest.net
http://www.ipcabc.org
Occupational Fields: sheet metal worker

Association of Western Pulp and Paper Workers,
   Local #5, James River Corporation
Camas Mill
Northeast Fourth and Adams
Camas, WA 98607
360-817-2157
Occupational Fields: sheet metal worker

Fluor Daniel Hanford
M/S R2-88
PO Box 1500
Richland, WA 99352-1505
509-376-1523
Occupational Fields: sheet metal worker

INTALCO Aluminum Corporation
PO Box 937
Ferndale, WA 98248
360-384-7296
Occupational Fields: sheet metal worker

Northeastern Washington and Northern Idaho
   Sheet Metal
East 7209 Trent Avenue
Spokane, WA 99212
509-533-8081
Occupational Fields: sheet metal worker

Northwest Washington Marine Sheet Metal
13513 Northeast 126th Place, A-1
Kirkland, WA 98034-8725
425-820-2306
Occupational Fields: sheet metal worker

Seattle, City of
700 Fifth Avenue, Suite 3100, Room SSCB-220
Seattle, WA 98104-5031
206-386-1607
Occupational Fields: sheet metal worker

Sno-King Sheet Metal Workers
13513 Northeast 126th Place
Kirkland, WA 98034-8725
425-823-5737
Occupational Fields: heating, ventilation, and air
   conditioning mechanic; sheet metal worker

Western Washington Sheet Metal
PO Box 5757
Lacey, WA 98503
360-459-9118
Occupational Fields: sheet metal worker

WEST VIRGINIA
Construction Trades Training Center
2307 Seventh Avenue
Charleston, WV 25312-1811
304-346-3863
Occupational Fields: sheet metal worker

WISCONSIN
Air Comfort Inc.
5525 Bjorksten Plaza
Madison, WI 53711
608-274-5566
Occupational Fields: sheet metal worker

Consolidated Papers Inc.
231 First Avenue, North
Wisconsin Rapids, WI 54495

715-442-3111
Occupational Fields: sheet metal worker

**Milwaukee Area Joint Apprenticeship and Training
    Committee For the Sheet Metal Industry**
5425 West Vliet Street
Milwaukee, WI 53208
414-778-1100
Fax: 414-778-0987
Occupational Fields: sheet metal worker

Repap USA Inc.
433 North Main Street
Kimberly, WI 54136-1440
414-788-3511
Fax: 414-788-5368
Occupational Fields: sheet metal worker

Rhinelander Paper Company
515 West Davenport Street
Rhinelander, WI 54501
715-369-4100
Occupational Fields: sheet metal worker

CANADA
BRITISH COLUMBIA
Sheet Metal Workers Training Centre
4415 Dawson Street
Burnaby, BC V5C 4B8
604-291-0656
Fax: 604-291-0602
smwtc@telus.net
Occupational Fields: sheet metal worker

NEW BRUNSWICK
**Department of Training and Employment
    Development Apprenticeship and Occupational
    Certification**
PO Box 6000
Chestnut Complex
Fredericton, NB E3B 5H1
506-453-2260
Fax: 506-453-5317
aoc-acp@gnb.ca
Occupational Fields: sheet metal worker

SHIPBUILDING AND SHIP MAINTENANCE INDUSTRY WORKERS

RELATED SECTIONS: *boilermakers; carpenters; engineers and engineering technicians; ironworkers; machinists; mechanics; metalworkers; millwrights; painters and paperhangers; pile drivers; pipe trades workers; railroad workers; sheet metal workers; tool, die, mold, and pattern makers; truck drivers; welders*

Workers in various trades, including *welders, pipe fitters,* and *mechanics,* are involved in the building of ships. Some workers specialize in building ships. *Shipfitters* manufacture metal bulkheads, frames, and other structural parts, and then secure those parts in position for riveting or welding. Some shipfitters create molds for manufacturing unusual parts.

Shipwrights are carpenters who build and repair ship parts.

Engineers, also known as *marine engineers,* operate, maintain, and repair engines, boilers, and other machines. *Assistant engineers* stand watch for about four hours at a time and look after the general performance of the ship's machines. *Marine oilers,* working under the supervision of the engineers, oil the moving parts of machinery, read gauges, compile data, and sometimes fine-tune and repair engines and motors.

Riggers install and repair rigging, the lines and chains used to secure masts and other structures on a ship. Some riggers also install machines, equipment, and structural parts on ships.

Shipbuilders work mostly indoors and run some risk of injury from power tools, cuts from sharp steel and various building materials, and other hazards. Workers who travel onboard ships risk falling overboard, being on a sinking vessel, having to abandon ship suddenly, or being stranded if the ship runs aground. Attention to safety procedures is important.

Workers who travel with the ship are sometimes away from home for long periods of time (except those who work on rivers and harbors), but they are compensated with extended shore leave. Many of them are employed for only one voyage at a time and have no guarantee of work afterward. Sometimes these workers put in long shifts, anywhere from eight hours to a week or a month of six- or 12-hour shifts, and then have a long period off. The work must be done despite inclement weather, and often the environment on the ship is cold and wet.

Apprentices to this trade work under the supervision of experienced workers. They participate in course work and on-the-job training. Typically, the course of study runs for three to four years. Apprentices learning to fabricate metal parts must master welding, forging, form-

ing, blueprint reading, designing, testing, and other skills. Engineers must pass a licensing examination; the test can be taken by applicants with at least three years of experience at sea and a thorough knowledge of the subject matter. Seamen without a license may work in the engineering department and enroll in training courses, which are usually sponsored by a trade union.

In general an applicant should

- apply in person
- be at least 18 years old
- be a high school graduate or hold a GED certificate
- be in good physical condition

APPRENTICESHIP SALARIES

Between $8 an hour and $14 an hour for beginning apprentices and up to $20 an hour for experienced apprentices.

POSTAPPRENTICESHIP SALARIES

About $15 an hour, up to $22 an hour.

JOB OUTLOOK

Employment in this industry is expected to decline slightly, although ships will likely remain an important component of the world's transportation system. The U.S. Navy will continue to build and operate ships. There is keen competition for some jobs in water transportation.

For more information on apprenticeships for workers in the shipbuilding and ship maintenance industry, contact local job centers, your state bureau of apprenticeship training, or the national organizations and individual programs listed below.

NATIONAL PROGRAMS
Shipbuilders Council of America
1455 F Street, NW, Suite 225
Washington, DC 20005

202-347-5462
Fax: 202-347-5464
mallen@dc.bjllp.com
http://www.shipbuilders.org
Occupational Fields: shipbuilder

APPRENTICESHIP PROFILE
Capitol District Carpenters, Shipwrights, Millwrights, Drywall, Metal Stud Acoustical, Ceiling and Insulation
Joint Apprenticeship and Training Committee
2201 South 78th Street, Building B-512
Tacoma, WA 98409
253-472-2629
Fax: 253-475-2785

General Nature of the Job
Shipwrights are specialized carpenters who finish the cabinets and other interior work on sailing vessels. The trade has changed rapidly during the past few decades to accommodate the trend toward vessels made of steel and fiberglass. Shipwrights now spend much of their time welding and performing other tasks that have not traditionally been the job of carpenters. An apprentice in this trade learns many skills, such as how to weld the hull of a ship.

"Apprentices work through the whole project. They'll insulate the hull and do interior work, all the cabinetry and partitions inside. Usually by the time they're in the latter part of their apprenticeship, they find a particular area and specialize," explains Richard DeWalt, coordinator of the Capitol District Shipwrights Joint Apprenticeship and Training Committee in Tacoma, Washington.

The apprenticeship program is a cooperative venture of the region's shipbuilding companies, the Capitol District Carpenters Union, and Bates Technical College. It has been in operation for about 50 years. Apprentices spend 160 hours at the college each year, performing mostly hands-on work and taking a few classes that pertain to their trade. By the time they finish the four-year program, they have also completed 8,000 hours of on-the-job training at a local shipyard. Graduates receive journeyman certification as shipwrights and qualify for journeyman standing in the Brotherhood of Carpenters.

Typical Day
For one week every three months, apprentices attend Bates Technical College from 7:30 A.M. to 4:00 P.M. The

carpenter training facility features a classroom, a computer lab, and a shop. There, students learn to work with the many tools of the carpenter's trade, including hammers, screwdrivers, levels, T-squares, radial arm saws, table saws, band saws, planers, and joiners. Unlike some other carpentry students, apprentice shipwrights spend a great deal of time working with the school's plasma cutter and twelve welders. In class they study general carpentry topics, such as how to read blueprints and how to work safely with power tools, and some specialized subjects, such as lofting (laying out a boat). Because most of the training is hands-on, apprentices are evaluated on their performance, not on examinations.

When they're not in the classroom, apprentices usually work in shipyards on the waterfront. They tend to stay with just one shipyard instead of learning a little from one employer and then moving on, as apprentices do in some other trades. The workday usually begins at about 6:00 A.M., and there are coffee breaks and a longer break for lunch.

Apprentices are closely supervised by the journeymen shipwrights who serve as their mentors; usually an apprentice and a journeyman work as partners because the job is too difficult for one person to handle alone. Shipwrights must be physically fit to handle metal, fiberglass, and other building materials. They're part of a larger crew working to finish the boat together: electricians, riggers, pipe fitters, machinists, and other specialists.

"There's a lot of heavy lifting, long hours, overtime, poor weather conditions. It's dangerous, working with all that machinery. There are people working around you and over your head. You're stumbling over everybody. You'll have people in different trades working side by side," Richard says.

Ships are most often built under the shelter of a roof, then moved to the water when they're finished. The construction occurs in many stages, and apprentices remain with each task until it's finished. Richard remarks that variety is one of the more appealing aspects of a shipwright's trade: "The beauty of building something is you have completion to it, and then you start something new."

Path to Becoming an Apprentice
Prospective students submit applications through the apprenticeship committee at the Capitol District Training Center, which is located on the campus of Bates Technical College. Then they take a three-hour assessment test of their writing, reading, and mathematical skills to see if they meet the program's eligibility requirements. They

also must pass a drug test and complete a five-day Pre-Employment Safety and Orientation class. Their names are placed on a waiting list, ranked in order of the scores on the preliminary tests, with adjustments to meet affirmative action goals. When an apprenticeship position opens, an applicant is notified, indentured into the program, and usually is sent to join a local labor union, which dispatches the apprentice to the job. Apprentices begin school only after they have started on-the-job training with a shipbuilding company. "Basically, they need to be sponsored by someone to get into the program," Richard explains.

Under certain circumstances, applicants can bypass some of these preliminary steps. Graduates of Job Corps and other programs approved by the apprenticeship committee can enter the apprenticeship directly if they meet the minimum qualifications; some transfers are accepted from other apprenticeship programs; and under certain conditions, nonunion employers can arrange to have their employees trained through this program. These employees can enter the apprenticeship directly. Most apprentices are in the union, but union membership is not required.

Applicants must be at least 17 years old and need have no particular educational background. Richard recommends taking mathematics and shop classes to prepare for a career as a shipwright, though: "Mathematics is a big one. You're doing that all day. Shop class goes without saying." He adds that aptitude is more important than previous education, however. "I've instructed for 18 years. I'd rather have someone with a good general education, and I'll teach them the trade," he says.

If you'd like to become a shipwright, but you fail to meet the eligibility requirements, you can enroll in the college's pre-apprenticeship boat-building program. Students in this program spend up to two years taking vocational classes and building boats at the carpentry shop on campus. "They are actually building smaller boats, using wood, aluminum, and fiberglass. They'll auction them off," Richard says. Proceeds from the sale of these boats help fund the program.

Salary Range

In the Seattle-Tacoma area, journeymen shipwrights earn about $25 an hour. Richard says the cost of living is relatively high in the region, but nevertheless, "It's a good, livable wage that can support your family." Apprentices start at $14 an hour and receive periodic raises until they're earning 100 percent of the journeyman scale by the time they graduate. During training, apprentices are provided with medical insurance and a retirement plan. They also receive free tuition at the college; it's paid out of the Training Trust Fund financed by employers affiliated with the program.

Apprentices do have to buy about $100 worth of books and must provide their own work boots. Employers provide other safety gear, including hard hats, safety harnesses for working on scaffolds, and welders' helmets.

Advice

Richard says it's possible to become a shipwright by learning related skills on some other job, but an "apprenticeship is the best way to go." He points out that apprentices have a contract that ensures they'll be employed for a specific length of time, until they're better qualified to compete for jobs. In addition, the apprenticeship provides well-rounded training at the school, covering a range of job skills that a person might not learn from one employer. Finally, apprentices can receive college credit for their training, which can count toward a bachelor's degree.

He recommends that workers accept responsibility for developing their own job skills. "Learning is a lifelong thing, and you've got to keep training. If you've got weaknesses, be willing to invest some time in it."

Future Goals

"Shipwright apprentices pretty much stay with one employer," Richard says. The company that provides on-the-job training usually offers the apprentice a job after graduation. Some apprentices move to Seattle, where the shipbuilding industry provides many advancement opportunities. Graduates of the training program can work their way up to positions as foremen or supervisors. They also have the option of working as cabinetmakers or moving into general carpentry but would need an extra year or so of studies to be journeymen carpenters, mostly to learn how to build forms and other structures for concrete work.

CALIFORNIA
Arques School of Traditional Boatbuilding
PO Box 2010
Sausalito, CA 94966
415-331-7134
Fax: 415-331-7134
arques@arqueschl.org
http://www.arqueschl.org
Occupational Fields: boatbuilder

CONNECTICUT

General Dynamics
Electric Boat Division
75 Eastern Point Road
Groton, CT 06340-4905
860-433-3000
Fax: 860-433-1400
http://www.gdeb.com
Occupational Fields: shipfitter (marine), rigger (marine)

ILLINOIS

Brooks Erection and Construction
3314 State Route 162
PO Box 1246
Granite City, IL 62014
618-452-3000
Occupational Fields: shipwright

KANSAS

Construction Design Inc.
5621 Kansas Avenue
Kansas City, KS 66106
913-287-0334
Occupational Fields: shipwright

MAINE

Bath Iron Works
700 Washington Street
Bath, ME 04530-2574
207-442-1820
Fax: 207-442-1737
http://www.gdbiw.com
Occupational Fields: shipfitter, hull outfit designer

MARYLAND

Bethlehem Steel Corporation, Sparrows Point
5111 North Point Boulevard
Baltimore, MD 21219
410-388-3000
Occupational Fields: shipwright

Industrial Union of Marine and Shipbuilding Workers of America
28111 Cherry Hill Road
Baltimore, MD 21225-1207
410-355-2502
Occupational Fields: shipbuilder

Industrial Union of Marine and Shipbuilding Workers of America
719 Eastfort Avenue
Baltimore, MD 21230
410-732-4676
Occupational Fields: shipbuilder

MASSACHUSETTS

Industrial Union of Marine and Shipbuilding Workers of America
480 Quincy Avenue
Quincy, MA 02169-8130
617-770-0393
Occupational Fields: shipwright

MISSOURI

All Temp Inc.
4915 Stilwell
Kansas City, MO 64120
Occupational Fields: shipwright

Babcock and Wilcox Construction
13600 Wyandotte Street
Kansas City, MO 65145
816-941-2073
Occupational Fields: shipwright

Boilermakers, Iron Ship Builders, Blacksmiths, Forgers and Helpers Union
Local Lodge #83
5910 East 86th Street
Kansas City, MO 64138
Fax: 816-523-2832
Occupational Fields: shipwright

Commercial Mechanical Inc.
4920 East 59th Street
Kansas City, MO 64130
816-444-2058
Occupational Fields: shipwright

Shamrad Metal Fabricators
801 Lafayette Street
St. Joseph, MO 64503

816-279-6354
Fax: 816-364-2273
shamrad@samradmetal.com
http://www.shamradmetal.com
Occupational Fields: shipwright

NEBRASKA
Team Industrial Services
2618 North 113th Street
Omaha, NE 68164
402-493-8899
Occupational Fields: shipwright

OHIO
Boilermakers Union, Local #1191
818 Mulberry Road, SE
Canton, OH 44707-3256
330-454-1180
Occupational Fields: shipyard worker, construction worker

RHODE ISLAND
General Dynamics
Employment Office
Quonset Point Facility
North Kingstown, RI 02852
401-268-2400
Fax: 401-268-2323
http://www.generaldynamics.com/overview/marine/eb/
    quonset.htm
Occupational Fields: shipwright

VIRGINIA
**Newport News Shipbuilding-Northrop Grumman
    Communications**
4101 Washington Avenue
Newport News, VA 23607
757-380-2000
http://www.northropgrumman.com
Occupational Fields: shipwright, rigger

WASHINGTON
**Capitol District Carpenters, Shipwrights, Millwrights,
    Drywall, Metal Stud Acoustical, Ceiling and
    Insulation**
2201 South 78th Street, Building B-512
Tacoma, WA 98409
253-472-2629
Occupational Fields: shipwright

King County Shipwrights and Boatbuilders Union
2415 Western Avenue
Seattle, WA 98121
206-441-8266
Occupational Fields: shipwright, boatbuilder

**Longview-Kelso Carpenters, Millmen, Shipwrights
    and Millwrights**
1316 Commerce Avenue
Longview, WA 98632
360-423-5030
Occupational Fields: shipwright

WISCONSIN
Azco Inc.
PO Box 567
Appleton, WI 54911
414-734-5791
http://www.azco-inc.com
Occupational Fields: shipwright

CANADA
BRITISH COLUMBIA
Quadrant Marine Institute Inc.
#14 - 2300 Canoe Cove Road
Sidney, BC V8L 3X9
250-656-2824
Fax: 250-656-5092
http://www.quadrantmarine.com
Occupational Fields: marine repair technician

SOCIAL ACTIVISTS AND HUMAN SERVICES WORKERS

RELATED SECTIONS: *agricultural workers, business workers, child care workers and educators, communications specialists, health care workers, herbalists, midwives*

Social activists strive to improve the circumstances of the poor, the homeless, the hungry, the mentally ill, battered women, children in jeopardy, and others who are disadvantaged or in need. They also work to protect natural resources, including forests, oceans, and endangered species, and cultural traditions. Many of these organizations work both to improve conditions for human beings and to protect the Earth.

Human services workers usually perform their duties under the oversight of social workers or psychologists, often for government agencies, such as welfare offices. These careers include social service technicians, case management aides, social work assistants, residential counselors, mental health technicians, child abuse workers, alcohol and drug abuse counselors, gerontology aides, community outreach workers, and others who help clients obtain benefits or services.

Organizations that help people may focus on issues such as helping the poor receive health care, including childhood immunizations; improving wage and labor laws, often by organizing unions; administering food banks or emergency fuel programs; encouraging people to vote; pressuring police and courts to establish more effective drug-prevention strategies; or establishing alternative schools that offer better educational opportunities for disadvantaged children. For example, an organization might recruit volunteers, potential buyers, and other workers to purchase and renovate abandoned buildings, which would then be available at affordable prices to low- or moderate-income applicants who had helped with the project. The organization might help applicants obtain loans or arrange other financing to make the purchase.

Workers for organizations concerned with protecting and improving the environment may learn on the job with distinguished scientists, helping them collect data and disseminate information intended to educate the public and government officials. Environmental organizations usually aim to encourage sustainable agriculture and to pressure other industries to do little or no harm to the planet's ecosystems. For instance, they might compel the owners of a factory to clean up a site where toxic substances have been dumped or to cancel plans to build an incinerator that would emit harmful gases.

Social activists frequently organize grassroots campaigns to exert pressure on lawmakers, industry, and other entities to change policies and laws. Fund-raising skills; organizing experience; leadership qualities; research, writing, and public speaking abilities; and an aptitude for persuasion are useful attributes.

Social activists often participate in hands-on projects—such as building houses, collecting scientific data, or handing out pamphlets from door to door—which may last for weeks or months. The project site may be near home or far away—a neighborhood across town, a seashore, a mountain wilderness. A background in science, medicine, communications, the social sciences, or a trade such as carpentry can be helpful.

The work is often rewarding but emotionally draining. Organizations may be understaffed and may lack adequate equipment or facilities. Human services workers usually work forty hours a week but may be required to work evenings, nights, weekends, or holidays.

On-the-job training and internships—which may be paid or unpaid—are common ways of entering this field. Some organizations that offer training in social activism operate internationally but have offices in the United States. Trainees can learn and work in this country but have the option of working in other countries if they so desire.

In general an applicant should

- be at least 18 years old
- be a high school graduate or hold a GED certificate
- have a strong commitment to the cause
- have a strong sense of responsibility
- have good communication skills
- be able to work as a member of a team
- have empathy, objectivity, and the ability to listen well
- respect human and natural diversity

APPRENTICESHIP SALARIES

Between about $7 and $9 an hour, sometimes with benefits.

215

POSTAPPRENTICESHIP SALARIES

About $12 to $15 an hour, sometimes with benefits. Earnings vary, depending on factors such as skill level, the employer, and geographic location.

JOB OUTLOOK

Generally good for human services workers. Opportunities will arise because of the growing number of older people, which will create a need for more services. Job training programs and residential care facilities for the physically and mentally disabled will also employ more human services workers in the coming decade. In general, the human services field is expected to expand more rapidly than most other occupations through the year 2012, and a shortage of qualified applicants is predicted.

For more information on apprenticeships for social activists and human services workers, contact the individual programs listed below, local job centers, your state bureau of apprenticeship training, or organizations devoted to encouraging social and political change.

NATIONAL PROGRAMS

National Organization for Human Services
5601 Brodie Lane, Suite 620-215
Austin, Texas 78745
512-692-9361
Fax: 512-692-9445
http://www.nohse.org
Occupational Fields: activist

APPRENTICESHIP PROFILE

International Alliance for Sustainable Agriculture
Sustainable Agriculture Internships
1701 University Avenue, SE
University of Minnesota
Minneapolis, MN 55414-2076
612-331-1099
Fax: 612-379-1527
iasa@mtn.org

General Nature of the Job

Social activism is a way to get involved and make a difference in the world around you. It's a field for people who care deeply and have the energy and commitment to work for a cause. It can involve everything from giving public speeches to conducting research to orchestrating a major fund-raising effort. There's room for people with all types of skills in this field, and it offers a wide range of experiences that can be applied to various careers. It also offers opportunities to make many friends and constantly broaden your horizons.

Students from overseas often work at the International Alliance for Sustainable Agriculture, which is located on the campus of the University of Minnesota in Minneapolis. Interns are usually assigned to open the mail for a while to give them insight into the many organizations that correspond with the Alliance. "People write us from all over the world. We've developed some of the first resources on sustainable agriculture. We're known for that," founder Terry Gips explains.

Because it operates on a limited budget, the organization depends on interns and volunteers to perform much of the work on its numerous projects. Internships usually last for at least three months and can run for a year or more, depending on the individual's needs. Interns may work on projects that are already up and running, or projects may be designed to match their interests and goals.

The Alliance publishes a newsletter and various books, and its slide and video programs are shown at more than 100 public gatherings each year. The organization's Resource Information Center processes about 2,000 information requests annually. Some of its past programs have included a campaign to promote alternatives to petrochemicals, which involved promotion of a training seminar called The Natural Step. The seminar emphasized the need for societies to balance their use of the world's natural resources. Another project, Skiers Ending Hunger, raised awareness and money to support local food programs and sustainable development projects in Africa, Asia, Latin America, and among the Hopi Indians of Arizona.

Interns help with all those endeavors and can also work as volunteer coordinators, graphic designers, writers, researchers, marketers, public relations specialists, translators, membership developers, computer operators, office help, or in many other areas. In addition to the in-depth knowledge they gain about their individual projects, interns learn about sustainable agriculture in general and see how nonprofit organizations operate.

Typical Day

The organization's purpose, operations, and method of handling internships has always been unconventional. Interns with the Alliance set their own schedules and are expected to work conscientiously without much supervision, although each is overseen and coached to some degree by a mentor. Terry explains, "We want people who will be mature self-starters. We want them to come in when they tell us they will. We get good enough interns so we can let them go, and often they turn out work that's even better than we expected."

Interns often attend educational slide shows, presentations, and other events, particularly during the summer. Sometimes they go as a group, but they're just as apt to go alone, choosing topics that interest them individually. They are encouraged to write reports and keep diaries documenting their experiences and insights. Terry remarks, "I know how valuable it is to write it up. It's one thing to go do something, and it's another to think about what they're doing" and organize it into a report.

For example, an intern compiling research on pesticides might write or call organizations and individuals, requesting information, and perhaps attend lectures on the subject. The trainee would compile a report, and a supervisor would evaluate it and discuss ways in which the student's work could be improved. Information from the report might be published in the organization's newsletter, used in one of its publications, incorporated into a speech, entered in a database, or distributed as a fact sheet to people in other nations.

Path to Becoming an Apprentice

Some students are referred to the organization through the United Way. Others learn about it through presentations at their schools. Prospective interns submit a letter outlining their interests, a resume, a writing sample, and three references. Anyone who is at least in junior high school can apply. There is no upper age limit, and no experience or advanced education is necessary.

"The more diverse, the better," says Terry. "It's good for the interns to work together. They get to be friends." Interns meet people from other nations and have the option of using their connections afterward to obtain employment in other countries.

Terry recalls one trainee who is now in South America, thanks in part to his experience with the Alliance. "He's a delightful person. His girlfriend was an intern, and he started to come in because she was here. He got excited about what we were doing." During his time with the Alliance, the student started an organic farm, worked in the resource center, developed the organization's World Wide Web site, conducted research, and developed presentations for The Natural Step program. When he returns from South America, he plans to sign on to help the Alliance again.

Salary Range

Interns with the Alliance are paid for their work when the grant proposals that fund their projects provide enough

money or when their schools offer to pay. These interns usually earn about $500 to $1,000 a month. Other interns volunteer their time, because in addition to working for a worthy cause, they receive on-the-job experience, college or high school credit, letters of reference, job connections, and similar benefits.

Earnings for social activists vary widely, but in general are quite low compared with other fields. Workers who advance to responsible positions, however, can often earn a livable wage. For example, the executive director of a nonprofit organization promoting environmental issues can expect to be paid between $30,000 and $40,000 a year. Some workers earn significantly less, because many nonprofit organizations operate on shoestring budgets.

Advice

Terry says that enthusiasm is the most important quality for an intern with his organization. "Be interested in sustainability, caring about people, caring about the Earth. It's important that they be really interested in learning. People who do better are people who really care. For them, it's fabulous to have access to so many resources. We get such a mix of people. Some just want to use their computer skills. Some have very special scientific knowledge, and some are generalists."

As one who has completed more than one internship, Terry strongly believes in the value of such an experience. The organization's internship program has been carefully developed over the years to accommodate the needs of a broad range of students and to help the Alliance achieve its goals. "I've always believed in interns," Terry says. "We've had an outstanding program."

Future Goals

After working with the International Alliance for Sustainable Agriculture, trainees can enter any number of related careers. "It's an interesting mix. Many want to go on to graduate study or into sustainable agriculture work, government, business, farming, nonprofit organizations, teaching, or research. Overseas development work is a popular one. We write letters of reference and help them get jobs afterward. I get to know each one," Terry says.

ARIZONA
Tohono Chul Park
7366 North Paseo del Norte
Tucson, Arizona, 85704
520-742-6455
Fax: 520-797-1213

http://www.tohonochulpark.org
Occupational Fields: activist, administrator

CALIFORNIA
Center for Third World Organizing, Main Office
1218 East 21st Street
Oakland, CA 94606
510-893-7583
http://www.ctwo.org
Occupational Fields: activist

Coro Foundation
690 Market Street
San Francisco, CA 94104-5101
415-986-0521
Fax: 415-546-1906
Occupational Fields: activist, politician, public
  administrator, journalist

International Museum of Women
PO Box 190038
San Francisco, CA 94119
415-543-4669
Fax: 415-543-4668
http://www.imow.org
Occupational Fields: administrator

Salvation Army—Southern California Division
9000 West James M. Woods Boulevard
Los Angeles, CA 90015
213-607-7304
Fax: 213-627-1440
http://www.salvationarmysocal.org
Occupational Fields: activist, administrator

Sustainable Business Institute
467 Saratoga Avenue, Suite 1411
San Jose, California, 95129
408-626-7626
Fax: 408-626-7227
http://www.sustainablebusiness.org
Occupational Fields: activist, administrator

COLORADO
Center for Third World Organizing, Denver Office
1201G Santa Fe Drive
Denver, CO 80204
303-893-2149
Fax: 303-893-9713

http://www.ctwo.org
Occupational Fields: activist

CONNECTICUT
Hartford Food System
191 Franklin Avenue
Hartford, CT 06114-1380
860-296-9325
Fax: 860-296-8326
http://www.hartfordfood.org
Occupational Fields: activist, administrator

DISTRICT OF COLUMBIA
Ecoventures International
1519 Connecticut Avenue, NW, Suite 301
Washington, DC 20036
202-667-0802
Fax: 202-667-0803
http://www.eco-ventures.org
Occupational Fields: activist, administrator

EnviroCitizen
1609 Connecticut Avenue, NW, Suite 400
Washington, DC 20009
202-986-1650
Fax: 202-986-1656
http://www.envirocitizen.org
Occupational Fields: activist, administrator

Girls Inc.
1001 Connecticut Avenue, NW, Suite 740
Washington, DC 20036
202-463-1881
Fax: 202-463-8994
http://www.girlsinc.org
Occupational Fields: activist, administrator

GlobalGiving
1751 T Street, NW
Washington, DC 20009
301-652-8455
Fax: 301-652-8420
http://www.globalgiving.com
Occupational Fields: activist, administrator

League of Conservation Voters
1920 L Street, NW, Suite 800
Washington, DC 20036
202-785-8683

Fax: 202-835-0491
http://www.lcv.org
Occupational Fields: activist, administrator

Polaris Project
PO Box 77892
Washington, DC 20013-8892
202-547-7909
Fax: 202-547-6654
http://www.PolarisProject.org
Occupational Fields: activist, administrator

Public Education Center Inc.
1100 Connecticut Avenue, NW, Suite 1310
Washington, DC 20036-4119
202-466-4310
Fax: 202-466-4344
http://www.publicedcenter.org
Occupational Fields: activist, administrator, teacher

Vital Voices Global Partnership
1050 Connecticut Avenue, NW, 10th Floor
Washington, DC 20036
202-772-4162
Fax: 202-772-2353
http://www.vitalvoices.org
Occupational Fields: activist, administrator

FLORIDA
Cooperative Feeding Program
1 NW 33rd Terrace
Ft. Lauderdale, FL 33311
954-792-2328
Fax: 954-792-9982
http://FeedingBroward.org
Occupational Fields: activist, administrator

GEORGIA
GMAAC—Resources for Refugee Youth
901 Rowland Street
Clarkston, GA 30021
404-299-6646
Fax: 404-299-6894
http://www.gmaac.org
Occupational Fields: activist, administrator

Soccer in the Streets
2323 Perimeter Park Drive, NE
Atlanta, GA 30341

678-993-2113
Fax: 770-452-1946
http://www.soccerstreets.org
Occupational Fields: activist, administrator, coach

Southern Crescent Sexual Assault Center
PO Box 1788
Jonesboro, GA 30237
770-603-4045
Fax: 770-477-4545
Occupational Fields: activist, administrator

IDAHO
Wood River Land Trust
119 East Bullion Street
Hailey, ID 83333
http://www.woodriverlandtrust.org
Occupational Fields: activist, administrator, conservation worker

ILLINOIS
American Red Cross of Greater Chicago
2200 West Harrison
Chicago, IL 60612
312-729-6115
Fax: 312-729-6306
http://www.chicagoredcross.org
Occupational Fields: activist, administrator

Association of Community Organizations for Reform Now
117 West Harrison, Suite 200
Chicago, IL 60605
312-939-7488
Fax: 312-939-8256
http://www.acorn.org
Occupational Fields: activist, organizer

Chicago Children's Museum
700 East Grand Avenue, Suite 127
Chicago, IL 60611
312-464-7652
Fax: 312-832-7182
http://www.chichildrensmuseum.org
Occupational Fields: administrator, organizer, teacher

Kids in Danger
116 West Illinois, Suite 5E
Chicago, IL 60610

312-595-0649
http://kidsindanger.org
Occupational Fields: activist, administrator

LOUISIANA
Louisiana SPCA
1319 Japonica Street
New Orleans, LA 70117
504-944-7445 ext. 217
Fax: 504-947-6690
http://www.la-spca.org
Occupational Fields: activist, administrator

MAINE
Maine Lake Monitors
24 Maple Hill Road
Auburn, ME 04210
207-783-7733
http://www.MaineVolunteerLakeMonitors.org
Occupational Fields: activist, administrator

MARYLAND
Annie E. Casey Foundation
701 St. Paul Street
Baltimore, MD 21202
http://www.aecf.org
Occupational Fields: activist, administrator

MASSACHUSETTS
Alma Linguae Academies Inc.
PO Box 382188
17 Franklin Street
Somerville, MA 02238-2188
617-497-9399
Fax: 617-497-9399
Occupational Fields: administrator, tutor

Boston Lyric Opera
45 Franklin Street, 4th Floor
Boston, MA 02110
617-542-4912
Fax: 617-542-4913
http://www.blo.org
Occupational Fields: administrator

Center on Media and Child Health
300 Longwood Avenue
Boston, MA 02115

617-355-2000
Fax: 617-730-0004
cmch@childrens.harvard.edu
http://www.cmch.tv
Occupational Fields: activist, administrator

Earthwatch
680 Mount Auburn Street
Watertown, MA 02272-9104
800-776-0188
Fax: 617-926-8532
http://www.earthwatch.org
*Occupational Fields: activist, office administrator,
    publisher, marketer, teacher*

Gould Farm Community
PO Box 157
Monterey, MA 01245
413-528-1804
Fax: 413-528-5051
http://www.gouldfarm.org
Occupational Fields: activist, administrator

Interlock Media
Athenaeum Building, Box 219
215 First Street
Cambridge, MA 02142
617-864-5625
Fax: 617-864-2066
http://www.interlockmedia.com
Occupational Fields: activist, administrator

International Health Organization Inc.
60 Leo M. Birmingham Parkway, Suite 105
Boston, MA 02135
617-254-5077
Fax: 617-254-2767
http://www.ihousa.org
Occupational Fields: activist, administrator

Massachusetts Budget & Policy Center
37 Temple Place, 3rd Floor
Boston, MA 02111
617-426-1228
Fax: 617-695-1295
http://www.massbudget.org
Occupational Fields: activist, administrator, lobbyist

Museum of Science
Science Park
Boston, MA 02114

617-589-0380
Fax: 617-589-0454
http://www.mos.org
Occupational Fields: administrator, teacher

MINNESOTA

Honor the Earth
2104 Stevens Avenue South
Minneapolis, MN 55404
612-879-7529
http://www.honorearth.org
Occupational Fields: activist, administrator

International Alliance for Sustainable Agriculture
1701 University Avenue, SE
University of Minnesota
Minneapolis, MN 55414-2076
612-331-1099
Fax: 612-379-1527
Occupational Fields: activist

Land Stewardship Project
2200 Fourth Street
White Bear Lake, MN 55110-3011
612-653-0618
Fax: 612-653-0589
Occupational Fields: activist

Organizing Apprenticeship
1885 University Avenue, West
St. Paul, MN 55104-3403
612-641-1830
Occupational Fields: activist

Planned Parenthood of Minnesota/South Dakota
1965 Ford Parkway
St. Paul, MN 55116
651-698-2401
Fax: 651-698-2405
http://www.ppmsd.org
Occupational Fields: activist, administrator

MONTANA

Project Vote Smart
One Common Ground
Philipsburg, MT 59858
406-859-8683
Fax: 406-859-8680

http://www.vote-smart.org
Occupational Fields: activist, administrator

NEVADA

Project MANA
948 Incline Way
Incline Village, NV 89451
775-298-0008
Fax: 775-298-0009
http://www.projectmana.org
Occupational Fields: activist, administrator

NEW HAMPSHIRE

Squam Lakes Natural Science Center
PO Box 173
Holderness, NH 03245
603-968-7194
Fax: 603-968-2229
http://www.nhnature.org
Occupational Fields: activist, administrator

Student Conservation Association
689 River Road
PO Box 550
Charlestown, NH 03603
603-543-1700
Fax: 603-543-1828
http://www.theSCA.org
Occupational Fields: activist, administrator

NEW JERSEY

American Cancer Society
95 Schwenk Drive
Kingston, NY 12401
800-ACS-2345
Fax: 845-331-4109
http://www.cancer.org
Occupational Fields: activist, administrator

United Way of Passaic County
20 Mill Street
Paterson, NJ 07501
Fax: 973-279-0059
http://www.unitedwaypassaic.org
Occupational Fields: activist, administrator

Urban League of Essex County
ULEC-CEO Search Comm., Govt. & Public Affairs
65 Bergen St., Suite 1338

Newark, NJ 07107
Fax: 973-872-7261
Occupational Fields: activist, administrator

NEW YORK
Farm Sanctuary
PO Box 150
Watkins Glen, NY 14891
607-583-2225
Fax: 607-583-2041
http://www.farmsanctuary.org
Occupational Fields: activist, administrator

Southampton College
Long Island University
239 Montauk Highway
Southampton, NY 11968-4198
516-283-4000
Fax: 516-283-4081
http://www.southampton.liunet.edu
Occupational Fields: activist, museum curator, herbalist, journalist, alternative energy specialist

Wittenberg Center for Alternative Resources
188 Wittenberg Road
Bearsville, NY 12409
914-679-9764
http://www.wittenbergcenter.org
Occupational Fields: social activist, horticulturist, environmentalist, Native American specialist

NORTH CAROLINA
Center for Purposeful Living
3983 Old Greensboro
Winston-Salem, NC 27101
336-761-8745
Fax: 336-722-7882
http://www.purposeful.org
Occupational Fields: activist, administrator

Earthhaven Learning Center
1025 Camp Elliott Road
Black Mountain, NC 28711
828-669-9935
http://www.earthavenlearningcenter.org
Occupational Fields: activist, administrator, ecologist, teacher

OHIO
Ohio Women's Policy and Research Commission
30 East Broad Street, Suite 2701
Columbus, OH 43266-0920
Fax: 614-466-5434
Occupational Fields: writer, researcher, data processor, legislative assistant, public relations specialist

OREGON
Sisters in Portland Impacting Real Issues Together (SPIRIT)
5736 Albina Avenue
Portland, OR 97217
503-283-5340
Occupational Fields: activist

RHODE ISLAND
Service Employees International Union
1704 Broad Street
Cranston, RI 02905-2720
401-941-6150
Occupational Fields: legislative lobbyist

TEXAS
Project Row Houses
2500 Holman Street
Houston, TX 77251
713-526-7662
Fax: 713-526-1623
http://www.projectrowhouses.org
Occupational Fields: activist, administrator

CANADA
ALBERTA
Alberta Mentor Foundation for Youth
200, 701 14th Street NW
Calgary, AB T2N 2A4
403-270-3637
Occupational Fields: activist, administrator

BRITISH COLUMBIA
Science Horizons Youth Internship Program
Environment Canada
Pacific Wildlife Research Centre

Canadian Wildlife Service
5421 Robertson Road
RR 1
Delta, BC V4K 3N2
Fax: 604-946-7022
Occupational Fields: activist

NOVA SCOTIA
Science Horizons Youth Internship Program
Environment Canada
45 Alderney Drive, 16th Floor
Dartmouth, NS B2Y 2N6
Fax: 902-426-6434
Occupational Fields: activist

ONTARIO
Amnesty International
312 Laurier Ave East
Ottawa, ON K1N 1H9
Fax: 613-746-2411
http://www.amnesty.ca
Occupational Fields: activist, administrator

Ecologial Monitoring and Assessment Network
Science Horizons Youth Internship Program
EMAN Coordinating Office
867 Lakeshore Road
Burlington, ON L7R 4A6
Fax: 905-336-4499
Occupational Fields: activist

Energy Probe International
33 Brunswick Road
Toronto, ON M2N 3P1
http://www.planetfriendly.net/gwd.php?id=639
Occupational Fields: activist

National Water Research Institute
Science Horizons Youth Internship Program
National Water Research Institute
PO Box 5050
Burlington, ON L7R 4A6
Fax: 905-336-4420
Occupational Fields: activist

Science Horizons Youth Internship Program
National Wildlife Research Centre
1125 Colonel By Drive, Raven Road

Carleton University
Ottawa, ON K1A 0H3
Fax: 613-998-0315
Occupational Fields: activist

Science Horizons Youth Internship Program
Office of the Regional Science Advisor
Environment Canada-Ontario Region
4905 Dufferin Street
Toronto, ON M3H 5T4
Fax: 416-739-4691
Occupational Fields: activist

QUEBEC
Science Horizons Youth Internship Program
Environment Canada
Canadian Wildlife Service
1141 Route de l'Église, 9th Floor
PO Box 10,100
Sainte-Foy, QC G1V 4H5
Fax: 418-649-6475
Occupational Fields: activist

Science Horizons Youth Internship Program
Environmental Protection Service
Environmental Technology Advancement
    Directorate
18th Floor, Place Vincent Massey
351 St. Joseph Boulevard
Hull, QC K1A 0H3
Fax: 819-953-9029
Occupational Fields: activist

Science Horizons Youth Internship Program
Knowledge Integration Directorate
70 Cremazie, 7th Floor
Gatineau, QC K1A 0H3
Fax: 819-994-4396
Occupational Fields: activist

Science Horizons Youth Internship Program
Water Priorities Branch
7th Floor, Place Vincent Massey
351 St. Joseph Boulevard
Hull, QC K1A 0H3
Fax: 819-953-0461
Occupational Fields: activist

SASKATCHEWAN

Science Horizons Youth Internship Program
Environment Canada
Environmental Conservation Branch
2365 Albert Street, Room 300
Regina, SK S4P 4K1
Fax: 306-780-7614
Occupational Fields: activist

THEATER WORKERS

RELATED SECTIONS: *artists and artisans, book arts workers, communications specialists, cosmetologists, crafts and trades workers at living historical sites and farms, electricians and line workers, electronics technicians, museum and gallery workers, printing industry workers*

The success of a theatrical production—whether for a feature film, television show, or for performance on stage in a theater—depends largely on the team of people working behind the scenes.

Stage technicians prepare stages for performances in arenas, stadiums, studios, theaters, and other entertainment venues. They also prepare sets for motion picture and television filming. They build, repair, paint, erect, and disassemble sets; install and maintain stage lighting, sound, and electrical systems; collect, devise, build, and repair props and manage them during performances; rig scenery and repair and maintain rigging systems; and construct and repair physical special effects, such as lasers, pyrotechnics, and makeup.

Broadcast technicians, also known as *operators* and *engineers,* install, operate, maintain, and repair electronic equipment that transmits television and radio programs. Those who create movie sound tracks are called *sound mixers* or *re-recording mixers.* Broadcast technicians must be proficient with microphones, television cameras, tape recorders, transmitters, light and sound effects, and other equipment. They may specialize in transmission, audio control, video and sound recording, special effects, or field transmission. Usually they work indoors but may occasionally be called to an outdoor site. This occupation often involves stress because of the need to meet production deadlines. Some broadcast technicians are self-employed, but most work for television, radio, or motion picture companies. There is a relatively high turnover rate in this trade.

Motion picture machine projectionists, also called *motion picture operators,* set up and operate various kinds of projection and sound equipment that produce coordinated effects on screen in multiplex, single-screen, and drive-in theaters. In some states they must be licensed.

Motion picture camera operators make films for the movie industry, television news, documentaries, and other projects. Some specialize in filming animated motion pictures or other optical effects. *Still photographers* make portraits and other photographs to be used in planning and publicizing the film or other performance. Photographers use filters, tripods, special lights, and assorted other pieces of equipment to achieve the desired effect on film. Photographers and camera operators often spend much time working in crowded darkrooms full of chemical fumes. They must also carry heavy equipment.

Theater managers ensure that business functions run smoothly at theaters that show motion pictures or feature live performances. They oversee box office cashiers, ticket takers, ushers, and other employees; count and deposit money from ticket sales; order food and other supplies for refreshment counters; and supervise the maintenance and cleaning of the building. Managers are on hand before and during performances to answer questions from patrons and to handle problems that arise, such as locating additional staff members or stage materials that are needed on short notice. Other workers involved with the business side of the theatrical industry include managing directors, company managers, and booking managers.

Many workers in the theatrical industry belong to the International Alliance of Theatrical Stage Employees, Moving Picture Technicians, Artists and Allied Crafts of the United States and Canada (IATSE), which offers training for various occupations, including film and television producers, wardrobe and costume designers, hair stylists, makeup artists, animators, exhibition specialists, treasurers, ticket sellers, publicists, and press agents.

Many jobs in the theatrical industry require no formal training; apprenticeships and on-the-job training are common ways of gaining entry into the profession. It is common to enter the motion picture industry as an assistant and advance to other positions by learning on the job. Broadcast technicians frequently start by working for small television or radio stations. Formal apprenticeships in the theater typically run for two to three years.

In general an applicant should

- have some theater experience
- be at least 18 years old
- be a high school graduate or hold a GED certificate
- be physically able to perform the work

APPRENTICESHIP SALARIES
Between about $8 an hour and $20 an hour.

POSTAPPRENTICESHIP SALARIES

About $12 an hour, up to $40 or more an hour. Earnings vary, depending on the position, the employer, skill level, and geographic location.

NATIONAL PROGRAMS

International Alliance of Theatrical Stage Employees
1430 Broadway, 20th Floor
New York, NY 10018
212-730-1770
Fax: 212-730-7809
http://www.iatse-intl.org

JOB OUTLOOK

Generally fair, because there is a continuing demand for films, plays, and other performances. Most positions for theater workers will grow about as fast as the average position through 2012.

For more information on apprenticeships for theatrical workers, contact the individual programs listed below, local job centers, your state bureau of apprenticeship training, or local theaters and production companies.

APPRENTICESHIP PROFILE

**International Association of Theatrical Stage
   Employees, Local #28**
Joint Apprenticeship Training Council
6800 Southeast 32nd Street
Portland, OR 97207
503-295-2828
Fax: 503-238-6644
http://www.iatse28.org

General Nature of the Job

Linda Miyahira is in the final year of her apprenticeship with the International Association of Theatrical Stage Employees (IATSE), which has been a strong union for more than a century. She has worked concerts, theatrical productions, and conventions. Her job requires skills in carpentry, electrical work, props, sound, high rigging, and other areas of expertise. She carries assorted tools with her from job to job—wrenches, multitools, hammers, screwdrivers—to assemble and disassemble lights, sound equipment, scenery, and special effects.

"Stagehands unload the trucks, set up the stage and equipment, and then tear it all down at the end of the

show and reload the trucks," she explains. "We also work during the show, running lighting boards or sound boards, operating spotlights, moving set pieces, performing costume changes, and overseeing the safety of everyone on stage and backstage.

"The purpose of the job is to not be seen by the audience. When I'm backstage doing a special effect, like using an ice machine to create fog or pulling a curtain to reveal a set piece, I feel like a magician. I can hear the audience laughing and enjoying themselves because of what I've done, yet they don't know that I did it. We are ghosts that wander around backstage in black clothing, making the lights dance and the scenery move and the costumes change and the lyrics clear for the audience to enjoy.

"Being a stagehand means enjoying the same show over and over and over. It means being able to tolerate and perhaps be amused by the antics and eccentricities of the artists who are performing. It means being able to communicate and take orders and give instruction. It means having odd working hours, unemployment, and over-employment. A stagehand sometimes runs fast and hard and at other times remains completely motionless. Sometimes it's like being married to your coworkers. There are times when we work together for 16 hours a day, five or six days in a row, in a dark and windowless building. Floods and heat waves can happen outside, but we don't know it."

As an apprentice, Linda also spends four hours in classes two to four times each month to learn the various aspects of the job and why things are done in certain ways. For example, she has studied electricity to prepare for the examination she must pass to become a journeyman stagehand after working at least 8,000 hours on the job. Apprentices who have previous experience in the field can complete the program at an accelerated pace, sometimes as little as six months, but most finish in two to three years. A high school diploma or GED is required for all applicants.

Typical Day

Linda's schedule varies constantly. Her workday can start at almost any time, from early in the morning to late in the evening. A typical week might begin with a call on Sunday morning from her business agent, informing her that she will work a rock concert on Tuesday and an opera on Wednesday.

She and 40 other stagehands begin unloading the truck at 8:00 A.M. on Tuesday. They take a coffee break after a few hours of work and stop for lunch at 1:00 P.M., when part of the crew is sent home. Linda stays to help set up the band's gear, wardrobe, and other details. After three hours, five more people go home. The others wait during a sound check, make adjustments on the stage, and stop for dinner. Five workers return at 7:00 P.M. to run the spotlights during the show, help change the set between bands, and operate special effects. By 10:00 P.M. the entire crew is back on the job, tearing down the stage and loading everything into the truck, which leaves by 2:00 A.M.

At 9:00 A.M. the next day, Linda arrives at the auditorium to help thirty stagehands unload more trucks. They take a coffee break, an hour for lunch at 1:00 P.M., and an hour for dinner at 6:00 P.M. They go home at 11:00 P.M.; and return the next day. Linda works four days there, then has no work until she returns to help load-out the opera three weeks later.

"A stagehand's life is always up in the air," she comments. "I may get cut after four hours, or I may be there for 10 hours. The show has a deadline, because tickets have been sold. Yes, there are times that we go without meal breaks or without substantial periods of sleep. As a union member I receive financial compensation for these inconveniences. It's difficult on relationships and on your health. It is impossible to go to school or have a second job and be a full-time stagehand. In Portland the work is too uneven. Some days the business agent needs three hundred workers, and other times there is no work at all. The work is feast or famine. It is a labor of love."

Path to Becoming an Apprentice

Linda wanted to be an actor since her childhood but also enjoyed working backstage for high school productions and in community theater. She was studying for a bachelor's degree in theater, expecting to focus on acting, when a large auditorium opened in Portland and began staging rock-and-roll concerts. Linda soon realized that acting was not her first love, and she decided to take a chance and become a full-time stagehand. That meant signing up for an apprenticeship, which would provide her with practical experience.

"Most people become stagehands either by working backstage in high school or college or by helping young rock-and-roll bands in local clubs. Someone who has a college degree in theater but no on-the-job training will have to learn a lot very quickly. College is a great place to prepare a stagehand for theatrical work, such as stage managing or designing, but as I discovered, it doesn't help in the world of concerts or conventions," she explains.

Salary Range

In Portland an apprentice earns $14.13 an hour and pays $75 or $126 a quarter in union dues. A journeyman makes $14.87 an hour and pays dues of $150 a quarter. Workers receive no paid holidays or sick leave, but they have a 401(k) plan, an annuity program, health care, and life insurance. "Considering the cost of living in Portland, our wage is a good wage, but the work is not always steady," Linda says.

Advice

Linda strongly recommends learning the trade through a combination of on-the-job training and classes, which can sometimes be set up as an apprenticeship through a college. "While it is not necessary to have a degree to hold a well-paid position as a stagehand, I believe the knowledge learned is immense," she says. "And on-the-job training is also vital for a stagehand. To someone who has an appreciation for dance, music, acting, and technical theater, being a stagehand is a dream come true."

In addition, Linda advises trainees to learn from the rest of the crew. "I found that stagehands are willing and often eager to show newcomers what to do. If you listen, pay attention, and learn, you will do well. If you talk too much and brag, you will be loudly ridiculed."

Future Goals

Eventually Linda might become a stage manager, producer, or production assistant, perhaps traveling on the road with a show. Specializing in lighting and sound equipment is a tempting option for some stagehands; it could mean traveling with a show, designing or maintaining equipment, or purchasing equipment and renting it to theatrical productions. Linda intends to try her hand at writing plays but would still continue working as a stagehand. "I really like where I am right now. I can see myself doing this in five to ten years," she says.

ALABAMA

International Alliance of Theatrical Stage Employees, Local #78
PO Box 10251
Birmingham, AL 35202
205-251-1312
Fax: 205-322-8447
Occupational Fields: stage technician

International Alliance of Theatrical Stage Employees, Local #142
3609 York Road
Mobile, AL 36605

334-479-8096
Fax: 334-476-9614
Occupational Fields: stage technician

International Alliance of Theatrical Stage Employees, Local #900
3809 Panorama Drive
PO Box 12
Huntsville, AL 35804
256-536-8025
Fax: 256-536-2487
modernm@bellsouth.net
Occupational Fields: various theater workers

ALASKA
International Alliance of Theatrical Stage Employees, Local #918
430 West Seventh Avenue
Anchorage, AK 99501
907-278-3146
Fax: 907-278-3145
Occupational Fields: stage technician

North County Productions
935 Orca Street
Anchorage, AK 99501
907-243-7545
Occupational Fields: lighting technician, sound technician

ARIZONA
International Alliance of Theatrical Stage Employees, Local #336
2515 East Waltann Lane
Phoenix, AZ 85032
623-465-9374
Fax: 602-253-4145
iatse336@uswest.net
http://www.iatse-336.org
Occupational Fields: stage technician

International Alliance of Theatrical Stage Employees, Local #415
PO Box 990
Tucson, AZ 85702
520-882-9126
Fax: 520-882-9127
Occupational Fields: various theater workers

International Alliance of Theatrical Stage Employees, Local #485
PO Box 5705
Tucson, AZ 85703-5705
520-743-8407
Fax: 520-743-8427
iatse485@juno.org
Occupational Fields: studio mechanic

International Alliance of Theatrical Stage Employees, Local #875, Mesa
11328 East Renfield Avenue
Mesa, AZ 85212
480-380-3933
Fax: 480-464-8262
Occupational Fields: various theater workers

ARKANSAS
International Alliance of Theatrical Stage Employees, Local #204
PO Box 848
Mabelvale, AR 72103
501-455-1839
Fax: 501-455-5430
Occupational Fields: various theater workers

CALIFORNIA
International Alliance of Theatrical Stage Employees, Local #16
240 Second Street, First Floor
San Francisco, CA 94105415-441-6400
Fax: 415-243-1079
http://www.local16.org
Occupational Fields: stage technician

International Alliance of Theatrical Stage Employees, Local #33
1720 West Magnolia Boulevard
Burbank, CA 91506-1871
818-841-9233
Fax: 818-567-1138
Occupational Fields: stage technician

International Alliance of Theatrical Stage Employees, Local #44
12021 Riverside Drive
Valley Village, CA 91607

818-769-2500
Occupational Fields: property craftsperson

International Alliance of Theatrical Stage Employees, Local #50
PO Box 163086
Sacramento, CA 95816
916-444-7654
Fax: 916-444-7654
Occupational Fields: various theater workers

International Alliance of Theatrical Stage Employees, Local #80
2520 West Olive
Burbank, CA 91505-4523
818-526-0700
Fax: 818-526-0719
Occupational Fields: motion picture studio grip

International Alliance of Theatrical Stage Employees, Local #107
8130 Baldwin Street
Oakland, CA 94621
510-351-1858
Fax: 510-430-9830
http://www.iatse107.org
Occupational Fields: stage technician

International Alliance of Theatrical Stage Employees, Local #122
3737 Camino Del Rio South, Suite 106
San Diego, CA 92108
619-640-0042
Occupational Fields: stage technician

International Alliance of Theatrical Stage Employees, Local #134
PO Box 28585
San Jose, CA 95159-8585
408-294-1134
Fax: 408-294-1250
localsec@jps.net
http://www.union.sjsu.edu/iatse134
Occupational Fields: various theater workers

International Alliance of Theatrical Stage Employees, Local #150
PO Box 5143
Culver City, CA 90231-5143

818-557-1677
Fax: 310-398-9445
Occupational Fields: motion picture operator

International Alliance of Theatrical Stage Employees, Local #158
PO Box 5274
Fresno, CA 93755
559-229-6445
Fax: 559-228-8881
Occupational Fields: stage technician

International Alliance of Theatrical Stage Employees, Local #166
PO Box 2166
Sebastopol, CA 95473-2166
209-830-8609
Fax: 209-830-8995
Occupational Fields: motion picture operator

International Alliance of Theatrical Stage Employees, Local #169
PO Box 29284
Oakland, CA 94604
510-522-6078
Occupational Fields: motion picture operator

International Alliance of Theatrical Stage Employees, Local #215
PO Box 555
Bakersfield, CA 93302
661-862-0215
Fax: 661-863-0569
Occupational Fields: various theater workers

International Alliance of Theatrical Stage Employees, Local #297
7944 Pasadena Avenue
La Mesa, CA 92941
619-464-5449
Occupational Fields: motion picture operator

International Alliance of Theatrical Stage Employees, Local #442
PO Box 413
Santa Barbara, CA 93102
805-898-0442
Fax: 805-898-0442
kaessy@verizon.net

http://www.iatse442.org
Occupational Fields: various theater workers

International Alliance of Theatrical Stage Employees, Local #504
671 South Manchester
Anaheim, CA 92802
714-774-5004
Fax: 714-774-7683
Occupational Fields: various theater workers

International Alliance of Theatrical Stage Employees, Local #521
2084 Junipero Avenue
Signal Hill, CA 90755
562-494-4227
Occupational Fields: motion picture operator

International Alliance of Theatrical Stage Employees, Local #564
PO Box 202
Merced, CA 95341-0202
209-573-8985
Fax: 209-383-5034
Occupational Fields: various theater workers

International Alliance of Theatrical Stage Employees, Local #611
PO Box 7571
Santa Cruz, CA 95061
831-458-0338
Fax: 831-401-2377
Occupational Fields: various theater workers

International Alliance of Theatrical Stage Employees, Local #614
PO Box 883
San Bernardino, CA 92405
909-888-1828
http://www.schuengineering.com/index.htm
Occupational Fields: stage technician

International Alliance of Theatrical Stage Employees, Local #683
9795 Cabrini Drive, Suite 204
Burbank, CA 91504
818-252-5628
Fax: 818-252-4962
Occupational Fields: laboratory film technician, video technician

International Alliance of Theatrical Stage Employees, Local #695
5439 Cahuenga Boulevard
North Hollywood, CA 91601
818-985-9204
Fax: 818-760-4681
Occupational Fields: various theater workers

International Alliance of Theatrical Stage Employees, Local #705
4731 Laurel Canyon Boulevard, Suite 201
Valley Village, CA 91607-3911
818-487-5655
Fax: 818-487-5663
Occupational Fields: motion picture costumer

International Alliance of Theatrical Stage Employees, Local #706
PO Box 6309
Burbank, CA 91510-6309
818-606-0005
Fax: 818-295-3930
info@ialocal706.org
http://www.local706.com
Occupational Fields: makeup artist, hair stylist

International Alliance of Theatrical Stage Employees, Local #707
PO Box 2810
Rancho Mirage, CA 92270
760-568-0033
Fax: 760-346-0042
Occupational Fields: various theater workers

International Alliance of Theatrical Stage Employees, Local #728
14629 Nordhoff Street
Panorama City, CA 91402
818-891-0728
Fax: 818-891-5288
loc728@iatse728.org
http://www.iatse728.org
Occupational Fields: lighting technician, rigger, floorman, lamp operator

International Alliance of Theatrical Stage Employees, Locals #729
1811 West Burbank Boulevard
Burbank, CA 91506-1314
818-842-7729

Fax: 818-846-3729
ialocal729@earthlink.net
http://www.ialocal729.com
Occupational Fields: motion picture set painter, sign writer, script supervisor, continuity coordinator, art director

International Alliance of Theatrical Stage Employees, Local #784
1182 Market Street, Suite 213
San Francisco, CA 94102-4919
415-861-8379
Fax: 415-861-8384
twu784@earthlink.net
Occupational Fields: wardrobe designer

International Alliance of Theatrical Stage Employees, Local #839
4729 Lankershim Boulevard
North Hollywood, CA 91602-1864
818-766-7151
Fax: 818-506-4805
mpsc839@mindspring.com
http://www.mpsc839.org/mpsc839
Occupational Fields: motion picture studio cartoonist

International Alliance of Theatrical Stage Employees, Local #874
PO Box 188787
Sacramento, CA 95818
916-804-8871
Fax: 916-991-7323
Occupational Fields: wardrobe designer

International Alliance of Theatrical Stage Employees, Local #905
PO Box 19479
San Diego, CA 92159-0479
619-885-0095
Fax: 619-293-0373
Occupational Fields: wardrobe designer

International Alliance of Theatrical Stage Employees, Local #916
7001 World Way West, Suite 109
Los Angeles, CA 90045-1745
310-645-5568
Fax: 310-645-1745
Occupational Fields: airline motion picture worker

International Alliance of Theatrical Stage Employees, Local #923
PO Box 9031
Anaheim, CA 92812
909-822-8892
Fax: 949-380-1439
iatselocal923@aol.com
Occupational Fields: sound technician, figure maintenance technician

International Alliance of Theatrical Stage Employees, Locals #768, #816, #818, #847, #854, and #892
13245 Riverside Drive, Suite 300
818-789-8735
Fax: 818-789-1928
Occupational Fields: motion picture craftsperson, wardrobe designer, studio arts craftsperson, scenic artist, theatrical publicist, motion picture set designer, model maker, story analyst

International Alliance of Theatrical Stage Employees, Stage Hands, Electrical Light Technicians
1438 North Gower Street
Hollywood, CA 90028-8362
Occupational Fields: stage technician, lighting technician

International Alliance of Theatrical Stage Employees, Local B18
965 Mission Street, Suite 207
San Francisco, CA 94103
415-974-0860
Fax: 415-974-0852
Occupational Fields: theatre employees

International Alliance of Theatrical Stage Employees, Local B66
PO Box 19063
Sacramento, CA 95819-0063
916-486-4809
Fax: 916-683-9618
Occupational Fields: theatre employees

International Alliance of Theatrical Stage Employees, Local B192
10999 Riverside Drive, Suite 301
North Hollywood, CA 91602
818-509-9192
Fax: 818-509-9873
Occupational Fields: amusement area employees

International Alliance of Theatrical Stage Employees, USA829
5225 Wilshire Boulevard, Suite 506
Los Angeles, CA 90036
323-965-0957
Fax: 323-965-0958
usamail@usa829.org
http://www.usa829.org
Occupational Fields: theatre employees

International Cinematographers Guild, Local #600
7715 Sunset Boulevard, Suite 300
Hollywood, CA 90046
323-876-0160
Fax: 323-876-6383
admin@cameraguild.com
http://www.cameraguild.com
Occupational Fields: cinematographers

San Francisco Opera Center
Auditions Coordinator
301 Van Ness Avenue
San Francisco, CA 94102-4509
415-861-4008
Fax: 415-621-7508
http://www.sfopera.com
Occupational Fields: stage manager, technical producer, administrator

COLORADO

International Alliance of Theatrical Stage Employees, Local #7
910 15th Street
Denver, CO 80202
303-534-2423
Fax: 303-534-0216
Occupational Fields: stage technician

International Alliance of Theatrical Stage Employees, Local #47
PO Box 1488
Pueblo, CO 81002
719-584-0860
Fax: 719-584-0820
Occupational Fields: stage technician

International Alliance of Theatrical Stage Employees, Local #62
PO Box 522
Colorado Springs, CO 80901-0522

719-520-1059
Fax: 719-520-1090
president@iatse62.com
http://www.iatse62.com
Occupational Fields: various theater workers

International Alliance of Theatrical Stage Employees, Local #230, Boulder
4500 19th Street, Suite 249
Boulder, CO 80302
Occupational Fields: motion picture operator

International Alliance of Theatrical Stage Employees, Local #719
12010 West 52nd Place, Unit 7
Arvada, CO 80002
303-431-7561
Fax: 303-989-6150
Occupational Fields: wardrobe designer

CONNECTICUT

International Alliance of Theatrical Stage Employees, Local #74
247 College Street
PO Box 9075
New Haven, CT 06532
203-773-9139
Fax: 203-773-9139
Occupational Fields: stage technician

International Alliance of Theatrical Stage Employees, Local #84
1145 D. New Britain Avenue
West Hartford, CT 06110
860-233-8821
Fax: 860-233-8827
Occupational Fields: stage technician

International Alliance of Theatrical Stage Employees, Local #109
PO Box 614
Stratford, CT 06497-0614
203-878-1109
Occupational Fields: stage technician

International Alliance of Theatrical Stage Employees, Local #133
PO Box 63
Norwalk, CT 06852

203-964-0133
Fax: 203-975-0133
Occupational Fields: *various theater workers*

**International Alliance of Theatrical Stage Employees,
Local #133, Stage Hands**
61 Atlantic Street
Stamford, CT 06901-2403
203-964-0133
Occupational Fields: *stage technician*

**International Alliance of Theatrical Stage Employees,
Local #486**
43 Brownleigh Road
West Hartford, CT 06117
Occupational Fields: *motion picture operator*

**International Alliance of Theatrical Stage Employees,
Local #538**
PO Box 124
Danielson, CT 06457
203-320-5223
Occupational Fields: *various theater workers*

DISTRICT OF COLUMBIA
**International Alliance of Theatrical Stage Employees,
Local #815, Cliffbourne Place**
2512 Cliffbourne Place, NW, Suite 2A
Washington, DC 20009-1512
Occupational Fields: *electronics technician, sound
technician, computer service technician*

**International Alliance of Theatrical Stage Employees,
Local #815, Ninth Street**
5900 Ninth Street, NW, Suite 4
Washington, DC 20011-1949
Occupational Fields: *electronics technician, sound
technician, computer service technician*

**International Alliance of Theatrical Stage Employees,
Local #819**
Box 5645
Friendship Station
Washington, DC 20016
202-966-4110
Fax: 301-926-0251
Occupational Fields: *television broadcast studio
employee*

**International Alliance of Theatrical Stage Employees,
Local #868**
PO Box 58129
Washington, DC 20037
703-869-9405
Fax: 301-322-3547
Occupational Fields: *treasurers, ticket sellers*

FLORIDA
**International Alliance of Theatrical Stage Employees,
Local #60, Gonzalez**
PO Box 1084
Pensacola, FL 32591
850-484-9050
Fax: 850-484-9050
Occupational Fields: *various theater workers*

**International Alliance of Theatrical Stage Employees,
Local #115**
3610 River Hall Drive
PO Box 462
Jacksonville, FL 32201
904-443-0060
Fax: 904-739-0592
Occupational Fields: *various theater workers*

**International Alliance of Theatrical Stage Employees,
Local #316**
PO Box 170310
Hialeah Gardens, FL 33017-0310
305-822-9918
Occupational Fields: *motion picture projectionist, motion
picture operator, video technician*

**International Alliance of Theatrical Stage Employees,
Local #321**
1211 North Westshore Boulevard, Suite 509
Tampa, FL 33607
813-877-2788
Fax: 813-289-8664
Occupational Fields: *various theater workers*

**International Alliance of Theatrical Stage Employees,
Local #412**
Postal Drawer Q
Sarasota, FL 34230
941-359-1254
Fax: 813-955-5844
Occupational Fields: *various theater workers*

International Alliance of Theatrical Stage Employees, Local #477
10705 Northwest 33rd Street, Suite 110
Miami, FL 33172
305-594-8585
Fax: 305-597-9278
Occupational Fields: studio mechanic

International Alliance of Theatrical Stage Employees, Local #500
4520 Northeast 18th Avenue, 3rd Floor
Fort Lauderdale, FL 33334
954-463-6175
Fax: 954-463-6426
Occupational Fields: various theater workers

International Alliance of Theatrical Stage Employees, Local #558
PO Box 534
Daytona Beach, FL 32115
386-767-2022
Fax: 386-767-2022
Occupational Fields: various theater workers

International Alliance of Theatrical Stage Employees, Local #600
7463 Conroy-Windermere Road, Suite A
Orlando, FL 32835
407-295-5577
Fax: 407-295-5335
Occupational Fields: motion picture photographer

International Alliance of Theatrical Stage Employees, Local #623
PO Box 19009
Palm Beach, FL 33416
561-968-1126
Fax: 561-694-7774
Occupational Fields: various theater workers

International Alliance of Theatrical Stage Employees, Local #631
5385 Conroy Road, Suite 200
Orlando, FL 32811-3719
407-422-2747
Fax: 407-843-9170
Occupational Fields: various theater workers

International Alliance of Theatrical Stage Employees, Local #647
PO Box 700
Estero, FL 33928

239-275-4555
Occupational Fields: stage technician

International Alliance of Theatrical Stage Employees, Local #853
1311 Northeast 213 Terrace, Apartment 1206
Miami Beach, FL 33179
305-651-9618
Occupational Fields: wardrobe designer

GEORGIA
International Alliance of Theatrical Stage Employees, Local #320
1513 Paulsen Street
Savannah, GA 31401
912-232-2203
Fax: 208-979-8533
iatse@earthlink.net
Occupational Fields: various theater workers

International Alliance of Theatrical Stage Employees, Local #824
PO Box 422
Athens, GA 30603
706-338-0818
Occupational Fields: theatre employees

International Alliance of Theatrical Stage Employees, Local #859
3993 Reynolds Road
Douglasville, GA 30135
678-838-3164
Fax: 678-838-1456
Occupational Fields: wardrobe designers

International Alliance of Theatrical Stage Employees, Locals #927 and #834
659 Auburn Avenue, NE, Apartment 262
Atlanta, GA 30312
404-870-9911
Fax: 404-870-9906
Occupational Fields: exhibit specialist, stage technician

INDIANA
International Alliance of Theatrical Stage Employees, Local #30
1701 West 18th Street
Indianapolis, IN 46202-1056
317-638-3226

Fax: 317-638-6126
Occupational Fields: stage technician

International Alliance of Theatrical Stage Employees, Local #125
1846 West 59th Place
Merrillville, IN 46410
219-942-9652
Fax: 219-987-4375
Occupational Fields: various theater workers

International Alliance of Theatrical Stage Employees, Local #187
211 North Michigan Street
PO Box 474
South Bend, IN 46624
219-234-2187
Occupational Fields: various theater workers

MAINE
Video Services Unlimited
1065 Riverside Drive
Auburn, ME 04210-9657
207-782-5650
Occupational Fields: video production assistant

MARYLAND
International Alliance of Theatrical Stage Employees, Local #22
11247-B Lockwood Drive
Silver Spring, MD 20901-4556
301-593-4650
Fax: 301-681-7141
Occupational Fields: stage technician

MASSACHUSETTS
Berkshire Theatre Festival
East Street
Stockbridge, MA 01262
413-298-5536
Fax: 413-298-3368
http://www.berkshiretheatre.org
Occupational Fields: scenery designer, wardrobe designer, prop designer, lighting technician

International Alliance of Theatrical Stage Employees, Locals #11 and #775
120 Boylston Street, Second Floor
Boston, MA 02116-4611

617-426-5595
Fax: 617-426-6252
Occupational Fields: stage technician, wardrobe designer

International Alliance of Theatrical Stage Employees, Local #921
186 Lincoln Street
Boston, MA 02111-2403
Occupational Fields: various theater workers

NEBRASKA
Omaha Community Playhouse
6915 Cass Street
Omaha, NE 68132-2649
402-553-4890
Occupational Fields: theater technician

NEVADA
International Alliance of Theatrical Stage Employees, #363
30 Mary Street, #14
PO Box 9840
Reno, NV 89507
775-786-2286
Fax: 775-786-7150
Occupational Fields: various theater workers

International Alliance of Theatrical Stage Employees, Local #720
3000 South Valley View Boulevard
Las Vegas, NV 89102-7898
775-873-3450
Fax: 775-873-4703
Occupational Fields: various theater workers

NEW JERSEY
International Alliance of Theatrical Stage Employees, Local #21, Vauxhall
Millburn Mall
2933 Vauxhall Road
Vauxhall, NJ 07088
Occupational Fields: stage technician

International Alliance of Theatrical Stage Employees, Local #77, Stage Hands
308 Pennsylvania Avenue
Absecon, NJ 08201-1221

609-646-7754
Occupational Fields: stage technician

International Alliance of Theatrical Stage Employees, Local #917
4119 Atlantic Avenue
Atlantic City, NJ 08401-5863
609-345-0550
Fax: 609-345-4554
Occupational Fields: casino worker, hotel worker

International Alliance of Theatrical Stage Employees, Local Union
Bridgewater Commons Mall
Somerville, NJ 08876-5863
908-429-8855
Occupational Fields: various theater workers

NEW MEXICO

Santa Fe Opera
Personnel Office
PO Box 2408
Santa Fe, NM 87504-2408
505-986-5955
Occupational Fields: various theater workers

NEW YORK

International Alliance of Theatrical Stage Employees, Local #1
320 West 46th Street, 3rd Floor
New York, NY 10036-3845
212-333-2500
Fax: 212-586-2437
Occupational Fields: stage technician

International Alliance of Theatrical Stage Employees, Local #4
2917 Glenwood Road
Brooklyn, NY 11210-2631
718-252-8777
Fax: 718-421-5605
Occupational Fields: stage technician

International Alliance of Theatrical Stage Employees, Local #52
326 West 48th Street
New York, NY 10036-1314
212-399-0980

Fax: 212-315-1073
Occupational Fields: stage technician, motion picture operator, studio mechanic

International Alliance of Theatrical Stage Employees, Locals #161 and #600
80 Eighth Avenue, 14th Floor
New York, NY 10011-5126
212-647-7300
Occupational Fields: script supervisor, motion picture producer, continuity coordinator, motion picture photographer

International Alliance of Theatrical Stage Employees, National Headquarters
1430 Broadway, 20th Floor
New York, NY 10018
212-730-1770
Fax: 212-921-7699
Occupational Fields: stage technician, film and television producer, cameraman, projectionist, wardrobe designer, animator, makeup artist, public relations specialist, producer

NORTH CAROLINA

International Alliance of Theatrical Stage Employees, Local #322
4037 East Independence Boulevard, Suite 601
Charlotte, NC 28205-7375
704-537-8329
Fax: 704-377-6452
Occupational Fields: various theater workers

International Alliance of Theatrical Stage Employees, Local #417
309 Robert Street
Cary, NC 27511-3233
919-481-0417
Occupational Fields: various theater workers

OREGON

International Alliance of Theatrical Stage Employees, Local #28
4949 Southeast 26th
Portland, OR 97202
503-295-2828
Fax: 503-238-6644
http://www.iatse28.org
Occupational Fields: various theater workers

PENNSYLVANIA

International Alliance of Theatrical Stage Employees, Local #3
Five Foster Plaza
Pittsburgh, PA 15220-2740
412-281-4568
Occupational Fields: various theater workers

International Alliance of Theatrical Stage Employees, Local #3
765 Somerville Drive
PO Box 352
Pittsburgh, PA 15230
412-281-4568
Fax: 412-281-4571
Occupational Fields: stage technician

International Alliance of Theatrical Stage Employees, Local #98
98 Harrisburg
Harrisburg, PA 17113-1562
717-232-9070
Occupational Fields: various theater workers

International Alliance of Theatrical Stage Employees, Local #489
PO Box 100056
Pittsburgh, PA 15233
412-321-2150
Occupational Fields: studio mechanic

State College Community Theatre
Boal Barn Playhouse
Boalsburg, PA 16827
814-466-7141
Occupational Fields: stage manager, scene constructor and painter, lighting technician, props technician, wardrobe designer painter

TEXAS

International Alliance of Theatrical Stage Employees, Locals #51 and #484
440 Louisiana Street
PO Box 403
Houston, TX 77001-0403
713-229-8277
Fax: 713-229-8138
Occupational Fields: stage technician, studio mechanic

International Alliance of Theatrical Stage Employees, Local #76
206 San Pedro Avenue, Suite 306
San Antonio, TX 78205
210-223-3911
Fax: 210-225-6115
Occupational Fields: stage technician

International Alliance of Theatrical Stage Employees, Local #127
Dallas Stage Employees
2805 Canton Street
Dallas, TX 75226
214-742-4741
Fax: 214-747-4792
Occupational Fields: stage technician

International Alliance of Theatrical Stage Employees, Local #153
Cielo Vista Cinema
PO Box 1130
El Paso, TX 79947
915-544-6818
Fax: 915-544-8323
Occupational Fields: various theater workers

UTAH

International Alliance of Theatrical Stage Employees, Local #99
526 West, 800 South, Suite 2002
Salt Lake City, UT 84101-1285
801-359-0513
Fax: 801-532-6227
http://www.xmission.com/~utp
Occupational Fields: stage technician

WASHINGTON

International Alliance of Theatrical Stage Employees, Locals #15, #154, #488, and #887
Pacific Northwest Chapter
2800 First Avenue
Seattle, WA 98121
206-448-0668
Fax: 206-448-0257
Occupational Fields: studio mechanic, stage technician, wardrobe designer, motion picture operator

CANADA
ALBERTA
International Alliance of Theatrical Stage Employees, Local #210
10428 123 Street
Edmonton, AB T5N 1N7
780-423-1863
http://www.iatse210.com
Occupational Fields: stage employees

International Alliance of Theatrical Stage Employees, Local #212
B8-141, 2526 Battleford Avenue, SW
Calgary, AB T3E 7J4
403-250-2199
Fax: 403-250-9769
ia212@iatse212.com
http://www.iatse212.com
Occupational Fields: stage employees

BRITISH COLUMBIA
International Alliance of Theatrical Stage Employees, Local #118
Cambie Street, Suite 202-601
Vancouver, BC V6B 2P1
604-685-9553
Fax: 604-685-9554
info@iatse118.com
http://www.iatse118.com
Occupational Fields: stage employees

International Alliance of Theatrical Stage Employees, Local #168
PO Box 5822, Station B
Victoria, BC V8R 6S8
250-381-3168
Fax: 866-618-3848
sec-treas@iatse168.com
http://www.iatse168.com
Occupational Fields: stage employees

International Alliance of Theatrical Stage Employees, Local #669
555 Brooksbank Avenue, 6/210
North Vancouver, BC V7J 3S5
604-983-5580
Fax: 604-983-5579
camera@ia669.com

http://www.ia669.com
Occupational Fields: camerapersons

International Alliance of Theatrical Stage Employees, Local #891
1640 Boundary Road
Burnaby, BC V5K 4V4
604-664-8910
Fax: 604-298-3456
Occupational Fields: stage employees

NOVA SCOTIA
International Alliance of Theatrical Stage Employees, Local #680
PO Box 711
Halifax, NS B3J 2T3
902-455-5016
Fax: 902-455-0398
Occupational Fields: stage employees

International Alliance of Theatrical Stage Employees, Local #849
15 Mcquade Lake Crescent, 2nd Floor
Halifax, NS B3S 1C4
902-425-2739
Fax: 902-425-7696
admin@iatse849.com
http://www.iatse849.com
Occupational Fields: motion picture studio production technicians

ONTARIO
International Alliance of Theatrical Stage Employees, Local #58
5 Lower Sherbourne, Suite 201
Toronto, ON M5A 2P3
416-364-5565
Fax: 416-364-5987
president@iatse58.org
http://www.iatse58.org
Occupational Fields: stage employees

International Alliance of Theatrical Stage Employees, Local #173
13 Carr Drive
Ajax, ON L1T 3E1
416-697-0330
Occupational Fields: motion picture projectionists, operators, and video technicians

International Alliance of Theatrical Stage Employees, Local #411
629 Eastern Avenue, Building C, #300
Toronto, ON M4M 1E4
416-645-8025
Fax: 416-645-8026
http://www.iatse411.ca
Occupational Fields: production coordinators, craftservice providers, honeywagon operators

International Alliance of Theatrical Stage Employees, Local #667
9 Gloucester Street
Toronto, ON M4Y 1L8
416-368-0072
Fax: 416-368-6932
camera@iatse667.com
http://www.iatse667.com
Occupational Fields: camerapersons

International Alliance of Theatrical Stage Employees, Local #828
Box 69503
109 Thomas Street
Oakville, ON L6J 7R4
905-845-2913
Fax: 905-845-2980
http://www.iatse828.org
Occupational Fields: scenic artists, propmakers

International Alliance of Theatrical Stage Employees, Local #873
474 Adelaide Street East
Toronto, ON M5A 1N6
416-368-1873
Fax: 416-368-8457
http://www.iatse873.com
Occupational Fields: motion picture studio production technicians

International Alliance of Theatrical Stage Employees, Local #B173
735 Don Mills Road, #1708
Toronto, ON M3C 1T1
416-423-9573
Fax: 416-423-9573
Occupational Fields: stage employees

PRINCE EDWARD ISLAND
International Alliance of Theatrical Stage Employees, Local #906
PO Box 2406
Charlottetown, PE C1A 8C1
902-892-3298
Fax: 902-368-7180
Occupational Fields: stage employees

TILE SETTERS

RELATED SECTIONS: *artists and artisans, bricklayers, carpenters, crafts and trades workers at living historical sites and farms, drywallers and lathers, floor layers, glaziers, insulators and asbestos workers, laborers, masons, painters and paperhangers, plasterers*

Tile setters install ceramic, marble, and quarry tile in bathrooms, kitchens, office lobbies, schools, hospitals, shopping centers, and other buildings. Some tile setters specialize in projects such as hospitals, offices, or residential sites. Tile has been valued for thousands of years, because it is durable, easy to clean, waterproof, and attractive. Tile helpers, also known as tile finishers, are workers who assist tile setters by carrying materials, cleaning surfaces, grouting, and performing other simple tasks.

Mosaic tile workers produce decorative and protective patterns with tiles of various colors, typically in creative, artistic designs. They often work with small, ceramic squares. This art form has been popular since the days of ancient Babylon and Persia.

Marble setters spread plaster on the back of marble pieces, apply them to interior and exterior surfaces of buildings, and fill the joints with grout.

Terrazzo workers employ a decorative technique developed in Venice, Italy, during the 16th century. They usually establish a concrete foundation, add a sandy concrete layer, and finish with a mixture of mortar and broken stone (most often marble or granite). Stone of varied colors is used to create elegant designs, which are typically polished with grinding machines. Terrazzo is most popular in Florida and California.

One method of setting tile begins with the worker tacking a metal mesh to the building surface, troweling cement plaster over the mesh, and scratching the plaster before it dries. The worker then coats the back of tiles with cement and presses them in place on the plaster, making sure to align them perfectly and match their patterns.

A second method is done on smooth, solid surfaces, such as plaster, drywall, or concrete. Cement adhesive or a sticky paste called "mastic" is applied to the surface or to the back of the tiles, which are then attached to the surface. The joints are filled with grouting cement.

Both methods sometimes involve using saws to cut tiles to fit around pipes, washbasins, and other objects. For renovation projects, old tile, adhesives, and grout must first be chiseled or scraped away before new tile can be placed. Tile setters usually work indoors in fairly clean surroundings. Terrazzo workers and marble setters work both indoors and outdoors. The work involves standing, bending, kneeling, and reaching but does not require great physical strength. In general this occupation is not as dangerous as some other construction trades, although tile setters risk injury from falling off ladders and working with tools and rough tiles.

Many tile setters are employed by contractors, but about half are self-employed. Some tile setters belong to labor unions, such as the International Union of Bricklayers and Allied Craftsmen or the United Brotherhood of Carpenters and Joiners of America. Union tile setters are generally paid by the hour; nonunion workers are usually paid by the amount of work completed; and self-employed tile setters are often paid a fixed price per project.

Unions and other organizations in the building and construction trades offer apprenticeships and on-the-job training for tile setters. Apprentices to this trade work under the supervision of experienced tile setters. They participate in course work and on-the-job training, moving from simple tasks, such as mixing cement, to more skilled tasks, such as cutting and installing tile. Typically the course of study runs for three years and includes instruction in blueprint reading, mathematics, and other pertinent subjects.

In general an applicant should

- apply in person
- be at least 18 years old
- be a high school graduate or hold a GED certificate
- be in good physical condition
- have a keen sense of color harmony
- have manual dexterity
- have an aptitude for calculating weights, angles, and dimensions
- have an artistic flair
- be able and willing to work efficiently and without much supervision

APPRENTICESHIP SALARIES

Between about $7 an hour and $13 an hour, or about half the rate paid to experienced workers. Experienced apprentices earn between about $17 an hour and $26 an hour.

POSTAPPRENTICESHIP SALARIES
About $10 an hour, up to $30 an hour.

JOB OUTLOOK
Generally good, because the continued growth in construction means there will continue to be demand for tile and related finishes. Tile is being used more frequently in new construction, particularly in more high-priced residences. There is less demand for tile setters than for other construction workers, however, and turnover in this trade is fairly low.

For more information on apprenticeships for tile setters, contact the national organizations and individual programs listed below, local job centers, your state bureau of apprenticeship training, or local tile setting contractors.

NATIONAL PROGRAMS
Bricklayers and Allied Craftsworkers, National Training Center
PO Box 755
Cascade, MD 21719
800-562-7464
http://www.bacweb.org
Occupational Fields: terrazzo worker, tile setter

International Masonry Institute
The James Brice House
42 East Street
Annapolis, MD 21401
800-562-7464
http://www.imiweb.org
Occupational Fields: bricklayer, tile setter

International Union of Bricklayers and Allied Craftsmen
776 I Street, NW
Washington, DC 20006
202-783-3788
http://www.bacweb.org
Occupational Fields: bricklayer, tile setter

APPRENTICESHIP PROFILE
International Union of Bricklayers and Allied Craftworkers, Local #1
Western Washington Masonry Trades Joint Apprenticeship and Training Committee
6314 7th Avenue, South
Seattle, WA 98108

800-636-5481
Fax: 206-762-8811

General Nature of the Job
Tile setters install various types of tile to provide a beautiful, waterproof finish in bathrooms, kitchens, the lobbies of office buildings, on roofs, around fireplaces, and in many other settings. This skilled masonry trade can be highly artistic; some tile setters specialize in creating decorative designs with colored ceramic or marble pieces. The job can also be physically demanding. Eric Hughes remembers a project at a local hospital, where he mixed mortar outdoors and transported it indoors in a wheelbarrow, balancing the 300-pound load on planks laid end to end down two flights of stairs.

"You're just trying to slow it down as much as you can to make those ninety-degree corners," he says. "You have to be physically fit for this job. You've got to carry the weight. Unless a person can haul a hundred pounds, it's not for them."

In addition to handling heavy wheelbarrows and lifting 100-pound sacks of dry cement and sand, tile setters carry packages of tile, shovel sand and mortar, and use grinders to roughen the surfaces of floors and walls to make the tile adhere securely. They apply mortar with trowels and use saws to cut the tile into precise shapes to fit around corners, toilets and other fixtures, and water pipes. The trade requires great precision and the ability to plan ahead, since the rows of tile must line up perfectly and fit in the allotted space.

Eric has learned most of his tile-setting skills through a four-year training program administered jointly by the Western Washington Masonry Trades Apprenticeship Committee and the International Union of Bricklayers and Allied Craftworkers, Local #1. He hopes to complete his 6,000 hours of on-the-job training and 576 hours of classroom studies at South Seattle Community College this year. Although tile setters are not required to be licensed or certified in the state of Washington, Eric's apprenticeship certification will allow him to join the union.

Typical Day
Eric commutes about two hours every day, either to college or to various job sites. His college classes begin at 7:00 A.M., and his work schedule begins at 6:30 A.M. He takes a 30-minute lunch break and usually has a coffee break in the morning and afternoon.

For about eight hours every other Saturday, Eric attends classes at South Seattle Community College. There, he studies trade mathematics, architectural drawing, blue-print reading, layout work, sketching, trade terminology, handbook reading, how to use and care for the tools of the trade, the use and preparation of materials, and first aid. He might attend morning lectures, then drive to a site to work on a volunteer project, such as finishing a monument in a local park. Sometimes the work is done outdoors in all sorts of weather, including blowing snow, sleet, and rain. Apprentices also complete mock-up projects, which provide hands-on experience under the supervision of an instructor.

During the rest of the week, Eric works on construction projects and is paid for his time. The apprenticeship committee encourages trainees to work with various contractors and on various types of projects where they will learn all the skills of the trade. Eric sometimes receives a call from an employer who needs an apprentice to help with a job. Sometimes the union puts him in touch with potential employers. Other times, he finds his own work by keeping in contact with journeymen tile setters of his acquaintance.

When Eric arrives on a job, the preliminary work has usually been done. The general contractor tells him where to begin, what tasks are priorities, what problems he's likely to encounter, and when the work must be finished. Eric checks the walls and floors to be sure they're straight and decides what preparatory work must be done before tile can be installed. For instance, he might have to slope the floor of a shower stall to make the water drain properly. Most jobs are complex and require careful planning and organization; Eric relies on the advice of his more experienced coworkers to ensure that everything is done properly.

Path to Becoming an Apprentice

Eric, who is now 35 years old, had another career before he decided to become a tile setter. He earned a college degree in culinary arts and became the manager of a fine-dining establishment, but he explains, "I just got tired of dealing with the things I was dealing with." He began working with an acquaintance who was a building contractor, but to keep that job, he had to join the local union. To join the union, he had to complete apprenticeship training.

Eric says the construction trades classes he took in high school, such as welding, and his on-the-job experience in drywall and carpentry during those years have proved useful in his career as a tile setter. Apprentices can enroll in a few extra classes to obtain a college degree, but Eric is not pursuing that option, since he already has a degree.

Applicants to the apprenticeship program must be at least 17 years old and have a high school diploma or GED, a driver's license, and a Social Security card. They participate in an orientation seminar and are interviewed briefly, then take a physical test, which includes climbing ladders and pushing a wheelbarrow full of sand. Those who pass are placed on an eligibility list until an apprenticeship position opens. They participate in 12 weeks of preparatory classes before being indentured. During the initial 1,200-hour probationary period, the apprentice or the sponsor can terminate the contract without a formal hearing or having to state a cause. The apprenticeship committee has an affirmative action plan to encourage applications by minorities and women.

Salary Range

Wages for apprentice tile setters start at 50 percent of journeyman scale and are raised periodically until the apprentice is earning 95 percent of journeyman scale. The apprenticeship committee grants raises based on classroom attendance, work attendance, hourly progress reports, attitude, instructor and employer evaluations, on-the-job training progress, and supplemental training.

In the Seattle area a journeyman tile setter can earn about $23 an hour plus dental and medical benefits and a national and local pension administered by the union. Workers do incur some expenses that cut into their income, though. They're required to pay union dues and provide their own tools and transportation. Eric estimates that he drives 35,000 to 40,000 miles a year in connection with his job. He has also been without income for up to eight weeks between projects.

Advice

Although he already had a job when he entered the apprenticeship, Eric says the program has provided him with the necessary skills of his profession. "The training is very valuable. I would have had to look around a lot more for a mentor without it," he notes. He advises apprentices to remember that, no matter what the type of schooling, "You get out of it what you put into it." At work, he adds, professionalism is important: "It's my own job to sell myself to make sure I have a job down the road. If you don't produce a good product in a timely and effective manner, you'll lose your job."

For tile setters he offers a bit of specific advice: "Wear your kneepads. We're on our knees all the time. There's plenty of guys out there that have knee problems from kneeling and getting up and down all day long."

Future Goals

Eric doesn't anticipate any major changes in his career during the next few years. "I will continue to work for somebody else, I think, though I might get a license to dabble on my own occasionally," he says. After completing the apprenticeship training, he'll know the basics of the job, but he expects to work about 10 years before considering himself an expert in the trade.

CALIFORNIA

International Union of Bricklayers and Allied Craftsworkers, Local #3
8400 Enterprise Way, Suite 103
Oakland, CA 94621
510-632-8781
Occupational Fields: tile setter, tile finisher

DISTRICT OF COLUMBIA

International Union of Bricklayers and Allied Craftsworkers, National Headquarters
1776 I Street, NW
Washington, DC 20006
202-783-3788
http://www.bacweb.org
Occupational Fields: terrazzo worker, tile setter

ILLINOIS

International Union of Bricklayers and Allied Craftsworkers
1950 West 43rd Street
Chicago, IL 60609
773-650-1894
http://www.bacillinoisdistrictcouncil.org
Occupational Fields: terrazzo worker, tile setter

Mosaic Terrazzo Workers Union
5814 West Grand Avenue
Chicago, IL 60639
773-237-2292
Occupational Fields: terrazzo worker

INDIANA

Bricklayers, Masons, and Tile Setters Union, Local #3
620 North East Street
Indianapolis, IN 46202-3421
317-262-4640
Occupational Fields: tile setter, marble setter, terrazzo worker

International Union of Bricklayers and Allied Craftworkers, Local #19
2900 North Granville Avenue
Muncie, IN 47303
765-284-2926
Occupational Fields: tile setter, stone setter, marble mason

Terre Haute Bricklayers and Allied Craftsmen Joint Apprenticeship Council
2112 South Third Street
PO Box 2205
Terre Haute, IN 47802
812-232-1492
Occupational Fields: tile setter

IOWA

Iowa Tile, Marble, and Terrazzo Workers
3839 Delaware Avenue
Des Moines, IA 50313
515-265-3467
Occupational Fields: tile setter

MARYLAND

International Masonry Institute
The James Brice House
42 East Street
Annapolis, MD 21401
800-JOBS-IMI
http://www.imiweb.org
Occupational Fields: terrazzo worker, tile setter

International Union of Bricklayers and Allied Craftworkers
National Training Center
PO Box 755
Cascade, MD 21719
800-562-7464
http://www.bacweb.org
Occupational Fields: terrazzo worker, tile setter

International Union of Bricklayers and Allied Craftworkers, Local #1
5200 Westland Boulevard
Arbutus, MD 21227-2360

410-536-2005
Occupational Fields: tile setter

MASSACHUSETTS

International Masonry Institute, Massachusetts
84 Myron Street
Springfield, MA 01089
413-737-5999
Fax: 413-737-6027
Occupational Fields: tile setter, marble setter, terrazzo
worker

**International Union of Bricklayers and Allied
Craftworkers, Local #3**
550 Medford Street
Charlestown, MA 02129-1405
617-242-5507
Fax: 617-242-0021
Occupational Fields: tile setter, marble setter, terrazzo
worker

MINNESOTA

Bricklayers and Tile Setters Union
2002 London Road
Duluth, MN 55812-2144
218-724-8374
Occupational Fields: tile setter

MONTANA

Tile Setters Union
1038 22nd Avenue, South
Great Falls, MT 59405-5951
406-727-1016
Occupational Fields: tile setter

NEVADA

Bricklayers and Tilesetters Union
3640 South Highland Drive
Las Vegas, NV 89103
702-873-0332
Occupational Fields: tile setter, marble setter

Bricklayers and Tilesetters Union
1150 Terminal Way
Reno, NV 89502
702-323-5451
Occupational Fields: tile setter

NEW JERSEY

International Masonry Institute, New Jersey
3281 Route 206, South
Bordentown, NJ 08505
609-291-8000
Fax: 609-291-8228
Occupational Fields: tile setter, marble worker, terrazzo
worker

NEW YORK

Eastern Contractors Association
Six Airline Drive
Albany, NY 12205-1004
518-869-0961
Fax: 518-869-2378
Occupational Fields: tile setter, terrazzo worker

OHIO

**International Union of Bricklayers and Allied
Craftworkers, Local #5**
4205 Chester Avenue
Cleveland, OH 44103
216-361-1652
Fax: 216-361-1675
brick5@core.com
Occupational Fields: tile setter, terrazzo worker

OREGON

Oregon and Southwest Washington Cement Masons
20210 Southwest Teton
Tualatin, OR 97062
503-691-9618
Fax: 503-691-5773
Occupational Fields: tile setter

Oregon and Southwest Washington Mason Trades
2215 Southeast Division Street
Portland, OR 97202
503-232-0358
Fax: 503-238-6644
Occupational Fields: tile setter

PENNSYLVANIA

**International Union of Bricklayers and Allied
Craftworkers**
2706 Black Lake Place
Philadelphia, PA

215-856-9505
Fax: 215-856-9515
http://www.bac1pa-de.org
Occupational Fields: tile setters, terrazzo worker

TEXAS
International Union of Bricklayers and Allied Craftworkers
District Council, Texas
International Masonry Institute
9105 Edgebrook Street
Houston, TX 77075-1241
713-941-5668
Occupational Fields: tile setter, stone mason, marble mason

Bricklayers and Tile Setters Union, Local #2
611 North Flores
San Antonio, TX 78205
210-227-5422
Occupational Fields: tile setter

WASHINGTON
Inland Northwest Masonry Apprenticeship Committee
East 102 Boone, Suite 101
Spokane, WA 99202
509-327-2774
Fax: 509-327-6451
Occupational Fields: tile setter

INTALCO Aluminum Corporation
450 Mountain View Road
Ferndale, WA 98248
360-384-7296
Fax: 360-284-6412
Occupational Fields: tile setter

International Masonry Institute, Washington State
6770 East Marginal Way, South, Building C
Seattle, WA 98108
206-767-3986
Fax: 206-762-0393
Occupational Fields: tile setter, marble worker, terrazzo worker

Seattle Cement Masons
552 Denny Way, Suite 102
Seattle, WA 98109
206-441-9386
Fax: 206-441-9018
Occupational Fields: tile setter

WISCONSIN
Bricklayers Union, Local #19
2233 Birch Street
Eau Claire, WI 54703
715-835-5164
Occupational Fields: tile setter

CANADA
ALBERTA
International Union of Bricklayers and Allied Craftworkers, Local #1
10576 104th Street, NW
Edmonton, AB T5H 2W1
780-426-7545
Fax: 780-425-9201
Occupational Fields: tile setter

ONTARIO
International Union of Bricklayers and Allied Craftworkers, Local #6
3454 Sandwich Street
Windsor, ON N9C 1B3
519-256-3070
Fax: 519-256-3070
Occupational Fields: tile setter

TOOL, DIE, MOLD, AND PATTERN MAKERS

RELATED SECTIONS: *auto body workers, boilermakers, carpenters, elevator constructors, engineers and engineering technicians, farriers, ironworkers, machinists, mechanics, metalworkers, millwrights, operating engineers and stationary engineers, pipe trades workers, sheet metal workers, shipbuilding and ship maintenance workers, welders*

Tool and die makers, also known as *mold makers* and *pattern makers*, design, produce, and repair machine tools and dies. They also repair gauges, jigs, and fixtures. They are often regarded as very specialized machinists.

Toolmakers produce tools that cut and shape metal and other materials. They make jigs (patterns that guide tools), fixtures (devices that clamp work pieces in place), and gauges. Die makers make metal forms called "dies," which are used in stamping and forging. In addition, they produce metal molds used in die-casting and in molding ceramics, plastics, and other materials. Experienced workers may become tool designers or tool programmers.

Metalworking and plastics-working machine operators run machines that produce the parts used in various manufactured products. This machinery cuts and forms various metal parts. Setup workers prepare the machinery for production and adjust it as it operates. Operators and tenders run the machinery and make small adjustments. They may operate a variety of machines or specialize in one or two.

A tool and die maker often produces items single-handedly. The worker reads the blueprints or other specifications, plans the steps to produce the item, and measures and marks the metal. Machines, such as lathes or milling machines, are set up to cut, drill, or otherwise shape the metal. Some parts are finished by filing or grinding, then they are assembled.

Machinery that can be programmed to shape parts automatically is becoming more common in this industry. In manufacturing plants with this type of machinery, tool and die makers sometimes help write computer programs for the machines, in addition to checking and assembling the product.

Most tool and die makers work in factories, particularly those that produce aircraft, motor vehicles, metalworking machines, and items made of plastic. The work is typically done in tool rooms, which are relatively quiet, with only a few machines in operation. To reduce the risk of injury from power tools and flying debris, workers generally wear safety glasses, earplugs, and other protective gear. The job requires hours of standing and some heavy lifting. Weekend work and overtime are becoming increasingly common.

Many workers in this trade belong to labor unions, such as the International Association of Machinists and Aerospace Workers; the United Electrical, Radio and Machine Workers of America; the United Automobile, Aerospace and Agricultural Implement Workers of America; the International Brotherhood of Electrical Workers; and the United Steelworkers.

Apprenticeship is the recommended way of entering this trade, although many machinists also become tool and die makers. Apprentices work under the supervision of experienced tool and die makers. Typically, the course of study runs for four to five years and includes at least 144 hours of classroom instruction annually, covering subjects such as mechanical drawing and metalworking. The trade requires an unusually broad understanding of machining, mathematics, blueprint reading, metals, alloys, tools, and measuring instruments.

In general an applicant should

- apply in person
- be at least 18 years old
- be a high school graduate or hold a GED certificate
- be physically capable of performing the work
- have the ability to work with minimal supervision
- be able to work swiftly and efficiently
- be able to pay keen attention to detail
- possess great patience
- have good eyesight

APPRENTICESHIP SALARIES
Between $5 an hour and $18 an hour.

POSTAPPRENTICESHIP SALARIES
About $20 an hour, with the highest paid employees making more than $30 an hour.

JOB OUTLOOK

Although excellent opportunities for employment will exist in this field, little growth is expected because automated equipment has reduced the number of jobs, even though the demand for machined metal parts is expected to increase. Also, U.S. companies are facing increased competition from foreign manufacturers exporting metal products and finished goods into this country. Jobs will be opening, however, as tool and die makers retire; a large number of the workers in this trade are at least 50 years old. In some areas, employers are having difficulty finding qualified applicants. Jobs are most numerous in the Northeast and the Midwest.

For more information on apprenticeships for tool, die, mold, and pattern makers, contact local job centers, your state bureau of apprenticeship training, or the national organizations and individual programs listed below.

NATIONAL PROGRAMS

International Association of Tool Craftsmen
3718 Wright Avenue
Racine, WI 53405-3304
414-637-4371
Occupational Fields: tool maker, die maker

National Tooling and Machining Association
9300 Livingston Road
Ft. Washington, MD 20744
http://www.ntma.org
Occupational Fields: tool maker, die maker

APPRENTICESHIP PROFILE

Siemens Electromechanical Components
308 Robey Street
Franklin, KY 42134
502-586-4451
Fax: 502-586-1089
http://www.siemens.com

General Nature of the Job

At Siemens Electromechanical Components in Franklin, students learn to build, repair, and maintain tools, dies, and molds used in industrial and automation equipment. A die is a metal form used to shape metal that is being stamped or forged. Molds are forms used to shape metal, plastic, or ceramic materials. The trade requires great precision. In addition to milling machines, lathes, and other power tools, workers commonly use hand tools such as scribes, micrometers, rules, protractors, scales, calipers, wrenches, and punches. It's a job for people who love working with their hands, building things, and seeing their creations function in the way they anticipated. "It's different every day. At times it may get repetitive, but usually it's quite varied," says Mike Greer, training manager.

Siemens spent $1.5 million to build this training center in 1992 because managers believed most U.S. training programs for tool and die makers did not teach workers to perform with the degree of skill the company required. The corporation needed employees who could produce large quantities of high-quality electrical parts. An apprenticeship was designed to train workers specifically for the plant in Franklin.

The Siemens Corporation also operates apprenticeship programs in Santa Clara, California; Lake Mary, Florida; Raleigh, North Carolina; and Alpharetta, Georgia. Ten more are expected to be up and running in this country within the next few years. The programs are structured to meet the needs of each factory and are not all for tool and die makers.

In Franklin the apprenticeships have been designed in cooperation with the Kentucky Advanced Technology Center in nearby Bowling Green. Unlike most tool and die apprenticeships in this country, which last four to five years, the training at Siemens is completed in two and a half years. Of 5,000 total hours, 960 are spent in classroom study; the remainder are spent in on-the-job training. The plant also offers school-to-work apprenticeships for juniors and seniors in high school.

Typical Day

For eight hours each week, apprentices are paid to attend classes designed for this program at the Kentucky Advanced Technology Center. This portion of the training involves studies in technical mathematics, physics, machining technology, computer numerical control, plastics and molding, welding, technical drawing, computer-aided drawing, industrial electronics, computers, fluid power, and automated systems.

Apprentices spend the remaining four days of the week in the training center or working in the factory. They report for work at 7:00 A.M., take a 10-minute break in the morning and afternoon, have 30 minutes to eat lunch, and are finished at 3:30 P.M. The training is project-oriented; apprentices learn theories and skills, then apply them to hands-on tasks. "Depending on the project, it may take two weeks, or it may take two days," Mike says.

Apprentices are graded on each project, before proceeding to the next one.

First-year apprentices work mostly in the training center, learning bench working and the fundamentals of machining. The training center is also where students learn about quality control, automated assembly, metal stamping, plastics and molding, plating and processing, toolmaking, tool design, and maintenance. During this first year, apprentices must pass six tests that demonstrate their proficiency with basic skills, in addition to two tests on theoretical subjects.

Second-year apprentices spend part of their time rotating through the factory's 10 departments, where mentors help them learn how each one functions and how it relates to the other departments. Students also perform some of the work done there. For instance, apprentices set dies and operate presses in the metal stamping department. In this second year, apprentices must complete a seven-hour, intermediate examination to demonstrate their machining skills and general knowledge.

During their third year apprentices learn advanced machining, how to work on production tools, and other skills. They finish with a 12- to 14-hour examination; if they fail this test, they study for three to six additional months and try again. So far, Mike says, every apprentice has passed the final exam.

Path to Becoming an Apprentice

Apprentices come from various backgrounds. Many are already employed at the factory and want to move into tool and die work. Others look forward to having a job with Siemens when they finish. "Some have experience with tool and die. Others just have some idea that it's what they want to do," Mike comments. There are usually about 30 to 40 adult apprentices, ranging in age from 18 to 50, in the program.

The school-to-work component of the program offers apprenticeships for high school juniors and seniors. "It gives the student an opportunity to see what tool and die is all about and to experience what it's like working in the real world. This gives them an opportunity to be in a factory, working with their hands," Mike explains. There are usually six to eight students in the school-to-work program.

Except for school-to-work students, apprentices must be at least 18 years old and have a high school diploma or GED. Applicants go through a two-hour orientation and take a four-hour test in mechanics or electricity to determine whether they show aptitude for this career. The top 35 are interviewed, and 10 or 15 are invited to enroll in the program. This entrance examination is adminis-

tered once each year; applicants can send a resume to be kept on file, and they will be notified when the next test is scheduled.

Salary Range

People commonly enter the tool-and-die field by working a part-time job while attending vocational school for two years, then working in a contract shop for about $6 to $8 an hour for a couple of years before being promoted. In contrast, adult apprentices at Siemens Electromechanical Components are paid about that amount while they're learning, both in class and on the job, and they have no student loans to pay back; the company pays for their tuition and books. Students who complete the training are also credited with 43 hours toward an industrial manufacturing degree at Western Kentucky University. During their training, apprentices are provided with health insurance, a 401(k) plan, and paid vacations. Journeymen tool and die makers typically earn $12 to $20 an hour, depending on experience.

Advice

Mike suggests that if you're considering becoming a tool and die maker, you should evaluate your talents and interests. "The advice I would give people considering a career in this field is that they should first like the idea of working with their hands in a highly skilled trade. Aptitude is very important, with strong mechanical reasoning a big plus. It's a definite benefit if they've done math and physics in high school, and if they've had hobbies where they're used to working with their hands—wood shop, auto shop, model building."

He adds that graduates of the program have a good chance of moving up in the company. "Their chances of promotion definitely improve because of this training. I think at least 90 percent of our students are successful in their careers."

Future Goals

Most apprentices in this program continue working for the Siemens Corporation after graduation. "We spend probably $60,000 to $70,000 on each student during their training, so placement is a priority," Mike notes. All apprentices sign a contract to work for Siemens for at least two years after their training is complete. Those who work less than two years must pay back $10,000 of the training expenses or a percentage of that amount, prorated to reflect the amount of time they worked for the company. Graduates begin in the company tool room, quality control, automated assembly, precision process operations, or as maintenance mechanics and can be promoted to quality engineers, lead tool makers, supervisors, or lead technicians.

ARIZONA

National Tool and Machine, Tucson
1889 West Prince Road
Tucson, AZ 85705
520-888-8860
Occupational Fields: die caster, die maker, tool maker, numerical control machine operator

Oberg Arizona Inc.
208 South McKemy Avenue
Chandler, AZ 85226-3407
602-961-1300
Occupational Fields: die maker, reel-to-reel plater, press operator, grinder operator, grinder set-up operator and wire drawing)

Rubbermaid Office Products Inc.
17300 West Broadway Road
PO Box 1489
Goodyear, AZ 85338
602-925-0692
Occupational Fields: mold maker, plastic die caster

Sesco Serigraphics
3315 West Vernon Avenue
Phoenix, AZ 85009
602-233-9483
Occupational Fields: die caster, die maker

The Tech Group
7975 North Hayden Road, Suite D-100
Scottsdale, AZ 85258-3241
480-281-4500
Fax: 480-281-4502
http://www.techgroup.com
Occupational Fields: plastic process technician

Tech Mold Inc.
1735 West 10th Street
Tempe, AZ 85281-5207
480-968-8691
Occupational Fields: die caster, die maker

Tooling Inc.
129 South Rockford Drive
Tempe, AZ 85281-3013

602-921-9939
Occupational Fields: die caster, die maker

Trans-Matic Manufacturing Company
1840 West Drake Drive
Tempe, AZ 85283
602-491-6977
Occupational Fields: tool maker, die maker

CONNECTICUT

General Dynamics
Electric Boat Division
75 Eastern Point Road
Groton, CT 06340-4905
860-433-3000
Fax: 860-433-1400
Occupational Fields: pattern maker (marine), tool maker, loftsperson

Pratt and Whitney Aircraft Group
400 Main Street
Hartford, CT 06108-0968
860-565-4321
Fax: 860-565-8896
http://www.pratt-whitney.com
Occupational Fields: tool maker, die maker

FLORIDA

Automation and Tooling Technology
4822 Victor Street
Jacksonville, FL 32207
Occupational Fields: tool maker, die maker

Centerline Tool and Engineering
3107 29th Avenue, East
Bradenton, FL 34203
941-749-5519
Occupational Fields: tool maker

Clairson Industries Corporation
2811 Northeast 14th Street
Ocala, FL 32670
352-732-3244
Occupational Fields: mold maker

Container Corporation of America
North Eighth Street
Fernandina Beach, FL 32034
904-261-5551
Occupational Fields: mold maker

Hudson Tool and Die Company
1327 North U.S. Highway One
Ormond Beach, FL 32174
386-675-2000
Fax: 386-676-6212
http://www.hudsontool.com
Occupational Fields: tool maker, die maker

Hurricane Tool Inc.
2071 Emerson Street, Unit Six
Jacksonville, FL 32207
Occupational Fields: tool maker

Industrial Tool and Die Company
968 Hall Park Road
PO Drawer G
Green Cove Springs, FL 32043
904-284-4737
Occupational Fields: tool maker, die maker

Jepsen Tool Company Inc.
6864 Phillips Parkway Drive, South
Jacksonville, FL 32256
904-262-2793
Occupational Fields: tool maker

Mandarin Tool and Die Inc.
11616 Columbia Park Drive, West
PO Box 23374
Jacksonville, FL 32241
904-262-7464
Occupational Fields: tool maker, die maker

North Florida Tool Engineering Inc.
4007 Saint Augustine Road
Jacksonville, FL 32207
904-398-5710
Occupational Fields: tool maker

Prima Die Casting
5300 115th Avenue, North
Clearwater, FL 33760
813-572-7040
http://www.primadiecast.com
Occupational Fields: die maker

Robbins Tooling Service
6541 Powers Avenue
Jacksonville, FL 32217
Occupational Fields: tool maker

S and S Industries-Toot Tooling
166 Industrial Loop
PO Box 1416
Orange Park, FL 32067-1416
904-264-8677
Occupational Fields: tool maker

Siewert Tool and Die Inc.
3388 Phillips Highway
Jacksonville, FL 32207
904-399-8425
Occupational Fields: tool maker, die maker

Tallahassee Tool and Die Inc.
3143-B West Tharpe Street
Tallahassee, FL 32304
Occupational Fields: tool maker, die maker

GEORGIA
United Auto Workers, Local #10
5407 Buford Highway, NE
Doraville, GA 30340-1125
770-457-3128
Occupational Fields: tool maker

ILLINOIS
Bohl Machine and Tool Company
7509 50th Street
Milan, IL 61264
309-799-5122
Occupational Fields: tool maker, die maker

East Moline Metal Products
1201 Seventh Street
Moline, IL 61244
309-752-1350
Occupational Fields: tool maker, die maker

General Pattern Corporation
235 40th Street
Moline, IL 61265
309-762-1581
Occupational Fields: pattern maker

Gett Industries, Limited
7307 50th Street
Milan, IL 61264
309-799-5131
Occupational Fields: tool maker, die maker

Quad City Engineering Company
1101 12th Avenue
Rock Island, IL 61201
309-786-7785
Occupational Fields: tool maker, die maker

Reynolds Manufacturing
501 38th Street
Rock Island, IL 61201
309-788-7443
Occupational Fields: tool maker, die maker

Standard Machine and Tool
3600 Coaltown Road
Moline, IL 61265
309-762-6431
Occupational Fields: tool maker, die maker

Tooling and Manufacturing Association
1177 South Dee Road
Park Ridge, IL 60068
847-825-1120
http://www.tmanet.org
Occupational Fields: tool maker, die maker

Wessel Pattern Company
333 Ninth
Moline, IL 61265
309-762-4762
Occupational Fields: pattern maker

INDIANA

Allison Engine Company
2355 South Tibbs Avenue
Indianapolis, IN 46206
317-230-5112
Fax: 317-230-3577
Occupational Fields: tool maker, die maker

Bentler Tool and Die
1818 Lakeview Drive
Fort Wayne, IN 46808
219-432-5569
Occupational Fields: tool maker, die maker

Chrysler Corporation
Kokomo Casting Plant
PO Box 9007
Kokomo, IN 46902-9007

765-454-1632
Occupational Fields: die maker

Cole Pattern and Engineering Company Inc.
2817 Goshen Road
Fort Wayne, IN 46808
260-482-2958
Occupational Fields: pattern maker

Crescent Plastics Inc.
955 Diamond Avenue
Evansville, IN 47711
812-428-9339
Fax: 812-428-9354
http://www.crescentplastics.com
Occupational Fields: tool maker

Cummins Engine Company
PO Box 3005
Mail Code 11861
Columbus, IN 47202-3005
812-377-5784
Occupational Fields: tool maker, tool designer, model maker

Cuttfield Industries Inc.
816 Division Street
Evansville, IN 47711
812-426-0323
Occupational Fields: die maker, tool maker

Dana Corporation
Spicer Axle Division
PO Box 70
Fort Wayne, IN 46801
219-481-3017
http://www.dana.com
Occupational Fields: tool maker

Delco Electronics
700 East Firmin Street
Kokomo, IN 46904-9005
317-451-2915
Occupational Fields: tool maker, die maker, model maker

Delphi Energy and Engine Management Systems
2401 Columbus Avenue
Anderson, IN 46018
317-646-3628
Occupational Fields: tool maker, die maker, pattern maker

Excel Tool Inc.
2020 First Avenue
Seymour, IN 47274
812-522-6880
Occupational Fields: tool maker, die maker

General Motors Corporation, Allison Transmission Division
4700 West 10th Street
PO Box 894
Indianapolis, IN 46206-0894
317-242-5321
Occupational Fields: tool maker, die maker

General Motors Corporation, Indianapolis
Metal Fabricating Division
PO Box 388
Indianapolis, IN 46206
317-269-5956
Occupational Fields: tool maker, die maker, pattern maker (wood)

General Motors Corporation, Marion
Metal Fabricating Division
2400 West Second Street
Marion, IN 46952-3295
317-668-2080
Occupational Fields: tool maker, die maker, pattern maker

Global Tool and Automation
3000 Engle Road
Fort Wayne, IN 46809
260-747-0531
http://www.gtacorp.com
Occupational Fields: tool maker, die maker

GM Powertrain
Training Programs
PO Box 271
Bedford, IN 47421
812-279-7261
Fax: 812-279-7334
Occupational Fields: die maker

Hamblen Gage Corporation
4901 Raymond Street
Indianapolis, IN 46241
317-241-9444
Fax: 317-240-1273
Occupational Fields: tool maker

Hittle Machine and Tool Company Inc.
2122 Doctor Martin Luther King Drive
Indianapolis, IN 46202
317-926-4594
Occupational Fields: tool maker, die maker

Salem Tool and Manufacturing
15333 West Commerce
PO Box 547
Daleville, IN 47334
317-378-0281
Occupational Fields: tool maker, die maker

South Bend Plastics
1810 Clover Road
Mishawaka, IN 46545
219-259-1991
Occupational Fields: mold maker

Whirlpool Corporation
Employment and Wage Administration
5401 U.S. Highway 41, North
Evansville, IN 47727
812-426-4496
Fax: 812-426-4957
Occupational Fields: tool maker, tool and gauge inspector

Zimmer Inc.
Employee Relations
PO Box 708
Warsaw, IN 47580
219-267-6131
Occupational Fields: tool maker, die maker

Zollner Company Unlimited Partnership
2425 Coliseum Boulevard, South
Fort Wayne, IN 46803
219-426-8081
Occupational Fields: die maker, tool maker, tool grinder

IOWA

A and S Tool and Die
PO Box 725
Bettendorf, IA 62722
319-355-1313
Occupational Fields: tool maker, die maker

Aluminum Company of America (ALCOA)
PO Box 3567
Davenport, IA 52808

319-359-2956
http://www.alcoa.com
Occupational Fields: roll grinder

American Tool of Cedar Rapids
5431 Center Point Road, NE
Cedar Rapids, IA 52402
319-393-1860
Occupational Fields: tool grinder

Atwood Industries Inc.
800 Highway 150, South
West Union, IA 52175
319-422-5641
http://www.atwoodindustries.com
Occupational Fields: tool maker, die maker

Benco Manufacturing
West Eighth Street
Belle Plaine, IA 52208
319-444-3505
Occupational Fields: tool maker, die maker

Berry Industries
209 Roosevelt Street
PO Box 161
Cedar Falls, IA 50613
319-268-0107
Occupational Fields: tool maker, die maker

Beuse's Pattern Works
304 South Cody Road
PO Box 216
LeClaire, IA 52802
319-289-5515
Occupational Fields: pattern maker

Blackhawk Foundry and Machine
323 South Clark Street
Davenport, IA 50208
319-323-3621
Occupational Fields: pattern maker

BTR Sealing Systems
3200 Main Street
PO Box 2230
Keokuk, IA 52632
319-524-4560, x393
Occupational Fields: tool maker, die maker

Cascade Die Mold Inc.
Monticello Industrial Park
PO Box 31
Monticello, IA 52110
319-465-4844
Occupational Fields: mold maker

Deco Products Company
506 Sandord Street
Decorah, IA 52101-2006
319-382-4264
Fax: 319-382-9845
http://www.decoprod.com
Occupational Fields: tool maker, die maker

Deere and Company, Des Moines
PO Box 1596
Des Moines, IA 50306
515-289-3208
Occupational Fields: tool maker, die maker

Deere and Company, Ottumwa
923 East Vine Street
Ottumwa, IA 52501-8002
515-684-4641
Occupational Fields: tool maker, die maker

Douglas Machine and Engineering
1721 West Fifth Street
PO Box 3528
Davenport, IA 52808
319-324-0611
http://www.doug-machine.com
Occupational Fields: tool maker, die maker, tool designer

Dubuque Stamping and Manufacturing Inc.
32nd and Jackson Streets
PO Box 798
Dubuque, IA 52004-0798
319-583-5716
Fax: 319-556-8729
Occupational Fields: tool maker, die maker

Eagle Engineering Inc.
521 North Ninth Avenue
PO Box 64
Eldridge, IA 52748
319-285-7515
http://www.eagleengineeringinc.com
Occupational Fields: tool maker, die maker, tool designer

Eagle Tool Company
400 Sixth Avenue
PO Box 146
Dyersville, IA 52040
319-875-2500
http://www.eagletl.com
Occupational Fields: mold maker

Eaton Corporation
700 Luick's Lane
Box 303
Belmond, IA 50421
515-444-3535
Occupational Fields: tool maker, die maker

Fleetguard Inc.
311 North Park
Lake Mills, IA 50450
515-592-1300
Occupational Fields: tool maker, die maker

General Machine and Tool
Highway Three, East
Waverly, IA 50677
319-352-1509
Occupational Fields: tool maker, die maker

Glacier Vandervell Inc.
West Highway 83
Atlantic, IA 50022
712-243-5060
Occupational Fields: tool maker, die maker

Headco Machine Works
2666 Kindustry Park Road
Keokuk, IA 52632
319-524-1804
Occupational Fields: tool maker, die maker

Industrial Standard Tooling
105 East Ninth Street
Box 1842
Waterloo, IA 50703
Occupational Fields: tool maker, die maker

JR Custom Machine
Two Kohles Court
Bettendorf, IA 52722
319-355-3997
Occupational Fields: tool maker, die maker

Kalona Plastics Inc.
Highway One, South
PO Box 790
Kalona, IA 52247
319-656-4500
Occupational Fields: mold maker

Kauffman Pattern Company
108 Terrace Drive
Box 161
Blue Grass, IA 52726
319-381-1156
Occupational Fields: pattern maker

Lennox Industries
PO Box 250
Marshalltown, IA 50158
515-754-4011
Occupational Fields: tool maker, die maker

Liberty Pattern Company Inc.
430 Main Street
PO Box 67
New Liberty, IA 52765-0067
319-843-3569
Fax: 319-843-3579
Occupational Fields: pattern maker

Lund International
PO Box 430
Ottumwa, IA 52501
515-682-7576
Occupational Fields: tool maker, die maker

Maytag Company
One Dependability Square
Newton, IA 50208
515-792-7000
Occupational Fields: tool maker, die maker

Midwest Industries Inc.
Highways 59 and 175
Ida Grove, IA 51445
712-364-3365
Occupational Fields: tool maker, die maker

MSI Mold Builders
12300 Sixth Street
Cedar Rapids, IA 52404
319-848-7001

http://www.msimoldbuilders.com
Occupational Fields: mold maker

North East Machine and Tool
Highway 218
Janesville, IA 50647
319-987-2003
Occupational Fields: tool maker, die maker

North Liberty Plastics Inc.
1140 240th Street
North Liberty, IA 52317
319-373-9491
Occupational Fields: mold maker

Oral B Laboratories
1823 Lower Muscatine Road
Iowa City, IA 52240
319-338-5411
Occupational Fields: mold maker

Pella Corporation
102 Main
Pella, IA 50219
515-628-1000
Occupational Fields: tool maker, die maker

Premier Tooling
8853 Kapp Drive
Peosta, IA 52068
319-557-7006
Occupational Fields: mold maker

Progressive Tool and Die
1624 Blackhawk
Waterloo, IA 52704
319-234-6619
Occupational Fields: tool maker, die maker, tool designer

Riverside Plastics
900 Washington
PO Box 220
Bonaparte, IA 52620
319-592-3166
Occupational Fields: mold maker

Saturn Tool and Die
134 Lincoln
Waterloo, IA 50613

319-266-1905
http://www.saturntool.com
Occupational Fields: tool maker, die maker

Scheaffer Eaton Textron
301 Avenue H
Fort Madison, IA 52627
Occupational Fields: tool maker, die maker, mold maker

Schult Engineering
107 North River Drive
Princeton, IA 52768
319-289-5808
Occupational Fields: pattern maker

Swan Engineering and Machine Company
2611 State Street
Bettendorf, IA 52722
319-355-2671, x128
Occupational Fields: tool maker, die maker, tool designer

Techniplas Inc.
3401 South Convenience Boulevard
Ankeny, IA 50021
515-964-2675
Occupational Fields: mold maker

Traer Manufacturing
Highway 63, South
Traer, IA 50675
319-647-3601
Occupational Fields: tool maker, die maker

Trentz Tool and Die
403 Clinton Avenue
Delmar, IA 52037
319-674-4295
Occupational Fields: tool maker, die maker

Uelner Precision Tools and Dies
4545 Futuro Court
Dubuque, IA 52001
319-583-5125
Occupational Fields: mold maker

Victor Manufacturing
1951 A Avenue
PO Box 338
Victor, IA 52347

319-647-3601
Occupational Fields: tool maker, die maker

Victor Plastics Inc.
Box 32, Rural Route One
Victor, IA 52347
319-647-3151
http://www.victorplastics.com
Occupational Fields: mold maker

Williamsburg Manufacturing
100 Park Avenue
PO Box 808
Williamsburg, IA 52361
319-668-2031
Occupational Fields: tool maker, die maker

Winegard Company
3000 Kirkwood Street
Burlington, IA 52601
319-754-0691
http://www.windegard.com
Occupational Fields: tool maker, die maker

Young Radiator
PO Box 460
Centerville, IA 52544
515-856-8634
Occupational Fields: tool maker, die maker

KANSAS

A1 Pattern and Model Works Inc.
113 West Washington Street
Arma, KS 66712-4014
316-347-8796
Fax: 316-347-4494
Occupational Fields: pattern maker

Applied Technology Development
212 South Mosley Street
Wichita, KS 67202-4708
316-267-0446
Occupational Fields: mold maker

CAC Mold Corporation
2005 South West Street
Wichita, KS 67213-1109

316-943-4285
Fax: 316-943-8546
Occupational Fields: mold maker

Coleman Outdoor Products Inc.
240 North Saint Francis Street
Wichita, KS 67202-2610
316-261-3211
Fax: 316-832-6160
http://www.coleman.com
Occupational Fields: tool maker

Friesen Tool Company Inc.
240 Wabash Street
Wichita, KS 67214-3946
316-262-6808
Occupational Fields: tool maker

Galaxy Tool Corporation
1111 Industrial Boulevard
Winfield, KS 67156-9133
316-221-6262
Occupational Fields: mold maker

General Motors Corporation
3201 Fairfax Trafficway
Kansas City, KS 66115-1399
913-573-7400
Occupational Fields: tool maker, die maker

Hallum Tooling Inc.
3838 May Street
PO Box 17308
Wichita, KS 67217-0308
316-942-1261
Fax: 316-942-4647
Occupational Fields: die maker, tool maker

Machinists Union
330 Laura Street
Wichita, KS 67211
316-262-7030
Occupational Fields: tool maker, die maker, mold maker

Manufacturing Services
2239 South Mead Street
Wichita, KS 67211-5021
316-267-4111
Occupational Fields: mold maker

Recreation Vehicle Products Inc.
PO Box 4020
Wichita, KS 67204-0020
316-832-3475
Occupational Fields: die maker, tool maker

Schuetz Tool and Die Inc.
807 Utah Street
Hiawatha, KS 66434-2323
785-7923
Fax: 785-742-7958
Occupational Fields: tool maker

Stettnisch Tool and Die
4209 Merriam Drive
Overland Park, KS 66203-1335
913-432-0111
Occupational Fields: die maker, tool maker

Wescon Products
2533 South West Street
PO Box 7710
Wichita, KS 67277-7710
316-942-7266
Fax: 316-942-0518
Occupational Fields: mold maker

Wichita Tool Company Inc.
2100 South West Street
Wichita, KS 67213-1112
316-942-5222
Fax: 316-942-1758
Occupational Fields: mold maker

KENTUCKY

Siemens Electromechanical Components
Robey Road
Franklin, KY 42134
502-586-4451
Occupational Fields: tool maker, die maker

Western Kentucky University
1 Big Red Way Street
Bowling Green, KY 42101-3576
502-745-0111
http://www.wku.edu
Occupational Fields: tool maker, die maker

MAINE

Jones and Vining of Maine Inc.
765 Webster Street
Lewiston, ME 04240
207-784-3547
Occupational Fields: last model maker

MARYLAND

**International Association of Machinists and
     Aerospace Workers**
9000 Machinists Place
Upper Marlboro, MD 20772-2687
301-967-4500
Fax: 301-967-3431
http://www.goiam.org
Occupational Fields: tool maker, die maker

Marada Industries Inc.
151 Airport Drive
Westminster, MD 21157
410-876-8000
Occupational Fields: tool maker, die maker

Poly Seal Corporation
8303 Pulaski Highway
Baltimore, MD 21237-2941
410-682-3000
Fax: 410-391-9581
Occupational Fields: tool maker, die maker

Suburban Tool Manufacturing Company
12 Emala Avenue
Middle River, MD 21220-2893
410-686-4894
Occupational Fields: tool maker, die maker

MICHIGAN

United Auto Workers
3731 Covington Road
Kalamazoo, MI 49002
616-381-2703
Occupational Fields: tool maker, die maker

NEW YORK

Check-Mate Industries Inc.
777 Mount Avenue
Wyandanch, NY 11798

800-229-6467
Fax: 631-491-1745
http://www.checkmateindustries.com
Occupational Fields: tool maker, die maker

NORTH CAROLINA
Eagle Electric Manufacturing Company Inc.
310 McNeill Road
Sanford, NC 27330
919-774-8015
Occupational Fields: tool maker, die maker

Ingersoll-Rand Company
1725 U.S. Highway One, South
Southern Pines, NC 28387-7040
910-692-8700
Occupational Fields: tool maker

Jeffery Tool and Mold Inc.
44 Buck Shoals Road, #G4
Arden, NC 28704-3307
704-891-2733
Occupational Fields: mold maker

Technical Design Associates Inc.
93 Schoolhouse Road
Horse Shoe, NC 28742
704-891-2696
Occupational Fields: tool designer

OHIO
Jefferson Smurfit Corporation
407 Charles Street
Middletown, OH 45042
513-424-4200
Occupational Fields: die maker

RHODE ISLAND
Tedco Inc.
70 Glen Road
Cranston, RI 02920
401-461-1118
Fax: 401-461-1119
http://www.tedco-inc.com
Occupational Fields: tool maker, mold maker

VERMONT
Rehav Inc.
PO Box 319
North Springfield, VT 05150
802-886-8595
Occupational Fields: tool maker

VIRGINIA
Newport News Shipbuilding
Admissions Office
4101 Washington Avenue
Newport News, VA 23607-2770
757-380-2000
Fax: 757-688-0305
Occupational Fields: heavy metal fabricator, forger (heat treater), mold maker

WASHINGTON
Ball Foster Glass Container Company
5801 East Marginal Way, South
Seattle, WA 98134
206-762-0660
Occupational Fields: mold maker

Boeing Commercial Airplane Group
M/S 2R-76
PO Box 3707
Seattle, WA 98124-2207
206-544-5537
Fax: 206-544-5511
Occupational Fields: tooling inspector, jig & fixture builder, tool maker, die maker, tool cutter

International Association of Machinists District #160
9135 15th Place, South
Seattle, WA 98108
206-762-7990
Fax: 206-764-0468
Occupational Fields: tool maker, die maker

Vancouver Machinists and Automotive Machinists
5000 East 18th Street
Vancouver, WA 98661
360-693-9172
Occupational Fields: mold maker, metal fabricator

WISCONSIN

Aluminum Casting and Engineering Company
2039 South Lenox Street
Milwaukee, WI 53207
414-744-3902
Occupational Fields: cast metal maker (foundry)

Apex Mold and Die Inc.
100 Industrial Lane
PO Box 169
Endeavor, WI 53930-0169
608-587-2333
Fax: 608-587-2410
Occupational Fields: tool maker, die maker

Bay Engineered Castings
1900 Enterprise Drive
De Pere, WI 54115-3102
414-337-2479
Fax: 414-336-3567
Occupational Fields: foundry worker

Beloit Precision Die Company Inc.
1525 Office Park Lane
Beloit, WI 53511
608-362-2261
Fax: 608-362-6207
Occupational Fields: tool maker, die maker

Briggs and Stratton
12301 West Wirth Street
Milwaukee, WI 53222
414-259-5333
Occupational Fields: tool maker, die maker, mold maker, stamp maker

Finn Pattern Company Inc.
2128 East Norse Avenue
Cudahy, WI 53110-2834
414-744-5700
Fax: 414-744-3616
Occupational Fields: pattern maker

General Pattern Inc.
4712 North 125th Street
Butler, WI 53007-1709
414-781-2970
Fax: 414-781-5590
Occupational Fields: mold maker

International Association of Machinists and Aerospace Workers
750 Windsor
Sun Prairie, WI 53590
608-244-1372
Occupational Fields: tool maker, die maker

International Association of Tool Craftsmen
3718 Wright Avenue
Racine, WI 53405-3304
414-637-4371
Occupational Fields: tool maker, die maker

J and L Fiber Service
809 Phillip Drive
Waukesha, WI 53186
414-544-1890
Occupational Fields: pattern setter

Kaysun Corporation
5500 West Drive
Manitowoc, WI 54221
920-682-6388
Fax: 682-8713
http://www.kaysun.com
Occupational Fields: mold maker, tool maker

National Tool Machine Association, Milwaukee Chapter
N93 W14430 Whittaker Drive
Menomonie Falls, WI 53051
Occupational Fields: tool maker, die maker

Phillips Plastics Corporation
1201 Hanley Road
Hudson, WI 54016
877-508-0252
Fax: 715381-3291
info@phillipsplastics.com
http://www.phillipsplastics.com
Occupational Fields: tool maker

Tri-Tec Corporation
455 West Madison Street
PO Box 70
Darien, WI 53114-0070
262-882-2000
http://www.triteccorp.com
Occupational Fields: tool maker, die maker

CANADA

NEW BRUNSWICK

Department of Training and Employment Development
Apprenticeship and Occupational Certification
PO Box 6000
Chestnut Complex
Fredericton, NB E3B 5H1
506-453-2260
Fax: 506-453-5317
aoc-acp@gnb.ca
Occupational Fields: tool maker, die maker

ONTARIO

St. Clair College
Windsor Campus
2000 Talbot Road West,
Windsor, ON N9A 6S4
519-966-1656
Fax: 519-972-3811
http://www.stclaircollege.ca/programs/apprenticeship/home_b.html
Occupational Fields: tool maker, die maker

TRUCK DRIVERS

RELATED SECTIONS: *auto body workers, mechanics, operating engineers and stationary engineers, railroad workers, shipbuilding and ship maintenance workers*

Truck drivers, also called *truckers,* pick up merchandise from factories, railroad terminals, warehouses, and other sites; transport it to trucking terminals where the cargo is sorted and routed; and deliver the merchandise to retail and wholesale outlets, residences, offices, and other destinations. They handle most of the merchandise produced in this nation, including fruits and vegetables, milk, lumber, logs, furniture, fuels, and hazardous materials.

Some local and regional drivers, called *driver-sales workers* or *route drivers,* not only deliver a product but also sell the product to customers. They might represent a company that sells ice cream or delivers dry cleaning, for example, or transport bakery goods to grocery stores and stock display racks there. These drivers are responsible for noting what merchandise is selling well, estimating how much and what type of goods will be sold, and making sure the merchandise on the shelf is fresh. Some service and stock vending machines work in settings such as schools and factories.

Truckers are responsible for making sure their vehicles have adequate oil and fuel; checking fire extinguishers and other safety equipment; examining the truck's lights, brakes, and windshield wipers; and inspecting the cargo to ensure that it has been loaded securely. On the road they are expected to drive carefully, conserve fuel when possible, and deliver the load swiftly.

Sometimes drivers unload the cargo at its destination. They may also accept money from customers and be responsible for turning in receipts and money at the end of the day. Long-distance truck drivers must file reports after each trip, giving details about the trip, their truck, and any accidents that occurred.

Some truckers work on schedules, while others await orders from dispatchers who tell them when and where they will drive. Some trucks make short runs within cities, making multiple deliveries each day. A truck driver who makes local runs is apt to work 50 hours or more a week and might be required to work early in the morning or late at night.

Others make longer runs throughout the region or across the country; they may be away from home for days or weeks at a time. On some long runs, two truckers travel together, taking turns driving almost nonstop and sleeping in a compartment behind the cab. A self-employed, long-distance trucker who owns the truck might spend more than seven out of 10 days on the road each year. U.S. law forbids long-distance truck drivers from working more than 60 hours per week or driving more than 10 hours, and requires breaks of at least eight hours.

Truck drivers are often required to take drug and alcohol tests or annual physical examinations. The job sometimes involves heavy lifting of cargo, long hours of sitting behind the wheel, loneliness, boredom, the stress of driving on slick highways or in heavy traffic, and the risk of accidents. Truckers who haul fuel must drive with extreme care and have particularly good driving records, since some fuels may explode or burn on impact in a traffic accident. Truckers often work nights, weekends, and holidays. The trucks are usually pleasant, with good ventilation and comfortable seats.

Truck drivers must meet federal and state standards and qualifications. Those who drive large trucks or transport hazardous waste must pass a written test and a performance test to obtain a commercial driver's license. Records of the driver's accident history and any violations are kept in a national data bank accessible to officials in every state. To participate in interstate commerce, a driver must pass a written examination and a physical examination, be at least 21 years old, not be using drugs except by prescription, have normal blood pressure, have good hearing and vision, have normal use of arms and legs (unless a waiver is granted), not have epilepsy, and not be a diabetic taking insulin.

Some trucking companies hire only drivers who are at least 25 years old, have several years of driving experience, are in good physical condition, have a high school diploma or GED, and are able to lift heavy items.

About 10 percent of truck drivers are self-employed and operate their own delivery services or subcontract with trucking companies. Most truckers work for trucking companies, wholesale and retail outlets, and other organizations. Local truck drivers are typically paid by the hour and make extra money for overtime work. Long-distance drivers are usually paid by the mile. Driver-sales workers are paid by the hour plus a commission on sales. Many truck drivers belong to unions, such as the International Brotherhood of Teamsters.

Apprenticeships and on-the-job training are common ways of entering this trade. Some beginning drivers work part-time or fill in for regular drivers who are on vacation or sick leave. Trainees work under the supervision of experienced truck drivers, starting by riding along in the passenger seat or by driving small trucks and moving on to larger trucks as their skills develop. Experienced truck drivers are generally rewarded with pay raises, better schedules, or premium routes, and some are promoted to manager or dispatcher.

In general an applicant should

- apply in person
- be at least 18 years old
- be a high school graduate or hold a GED certificate
- have good eyesight
- have a driver's license issued by the state in which the applicant resides
- have an excellent driving record
- be responsible and able to work with little or no supervision

APPRENTICESHIP SALARIES

About 60 percent of a journeyman's salary, with incremental increases.

POSTAPPRENTICESHIP SALARIES

Between $14 and $20 an hour for the majority of workers. Some truck drivers, however, earn more than $23 an hour. Earnings vary, depending on the number of hours worked, the number of nights worked away from home, the specific equipment, the trucking company, and geographic location.

JOB OUTLOOK

Generally good, because there are many job openings annually. The trend toward transporting trailers via railroad instead of having truck drivers deliver them has cut into the demand for drivers somewhat, but truck driving is expected to remain an integral component of the transportation industry. This occupation is expected to grow about as fast as the average for all occupations through 2012.

For more information on apprenticeships for truck drivers, contact the national organizations and individual programs listed below, local job centers, your state bureau of apprenticeship training, or local trucking companies.

NATIONAL PROGRAMS

American Trucking Associations Inc.
2200 Mill Road
Alexandria, VA 22314
703-838-1700
http://www.trucking.org
Occupational Fields: truck driver

International Brotherhood of Teamsters
25 Louisiana Avenue, NW
Washington, DC 20001
202-624-6800
http://www.teamster.org
Occupational Fields: truck driver, dock worker, truck mechanic, warehouse worker, dispatcher, production worker, various others

Online Truck Drivers' Job Bank
http://www.truck.net/jobs.html
Occupational Fields: truck driver, dispatcher, trainer, warehouse worker, truck mechanic

APPRENTICESHIP PROFILE

Teamsters Union, Local #533
Joint Apprenticeship and Training Trust
316 Vassar Street
Reno, NV 89502-2910
702-348-6060

General Nature of the Job

The workers who drive heavy trucks on road construction projects haul materials such as rocks, dirt, water, and asphalt. They also drive transport trucks to and from job sites, hauling equipment and the temporary barrier rails that direct traffic through the projects. They inspect their vehicles for mechanical problems twice each day, and they're responsible for ensuring that trucks are properly loaded. Sometimes they work long hours, and they're frequently away from home for days or weeks at a time, but the trade can provide a comfortable income and the opportunity to work outdoors, often in scenic locations.

Since the late 1980s, the Teamsters Union, Local #533, in Reno, Nevada, has operated an apprenticeship program that trains workers for jobs on road construction projects. "It teaches you to drive trucks, and that's a good living, especially if you stay with the same company," says Don Bouma, apprenticeship coordinator. "Some of those trucks are like Cadillacs. They have features like power steering and easy clutches."

The two-year program, which is limited to five apprentices at a time, includes 144 hours of classroom studies per year. Apprentices can opt to spend some of those 144 hours in classes such as cardiopulmonary resuscitation at Truckee Meadows Community College in Reno; these classes can count toward a college degree. Students spend the rest of their time in on-the-job training, 600 hours in each classification of work: water truck, dump truck, and "road trains" (trucks at least 100 feet long, usually consisting of more than one component, such as a truck tractor with a semitrailer, pulling a second trailer).

Typical Day

Usually, classes are scheduled in the evening, and training sessions are on Saturday or Sunday so they won't interfere with the apprentice's on-the-job training. Apprentices typically report for work at about 6:00 A.M., but some arrive at other times, depending on the schedule for their trucks. The apprentice starts by inspecting the vehicle's lights, brakes, battery, and other systems. At the end of the day, the driver inspects the truck again and reports any problems to a mechanic, who repairs them.

The truck must be loaded according to regulations to ensure that nothing will shift or fall onto the roadway during transit. Usually a laborer performs most of the work; the driver oversees the operation and might provide some assistance. For example, if a barrier rail weighing thousands of pounds were being loaded, the driver might guide it manually as a crane sets it on a flatbed truck. Drivers sometimes operate forklifts to load materials, and they're responsible for tying the load down securely.

Throughout the day the apprentice receives instructions from a dispatcher who coordinates all the trucks on the project, communicating with the drivers via radio. Assignments vary, depending on the type of truck. One apprentice might spend the day hauling trash to the landfill or moving dirt from one part of the site to another. An apprentice in a water truck would fill the water tank at a standpipe, drive to an area where base rock has been placed, spray water on it, and then spend a couple of hours washing the highway. Then the water truck might be assigned to repeat the process at another site that same day.

Some workers have a break for lunch, but frequently a truck driver is expected to take breaks of a few minutes during the numerous lulls during the day. "On some jobs you don't get a break all day. It depends on the job," Don says. On an asphalt project, for example, the crew can't stop until the job is done, or the quality of the work would suffer.

Path to Becoming an Apprentice

This is not a program for those fresh out of high school. Applicants must be at least 21 years old, and the union is considering raising the age requirement to about 25. A high school diploma or GED is also required. Applications are accepted throughout the year. Because only five apprentices are trained at a time, applicants are called for interviews only when an opening is available, and the apprenticeship is offered to the most promising individual. Interviews are usually conducted by two union representatives, two employer representatives, and one representative from the Associated General Contractors. Apprentices must join the union upon acceptance into the program. Women and minorities are encouraged to apply.

Because truck drivers inspect their vehicles for mechanical problems, some previous mechanical knowledge is helpful, but it's not required. "We do teach that. It's part of the class," Don says. During the first part of their training, apprentices spend time at a contractor's yard, where an instructor explains the responsibilities of the trade and supervises them as they practice driving trucks and pulling a trailer. They must earn a commercial driver's license by passing an examination administered by the Department of Transportation, and then they begin work at actual job sites.

Salary Range

Apprentices start at 60 percent of journeyman scale and receive raises every six months; they're earning 90 percent of journeyman scale by the time they complete the training. Journeyman truck drivers on construction projects earn $16.22 an hour and are provided with health insurance, paid holidays, and a pension plan. Drivers who work in very remote areas are paid an extra $2 to $3.50 an hour. After about five years of working with the same company, a truck driver can make about $40,000 a year.

Sometimes, however, a truck driver works only six hours a day; the union is currently negotiating with the state for more regular hours. Weather can also cut into profits, slowing or stopping construction, particularly during the winter when it's too cold to lay pavement. "It comes with the territory. Everybody knows that's what's going to happen. I used to just take two weeks and go hunting every year," Don says.

Advice

It's possible to graduate from some truck driving schools in as little as four weeks instead of learning through apprenticeship, but you're apt to practice mostly driving skills there and skip some important aspects of the truck driving trade. That will make you less attractive to prospective employers. Don says, "Employers like to get somebody who's trained, who they don't have to mess with."

As far as succeeding in the occupation goes, he says, "A positive attitude would definitely be beneficial. There are lots of new things out there. Every piece of equipment is different. You have to be open to change."

Future Goals

After graduation a driver might be offered work anywhere in northern Nevada or in a small part of nearby California. Road crews are constantly finishing one project and moving to the next, which might be hundreds of miles away. "You have to be able to accept work anywhere in Local #533's jurisdiction," Don says. "We have several drivers that just move with the company." Some workers live in their own camper trailers near the job site or rent an apartment or motel room nearby and drive home for the weekends. Others commute long distances to work every day. An assignment might last for a week, three weeks, or all summer, depending on the size of the project.

Drivers can expand the scope of their duties by earning endorsements that allow them to transport hazardous materials, for example; they can complete this training through the Teamsters Union. Skilled drivers can be promoted to dispatchers or foremen.

ALABAMA

Swift Transportation
5250 Truman Drive
Decatur, AL 30053
205-353-0173
Occupational Fields: truck driver

Teamsters Union, Local #991
112 South Broad Street
Mobile, Al 36602-1109
251-433-1521
Fax: 251-433-1524
Team991@aol.com

http://www.teamsterslocal991.org
Occupational Fields: truck driver, dock worker, truck mechanic, warehouse worker, dispatcher, production worker, various others

ALASKA

Teamsters Union, Local #959
520 East 34th Avenue
Anchorage, AK 99503
907-565-8122
Fax: 907-565-8265
Occupational Fields: truck driver, dock worker, truck mechanic, warehouse worker, dispatcher, production worker, various others

ARIZONA

Granite Construction Company
PO Box 27557
Tucson, AZ 85726
520-748-8000
Fax: 520-748-8230
Occupational Fields: truck driver

Swift Transportation Inc.
2200 South 75th Avenue
PO Box 29243
Phoenix, AZ 85038
800-882-7364
Occupational Fields: truck driver, dispatcher, trainer, warehouse worker, mechanic

Swift Transportation Inc.
6215 West Van Buren Street
Phoenix, AZ 85043-3522
602-352-1188
Occupational Fields: truck driver

Swift Transportation Inc.
5601 West Mohave Street
Phoenix, AZ 85043-9602
602-269-9700
Occupational Fields: truck driver

Teamsters Union
1820 West Broadway
Phoenix, AZ 85041
602-268-8801
Occupational Fields: heavy-truck driver

Teamsters Union, Local #104
1450 South 27th Avenue
PO Box 18090
Phoenix, AZ 85009
602-272-5561
Fax: 602-272-3744
team104az@aol.com
Occupational Fields: truck driver, dock worker, truck mechanic, warehouse worker, dispatcher, production worker, various others

Teamsters Union, Local #104
38 W. Elm Street
Tucson, AZ 85705
520-622-3616
Fax: 520-624-5262
Occupational Fields: truck driver, dock worker, truck mechanic, warehouse worker, dispatcher, production worker, various others

Teamsters Union, Local #104
2126 North Walgreen
Flagstaff, AZ 86004
928-527-9836
Fax: 928-527-9837
Occupational Fields: truck driver, dock worker, truck mechanic, warehouse worker, dispatcher, production worker, various others

Teamsters Union, Local #752
PO Box 811
Gilbert, AZ 85299-0811
602-352-0401
Fax: 602-352-1171
Occupational Fields: truck driver, dock worker, truck mechanic, warehouse worker, dispatcher, production worker, various others

United Metro Materials Inc.
701 North 44th Street
PO Box 52140
Phoenix, AZ 85072-2140
602-220-5345
Occupational Fields: heavy-truck driver

Utility and Transportation Contractors Association of Arizona
725 West McDowell, Suite B
Phoenix, AZ 85007
602-252-4574
Occupational Fields: heavy-truck driver

ARKANSAS
Teamsters Union, Local #373
4314 Phoenix
Fort Smith, AR 72903
501-646-1639
Fax: 501-646-4088
http://go.to/teamsters_373
Occupational Fields: truck driver, dock worker, truck mechanic, warehouse worker, dispatcher, production worker, various others

CALIFORNIA
Merced County Private Industry Training Department, Los Banos
848 Sixth Street
Los Banos, CA 93635
209-826-0636
http://www.co.merced.ca.us/pitd/pitdhome.htm
Occupational Fields: truck driver

Merced County Private Industry Training Department, Merced
1020 West Main Street
Merced, CA 95340
209-385-7326
http://www.co.merced.ca.us/pitd/pitdhome.htm
Occupational Fields: truck driver

Swift Transportation Inc.
9951 Banana Avenue
Fontana, CA 92335-5208
909-823-9669
Occupational Fields: truck driver

Swift Transportation Inc.
411 East 18th Street
Oakland, CA 94606-1850
510-839-3819
Occupational Fields: truck driver

Swift Transportation Inc.
781 Swift Way
Stockton, CA 95206-1172
209-943-1476
Occupational Fields: truck driver

Swift Transportation Inc.
1475 County Road 99
Willows, CA 95988-1172
916-934-0243
Occupational Fields: truck driver

Teamsters Union, Joint Council 38
1209 K Street
Modesto, CA 95354
209-577-0500
Occupational Fields: truck driver, dock worker, truck
mechanic, warehouse worker, dispatcher, production
worker, various others

Teamsters Union, Joint Council 42
626-974-4212
JCT42@aol.com
http://www.teamsters.info
Occupational Fields: truck driver, dock worker, truck
mechanic, warehouse worker, dispatcher, production
worker, various others

Teamsters Union, Local #63
845 Oak Park Road
Covina, CA 91724
626-859-4005
Fax: 626-859-4084
http://www.teamsters63.org
Occupational Fields: truck driver, dock worker, truck
mechanic, warehouse worker, dispatcher, production
worker, various others

Teamsters Union, Local #63
379 West Valley Boulevard
Rialto, CA 92376
909-877-4760
Fax: 909-877-2452
http://www.teamsters63.org
Occupational Fields: truck driver, dock worker, truck
mechanic, warehouse worker, dispatcher, production
worker, various others

Teamster Union, Local #87
3724 Buck Owens Boulevard
Bakersfield, CA 93308
661-327-8594
Fax: 661-327-0931
Occupational Fields: truck driver, dock worker, truck
mechanic, warehouse worker, dispatcher, production
worker, various others

Teamsters Union, Local #137
3540 South Market Street
Redding, CA 96001
530-243-0232
Fax: 530-243-3115
http://teamsters137.com
Occupational Fields: truck driver, dock worker, truck
mechanic, warehouse worker, dispatcher, production
worker, various others

Teamsters Union, Local #150
7120 East Parkway
Sacramento, CA 95823
916-392-7070
Fax: 916-392-7675
http://www.teamsters150.org
Occupational Fields: truck driver, dock worker, truck
mechanic, warehouse worker, dispatcher, production
worker, various others

Teamsters Union, Local #166
18597 Valley Boulevard
Bloomington, CA, 92316
909-877-8326
Fax: 909-877-2812
http://www.teamsterslocal166.org
Occupational Fields: truck driver, dock worker, truck
mechanic, warehouse worker, dispatcher, production
worker, various others

Teamsters Union, Local #186
1534 Eastman Avenue, Suite B
Ventura, California 93003-7760
805-644-0070
Fax: 805-644-0084
http://www.teamsters.info/local186/index.htm
Occupational Fields: truck driver, dock worker, truck
mechanic, warehouse worker, dispatcher, production
worker, various others

Teamsters Union, Local #228
4600 47th Avenue, Suite 205
Sacramento, CA 95824
916-395-0437
http://www.teamsterslocal228.com
Occupational Fields: truck driver, dock worker, truck
mechanic, warehouse worker, dispatcher, production
worker, various others

Teamsters Union, Local #381
115 West Bunny Avenue
Santa Maria, California 93458
805-922-7875
Fax: 805-922-6885
http://www.teamsters.info/local381/index.htm
Occupational Fields: truck driver, dock worker, truck mechanic, warehouse worker, dispatcher, production worker, various others

Teamsters Union, Local #386
1225 13th Street
Modesto, CA 95354
209-526-2755
Fax: 209-526-9485
http://www.teamsters386.org
Occupational Fields: truck driver, dock worker, truck mechanic, warehouse worker, dispatcher, production worker, various others

Teamsters Union, Local #396
880 Oak Park Road, Suite 200
Covina, California 91724
626-915-3636
Fax: 626-915-3635
L396team@aol.com
http://teamsterslocal396.com
Occupational Fields: truck driver, dock worker, truck mechanic, warehouse worker, dispatcher, production worker, various others

Teamsters Union, Local #399
4747 Vineland Avenue
North Hollywood, CA 91602
818-985-7374
http://www.hollywoodteamsters.org
Occupational Fields: truck driver, dock worker, truck mechanic, warehouse worker, dispatcher, production worker, various others

Teamsters Union, Local #431
1140 West Olive
Fresno, CA 93728
559-486-5410
Fax: 559-441-1743
teamsters431@teamsters431.org
Occupational Fields: truck driver, dock worker, truck mechanic, warehouse worker, dispatcher, production worker, various others

Teamsters Union, Local #439
1531 E Fremont Street
Stockton, CA 95205
209-948-9592
Fax: 209-948-3424
http://www.teamsters439.com
Occupational Fields: truck driver, dock worker, truck mechanic, warehouse worker, dispatcher, production worker, various others

Teamsters Union, Local #495
9101 East Whittier Boulevard, 2nd Floor
Pico Rivera, CA 90660
562-908-8727
Fax: 562-908-8737
office@teamsters495.org
http://www.teamsters495.org
Occupational Fields: truck driver, dock worker, truck mechanic, warehouse worker, dispatcher, production worker, various others

Teamsters Union, Local #517
1209 K Street
Modesto, CA 95354
209-577-0500
Occupational Fields: truck driver, dock worker, truck mechanic, warehouse worker, dispatcher, production worker, various others

Teamsters Union, Local #533
1209 K Street
Modesto, CA 95354
209-577-0500
Occupational Fields: truck driver, dock worker, truck mechanic, warehouse worker, dispatcher, production worker, various others

Teamsters Union, Local #542
4666 Mission Gorge Place
San Diego, CA 92120
619-582-0542
Fax: 619-582-0059
http://www.teamsters542.com
Occupational Fields: truck driver, dock worker, truck mechanic, warehouse worker, dispatcher, production worker, various others

Teamsters Union, Local #572
450 East Carson Plaza, Suite A
Carson, CA, 90746

310-515-0601
http://www.teamsters572.org
Occupational Fields: truck driver, dock worker, truck mechanic, warehouse worker, dispatcher, production worker, various others

Teamsters Union, Local #578
1936 West Chapman Avenue
Orange, CA 92868
714-939-1519
Fax: 714-939-1518
http://www.teamsters.info/local578/index.htm
Occupational Fields: truck driver, dock worker, truck mechanic, warehouse worker, dispatcher, production worker, various others

Teamsters Union, Local #630
750 South Stanford Avenue
Los Angeles, CA 90021-1468
http://www.teamsters630.org
Occupational Fields: truck driver, dock worker, truck mechanic, warehouse worker, dispatcher, production worker, various others

Teamsters Union, Local #683
2731 B Street
San Diego, CA 92102
619-232-7903
Fax: 619-232-8077
http://www.teamsters683.com
Occupational Fields: truck driver, dock worker, truck mechanic, warehouse worker, dispatcher, production worker, various others

Teamsters Union, Local #958
1399 Marion Street
Kingsburg, CA 93631
559-897-3148
Fax: 559-897-5537
http://www.teamsters948.com
Occupational Fields: truck driver, dock worker, truck mechanic, warehouse worker, dispatcher, production worker, various others

Teamsters Union, Local #958
1222 I Street
Modesto, CA 95354
209-522-9006
Fax: 209-523-3323

Occupational Fields: truck driver, dock worker, truck mechanic, warehouse worker, dispatcher, production worker, various others

Teamsters Union, Local #958
1933 W Caldwell, Suite 7
Visalia, CA 93277
559-625-1061
Fax: 559-625-9269
Occupational Fields: truck driver, dock worker, truck mechanic, warehouse worker, dispatcher, production worker, various others

COLORADO

Swift Transportation Inc.
6785 East 50th Avenue
Commerce City, CO 80022-4619
303-287-9099
Occupational Fields: truck driver

Swift Transportation Inc.
4600 Wabash Street
Denver, CO 80216-3445
303-320-3936
Occupational Fields: truck driver

Teamsters Joint Council 3
3245 Eliot Street
Denver, CO 80216
303-477-1623
Fax: 303-433-5950
teamsterslocal17.org
http://www.teamstersjc3.org
Occupational Fields: truck driver, dock worker, truck mechanic, warehouse worker, dispatcher, production worker, various others

Teamsters Union, Local #267
3101 Kintzley Court
LaPorte, CO 80535
970-482-2749
Fax: 970-482-2640
Occupational Fields: truck driver, dock worker, truck mechanic, warehouse worker, dispatcher, production worker, various others

Teamsters Union, Local #435
10 Lakeside Lane, Suite 3-A
Denver, CO 80212

303-458-6325
Fax: 303-480-1015
http://www.teamsterslocal435.org
Occupational Fields: truck driver, dock worker, truck
mechanic, warehouse worker, dispatcher, production
worker, various others

Teamsters Union, Local #961
3245 Eliot Street Room 201
Denver, CO 80216
303-458-1415
Fax: 303-458-0207
Occupational Fields: truck driver, dock worker, truck
mechanic, warehouse worker, dispatcher, production
worker, various others

Teamsters Union, Local #2004
3245 Eliot Street, Suite A
Denver, CO 80216
303-433-1718
Fax: 303-433-1748
http://www.teamsterslocal2004.org
Occupational Fields: truck driver, dock worker, truck
mechanic, warehouse worker, dispatcher, production
worker, various others

DISTRICT OF COLUMBIA
International Brotherhood of Teamsters
25 Louisiana Avenue, NW
Washington, DC 20001
202-624-6800
http://www.teamster.org
Occupational Fields: truck driver, dock worker, production
worker, various others

FLORIDA
Teamsters Union, Joint Council 75
5818 E Martin Luther King, Jr. Boulevard
Tampa, FL 33619-1033
813-621-1391
Fax: 813-349-1327
Teamstersjc75@aol.com
http://www.teamstersjc75.org
Occupational Fields: truck driver, dock worker, truck
mechanic, warehouse worker, dispatcher, production
worker, various others

Teamsters Union, Local #385
126 North Kirkman Road
Orlando, FL 32811
407-298-7037
Fax: 407-297-9097
http://www.local385.org
Occupational Fields: truck driver, dock worker, truck
mechanic, warehouse worker, dispatcher, production
worker, various others

Teamsters Union, Local #512
1210 North Lane Avenue
Jacksonville, FL 32254
904-786-7649
Fax: 904-781-2152
Teamsterslocal512.org
http://www.teamsterslocal512.org
Occupational Fields: truck driver, dock worker, truck
mechanic, warehouse worker, dispatcher, production
worker, various others

GEORGIA
Swift Transportation Inc.
1601 Pecan Lane
Albany, GA 31705-5004
912-435-7320
Occupational Fields: truck driver

Teamsters Union, Local #129
645 Henderson Drive, Suite 9
Cartersville, GA 30120
770-382-1129
Fax: 770-382-2042
http://www.teamsterslocal1129.org
Occupational Fields: truck driver, dock worker, truck
mechanic, warehouse worker, dispatcher, production
worker, various others

IDAHO
Teamsters Union, Local #483
225 North 16th Street, # 112
Boise, ID 83702
208-343-5439
Fax: 208-343-7993
teamsters483@rmci.net
Occupational Fields: truck driver, dock worker, truck
mechanic, warehouse worker, dispatcher, production
worker, various others

Teamsters Union, Local #983
518 E. Center Street
PO Box 1085
Pocatello, ID 83204
208-232-6891
Fax: 208-234-7242
Occupational Fields: truck driver, dock worker, truck mechanic, warehouse worker, dispatcher, production worker, various others

ILLINOIS

Teamsters Joint Council 25
1645 West Jackson
Chicago, IL 60612
312-421-2600
http://www.chicagoteamsters.org
Occupational Fields: truck driver, dock worker, truck mechanic, warehouse worker, dispatcher, production worker, various others

Teamsters Union, Local #325
5533-11th Street
Rockford, IL 61109
815-874-6307
Fax: 815-874-4694
http://www.teamsters325.com
Occupational Fields: truck driver, dock worker, truck mechanic, warehouse worker, dispatcher, production worker, various others

Teamsters Union, Local #705
1645 West Jackson Boulevard
Chicago, IL 60612
312-738-2800
http://www.teamsters325.com
Occupational Fields: truck driver, dock worker, truck mechanic, warehouse worker, dispatcher, production worker, various others

Teamsters Union, Local #710
4217 South Halsted Street
Chicago, IL 60609
773-254-3200
http://www.local710.org
Occupational Fields: truck driver, dock worker, truck mechanic, warehouse worker, dispatcher, production worker, various others

Teamsters Union, Local #726
1645 West Jackson Boulevard, Suite 603
Chicago Il. 60612
312-666-5772
Fax: 312-666-7581
teamsterslocal726@sbcglobal.net
Occupational Fields: truck driver, dock worker, truck mechanic, warehouse worker, dispatcher, production worker, various others

INDIANA

Swift Transportation Inc.
3210 Watling Street
East Chicago, IN 46312-1716
219-397-6651
Occupational Fields: truck driver

Swift Transportation Inc.
6500 Industrial Highway
Gary, IN 46406-1033
219-949-4800
Occupational Fields: truck driver

Swift Transportation Inc.
Rural Route One
Shoals, IN 47581-9801
812-247-2128
Occupational Fields: truck driver

Teamsters Union, Local #135
1233 Shelby Street
Indianapolis, IN 46203
http://www.local135.com
Occupational Fields: truck driver, dock worker, truck mechanic, warehouse worker, dispatcher, production worker, various others

MARYLAND

Teamsters Union, Local #570
6910 Eastern Avenue
Baltimore, MD 21224
410-284-5081
Fax: 410-282-7185
http://www.team570.com
Occupational Fields: truck driver, dock worker, truck mechanic, warehouse worker, dispatcher, production worker, various others

MASSACHUSETTS

Teamsters Joint Council 10 New England
544 Main Street
Boston, MA 02129-1113
617-242-9803
Fax: 617-241-7512
http://www.teamstersjc10.com
Occupational Fields: truck driver, dock worker, truck mechanic, warehouse worker, dispatcher, production worker, various others

Teamsters Union, Local #25
544 Main Street
Boston, MA 02129
617-241-8825
http://www.teamsterslocal25.com
Occupational Fields: truck driver, dock worker, truck mechanic, warehouse worker, dispatcher, production worker, various others

MONTANA

Teamsters Union, Local #2
422 East Mendenhall
PO Box 1045
Bozeman, MT 59715
406-586-6705
Occupational Fields: truck driver, dock worker, truck mechanic, warehouse worker, dispatcher, production worker, various others

Teamsters Union, Local #2
3345 Harrison Avenue
PO Box 3745
Butte, MT 59702-3745
406-494-2747
Fax: 406-494-4430
http://www.teamsterslocal2.org
Occupational Fields: truck driver, dock worker, truck mechanic, warehouse worker, dispatcher, production worker, various others

Teamsters Union, Local #2
1112 7th Street South
PO Box 2648
Great Falls, MT 59403
406-453-1431
Fax: 406-453-6652

Occupational Fields: truck driver, dock worker, truck mechanic, warehouse worker, dispatcher, production worker, various others

Teamsters Union, Local #2
727 West Central
PO Box 8144
Missoula, MT 59807
406-543-3472
Fax: 406-549-9778
Occupational Fields: truck driver, dock worker, truck mechanic, warehouse worker, dispatcher, production worker, various others

Teamsters Union, Local #190
437 Kuhlman Drive
PO Box 50969
Billings, MT 59105-0901
406-248-2658
Fax: 406-248-1503
teamsters190@teamsters190.com
http://www.Teamsters190.com
Occupational Fields: truck driver, dock worker, truck mechanic, warehouse worker, dispatcher, production worker, various others

Watkins and Shepard Trucking
6400 U.S. Highway 10, West
Missoula, MT 59801
406-728-6121
Occupational Fields: truck driver, dock worker, truck mechanic, warehouse worker, dispatcher, production worker, various others

NEVADA

Swift Transportation Inc.
1455 Hulda Way
Sparks, NV 89431-7124
702-359-5161
Occupational Fields: truck driver

Teamsters and Truck Drivers
307 Wall Street
Las Vegas, NV 89102-2533
702-385-1455
Occupational Fields: truck driver, dock worker, truck mechanic, warehouse worker, dispatcher, production worker, various others

Teamsters Union, Local #14
1250 Burnham Avenue, Floor 2
Las Vegas, NV 89104-1921
702-384-7841
Fax: 702-386-4848
http://www.teamsters14.com
Occupational Fields: *truck driver, dock worker, truck mechanic, warehouse worker, dispatcher, production worker, various others*

Teamsters Union, Local #631
700 North Lamb Boulevard
Las Vegas, NV 89110
702-453-6310
http://www.teamsterslocal631.org
Occupational Fields: *truck driver, dock worker, truck mechanic, warehouse worker, dispatcher, production worker, various others*

Teamsters Union
316 Vassar Street
Reno, NV 89502-2910
702-348-6060
Occupational Fields: *truck driver, dock worker, truck mechanic, warehouse worker, dispatcher, production worker, various others*

NEW JERSEY

Teamsters Union, Local #723
170 Changebridge Road, UnitB3-2
Montville, NJ 07045
973-575-5323
Fax: 973-882-8218
union723@aol.com
http://www.teamsterlocal723.com
Occupational Fields: *truck driver, dock worker, truck mechanic, warehouse worker, dispatcher, production worker, various others*

NEW MEXICO

Teamsters Union, Local #492
4269 Balloon Park Rd, NE
Albuquerque, NM 87109
505-344-1925
Fax: 505-344-2636
Occupational Fields: *truck driver, dock worker, truck mechanic, warehouse worker, dispatcher, production worker, various others*

NEW YORK

Swift Transportation Inc.
County House Road
Auburn, NY 13021-1968
315-255-3417
Occupational Fields: *truck driver*

Swift Transportation Inc.
323 North Burgher Avenue
Staten Island, NY 10310-2019
718-698-4916
Occupational Fields: *truck driver*

NORTH CAROLINA

Teamsters Union, Local #391
336-668-0441, ext.255
Sjones@teamsterslocal391.org
http://www.teamsterslocal391.org
Occupational Fields: *truck driver, dock worker, truck mechanic, warehouse worker, dispatcher, production worker, various others*

OKLAHOMA

Eastern Oklahoma Building and Construction Trades
2651 East 21st Street, Suite 405
Tulsa, OK 74114
Occupational Fields: *truck driver*

Swift Transportation Inc.
8236 West Interstate 40 Service Road
Oklahoma City, OK 73128-4239
405-495-0035
Occupational Fields: *truck driver*

Swift Transportation Inc.
9400 Northwest 10th Street
Oklahoma City, OK 73127-7458
405-495-0035
Occupational Fields: *truck driver*

Teamsters Union, Local #886
3528 West Reno
Oklahoma City, OK 73107
405-947-2333
http://www.teamsterslocal886.org
Occupational Fields: *truck driver, dock worker, truck mechanic, warehouse worker, dispatcher, production worker, various others*

OREGON

Swift Transportation Inc.
2021 Northwest Sundial Road
Troutdale, OR 97060-9513
503-661-3031
Occupational Fields: truck driver

PENNSYLVANIA

AAA School of Trucking
5000 Letterkenny Road
Chambersburg, PA 17201
717-261-4787
aaatruck@earthlink.net
Occupational Fields: truck driver

Swift Transportation Inc.
1076 Harrisburg Pike
Carlisle, PA 17013-1615
717-258-1936
Occupational Fields: truck driver

Teamsters Union, Local #249
4701 Butler Street
PO Box 40128
Pittsburgh, PA 15201-0128
412-682-3700
Fax: 412-682-3732
http://www.teamsters249.com
Occupational Fields: truck driver, dock worker, truck mechanic, warehouse worker, dispatcher, production worker, various others

RHODE ISLAND

Teamsters, Chauffers, and Helpers Union, Local #251
121 Brightridge Avenue
East Providence, RI 02914-3901
401-434-0454
Occupational Fields: truck driver

TENNESSEE

Teamsters Union, Local #515
4431 Bonny Oaks Drive
Chattanooga, TN 37416
423-894-3630
http://www.teamsterslocal515.org
Occupational Fields: truck driver, dock worker, truck mechanic, warehouse worker, dispatcher, production worker, various others

Teamsters Union, Local #549
2857 Highway 11-W
Blountville, TN 37617
423-323-4171
Fax: 423-279-0776
TLU549@aol.com
http://members.aol.com/_ht_a/tlu549/myhomepage
Occupational Fields: truck driver, dock worker, truck mechanic, warehouse worker, dispatcher, production worker, various others

TEXAS

Swift Transportation Inc.
901 Skyline Drive
Hutchins, TX 75141-9445
972-225-3285
Occupational Fields: truck driver

Swift Transportation Inc.
14415 Mines Road
Laredo, TX 78045-7848
210-717-9646
Occupational Fields: truck driver

Teamsters Union, Local #657
8214 Roughrider
San Antonio, TX 78239
210-590-2013
Fax: 210-590-4420
info@teamsters657.com
http://www.teamsters657.com
Occupational Fields: truck driver, dock worker, truck mechanic, warehouse worker, dispatcher, production worker, various others

Teamsters Union, Local #747
1419 FM 1960 Road
Houston, TX 77073
281-209-0300
Fax: 281-209-0320
http://www.ibt747.org
Occupational Fields: truck driver, dock worker, truck mechanic, warehouse worker, dispatcher, production worker, various others

Teamsters Union, Local #767
6109 Anglin Drive
Forest Hill, TX 76119
http://www.teamsterslocal767.com

Occupational Fields: truck driver, dock worker, truck mechanic, warehouse worker, dispatcher, production worker, various others

UTAH

Swift Transportation Inc.
1101 Industrial Parkway
Clearfield, UT 84015-7848
Occupational Fields: truck driver

Swift Transportation Inc.
2900 Parkway Boulevard
West Valley City, UT 84119-1968
801-972-8300
Occupational Fields: truck driver

Teamsters Union, Local #222
2641 South 3270 West Street
PO Box 30749
Salt Lake City, UT
801-972-1898
Fax: 801-972-8226
http://www.teamsterslocal222.org
Occupational Fields: truck driver, dock worker, truck mechanic, warehouse worker, dispatcher, production worker, various others

VIRGINIA

Swift Transportation Inc.
2841 Charles City Road
Richmond, VA 23231-4531
804-222-8579
Occupational Fields: truck driver

WASHINGTON

Teamsters Union, Local #38
2601 Everett Avenue
PO Box 1548
Everett, WA 98206
425-252-3800
Fax: 425-252-3889
http://www.teamsters38.org
Occupational Fields: truck driver, dock worker, truck mechanic, warehouse worker, dispatcher, production worker, various others

Teamsters Union, Local #58
2212 North East Andresen Road
Vancouver, WA 98661

360-693-2561
Fax: 360-695-0768
Occupational Fields: truck driver, dock worker, truck mechanic, warehouse worker, dispatcher, production worker, various others

Teamsters Union, Local #117
553 John Street
206-441-4860
Fax: 206-441-3153
http://www.teamsters117.org
Occupational Fields: truck driver, dock worker, truck mechanic, warehouse worker, dispatcher, production worker, various others

Teamsters Union, Local #174
553 John Street
Seattle, WA 98109
206-441-6060
Fax: 206-441-4853
TTY: 206-728-5409
http://www.teamsters174.org
Occupational Fields: truck driver, dock worker, truck mechanic, warehouse worker, dispatcher, production worker, various others

Teamsters Union, Local #231
1700 N. State Street
PO Box H
Bellingham, WA 98227-0298
360-734-7780
Fax: 360-734-7783
http://www.231teamsters.org
Occupational Fields: truck driver, dock worker, truck mechanic, warehouse worker, dispatcher, production worker, various others

Teamsters Union, Local #252
217 East Main Street
Centralia, WA 98531-4449
360-736-9979
Fax: 360-330-0377
Occupational Fields: truck driver, dock worker, truck mechanic, warehouse worker, dispatcher, production worker, various others

Teamsters Union, Local #313
220 South 27th Street
Tacoma, WA 98402
253-627-0103
Fax: 253-627-0106

http://www.teamsters313.org
Occupational Fields: truck driver, dock worker, truck mechanic, warehouse worker, dispatcher, production worker, various others

Teamsters Union, Local #556
1750 Portland Street
Walla Walla, WA 99362
509-525-5563
Fax: 509-525-8854
Occupational Fields: truck driver, dock worker, truck mechanic, warehouse worker, dispatcher, production worker, various others

Teamsters Union, Local #589
632 Fifth Street, Suite 4
Bremerton, WA 98337
360-377-3986
Fax: 360-377-4012
Occupational Fields: truck driver, dock worker, truck mechanic, warehouse worker, dispatcher, production worker, various others

Teamsters Union, Local #589
1303 South C Street
Port Angeles, WA 98363-7259
360-452-3388
Occupational Fields: truck driver

Teamsters Union, Local #690
1912 North Division Street
Spokane, WA 99207
509-455-9410
Fax: 509-326-9507
Occupational Fields: truck driver, dock worker, truck mechanic, warehouse worker, dispatcher, production worker, various others

Teamsters Union, Local #763
553 John Street
Seattle, WA 98109
206-441-0763
Fax: 206-441-6376
Occupational Fields: truck driver, dock worker, truck mechanic, warehouse worker, dispatcher, production worker, various others

Teamsters Union, Local #839
2508 West Sylvester, Suite E
PO Box 4090

Pasco, WA 99302
509-547-7513
Fax: 509-546-2560
Occupational Fields: truck driver, dock worker, truck mechanic, warehouse worker, dispatcher, production worker, various others

WEST VIRGINIA
Construction Trades Training Center
2307 Seventh Avenue
Charleston, WV 25312-1811
304-346-3863
Occupational Fields: truck driver

WISCONSIN
Teamsters Union, Local #43
1624 Yout Street
Racine, WI
262-633-6387
http://www.teamsterslocal43.com
Occupational Fields: truck driver, dock worker, truck mechanic, warehouse worker, dispatcher, production worker, various others

WYOMING
Teamsters Union, Local #17
3245 Eliot Street, Room 214
Denver, CO
303-433-6496
Fax: 303-433-5950
http://www.teamstersjc3.org
Occupational Fields: truck driver, dock worker, truck mechanic, warehouse worker, dispatcher, production worker, various others

CANADA
ALBERTA
Teamsters Union, Local #362
1200 A-58th Avenue SE
Calgary, AB T2H 2C9
403-259-4608
Fax: 403-255-9616
teamcal@teamsters362.com
Occupational Fields: truck driver, dock worker, truck mechanic, warehouse worker, dispatcher, production worker, various others

Teamsters Union, Local #362
15035-121A Avenue
Edmonton, AB T5V 1N1
780-455-2255
Fax: 780-455-6976
teamedm@teamsters362.com
Occupational Fields: truck driver, dock worker, truck mechanic, warehouse worker, dispatcher, production worker, various others

BRITISH COLUMBIA

Okanagan University College
Faculty of Industrial Trades & Services
1000 KLO Road,
Kelowna, BC C V1Y 4X8
250-862-5457
Fax: 250-862-5469
rwerger@ouc.bc.ca
www.ouc.bc.ca/trades
Occupational Fields: truck driver

Teamsters Union, Local #31
1 Grosvenor Square
Delta, BC V3M 5S1
604-540-6009
Fax: 604-540-6073
Occupational Fields: truck driver, dock worker, truck mechanic, warehouse worker, dispatcher, production worker, various others

Teamsters Union, Local #31
9 - 2480 Kenworth Road
Nanaimo, BC V9T 3Y3
250-758-1857
Fax: 250-758-4365
Occupational Fields: truck driver, dock worker, truck mechanic, warehouse worker, dispatcher, production worker, various others

Teamsters Union, Local #31
2700 Queensway Street, Suite 100
Prince George, BC V2L 1N2
250-563-5346
Fax: 250-563-2379
Occupational Fields: truck driver, dock worker, truck mechanic, warehouse worker, dispatcher, production worker, various others

NEW BRUNSWICK

Department of Training and Employment Development
Apprenticeship and Occupational Certification
PO Box 6000
Chestnut Complex
Fredericton, NB E3B 5H1
506-453-2260
Fax: 506-453-5317
aoc-acp@gnb.ca
Occupational Fields: truck driver

ONTARIO

Teamsters Union, Local #938
275 Matheson Boulevard East
Mississauga, ON L4Z 1X8
905-502-0062
Fax: 905-502-0076
info@teamsters938.org
http://www.teamsters938.org
Occupational Fields: truck driver, dock worker, truck mechanic, warehouse worker, dispatcher, production worker, various others

Teamsters Union, Local #938
1240 Philip Murray Avenue, Unit 9
Oshawa, ON L1J 6Z9
905-436-8887
Fax: 905-436-9555
http://www.teamsters938.org
Occupational Fields: truck driver, dock worker, truck mechanic, warehouse worker, dispatcher, production worker, various others

YUKON TERRITORIES

Teamsters Union, Local #31
407 Black Street
Whitehorse, YT Y1A 2N2
867-667-2473
Fax: 867-667-7112
Occupational Fields: truck driver, dock worker, truck mechanic, warehouse worker, dispatcher, production worker, various others

WELDERS

RELATED SECTIONS: *artists and artisans; auto body workers; boilermakers; carpenters; crafts and trades workers at living historical sites and farms; elevator constructors; farriers; ironworkers; machinists; mechanics; metalworkers; millwrights; operating engineers and stationary engineers; pile drivers; pipe trades workers; railroad workers; sheet metal workers; shipbuilding and ship maintenance workers; tool, die, mold, and pattern makers*

Welders cut and shape metal pieces and join metal parts, usually by applying heat. They work on structures and numerous manufactured products, including buildings, pipelines, bridges, ships, boilers, machinery, appliances, aircraft, spacecraft, and automobiles. *Welding machine operators* usually work in manufacturing plants, performing automated welding tasks. They set up the machine according to blueprints, layouts, or other specifications and oversee it to ensure that it functions properly. *Arc, plasma, and flame cutters* use electric arcs or burning gases to cut metal and to dismantle objects such as automobiles and railroad cars.

There are several types of welding. Gas welding is done with a gas torch, which generates an extremely hot flame that is used to melt welding rods (rod-shaped pieces of filler metal) to the edges of metal parts, thus fusing them together. Arc welding employs an electric current to melt the metal edges and the filler wire that joins them. Lasers, electron beams, and friction are used in other methods of welding.

Most welders work in manufacturing plants, on construction projects, or in repair shops. Some do manual welding and use a great deal of creativity to fabricate unusual or unique pieces; some welders plan their work after consulting blueprints or other instructions. Other welders, usually those who work in factories, perform the same task every day. On construction projects, welders help build bridges, nuclear power plants, refineries, and other structures by joining steel beams and reinforcing rods.

Welders work with various metals, including steel, cast iron, nickel, bronze, and aluminum; they use special techniques for different materials. The work involves bending, stooping, and crouching in uncomfortable positions. Workers wear protective clothing, goggles, safety shoes, and other gear to avoid burns from hot metal and tools and to avoid breathing toxic fumes emitted by heated metal. Welding machine operators wear less protective gear, because they are exposed to fewer hazards.

Most welders and cutters work for manufacturers, construction companies, service companies, or wholesalers. Welding machine operators work in factories, where they most commonly produce machines, metal parts, and vehicles. Some welders operate their own repair shops.

About one third of welders belong to labor unions, such as the International Association of Machinists and Aerospace Workers; the International Brotherhood of Boilermakers, Iron Ship Builders, Blacksmiths, Forgers and Helpers; the International Union, United Automobile, Aerospace and Agricultural Implement Workers of America; the United Association of Journeymen and Apprentices of the Plumbing and Pipe Fitting Industry of the United States and Canada; and the United Electrical, Radio, and Machine Workers of America.

Welders often enter this trade through apprenticeship or on-the-job training. Apprentices work under the supervision of experienced welders. Typically, the course of study runs for three to four years and includes instruction in blueprint reading, chemistry, mathematics, mechanical drawing, and metallurgy. Welders who finish the training and pass an examination may become certified, but certification is not always necessary. Skilled workers may advance to supervisory positions, become instructors, inspectors, or welding technicians.

In general an applicant should

- apply in person
- be at least 18 years old
- be a high school graduate or hold a GED certificate
- be physically capable of performing the work
- have manual dexterity
- have good eyesight
- have good hand-eye coordination
- be capable of concentrating for long periods of time

APPRENTICESHIP SALARIES
Between $7 an hour and $18 an hour.

POSTAPPRENTICESHIP SALARIES
About $11 an hour, up to $20 an hour.

JOB OUTLOOK
Generally stable, because welders will continue to be hired for construction and repair projects. Automated

welding could replace some manual welding positions, but manual welders will always be needed for some types of jobs.

For more information on apprenticeships for welders, contact local job centers, your state bureau of apprenticeship training, or the individual programs listed below.

APPRENTICESHIP PROFILE
Newport News Shipbuilding-Northrop Grumman Communications
4101 Washington Avenue
Newport News, VA 23607
757-380-3809
Fax: 757-688-0305
http://www.northropgrumman.com

General Nature of the Job
As a welder, Ozzy Reynolds is apt to be involved in every phase of shipbuilding. Welders use a wide range of techniques on various metals to join the bulkheads, decks, framing, and stiffeners into a finished ship. The trade requires precision and familiarity with the properties of metals, along with the physical stamina to spend hours crouching, kneeling, and working in awkward positions. Ozzy says many skills are important for a welder at the shipyard, but expertise in weld preparation is vital to meet the navy's high standards in shipbuilding.

Navy submarines and aircraft carriers are constructed here, other navy ships are overhauled, and commercial vessels are renovated and repaired. With more than 18,000 employees, Newport News Shipbuilding is Virginia's largest private employer. It's a city within a city, and the Apprentice School is much like a college, complete with intercollegiate athletic teams. Apprentices can become involved in football, basketball, wrestling, golf, parties, dances, the company's annual pig roast, student council, and many other social and recreational events.

These apprenticeships were designed to train workers primarily for this specific company; students don't travel to other job sites or work for other employers during their training period. The four-year apprenticeship consists of about 14 percent classroom work and 86 percent (6,000 hours) on-the-job training. The school also offers a design program, which extends the apprenticeship to five years. Apprentices who earn merit advancement can complete either program in a shorter length of time.

Typical Day
Apprentices work 40 hours a week, from 7:00 A.M. to 3:30 P.M., with a half-hour, unpaid lunch break. For two days each week, Ozzy attends classes until 10:30 A.M., then walks to the job site and works for the rest of the day. Classes provide him with a technical background in subjects such as hull construction, shielded metal arc welding, gas-metal arc welding, and nondestructive testing. After studying each topic in class, he applies what he has learned to actual projects at work.

Ozzy spends the remaining three days each week practicing his skills on the job, working under the supervision of a skilled welder. He learns to secure electrodes, weld pipes and various types of joints, and use tools such as fillet gauges, heating torches, burning torches, carbon-arc equipment, grinders, levels, and tape measures. Each project requires the careful completion of several steps. For instance, just to prepare for welding, Ozzy must set the correct weld amperage, set and adjust the power supply, adjust the gas flow, set and adjust the wire feeder, check the job for a proper fit, clean the weld area with a grinder, check the preheat and interpass, and observe the heat input.

To learn the complexities of his trade more fully, Ozzy rotates through the company's other departments, including shipfitting, steel fabrication, nondestructive testing, the welding engineering lab, and welding equipment maintenance. These rotations help him see the bigger picture and understand how other specialists fit into the shipbuilding process.

Path to Becoming an Apprentice
"I have always been fascinated by the capabilities of ships and the flotation principles associated with them," Ozzy says. "My high school physics course reinforced that curiosity and influenced me to pursue it." In high school he enjoyed classes that later proved helpful in his career: mathematical analysis, physics, drafting and computer assisted design, and computer literacy.

He explains that seeking an apprenticeship was a practical way to begin a career and earn an income at the same time: "I wanted to receive an education that would prepare me for an engineering career. However, I also have the responsibility of financially supporting my daughter and myself. I decided that an apprenticeship was the best route for me to take, and I applied to the Apprentice School."

Applicants to the program are required to have a high school diploma or GED and be at least 18 years old, except those who are high school seniors. They must have a solid background in several of the following subjects: algebra, geometry, trigonometry, physics, chemistry, mechanical drawing, computer science, and vocational and technical shop classes. Only the most qualified applicants are selected for admission after passing a physical exam and a test for use of alcohol and other drugs. Like all apprentices and employees at the shipyard, Ozzy works on defense contracts that are important to national security. He had to pass a background check and obtain a security clearance before he was admitted to the school.

Salary Range

Apprentices are paid for their time in class and on the job, starting at $11.06 and going up to more than $20 an hour by the end of the four-year program. During their four years of study, apprentices can earn more than $75,000.

All apprentices and workers qualify for full health and medical benefits. The company also offers life insurance, a pension plan, a 401(k) savings plan, an employee stock purchase plan, tuition reimbursement for employees earning undergraduate or graduate degrees, a prepaid legal plan, paid vacations, 10 paid holidays each year, and a counseling program to help employees cope with personal problems.

Advice

"I would advise anyone who is interested in an industrial career to pursue an apprenticeship, because the combination of classroom and on-the-job training is second to none," Ozzy says. "The academic training and practical experience at the Apprentice School will be the foundation of my career. The program gives me insight on both aspects of ship construction: design and production." In the future, he adds, the training for this career will probably be even more demanding, because each year the navy's expectations become more technical and involved.

Future Goals

Graduates of the apprenticeship program frequently continue as employees at the shipyard, where they can advance to production foreman, general foreman, or department superintendent. The company offers free night school and will pay the tuition of employees pursuing degrees at any of the colleges or universities in the area. Apprentices can receive college credit for some of the work completed in the training program. They often earn degrees in engineering, engineering technology, or business.

"A general misconception is that being a welding apprentice prepares you only to become a welder. However, the various special rotations that a welding apprentice receives can open doors for careers in welding engineering, welding equipment repair, quality control, and upper management within the company. My ultimate goal for the future is to earn a degree in naval engineering," Ozzy says. He anticipates a long career as a designer and naval engineer for Newport News Shipbuilding Company.

ALABAMA

Plumbers and Steamfitters Union, Local #52
5563 Wares Ferry Road
Montgomery, AL 36117
334-272-9500
Occupational Fields: welder

CALIFORNIA

Central Valley Automotive and Machinists
4669 East Hedges Avenue
Fresno, CA 93703
209-251-1968
Occupational Fields: combination welder

Central Valley Opportunity Center, Modesto
912 11th Street
Modesto, CA 95354
209-577-3210
Fax: 209-521-9954
Occupational Fields: welder

Central Valley Opportunity Center, Winton
Winton Small Business Incubator
6838 West Bridget Court
Winton, CA 95388
209-357-3716
Occupational Fields: welder

CONNECTICUT

General Dynamics
Electric Boat Division
75 Eastern Point Road
Groton, CT 06340-4905
860-433-3000
Fax: 860-433-1400
Occupational Fields: welder (marine)

DISTRICT OF COLUMBIA
Sheet Metal Workers International Association and Sheet Metal and Air Conditioning Contractors' National Association
1750 New York Avenue, NW
Washington, DC 20008
202-783-5880
http://www.smwia.org
Occupational Fields: welder

GEORGIA
Atlanta Ironworkers
109 Selig Drive, SW
Atlanta, GA 30336
404-505-0022
Occupational Fields: welder

United Auto Workers, Local #10
5407 Buford Highway, NE
Doraville, GA 30340-1125
404-457-3128
Occupational Fields: welder

Welding Services Inc.
2225 Skyland Court
Norcross, GA 30071
770-449-1706
Occupational Fields: welder

HAWAII
Honolulu, City and County of
Department of Civil Service
City Hall Annex
Honolulu, HI 96813
808-523-4233
Occupational Fields: welder

Operating Engineers
50 Waianuenue Avenue, First Floor
Hilo, HI 96720
808-935-8709
Occupational Fields: heavy duty welder, heavy duty repairer, construction equipment operator

Operating Engineers
1432 Middle Street, Room 103
Honolulu, HI 96819
808-847-5523

Occupational Fields: heavy duty welder, heavy duty repairer, construction equipment operator

ILLINOIS
Headco Machine Works
2601 Parkes Drive
Broadview, IL 60155
708-681-4400
Fax: 708-681-4439
http://www.headco.com
Occupational Fields: welder

INDIANA
Allison Engine Company
2355 South Tibbs Avenue
Indianapolis, IN 46206
317-230-5112
Fax: 317-230-3577
Occupational Fields: welder

Delco Electronics
700 East Firmin Street
Kokomo, IN 46904-9005
317-451-2915
Occupational Fields: welder

ILLINOIS
Headco Machine Works
2601 Parkes Drive
Broadview, IL 60155
708-681-4400
Fax: 708-681-4439
http://www.headco.com
Occupational Fields: welder

IOWA
Midwest Gas Company
401 Douglas Street
Sioux City, IA 51102
712-277-7624
Occupational Fields: welder

KANSAS
Colgate-Palmolive Company
18010 Kansas Avenue
Kansas City, KS 66105

913-573-6464
Fax: 913-573-6605
Occupational Fields: combination welder

MAINE

Bath Iron Works
700 Washington Street
Bath, ME 04530-2574
207-443-3311
Occupational Fields: welder

MARYLAND

Bethlehem Steel Corporation, Sparrows Point
5111 North Point Boulevard
Baltimore, MD 21219
410-388-3000
Occupational Fields: welder

MONTANA

Anaconda Foundry and Fabrication Company
1015 East Sixth Street
Anaconda, MT 59711-2658
406-563-8494
Fax: 406-563-3368
Occupational Fields: welder, fabricator, molder

PENNSYLVANIA

Ironworkers, Local #401
Training Facility
11600 Norcom Road
Philadelphia, PA 19154
Occupational Fields: welder, ironworker

VIRGINIA

Newport News Shipbuilding
Admissions Office
4101 Washington Avenue
Newport News, VA 23607-2770
757-380-2000
Fax: 757-688-0305
Occupational Fields: welder, welding equipment
   repairer

WASHINGTON

Boilermakers/Puget Sound Employers
6770 East Marginal Way, Room B122
Seattle, WA 98108
206-624-4707
Fax: 206-623-7176
Occupational Fields: welder, boilermaker, metal fabricator

CANADA
BRITISH COLUMBIA

College of the Rockies
2700 College Way, Box 8500
Cranbrook, BC V1C 5L7
250-489-2751
Fax: 250-489-1790
http://www.cotr.bc.ca
Occupational Fields: welder

Northwest Community College
Box 338
Hazelton, BC V0J 1Y0
250-842-5291
Fax: 250-842-5813
http://www.nwcc.bc.ca
Occupational Fields: welder

Okanagan University College
Faculty of Industrial Trades & Services
1000 KLO Road,
Kelowna, BC V1Y 4X8
250-862-5457
Fax: 250-862-5469
rwerger@ouc.bc.ca
http://www.ouc.bc.ca/trades
Occupational Fields: welder

NEW BRUNSWICK

Department of Training and Employment Development
   Apprenticeship and Occupational Certification
PO Box 6000
Chestnut Complex
Fredericton, NB E3B 5H1
506-453-2260
Fax: 506-453-5317
aoc-acp@gnb.ca
Occupational Fields: welder

APPRENTICESHIPS BY ELIGIBILITY

GOODWILL INDUSTRIES

Goodwill Industries is a nationwide network of independent, nonprofit organizations dedicated to providing "a hand up, not a hand out" to people who might otherwise have difficulty earning a living. Trainees include individuals with physical, mental, or emotional disabilities, including workers who have been injured on the job; the homeless; the elderly; the illiterate; and clients with little work experience, a criminal record, or a history of substance abuse. Each year, Goodwill Industries trains more than 30,000 people for the general work force and hires more than 60,000 employees.

Goodwill offers various types of learning experiences, including paid, on-the-job training and apprenticeships at some sites. For instance, a client might complete training and then be hired by a local business. In such a case, a job coach from Goodwill typically accompanies the new employee to the job site and remains there to supervise until the employee has mastered the task. The employee then works independently, but the job coach follows up with periodic visits to ensure that the employee is doing well. Other clients receive on-the-job training in Goodwill facilities, where they typically perform light industrial projects for local businesses, such as assembling computer parts or counting newsletters.

Programs are tailored to each local community, but they tend to include assessment of job skills and aptitudes, career planning, job training, help in preparing a resume and finding a job, follow-up services, and short-term employment for clients who are not ready to enter the general work force. Some sites offer special training for women seeking employment. Others feature training and placement services for temporary workers.

The specific training varies widely from site to site, but instruction in dozens of trades is available at nearly 200 locations nationwide. Training is offered in areas such as computer skills, clerical trades, financial services, telephone surveying, electronics, weeding and grounds maintenance, arts and crafts, flower arranging, wood products assembly, shrink-wrapping, retail sales, furniture refinishing, sand blasting, janitorial work, and food service occupations. A business training program might feature, for example, instruction in typing, business English, proofreading, bookkeeping, data entry, databases, spreadsheets, word processing, using a calculator, using a dictation machine, medical transcription, working with medical and dental insurance forms, and customer service.

In addition to job skills, clients are taught how to groom themselves, dress appropriately, behave properly, follow instructions, make decisions, communicate effectively, and establish a rapport with coworkers. Emphasis is placed on the importance of reporting for work on time, following safety procedures, working efficiently, and cultivating a good attitude about work in general.

Goodwill Industries was founded at the turn of the century by a Methodist minister, who helped immigrants and low-income people in Boston by training and hiring them to repair secondhand merchandise and sell it at a profit. The organization still sells an enormous quantity of used goods donated to its thrift stores; the profits help fund its job training programs. Some trainees receive on-the-job training by working in the thrift stores, where they learn to sort and price textiles and other merchandise, box books, process donations, sort and package breakable items, ship and receive merchandise, work in a recycling center, display merchandise, and operate a cash register. Others perform mass mailings and other contract services for businesses; that revenue also helps fund training programs. In addition, the organization receives some state and federal grants.

In general an applicant should

- be at least 17 years old
- have difficulty obtaining a job due to a disability, homelessness, lack of work experience, or a criminal record, for example.

APPRENTICESHIP SALARIES
Vary widely, depending on the trade, the geographic location, and the particular employer.

POSTAPPRENTICESHIP SALARIES
Vary widely, depending on the trade, the geographic location, the employer, and the skills of the worker. Workers who complete a Goodwill apprenticeship program usually earn more than the minimum wage.

For more information on Goodwill apprenticeships, contact the individual programs listed below, local job centers, or your state bureau of apprenticeship training.

PROGRAM PROFILE
Goodwill Industries of Southern New Jersey
Industrial Services Training Program
2835 Route 73, South

Maple Shade, NJ 08052
609-439-0200
Fax: 609-439-0843
svann@juno.com
http://www.goodwillnj.org

General Nature of the Program

People sign up for Goodwill's various job training programs for many reasons. Some have few work skills or have experienced a series of failures as they attempted to hold jobs. Many have low self-esteem. To qualify for the Industrial Services Training Program, clients must have mental or physical disabilities or other disadvantaging conditions.

Jennifer Taylor, a case manager with the Industrial Services Training Program offered by Goodwill Industries of Southern New Jersey, explains: "I feel the training is extremely important, because most people in the program don't know what to do on a job. Most have no work history at all. We're trying to teach them core work skills." Because they often come from homes where no one has a job, many of the clients have had few role models to help them understand how to succeed as employees. At the Outsourcing Support Center, they learn not only job skills but the importance of being punctual and showing up for work, how to follow instructions, how to develop effective relationships with supervisors and coworkers, and how to conduct themselves in an appropriate manner on the job.

The Industrial Services Training Program helps clients prepare for careers with companies that manufacture, assemble, or package a wide variety of products. While completing projects such as bulk mailings for local businesses, the trainees earn money, learn to solve problems, develop confidence, and cultivate the ability to work effectively. About 70 clients are usually enrolled in the program, and most will work here for quite some time. Those who are not ready for competitive employment after 150 days of training can remain in the program indefinitely. "We have become family for many of the clients," Jennifer says. "And they care about us, too. If I'm out sick for a day, everyone notices."

Typical Day

Students usually begin their day by packing a lunch, commuting to the Outsourcing Support Center, and picking up their name tags and work assignments. "The attendance here is unbelievable," says Jennifer. "The work day starts at 9:00 A.M., but the majority of clients are here by 8:00 A.M. They are so dedicated." Trainees take a 15-minute break at 10:15 and at least half an hour for lunch, and they're finished with work by 2:00 P.M.

The center features an office, a conference room, a lunch room, and a work room about the size of a gymnasium, where students sit at tables, working diligently. "It's very brightly lit and fairly spacious. Bustling with activity. We encourage people to work quietly, because the majority of jobs involve many steps, and it helps them focus," says Jennifer.

The staff assigns different projects every day, but trainees can request not to be chosen for jobs they dislike. Students occasionally use a pallet jack, a lubing machine, price guns, and X-acto knives, but most of the work is done by hand. "The staff decides the most efficient way to do it. Sometimes we have to do things the hard way. We tailor the jobs to meet our clients' needs," Jennifer explains. Trainees work under the direction of employment and industrial services experts. Some can work independently, but others require constant supervision.

They might unpack and inspect boxes of goods; collate, label, and mail thousands of copies of a company newsletter; or assemble 50,000 heating oil nozzles for a manufacturing firm. One project involved counting and repackaging about 800,000 bus schedules. Another involved forming an assembly line to collate baseball cards for the Philadelphia Phillies sports team. In 1997, workers assembled 10 million gears in printers for the program's largest client, the Okidata Computer Company.

The work is repetitious, but Jennifer says that doesn't bother the clients. "They enjoy the structure of doing the same thing all day long. The majority of our jobs are easy, so most of our people do very well."

Path to Becoming an Apprentice

Most clients learn about the training program by referral through the state Department of Vocational Rehabilitation, local Job Training Partnership Act (JTPA) offices, welfare and human services agencies, insurance companies, and private businesses. Goodwill Industries of Southern New Jersey serves about 300 people with disabilities and disadvantaging conditions each year. The organization features other training programs for computer skills, retail skills, and janitorial services. New clients are tested and counseled to discover their talents, aptitudes, skill levels, and career options. Then they usually spend a few days in each program to see which is best for them.

Participants in the Industrial Services Training Program must be at least sixteen years old, be no threat to themselves or others, be able to administer their own medications, and be able to communicate with the staff. On the trainees' first day in the program, the staff explains the routine and the work to be done, sometimes leading clients through the steps until they have a good grasp of their duties. From there the training progresses at a speed tailored to each person's needs and abilities.

Salary Range

Trainees are paid according to the amount of work they complete; the most efficient workers can earn $6 or more an hour. Combined with the supplemental income that most of them receive from other sources, such as Social Security, it can be enough to meet their living expenses.

After graduation, workers who find employment usually earn more than the minimum wage. In 1997 those who started new jobs earned an average of $6.72 an hour, about 33 percent more than the minimum wage of $5.15 an hour. Many of the clients move to a sheltered workshop, however, instead of competing for jobs.

Advice

For anyone with a disability or disadvantaging condition, Jennifer recommends checking into what Goodwill has to offer: "They should definitely give it a try. It will really increase their self-esteem. They can become more self-supportive. It gives them a positive outlook." A paying job generates income, but it also promotes confidence, dignity, self-respect, and independence. "Have an 'I can do it' attitude," Jennifer advises anyone considering this type of program.

Future Goals

Goodwill Industries of Southern New Jersey helps its vocational training clients find employment after graduation. The organization helps develop job search strategies; helps prepare resumes, cover letters, and job applications; provides references; gives advice about doing well in interviews; and explains how to dress and groom properly.

Graduates of the Industrial Services Training Program often find employment with production companies, where they work on assembly lines and in warehouses. They may also be qualified to work in food service occupations, in shoe stores and other retail outlets, and in many other fields. Every client in the computer and janitorial programs is placed in a job after training here.

Still, the transition from school to the competitive work force is frequently difficult, and many graduates

return to the center. To help them succeed in their new careers, the organization follows up by contacting them at least every 30, 60, and 90 days. "We become very close to the clients, and it usually goes beyond ninety days. We're involved in their lives, and we keep in touch with them. We care about them," Jennifer says.

ALABAMA
Alabama Goodwill Industries Inc.
2350 Green Springs Highway
Birmingham, AL 35205
205-323-6331
Fax: 205-324-9059

Goodwill Industries of Central Alabama Inc.
PO Box 9349
Montgomery, AL 36196
334-263-4633
Fax: 334-263-5817

Goodwill Industries of the Gulf Coast
2448 Gordon Smith Drive
Mobile, AL 36617
334-471-1581
Fax: 334-476-4303

ARIZONA
Goodwill Industries of Central Arizona Inc.
417 North 16th Street
Phoenix, AZ 85006
602-254-2222
Fax: 602-258-7047
Info@goodwillcentralAZ.org
http://www.goodwillaz.org

Goodwill Industries of Northern Arizona
2225 North Steves Boulevard
PO Box 1060
Flagstaff, AZ 86002
928-526-9188
Fax: 928-526-9240
http://www.goodwill.org/states/az/flagstaff.htm

Goodwill Industries of Southern Arizona Inc.
1940 East Silverlake Road, Suite 405
Tucson, AZ 85713
520-623-5174
Fax: 520-623-8528

ARKANSAS

Goodwill Industries of Arkansas Inc.
1110 West Seventh Street
Little Rock, AR 72201
501-372-5100
Fax: 501-372-5112
http://www.goodwill.org/states/ar/littlerock.htm

CALIFORNIA

Goodwill Industries of Long Beach and South Bay
800 West Pacific Coast Highway
Long Beach, CA 90806
562-435-3411
Fax: 562-495-1447
http://www.goodwill-lbsb.org

Goodwill Industries of Orange County
410 North Fairview
Santa Ana, CA 92703
714-547-6301
Fax: 714-541-6531
http://www.ocgoodwill.org

Goodwill Industries of Sacramento Valley Inc.
6648 Franklin Boulevard
Sacramento, CA 95823
916-395-9000
http://www.goodwillsacto.org

Goodwill Industries of San Diego County Inc.
3663 Rosecrans Street
San Diego, CA 92110
619-225-2200
Fax: 619-225-1934
http://www.sdgoodwill.org

Goodwill Industries of San Joaquin Valley Inc.
129 South Grant Street
Stockton, CA 95202
209-466-2311
Fax: 209-466-0547
http://www.goodwill-sjv.org

Goodwill Industries of Santa Cruz, Monterey, and San Luis Obispo Counties
Branch Office
880 Industrial Way
San Luis Obispo, CA 93401
805-544-0542

Fax: 805-544-0543
http://www.scgoodwill.org

Goodwill Industries of Santa Cruz, Monterey, and San Luis Obispo Counties
Corporate Office
350 Encinal Street
Santa Cruz, CA 95060
408-423-8611
Fax: 408-423-8968
http://www.scgoodwill.org

Goodwill Industries of South Central California
1401 Commercial Way, Suite 220
Bakersfield, CA 93309
805-837-0595
Fax: 805-837-0801
http://www.centcalgoodwill.org

Goodwill Industries of Southern California
Los Angeles Headquarters
342 San Fernando Road
Los Angeles, CA 90031
213-223-1211
http://www.goodwillsocal.org

Goodwill Industries of Southern California
San Fernando Valley
14565 Lanark Street
Panorama City, CA 91402
818-782-2520
http://www.goodwillsocal.org

Goodwill Industries of Southern California
Ventura/Santa Barbara Unit
350 Cactus Drive
Oxnard, CA 93030
805-983-3414
http://www.goodwillsocal.org

Goodwill Industries of the Greater East Bay Inc.
1301 30th Avenue
Oakland, CA 94601
510-534-6666
Fax: 510-534-0837
http://www.eastbaygoodwill.org

Goodwill Industries of the Inland Counties Inc.
83-203 Indio Boulevard, Suite 5
Indio, CA 92201
760-347-1236

Goodwill Industries of the Inland Counties Inc.
1020 Iowa Avenue, Suite C
Riverside, CA 92507
909-686-5484

Goodwill Industries of the Inland Counties Inc.
8210 Palm Lane
PO Box 760
San Bernardino, CA 92410
909-885-3831
Fax: 909-885-2953

Goodwill Industries of the Inland Counties Inc.
15421 Village Drive
Victorville, CA 92392
760-243-4163

Goodwill Industries of the Redwood Empire
11 West Barham Avenue
Santa Rosa, CA 95407
707-523-0550
Fax: 707-523-0552
http://www.gire.org

Goodwill of San Francisco, San Mateo, and Marin Counties
1500 Mission Street
San Francisco, CA 94103
Fax: 415-575-2170
http://www.sfgoodwill.org

Goodwill of Santa Clara County
Corporate Office
1080 North Seventh Street
San Jose, CA 95112
408-998-5774

COLORADO
Goodwill Industries of Colorado Springs
2320 West Colorado Avenue
PO 6300
Colorado Springs, CO 80934
719-635-4483
Fax: 719-635-5713
http://www.goodwill-colosprings.org

Goodwill Industries of Denver
6850 North Federal Boulevard
Denver, CO 80221

303-650-7700
Fax: 303-650-7749
http://www.goodwilldenver.org

Pueblo Goodwill Industries Inc.
250 South Santa Fe
Pueblo, CO 81003
719-543-4483
Fax: 719-545-5134
http://www.pueblogoodwill.com

CONNECTICUT
Easter Seal Goodwill Industries Rehabilitation Center Inc.
95 Hamilton Street
New Haven, CT 06511
203-777-2000
http://newhavengoodwill.easterseals.com

Goodwill Industries of Western Connecticut
165 Ocean Terrace
Bridgeport, CT 06605
203-368-6511
Fax: 203-335-9326
http://www.goodwillwct.org

DISTRICT OF COLUMBIA
Goodwill Industries, Greater Washington
2200 South Dakota Avenue, NE
Washington, DC 20018
202-636-4225
http://www.dcgoodwill.org

DELAWARE
Goodwill Industries of Delaware & Delaware County Inc.
Corporate Office
100 West 10th Street, Suite 211
Wilmington, DE 19801-1664
302-761-4644
http://www.goodwillde.org

FLORIDA
Goodwill Industries – Heart of Florida Inc.
Human Resources Department
809 South Florida Avenue

Lakeland, FL 33801
941-687-2500

Goodwill Industries – Manasota Inc.
15 West Oak Street
Arcadia, FL 33821
941-494-6152

Goodwill Industries – Manasota Inc.
3525 East First Street
Bradenton, FL 34208
941-746-5796

Goodwill Industries – Manasota Inc.
5512 Manatee Avenue, West
Bradenton, FL 34209
941-795-0912

Goodwill Industries – Manasota Inc.
5138 Cortez Road, West
Bradenton, FL 34210
941-794-1889

Goodwill Industries – Manasota Inc.
410 North Indiana Avenue
Englewood, FL 34223
941-473-1288

Goodwill Industries – Manasota Inc.
2210 North Tamiami Trail
Laurel, FL 34234
941-966-4359

Goodwill Industries – Manasota Inc.
1781 Dr. Martin Luther King, Jr., Way
Newtown, FL 34234
941-359-0327

Goodwill Industries – Manasota Inc.
1210 10th Street, East
Palmetto, FL 34221
941-723-2824

Goodwill Industries – Manasota Inc.
7241 South Tamiami Trail
Sarasota, FL 34231
941-923-0464

Goodwill Industries – Manasota Inc.
Corporate Office and CTC
7501 Bradenton Road

Sarasota, FL 34243
941-355-2721

Goodwill Industries – Manasota Inc.
700 North Beneva Road
Sarasota, FL 34232
941-366-4143
Fax: 941-358-5171

Goodwill Industries – Manasota Inc.
1752 South Tamiami Trail
Venice, FL 34239
941-493-2790

Goodwill Industries – Manasota Inc.
1040 South Sixth Street
Wauchula, FL 33873
813-773-4003

Goodwill Industries of Big Bend Inc.
300 Mabry Street
Tallahassee, FL 32304-3899
850-576-7145
Fax: 850-574-4260
http://www.goodwillbigbend.com

Goodwill Industries of Broward County Inc.
2104 West Commercial Boulevard
PO Box 100339
Fort Lauderdale, FL 33310-0339
954-486-1600
Fax: 954-497-3270
gwibci@msn.com

Goodwill Industries of Central Florida Inc.
6400 South Orange Avenue
PO Box 590557
Orlando, FL 32859-0557
407-857-0659
Fax: 407-851-8190
admin@goodwillcfl.org
http://www.goodwillcfl.org

Goodwill Industries of South Florida Inc.
2121 Northwest 21st Street
Miami, FL 33142
305-325-9114
Fax: 305-324-7319
info@goodwillmiami.org
http://www.goodwillmiami.org

Goodwill Industries of Southwest Florida Inc.
4940 Bayline Drive
North Fort Myers, FL 33917
941-995-2106
Fax: 941-995-5868
jamieford@goodwillswfl.org
http://www.goodwillswfl.org

Goodwill Industries of the Suncoast Inc.
10596 Gandy Boulevard
St. Petersburg, FL 33733
727-523-1512
Fax: 727-579-0850
http://www.goodwill-suncoast.org

Goodwill of North Florida
4527 Lenox Avenue
PO Box 60219
Jacksonville, FL 32236
904-384-1361
Fax: 904-387-3204
kphillip@goodwilljax.org
http://www.goodwilljax.org

Gulfstream Goodwill Industries Inc.
1715 Tiffany Drive, East
West Palm Beach, FL 33407-3277
561-848-7200
Fax: 561-848-0346
http://www.gulfstreamgoodwill.org

GEORGIA

Goodwill Industries of Atlanta Inc.
2201 Glenwood Avenue, SE
Atlanta, GA 30316
404-377-0441

Goodwill Industries of Middle Georgia and the CSRA
5171 Eisenhower Parkway
Macon, GA 31206
478-475-9995
Fax: 478-471-4845
http://www.goodwillworks.org

Goodwill Industries of South Georgia Inc.
2011 Krug Street
PO Box 50005
Albany, GA 31703-0006
912-432-0551
Fax: 912-883-6840

Goodwill Industries of the Coastal Empire Inc.
7220 Sallie Mood Drive
PO Box 15007
Savannah, GA 31406
912-354-6611
Fax: 912-354-3787
mail@goodwillsavannahga.org
http://goodwillsavannahga.org

Goodwill Industries of the Southern Rivers
1955 Northside Industrial Boulevard
Columbus, GA 31904
706-324-4366
Fax: 706-660-0429
gwicol@gwicol.org
http://www.gwicol.org

HAWAII

Employment Works
680 Ala Moana Boulevard
Honolulu, HI 96813
808-526-7149
http://www.aloha.net/~laurar

Goodwill Industries of Honolulu Inc.
Main Office
2610 Kilihau Street
Honolulu, HI 96819
808-836-0313
Fax: 808-833-4943
info@higoodwill.org
http://www.higoodwill.org

Goodwill Industries of Honolulu Inc., Haleiwa Location
66-437 Kam Highway
Haleiwa, HI 96712
808-637-7733

Island Career Center
1020 Isenberg Street
Honolulu, HI 96826
808-946-9675

IDAHO

Idaho Easter Seal Society, Boise
1455 North Cole Road
Boise, ID 83704-8537
208-378-9924
Fax: 208-378-9965

Idaho Easter Seal Society, Nampa
16 12th Avenue, South
Nampa, ID 83651
208-467-1637

Idaho Easter Seal Society, Pocatello
746 East Lander, Suite E
Pocatello, ID 83201
208-233-6824
Fax: 208-233-2208

ILLINOIS
Goodwill Industries of Central Illinois
2319 East War Memorial Drive
Peoria, IL 61614
309-682-1113
Fax: 309-682-8353

Goodwill Industries of Metropolitan Chicago Inc.
1001 West Van Buren Street
Chicago, IL 60607
312-491-2900
Fax: 312-491-2901

Goodwill Industries of Northern Illinois Inc.
1907 Kishwaukee Street
Rockford, IL 61108
815-965-3795
Fax: 815-965-7087

Land of Lincoln Goodwill Industries Inc.
800 North 10th Street
Springfield, IL 62791
217-789-0400
Fax: 217-789-7239

INDIANA
**Bridgepointe Goodwill Industries and Easter
Seal Society**
1329 Applegate Lane
PO Box 2117
Clarksville, IN 47129
812-283-7908
Fax: 812-283-6248

Calumet Goodwill Industries Inc.
114 State Street
Hammond, IN 46320

219-931-5230
Fax: 219-931-8104

Evansville Goodwill Industries Inc.
500 South Green River Road
Evansville, IN 47715
812-474-2222
Fax: 812-474-2233
http://www.evvgoodwill.org

Goodwill Industries of Central Indiana Inc.
1635 West Michigan Street
Indianapolis, IN 46222
317-524-4313
Fax: 317-524-4336
http://www.goodwill-indy.org

Goodwill Industries of Michiana Inc.
1805 Western Avenue
PO Box 3128
South Bend, IN 46619-0846
574-472-7300
Fax: 574-239-6667

Goodwill Industries of Northeast Indiana Inc.
1516 Magnavox Way
Fort Wayne, IN 46804
260-478-7617
Fax: 260-436-3800

Wabash Valley Goodwill Industries
2702 South Third Street
PO Box 2720
Terre Haute, IN 47802
812-235-1827
Fax: 812-235-1397
wvgoodwill@wvgoodwill.org
http://wvgoodwill.org

IOWA
Goodwill Industries of Central Iowa
4900 Northeast 22nd Street
Des Moines, IA 50313
515-265-5323
Fax: 515-265-0645
http://www.goodwill.org/states/ia/des_moines.htm

Goodwill Industries of Northeast Iowa Inc.
2640 Falls Avenue
Waterloo, IA 50701

319-234-4626
Fax: 319-234-2504

Goodwill Industries of Southeast Iowa
1410 First Avenue
PO Box 1696
Iowa City, IA 52244
319-337-4158
Fax: 319-337-7369
http://www.goodwillseiowa.org

Wall Street Mission Goodwill Industries
3100 West Fourth Street
PO Box 1438
Sioux City, IA 51102
712-258-4511
Fax: 712-258-7832

KANSAS
**Goodwill Industries and Easter Seal Society
    of Kansas Inc.**
3636 North Oliver
PO Box 8169
Wichita, KS 67208
316-744-9291
Fax: 316-744-1428
http://www.goodwilleastersealsks.org

KENTUCKY
Goodwill Industries of Kentucky, Bluegrass Division
275 Gold Rush Road
Lexington, KY 40503
606-277-3661
Fax: 606-277-2982

Goodwill Industries of Kentucky, Bluegrass Division
Richmond Rehabilitation Office
210 St. George Street, #109
Richmond, KY 40475
606-624-5525
Fax: 606-624-9475

**Goodwill Industries of Kentucky,
    Cumberland Division**
Tradewind Shopping Mall
370 South Highway 27
Somerset, KY 42501
606-678-0890

Goodwill Industries of Kentucky, Western Division
730 Fairview Avenue
Bowling Green, KY 42101
502-781-4930

Goodwill Industries of Kentucky, Western Division
Hopkinsville Rehabilitation Office
2208 Fort Campbell Boulevard
Hopkinsville, KY 42240
502-886-9190

Goodwill Industries of Kentucky Inc.
907 East Broadway
Louisville, KY 40204-3000
502-585-4945
Fax: 502-561-8035
Goodwill@gwik.org
http://www.gwik.org

LOUISIANA
Goodwill Industries Acadiana Inc.
5718 Cameron Street
Lafayette, LA 70596-2270
337-261-5811
Fax: 337-261-1911
lagoodwill@lagoodwill.com
http://www.lagoodwill.com

Goodwill Industries of Southeastern Louisiana Inc.
1000 South Jefferson Davis Parkway
PO Box 13006
New Orleans, LA 70185
504-482-4173
Fax: 504-484-7565
goodwill@communique.net

**North Louisiana Goodwill Industries
    Rehabilitation Center Inc.**
800 West 70th Street
Shreveport, LA 71106-2550
318-869-2575
Fax: 318-869-2574
http://www.nlagoodwill.org

MAINE
Goodwill Industries of Northern New England
353 Cumberland Avenue
PO Box 8600

Portland, ME 04104
207-774-6323
Fax: 207-761-8460
info@ginne.org
http://www.ginne.org

Goodwill Professional Services, Augusta
347 Leighton Road
Augusta, ME 04330
207-626-0170

Goodwill Professional Services, Waterville
18 Silver Street
Waterville, ME 04901
207-872-2128

MARYLAND
Baltimore Goodwill Industries Inc.
4001 Southwestern Boulevard
PO Box 2907
Baltimore, MD 21229-0907
410-247-3500
Fax: 410-247-6219

Goodwill Industries of Monocacy Valley Inc.
400 East Church Street
Frederick, MD 21701
301-662-0622
Fax: 301-846-0940

Horizon Goodwill Industries Inc.
14515 Pennsylvania Avenue
Hagerstown, MD 21740
301-733-7330
Fax: 301-739-7144
http://www.horizongoodwill.org

MASSACHUSETTS
Goodwill Industries of the Berkshires Inc.
20 Commercial Street
Pittsfield, MA 01201
413-442-0061
Fax: 413-449-3756
http://www.goodwill.org/states/ma/pittsfield.htm

Goodwill Industries of the Springfield/Hartford Area Inc.
285 Dorset Street
PO Box 80006

Springfield, MA 01108
413-788-6981
http://www.goodwillspringfield.org

Merrimack Valley Goodwill Industries Inc.
1705 Middlesex Street
Lowell, MA 01851
508-459-0351

Morgan Memorial Goodwill Industries
1010 Harrison Avenue
Boston, MA 02119
617-541-1429
http://www.goodwillmass.org

MICHIGAN
Goodwill Industries of Central Michigan Inc.
617 North Mechanic Street
Jackson, MI 49202
517-787-0570
Fax: 517-787-7254
http://www.gicm.org

Goodwill Industries of Greater Detroit
3132 Trumbull Avenue
Detroit, MI 48216
313-964-3900
Fax: 313-964-3909
http://www.goodwilldetroit.org

Goodwill Industries of Greater Grand Rapids Inc.
3036 Prairie Street, SW
Grandville, MI 49418
616-532-4200
Fax: 616-532-3044
http://www.goodwillgr.org

Goodwill Industries of Mid-Michigan Inc.
501 South Averill Avenue
Flint, MI 48506
810-762-9960
Fax: 810-762-9957
http://www.goodwillmidmichigan.org

Goodwill Industries of Northern Michigan Inc.
2889 Aero Park Drive
Traverse City, MI 49686
616-922-4805
Fax: 616-922-2053
http://www.goodwillnmi.org

Goodwill Industries of Southeastern Michigan –
LARC Activity Center Inc.
600 East Beecher Street
PO Box 805
Adrian, MI 49221
517-263-2135
Fax: 517-265-9740
http://www.goodwillsemi.org

Goodwill Industries of Southwestern Michigan
2700 North Pitcher Street
Kalamazoo, MI 49004-3498
616-382-0490
Fax: 616-382-6836
http://www.goodwillswmi.org

Goodwill Industries of St. Clair County Inc.
1013 26th Street
Port Huron, MI 48060
810-987-9333
Fax: 810-987-3121

Goodwill Industries of West Michigan Inc.
271 Apple Avenue
Muskegon, MI 49442
616-722-7871
Fax: 616-728-6408
http://www.goodwillwm.org

Michigan Heartland Goodwill Industries
4820 Wayne Road
Battle Creek, MI 49015
616-964-9455
Fax: 616-964-9519
http://www.mihgoodwill.org

MINNESOTA
Goodwill Industries Inc./Easter Seal Society
of Minnesota
2543 Como Avenue
St. Paul, MN 55108
612-646-2591
Fax: 612-649-0302
http://mnges.easterseals.com

Goodwill Industries Vocational Enterprises Inc.
700 Garfield Avenue
Duluth, MN 55802
218-722-6351

MISSISSIPPI
Goodwill Industries of Mississippi Inc.
104 East State Street
Ridgeland, MS 39157
601-853-8110
Fax: 601-853-8113
http://goodwill@netdoor.com

Goodwill Industries of South Mississippi Inc.
2407 31st Street
Gulfport, MS 39501
228-863-2323
Fax: 228-863-5621
http://www.goodwillsms.org

MISSOURI
Helping Hand of Goodwill Industries, Joseph
117 South Seventh Street
Joseph, MO 64501
816-842-7425

Helping Hand of Goodwill Industries, Kansas City
1817 Campbell Street
Kansas City, MO 64108
816-842-7425
http://www.mokangoodwill.org

Missouri Goodwill Industries
4140 Forest Park Boulevard
St. Louis, MO 63108
314-371-6320
http://www.mersgoodwill.org

MONTANA
Career Development Associates
815 Second Street, South
Great Falls, MT 59405
406-771-0026
Fax: 406-453-2160

Easter Seal Center, Billings
Alpine Village, 6A
1130 16th Street, West
Billings, MT 59102
406-252-9600

Easter Seal Center, Butte
507 Centennial
Butte, MT 59701
406-723-5780

Goodwill Industries/Northern Rocky Mountain Easter Seal Society
Corporate Office
4400 Central Avenue
Great Falls, MT 59405
406-761-3680
http://esgw-nrm.easterseals.com

Goodwill Industries Retail Store and Plant
1210 Ninth Street, South
Great Falls, MT 59404
406-453-0311

NEBRASKA
Central Nebraska Goodwill Industries Inc.
1804 South Eddy Street
Grand Island, NE 68801
308-384-7896
Fax: 308-384-9231
http://www.goodwill.org/states/ne/grand_island.htm

Eastern Nebraska and Southwest Iowa Goodwill Industries Inc.
1111 South 41st Street
Omaha, NE 68105-189
402-341-4609
Fax: 402-341-3061
http://www.goodwillomaha.com

Goodwill Industries Serving Southeast Nebraska Inc.
2100 Judson
Lincoln, NE 68521
402-438-2022
Fax: 402-438-2167

NEVADA
Goodwill Industries of Southern Nevada Inc.
3461 Boulder Highway, Suite J
Las Vegas, NV 89121
702-367-7272
Fax: 702-431-2557
http://www.sngoodwill.org

NEW JERSEY
Goodwill Industries of New Jersey Inc.
400 Worthington Avenue
Harrison, NJ 07029
201-481-2300
Fax: 201-481-9031
http://www.goodwillnj.org

Goodwill Industries of Southern New Jersey
2835 Route 73, South
Maple Shade, NJ 08052
609-439-0200
Fax: 609-439-0843

NEW MEXICO
Goodwill Industries of New Mexico
5000 San Mateo Boulevard, N. E.
Albuquerque, NM 87109
505-881-6401
Fax: 505-884-3157
http://www.goodwillnm.org

Goodwill Industries of Southern New Mexico
2305 East Nevada Street
PO Box 117
Las Cruces, NM 88004
505-524-1395

NEW YORK
Goodwill Industries of Greater New York
4-21 27th Avenue
Astoria, NY 11102
718-728-5400
http://www.goodwillny.org

Goodwill Industries of Greater Rochester Inc.
Association for the Blind and Visually Impaired
422 South Clinton Avenue
Rochester, NY 14620-1198
716-232-1111
Fax: 716-232-6707
http://www.abvi-goodwill.org

Goodwill Industries of Western New York Inc.
1119 Williams Street
Buffalo, NY 14206-1897
716-854-3494
Fax: 716-854-1988
http://www.goodwillwny.org

NORTH CAROLINA

Goodwill Industries of Eastern North Carolina Inc.
4808 Chin Page Road
Durham, NC 27703
919-941-9600
Fax: 919-941-9606
http://www.goodwillenc.org

Goodwill Industries of Northwest North Carolina Inc.
2701 University Parkway
PO Box 4299
Winston-Salem, NC 27115-4299
910-724-3621
Fax: 910-723-4848
http://goodwillnwnc.org

Goodwill Industries of the Southern Piedmont
PO Box 668768
Charlotte, NC 28266
704-372-3434
Fax: 704-372-3228
http://www.goodwillsp.org

Goodwill Industries Rehabilitation Center of Central North Carolina Inc.
1235 South Eugene Street
Greensboro, NC 27406
910-275-9801
Fax: 910-274-1352

NORTH DAKOTA

Easter Seal Society of North Dakota/Goodwill Industries Inc.
211 Collins
PO Box 1206
Mandan, ND 58554-1206
701-663-6828
Fax: 701-663-6859

OHIO

Goodwill Industries of Akron Inc.
36 South College Street
Akron, OH 44308-1763
216-762-8421
Fax: 216-762-7575
http://www.goodwillakron.org

Goodwill Industries of Ashtabula Inc.
621 Goodwill Drive
PO Box 2926
Ashtabula, OH 44004-1326
440-964-3565

Goodwill Industries of Greater Cleveland
2295 East 55th Street
Cleveland, OH 44103
216-431-8300
http://www.goodwill-cleveland.org

Goodwill Industries of Lima Inc.
949 South Main Street
Lima, OH 45804-1594
419-228-4821
Fax: 419-222-5269
http://www.limagoodwill.org

Goodwill Industries of Lorain County Inc.
1600 Broadway
Lorain, OH 44052
216-244-3174
Fax: 216-245-2670

Goodwill Industries of Northwest Ohio
525 Cherry Street
PO Box 336
Toledo, OH 43697
419-255-0070
Fax: 419-255-8152
http://www.goodwillnwohio.com

Goodwill Industries of South Central Ohio Inc.
457 East Main Street
PO Box 93
Chillicothe, OH 45601
614-775-3000
Fax: 614-775-3018

Goodwill Industries of Southern Ohio Inc.
1910 Robinson Avenue
Portsmouth, OH 45662
614-354-2897

Goodwill Industries of the Miami Valley
1511 Kuntz Road
Dayton, OH 45404-1297
937-461-4800

Fax: 937-461-2750
http://www.goodwilldayton.org

Goodwill Industries of Wayne County Inc.
1034 Nold Avenue
Wooster, OH 44691
330-264-1300
Fax: 330-262-5932

Goodwill Industries Rehabilitation Center Inc.
408 Ninth Street, SW
Canton, OH 44707-4799
330-454-9461

Goodwill Rehabilitation Center
1331 Edgehill Road
Columbus, OH 43212
614-294-5181
Fax: 614-294-6895
http://www.goodwillcolumbus.org

Licking/Knox Goodwill Industries Inc.
55 South Fifth Street
PO Box 828
Newark, OH 43058-0828
614-345-9861
Fax: 614-345-3191

Marion Goodwill Industries Inc.
340 West Fairground Street
Marion, OH 43302
614-387-7023
Fax: 614-382-0420

Ohio Valley Goodwill Industries
Rehabilitation Center
10600 Springfield Pike
Cincinnati, OH 45215
513-771-4800
Fax: 513-771-4959
http://www.cincinnatigoodwill.org

Sandusky Bay Area Goodwill Industries Inc.
419 West Market Street
Sandusky, OH 44870
419-625-4744
Fax: 419-625-4692
http://www.sbagoodwill.org

Youngstown Area Goodwill Industries Inc.
2747 Belmont Avenue
Youngstown, OH 44505-1819

330-759-7921
Fax: 330-759-0678
http://www.goodwill.org/states/oh/youngstown.
htm

Zanesville Welfare Organization and Goodwill Industries Inc.
18 Beaumont Street
Zanesville, OH 43701
614-454-0118

OKLAHOMA
Goodwill Industries of Muskogee, Oklahoma Inc.
2022 West Shawnee
Muskogee, OK 74401
918-683-5505
Fax: 918-683-4714

Goodwill Industries of Southwest Oklahoma Inc.
1210 Summit Avenue
Lawton, OK 73501
405-355-2163
Fax: 405-355-2166

Goodwill Industries of Tulsa Inc.
2800 Southwest Boulevard
Tulsa, OK 74107
918-584-7291
Fax: 918-583-9010

Oklahoma Goodwill Industries
410 Southwest Third
Oklahoma City, OH 73109
405-236-4451
Fax: 405-235-7215

OREGON
Goodwill Industries of Lane County
855 Seneca
Eugene, OR 97402
541-345-1801
Fax: 541-345-1739

Goodwill Industries of the Columbia Willamette
1943 Southeast Sixth Avenue
Portland, OR 97214-4508
503-238-6100
Fax: 503-238-1535

Southern Oregon Goodwill Industries
604 North Fir
Medford, OR 97501
541-772-3300

PENNSYLVANIA
Goodwill Employment Services, Montgomery/Bucks
501 Office Center Drive, Suite 250
Fort Washington, PA 19034
215-653-7095
http://www.yourgoodwill.org

Goodwill Employment Services, Schuylkill
91 South Progress Avenue
Pottsville, PA 17901
717-628-9097

Goodwill Industries of Central Pennsylvania Inc.
1150 Goodwill Drive
PO Box 3155
Harrisburg, PA 17105
717-232-1831

Goodwill Industries of Mid-Eastern Pennsylvania
310 North Wyomissing Avenue
Shillington, PA 19607
610-777-7875
Fax: 610-777-0441

Goodwill Industries of North Central Pennsylvania Inc.
90 Beaver Drive, Suite 213-B
PO Box 684
DuBois, PA 15801-0684
814-371-2821
Fax: 814-371-0616

Goodwill Industries of Northeastern Pennsylvania Inc.
300 Brook Street
Scranton, PA 18505
717-343-1166
Fax: 717-343-6765

Goodwill Industries of Pittsburgh
2400 East Carson Street
Pittsburgh, PA 15203-2112
412-481-7227
http://www.goodwillpitt.org

Goodwill Industries of Southeastern Pennsylvania
1048 North Plum Street
Lancaster, PA 17601
717-394-0647

Goodwill Industries of the Conemaugh Valley Inc.
920-922 Oak Street
Johnstown, PA 15902
814-536-3536

RHODE ISLAND
Goodwill Industries of Rhode Island Inc.
100 Houghton Street
North Providence, RI 02904
401-861-2080
Fax: 401-454-0889

SOUTH CAROLINA
Goodwill Industries of Lower South Carolina Inc.
5640 Rivers Avenue
North Charleston, SC 29406
843-566-0072
Fax: 843-566-0062
http://www.goodwillsc.org

Goodwill Industries of Upper South Carolina Inc.
100 Industrial Drive
Greenville, SC 29607
864-467-3200
Fax: 864-467-3206
goodwill@goodwillsc.org
http://www.goodwillsc.org

TENNESSEE
Chattanooga Goodwill Industries Inc.
3500 Dodds Avenue
Chattanooga, TN 37407
423-629-2501
Fax: 423-622-0840
http://www.goodwillchatt.org

Goodwill Industries-Knoxville Inc.
5508 Kingston Pike
PO Box 11066
Knoxville, TN 37939-1066
423-588-8567
http://www.gwiktn.org

Goodwill Industries of Middle Tennessee Inc.
905 Ninth Avenue, North
Nashville, TN 37208
615-742-4151
Fax: 615-254-3901
http://www.goodwillmidten.org

Goodwill Industries of Tenneva Area Inc.
2017 Brookside Lane
Kingsport, TN 37660
423-245-0600
Fax: 423-245-0200
http://www.goodwilltnva.org

Memphis Goodwill Industries Inc.
2605 Chelsea Avenue
Memphis, TN 38108
901-323-6221
Fax: 901-323-0751

TEXAS
Abilene Goodwill Industries Inc.
1730 North First
Abilene, TX 79603
915-676-7925
Fax: 915-676-7391

Goodwill Adult Learning Center
2462 Mansfield Highway
PO Box 1408
Fort Worth, TX 76101
817-332-7866
Fax: 817-534-4496
http://www.goodwillfortworth.org

Goodwill Industries of Amarillo Inc.
209 East 17th Street
PO Box 2926
Amarillo, TX 79105
806-372-4352
Fax: 806-372-7321

Goodwill Industries of Central East Texas
1011 West Frank
Lufkin, TX 75901
409-632-8838
Fax: 409-632-9561

Goodwill Industries of Central Texas
300 North Lamar Boulevard
Austin, TX 78703-4697

512-472-6224
Fax: 512-472-6521
http://www.austingoodwill.org

Goodwill Industries of Dallas Inc.
2800 North Hampton Road
Dallas, TX 75212
214-638-2800
Fax: 214-638-7926
http://www.goodwilldallas.org

Goodwill Industries of East Texas
409 West Locust
Tyler, TX 75702
903-593-8438
Fax: 903-593-8774
http://www.tylergoodwill.com

Goodwill Industries of El Paso Inc.
7015 Alameda Avenue
El Paso, TX 79915
915-778-3371
Fax: 915-772-2896
http://www.goodwillep.org

Goodwill Industries of Houston
5200 Jensen Drive
Houston, TX 77026
713-692-6221
http://www.goodwillhouston.org

Goodwill Industries of Lubbock Inc.
715 28th Street
Lubbock, TX 79404
806-744-8419
Fax: 806-741-1352
http://www.goodwill.org/states/tx/lubbock.htm

Goodwill Industries of Northeast Texas Inc.
2206 East Lamar Street
Sherman, TX 75090
903-893-3145
Fax: 903-892-0764

Goodwill Industries of San Antonio
3838 Pleasanton Road
PO Box 21340
San Antonio, TX 78221
210-924-8581
Fax: 210-924-3011
http://www.goodwillsa.org

Goodwill Industries of Southeast Texas
460 Wall Street
PO Box 3963
Beaumont, TX 77701
409-838-9911
http://www.goodwillbmt.org

Goodwill Industries of South Texas, Corpus Christi
2961 South Port Avenue
Corpus Christi, TX 78405
512-884-4068
Fax: 512-884-4090
http://www.goodwillsouthtexas.com

Goodwill Industries of South Texas, Pharr
101A East Expressway 83
Pharr, TX 78577
210-702-4404
http://www.goodwillsouthtexas.com

Goodwill Industries of the Pines Inc.
1419 South Green Street
Longview, TX 75602
903-757-5047

Heart of Texas Goodwill Industries Inc.
1000 East Waco Drive
PO Box 645
Waco, TX 76703
817-753-7337

North Texas Institute for Career Development, Arlington
1915 East Park Row
Arlington, TX 76010-4745
817-795-7594
http://www.goodwillfortworth.org

North Texas Institute for Career Development, Fort Worth
1701 East Lancaster
Fort Worth, TX 76102
817-332-2470
http://www.goodwillfortworth.org

VIRGINIA
Goodwill Industries of Danville Area Inc.
512 Westover Drive
Danville, VA 24541
434-792-2511

Fax: 434-792-2544
gdwill@gamewood.net
http://www.goodwill-danva.com

Goodwill Industries of Hampton Roads Inc.
5565 Virginia Beach Boulevard
Virginia Beach, VA 23462
757-248-9405
Fax: 757-248-9416
http://www.goodwillhr.org

Goodwill Industries of the Valleys
2520 Melrose Avenue, NW
Roanoke, VA 24017
540-581-0620
Fax: 540-581-0629
info@goodwill-the-valleys.com
http://www.goodwill-the-valleys.com

Rappahannock Goodwill Industries Inc.
1414 Caroline Street
PO Box 905
Fredericksburg, VA 22404
540-371-3070
Fax: 540-371-9433
http://www.fredgoodwill.org

Richmond Goodwill Industries Inc.
6301 Midlothian Turnpike
Richmond, VA 23225
804-745-6300
Fax: 804-276-6519
contact@goodwillrichmond.org
http://www.goodwillrichmond.org

WASHINGTON
Goodwill Industries of Longview
1362 Tennant Way
Longview, WA 98632-2424
360-425-6929
Fax: 360-425-9629, x20
http://www.tacomagoodwill.org

Goodwill Industries of the Blue Mountains
217 East Alder Street
Walla Walla, WA 99362
509-525-5992

Goodwill Industries of the Columbia Inc.
Corporate Office
307 West Columbia

Pasco, WA 99301-5634
509-547-7717
Fax: 509-545-5490
http://www.goodwillotc.org

Goodwill Industries of the Inland Northwest
130 East Third
Spokane, WA 99202
509-838-4246
Fax: 509-838-0176
http://www.giin.org

Goodwill Industries of the Yakima Valley
503 South First Street
Selah, WA 98942-1603
509-697-3711
Fax: 509-697-3727
http://www.tacomagoodwill.org

Goodwill-Tacoma Headquarters & Administration
714 South 27th Street
Tacoma, WA 98409-8193
206-272-5166
Fax: 206-627-1248
http://www.tacomagoodwill.org

WEST VIRGINIA
Goodwill Industries of Kanawha Valley Inc.
209 Virginia Street, West
Charleston, WV 25302
304-346-0811
Fax: 304-346-0815
http://www.goodwillkv.com

Goodwill Industries of KYOWVA Area Inc.
1005 Virginia Avenue
PO Box 7365
Huntington, WV 25776-7365
304-523-7461
Fax: 304-523-7060
http://www.goodwillhunting.org

WISCONSIN
Goodwill Industries of North Central Wisconsin Inc.
1800 Appleton Road
Menasha, WI 54952
920-731-6601

Fax: 920-731-3041
http://www.goodwillncw.org

Goodwill Industries of Northern Wisconsin and Upper Michigan Inc.
1428 Main Street
Marinette, WI 54143
715-732-0563
Fax: 715-732-1519
mdemuth@gwmarinette.org

Goodwill Industries of South Central Wisconsin Inc.
1302 Mendota Street
Madison, WI 53714-1024
608-246-3140
Fax: 608-246-1984
goodwilljobs@tda.net
http://goodwillscwi.org

Goodwill Industries of Southeastern Wisconsin, Milwaukee
6055 North 91st Street
Milwaukee, WI 53225-1799
414-353-6400
Fax: 414-353-2510
http://www.goodwillsew.com

Goodwill Industries of Southeastern Wisconsin, Mount Pleasant
2512 Willow Road
Mount Pleasant, WI 53177-1999
414-260-3995
http://www.goodwillsew.com

Goodwill Industries of Southeastern Wisconsin, Racine
5420 21st Street
Racine, WI 53406-5097
414-554-3155
http://www.goodwillsew.com

Kenosha County Job Center
8600 Sheridan Road
Kenosha, WI 53143-6504
414-697-2500

Milwaukee Job Center-South
611 West National Avenue
Milwaukee, WI 53204-1714
414-384-4000

WYOMING

Goodwill Industries of Wyoming Inc.
3301 East Nationway
Cheyenne, WY 82001
307-634-7751
Fax: 307-778-6135
http://www.goodwill.org/states/wy/cheyenne.htm

Wyoming Easter Seal Society, Casper
1240 West Collins Drive
Casper, WY 82604
307-234-1102
Fax: 307-265-7910

Wyoming Easter Seal Society, Gillette
400 South Gillette Avenue
Gillette, WY 82716
307-682-4624

Wyoming Easter Seal Society, Sheridan
267 North Main Street
Sheridan, WY 82801
307-672-2816
Fax: 307-672-3896

AMERICAN SAMOA

Goodwill Industries of American Samoa
PO Box 4569
Pago Pago, AS 96799
684-633-2238
Fax: 684-633-1061

GUAM

Goodwill Industries of Guam Inc.
130 Rehabilitation Center Street
Tamuning, GU 96911
671-646-1008
Fax: 671-649-1664

CANADA

ALBERTA

Goodwill Industries of Alberta
8761-51 Avenue
Edmonton, AB T6E 5H1
780-944-1414
Fax: 780-463-7396
http://www.goodwill.ab.ca

ONTARIO

Goodwill Industries Essex Kent Lambton Inc.
439 S. Palmerston Street
Sarnia, ON N7T 3P4
519-332-0440
Fax: 519-332-6029
http://goodwillekl.com

Goodwill Industries Niagara
111 Church Street
St. Catharines, ON L2R 3C9
905-685-8777
Fax: 905-685-7656
goodwill@iaw.on.ca

Goodwill Industries of Toronto
365 Bloor Street, East 14 Floor
Toronto, ON M4W 3L4
416-815-4767
Fax: 416-362-0720
http://www.goodwill.on.ca

Goodwill the Amity Group
225 King William Street
Hamilton, ON L8R 1B1
905-526-8481
Fax: 905-526-9342
amity@amity.on.ca
http://www.amity.on.ca

London Goodwill Industries Association
255 Horton Street
London, ON N6B 1L1
519-645-1455
Fax: 519-645-8610
info@goodwillindustries.ca
http://www.londongoodwill.on.ca

QUEBEC

Industries Goodwill Renaissance Montreal Inc.
7250 Boulevard St-Laurent
Montreal, QC H2R 2X9
514-276-3626
Fax: 514-276-5899
renmont@generation.net
http://www.renaissancequebec.ca

JOB CORPS

Job Corps is a federally funded job training and education program for young people between the ages of 16 and 24. It offers participants a chance to change their lives and obtain the work experience they need to be competitive in the job market. Participants enroll in the program because they are motivated to improve their academic, vocational, and social skills.

Job Corps operates more than 100 training centers, located in every state except Delaware, New Hampshire, Rhode Island, and Wyoming. Most students live at the centers and occasionally travel home for weekends and holidays, but some commute from nearby communities. The environment is supportive, and students are encouraged to set their own goals instead of competing with each other. Students work with advisors to plan their course of training. Participants work at their own pace, taking anywhere from six months to two years to complete their education and training. They arrive on campus at various times and graduate whenever they complete their training.

Participants earn while they learn and receive bonuses for demonstrating good performance and behavior, completing the training to enter a trade, and earning a diploma or GED. Job Corps features certified instructors who teach classes in basic reading, writing, and mathematics. National labor and business organizations provide vocational training at many centers.

Students who do well may enroll in advanced training or up to two years of college at no cost. For college work, the student generally lives at the Job Corps center and attends classes regularly at a college, earning credit toward an associate degree there.

In addition to classroom work, students receive hands-on instruction at the Job Corps centers and on-the-job training at nearby sites. For instance, a student learning plumbing or bricklaying would typically spend a day or two each week working on construction projects in neighboring communities.

Graduates of Job Corps programs have at least 800 hours of on-the-job training, know how to use hand tools and power tools safely, and have obtained a driver's license and the proper clothing and tools of their trades. Placement counselors are available to help students obtain employment after they complete their training. Because Job Corps is a national program, graduates have the option of relocating and receiving help in finding employment in any region of the country.

To participate in Job Corps, candidates must

- be 16 to 24 years old
- have signed consent from a parent or guardian if the candidate is less than 18 years old
- be economically disadvantaged
- be living in an environment that discourages or hampers the candidate from finding a job or a better education
- be a high-school dropout or need additional education or training to obtain meaningful employment
- be free of serious medical or behavioral problems
- be willing to sign a commitment not to take drugs or participate in violent acts
- be a U.S. citizen or lawfully admitted alien
- have a plan for child care if the applicant has a dependent child

The training available through Job Corps varies. Depending on the site, the trades offered may include:

- **Construction and Heavy Equipment:** construction estimator, surveyor assistant, solar installer, bricklayer, building and apartment maintenance worker, carpenter, cement mason, construction worker, electrician, floor layer, glazier, painter, plasterer, plumber, tile setter, heavy equipment operator, small-truck driver, truck driver.
- **Technical and Mechanical:** machinist, marine pipe fitter, welder, water and waste water attendant, air conditioning and refrigeration mechanic, aviation maintenance worker, auto body repair technician, auto repair technician, automotive and farm equipment mechanic, diesel mechanic, heavy equipment and construction equipment mechanic, small-engine mechanic, electrical appliance repairer, electronics assembler, electronics tester, computer service technician, computer programmer, cable television installer, telephone station installer.
- **Agricultural:** forester aide, horticultural worker, landscape technician.
- **Service and Skilled:** barber, cosmetologist, child care attendant, nursery school attendant, teacher's aide, security guard, correctional officer,

janitor, hotel clerk, furniture upholsterer, computer-assisted drafter, drafter, interior designer, visual artist, sign painter, lithograph printer, offset duplicating machine operator, printer, desktop publisher.

- **Food Preparation:** cook, culinary arts worker, food service worker, meat cutter.
- **Medical:** dental assistant, medical assistant, medical laboratory assistant, physical therapy assistant, respiratory therapy assistant, electrocardiograph technician, radiological technician, surgical technician, geriatric nursing assistant, home health aide, licensed practical nurse, nurse's aide, dispensing optician, phlebotomist, medical records clerk, medical records transcriptionist, medical secretary.
- **Business and Clerical:** accounting clerk, auto parts clerk, automobile and farm machinery sales person, bookkeeper, business technician, cashier-checker, clerk, computer operator, data entry worker, legal secretary, program aide, retail sales clerk, stenographer, teller, terminal operator, train clerk, ward clerk, word processor.

APPRENTICESHIP SALARIES

Vary widely. Job Corps programs often pay weekly or monthly stipends, as well as room and board.

POSTAPPRENTICESHIP SALARIES

Vary widely, depending on the trade, the geographic location, and the employer.

For further details on Job Corps, call the program's toll-free hot line at 1-800-733-JOBS.

PROGRAM PROFILE

Anaconda Job Corps Center

1407 Foster Creek Road
Anaconda, MT 59711
406-563-3476
Fax: 406-563-8243
anaco@jcdc.jobcorps.org
http://jobcorps.doleta.gov

General Nature of the Program

Rhonda Fisas learned most of the skills of her trade at the beautiful Anaconda Job Corps Center in the Deer Lodge National Forest of western Montana. There are about 100

Job Corps centers nationwide, where students receive free training in various fields, courtesy of the federal government. The Anaconda Job Corps offers training for bricklayers, carpenters, heavy-equipment mechanics, heavy-equipment operators, painters, welders, culinary workers, and workers who need business and technical skills, such as operating a computer. At the time Rhonda was enrolled there, in 1993, the Anaconda Job Corps was rated number one in the nation overall and in the percentage of students who were placed in jobs soon after graduation.

At the Anaconda complex, students live in dormitories and eat in a cafeteria. They study in classrooms, sometimes commute to nearby colleges for supplemental classes, practice their skills in a large shop at the campus, and travel to actual work sites to hone their skills on the job. In their free time they enjoy rafting trips, picnics, horseback riding, movies, and the center's gymnasium and recreational programs. Students have opportunities to travel home for weekends and holidays, but they must obtain passes to leave the complex at other times.

The centers are designed to help participants focus on why they enrolled there: to start careers that will take their lives in a new direction. Students work at their own pace and may take from six months to two years to complete their training. "It was like a big family. It was a lot of fun, a good experience," Rhonda says. "Everybody that graduates from there is ready to leave, but they're sad to leave. They're friends."

Typical Day

Students at the Anaconda Job Corps are usually out of bed by 6:00 A.M. Every morning they're required to make their beds neatly, clean their living spaces, and spend an hour or so helping to clean the complex. There is a roll call and safety meeting every day. On Mondays there's a tool inventory to make sure that students still have the tools that were issued to them.

The schedule alternates daily, with students either attending classes, receiving hands-on instruction in the shop, or traveling by truck to job sites. They take short breaks each morning and afternoon and have a longer break for lunch. By 4:30 P.M., everyone returns to the complex for another roll call, then gathers to watch a videotape of news about people in the center: who is having a birthday, who received a package from home, and other notes of interest.

Path to Becoming an Apprentice

Rhonda is a native of Billings, Montana, and had attended Eastern Montana College on a volleyball scholarship for one year after high school. When the scholarship was no longer available, she spent a year working for her mother, who is also a carpenter. Then she worked for three years as a nanny. "Finally they didn't need me anymore," she says. "I didn't want to go to college and go into debt, because I didn't know what I wanted to do for a living. I saw a Job Corps ad in the paper, and I called them. I found out it was a great deal."

Originally, Rhonda did not intend to enroll in the carpentry program, because she wanted to pursue a different career than her mother, but after meeting the instructors at Job Corps, she decided to give it a try. "I wasn't a natural at it," she explains. "I ended up sticking with it because it wasn't easy for me. It has taught me patience and how to think before I do something, and that if I don't know something, I should ask for help."

Since graduating from Job Corps, Rhonda has spent five more years as an apprentice with Cop Construction Company. She attends school for three weeks a year and expects to have accumulated enough hours this year to take the difficult examination to become a journeyman carpenter.

Salary Range

For new students, Job Corps will pay for transportation to its training centers. Students at the Anaconda Job Corps receive a clothing and entertainment allowance of about $30 a week and bonuses for certain achievements, in addition to room and board. They also build a savings account that is distributed to them in two payments upon graduation to help them start their new lives.

All students in Job Corps receive help in preparing a resume and getting business cards, advice about how to do well in job interviews, and general information about succeeding in the world of work. Upon graduation, the program even helps them find a job and join a union, if necessary. Because Job Corps is a nationwide organization, it offers placement services for graduates who wish to relocate anywhere in the United States.

"They placed me right away," Rhonda says. "They bend over backward to help you find a job." As an apprentice carpenter, Rhonda is now paid union scale and receives periodic raises and benefits.

Advice

For Rhonda, the Job Corps experience was a turning point in her life, and she recommends it to anyone who is highly motivated to learn a trade. She says the discipline she learned there has been one of the most important factors in her career. Success in this type of training program, she believes, is largely a question of attitude.

"Keep your focus on why you're there, and you'll do well," Rhonda advises. "There are some sacrifices that you have to make—you have to live at the campus, for instance—but you have to ask yourself what you're willing to do to get started in a good job. It just depends on how much you want it."

Future Goals

These days, Rhonda works on highway bridges and other construction projects. She is the only woman carpenter on her crew of 10 to 12 people, but she says most of her coworkers quickly learned to respect her when they realized she was qualified for the job and motivated to work hard. She says she strives to do her job well, because she's setting a precedent for other Job Corps students, and she's demonstrating to employers that Job Corps graduates are well worth hiring.

In the future, she says, "I want to have a family. I work to live; I don't live to work. But I would like to be a foreman or a boss. It's a lot of responsibility, but it teaches you how to handle people."

ALABAMA

Gadsden Job Corps Center
600 Valley Street
PO Box 286
Gadsden, AL 35902
256-547-6222
Fax: 256-547-9040
http://jobcorps.doleta.gov

Montgomery Job Corps Center
1145 Air Base Boulevard
Montgomery, AL 36108
334-262-8883
Fax: 334-265-2339

ALASKA

Alaska Job Corps Center
800 E. Lynn Martin Drive
Palmer, AK 99645
907-746-8800
Fax: 907-746-8810
http://www.alaskajobcorps.com

ARIZONA

Fred G. Acosta Job Corps Center
901 South Campbell Avenue
Tucson, AZ 85719

520-792-3015
Fax: 520-628-1552
http://www.acostajobcorps.com

Phoenix Job Corps Center
518 South Third Street
Phoenix, AZ 85004
602-254-5921
Fax: 602-340-1965

ARKANSAS

Cass Job Corps Center
21424 N. Highway 23
Ozark, AR 72949
479-667-3686
Fax: 479-667-3989
http://jobcorps.doleta.gov

Little Rock Job Corps Center
2020 Vance Street
Little Rock, AR 72206
501-376-4600
Fax: 501-376-6152
http://jobcorps.doleta.gov

Ouachita Job Corps Center
570 Job Corps Road
Royal, AR 71968
501-767-2707
Fax: 501-767-2768
http://jobcorps.doleta.gov

CALIFORNIA

Inland Empire Job Corps Center
3173 Kerry Street
San Bernardino, CA 92405
909-887-6305
Fax: 909-887-8635
http://www.iejcc.org

Long Beach Job Corps Center
1903 Santa Fe Avenue
Long Beach, CA 90810-4050
562-983-1777
Fax: 562-983-0053

Los Angeles Job Corps Center
1106 South Broadway
Los Angeles, CA 90015

213-748-0135
Fax: 213-741-5359
http://jobcorps.doleta.gov

Region Nine Main Office
U.S. Department of Labor, ETA
71 Stevenson Street, Suite 1015
PO Box 3768
San Francisco, CA 94119-3768
415-975-4680
Fax: 415-975-4715
http://jobcorps.doleta.gov

Sacramento Job Corps Center
3100 Meadowview Road
Sacramento, CA 95832
916-393-2880
Fax: 916-424-2872
http://jobcorps.doleta.gov

San Diego Job Corps Center
1325 Iris Avenue, Building 60
Imperial Beach, CA 91932
619-429-8500
Fax: 619-423-5194
http://www.sandiegojobcorps.org

San Jose Job Corps Center
3485 East Hills Drive
San Jose, CA 95127-2970
408-937-3200
http://jobcorps.doleta.gov

Treasure Island Job Corps Center
Building 363, First Floor
Treasure Island Station
San Francisco, CA 94130-5027
415-277-2400
Fax: 415-705-1776
http://jobcorps.doleta.gov

COLORADO

Collbran Job Corps Center
57608 Highway 330
Collbran, CO 81624-9702
970-487-3576
Fax: 970-487-3823

CONNECTICUT
Connecticut Job Corps Center
455 Wintergreen Avenue
New Haven, CT 06515
203-397-3775
Fax: 203-392-0299
http://jobcorps.doleta.gov

Hartford Job Corps Center
100 William Shorty Campbell Drive
Hartford, CT 06106
860-953-7210
860-953-7203
Fax: 860-953-7216

DISTRICT OF COLUMBIA
Potomac Job Corps Center
One D.C. Village Lane, SW
Washington, DC 20032
202-574-5000
Fax: 202-574-9451
http://www.jobcorpsregion2.com/Trades/Center-
    Potomac.html

FLORIDA
Gainesville Job Corps Center
5301 N.E. 40th Terrace
Gainesville, FL 32609-1670
352-377-2555
Fax: 352-374-8257
http://www.jobcorpsregion3.com/jcCenters/
    gainesvilleJCC.html

Homestead Job Corps Center
12350 S.W. 285th Street
Homestead, FL 33033
305-257-4800
Fax: 305-257-3920

Jacksonville Job Corps Center
4811 Payne Stewart Drive
Jacksonville, FL 32209
904-360-8200
Fax: 904-632-5498
http://www.jobcorpsregion3.com/jcCenters/
    jacksonvilleJCC.html

Miami Job Corps Center
3050 Northwest 183rd Street
Miami, FL 33055
305-626-7800
Fax: 305-626-7857
http://www.miamijobcorps.org

GEORGIA
Atlanta Job Corps Center
239 West Lake Avenue, NW
Atlanta, GA 30314
404-794-9512
Fax: 404-794-8426
http://www.jobcorpsregion3.com/jcCenters/
    atlantaJCC.html

Brunswick Job Corps Center
4401 Glynco Industrial Park
Brunswick, GA 31520
912-264-8843
Fax: 912-267-7192
http://jobcorps.doleta.gov

Turner Job Corps Center
2000 Schilling Avenue
Albany, GA 31708
229-883-8500
Fax: 229-434-0383Turner
http://jobcorps.doleta.gov

HAWAII
Hawaii Job Corps Center
41-467 Hihimanu Street
Waimanalo, HI 96795
808-259-6010
Fax: 808-259-7907
http://jobcorps.doleta.gov

IDAHO
Centennial Job Corps Civilian Center
3201 Ridgecrest Drive
Nampa, ID 83687
208-442-4500
Fax: 208-442-4506
http://jobcorps.doleta.gov

ILLINOIS

Golconda Job Corps Center
Route One, Box 104A
Golconda, IL 62938
618-285-6601
Fax: 618-285-3121
http://jobcorps.doleta.gov

Joliet Job Corps Center
1101 Mills Road
Joliet, IL 60433
815-727-7677
http://jobcorps.doleta.gov

Paul Simon Chicago Job Corps Center
3348 South Kedzie Avenue
Chicago, IL 60623
773-890-3100
Fax: 773-847-9823
http://www.jobcorpschicagokc.com/aboutjc/jccenters/
    chicago.htm

INDIANA

Atterbury Job Corps Center
PO Box 187
Edinburg, IN 46124
812-526-5581
Fax: 812-526-9551
http://jobcorps.doleta.gov

IndyPendence Job Corps Center
32 East Washington Street
Indianapolis, IN 46204
317-231-2365
Fax: 317-231-2375
http://jobcorps.doleta.gov

IOWA

Denison Job Corps Center
High 30 East
PO Box 608
Denison, IA 51442
712-263-4192
Fax: 712-263-6910
http://jobcorps.doleta.gov

KANSAS

Flint Hills Job Corps Center
4620 Eureka Drive
Manhatten, KS 66502
785-537-7222
Fax: 785-537-9517
http://www.fhjcc.com

KENTUCKY

Carl D. Perkins Job Corps Center
478 Meadows Branch
Prestonburg, KY 41653
800-491-4001
Fax: 606-886-6048
http://www.cdpjobcorps.com

Earl C. Clements Job Corps Center
2302 U.S. Highway 60 East
Morganfield, KY 42437
270-389-2419
Fax: 270-389-1134
http://www.jobcorpsregion2.com/Trades/Center-
    Clements.html

Frenchburg Job Corps Civilian Conservation Center
HCR 68 - Box 2170
Highway 77
Mariba, KY 40322
606-768-2111
Fax: 606-768-3080
http://www.jobcorpsregion2.com/Trades/Center-French.
    html

Great Onyx Job Corps Civilian Conservation Center
3115 Ollie Ridge Road
Mammoth Cave, KY 42259-9801
270-286-4514
Fax: 270-286-1120
http://www.jobcorpsregion2.com/Trades/Center-
    GreatOnyx.html

Muhlenburg Career Development Center
3875 State Route, Highway 181 North
Greenville, KY 42345
270-338-5460
Fax: 270-338-3615
http://www.muhlenbergjcc.org

Pine Knot Job Corps Civilian Conservation Center
PO Box 1990
U.S. Highway 27
Pine Knot, KY 42635-1990
606-354-2176
Fax: 606-354-2170
http://www.jobcorpsregion2.com/Trades/Center-
PineKnot.html

Whitney M. Young Jr. Job Corps Center
8460 Shelbyville Road
Simpsonville, KY 40067
502-722-8862
Fax: 502-722-3601
http://www.jobcorpsregion2.com/Trades/Center-
Whitney.html

LOUISIANA
Carville Job Corps Academy
5465 Point Clair Road
Carville, LA 70721
225-642-0699
Fax: 225-642-3098
http://jobcorps.doleta.gov

New Orleans Job Corps Center
3801 Hollygrove Street
New Orleans, LA 70118
504-486-0641
http://jobcorps.doleta.gov

Shreveport Job Corps Center
2816 Lillian Street
Shreveport, LA 71109
318-227-9331
Fax: 318-222-0768
http://jobcorps.doleta.gov

MAINE
Loring Job Corps Center
Rural Route One, Box 1727
Limestone, ME 04750
207-328-4212
Fax: 207-328-4219
http://www.nejobcorps.org/loring/index.asp

Penobscot Job Corps Center
1375 Union Street
Bangor, ME 04401
207-990-3000
Fax: 207-942-9829
http://www.penobscotjobcorpscenter.com

MARYLAND
Woodland Job Corps Center
3300 Fort Mead Road
Laurel, MD 20724
301-725-7900
Fax: 301-497-8978
http://www.jobcorpsregion2.com/Trades/Center-
Woodland.html

Woodstock Job Corps Center
PO Box 300
Randallstown, MD 21133-0395
410-461-1100
Fax: 410-461-5794
http://www.jobcorpsregion2.com/Trades/Center-
Woodstock.html

MASSACHUSETTS
Grafton Job Corps Center
191 Westboro Road
PO Box 575
North Grafton, MA 01536
508-839-9529
Fax: 508-839-9781

Shriver Job Corps Center
270 Jackson Road
Devens, MA 01434
978-772-7933
Fax: 978-784-2721

Westover Job Corps Center
103 Johnson Road
Chicopee, MA 01020
413-593-5731
Fax: 413-593-5170

MICHIGAN
Detroit Job Corps Center
11801 Woodrow Wilson Street
Detroit, MI 48206
313-852-0301
Fax: 313-865-8791

http://www.jobcorpschicagokc.com/aboutjc/jccenters/
detroit.htm

Flint/Genesee Job Corps Center
2400 North Saginaw Street
Flint, MI 48505
810-232-9102
Fax: 810-232-6835

Gerald R. Ford Job Corps Center
110 Hall Street, SE
Grand Rapids, MI 49507
616-243-6877
Fax: 616-243-1701
http://jobcorps.doleta.gov

MINNESOTA
Hubert Humphrey Job Corps Center
1480 North Snelling Avenue
St. Paul, MN 55108
612-642-1133
Fax: 612-642-0123
http://jobcorps.doleta.gov

MISSISSIPPI
Batesville Job Corps Center
821 Highway 51, South
Batesville, MS 38606
601-563-4656
http://jobcorps.doleta.gov

Gulfport Job Corps Center
3300 20th Street
Gulfport, MS 39501
601-864-9691
Fax: 601-864-9691
http://jobcorps.doleta.gov

Mississippi Job Corps Center
PO Box 817
Crystal Springs, MS 39059
601-892-3348
Fax: 601-892-3719
http://jobcorps.doleta.gov

MISSOURI
Excelsior Springs Job Corps Center
701 St. Louis Avenue
Excelsior Springs, MO 64024

816-630-5501
Fax: 816-637-1806
http://www.esjobcorps.com

Mingo Job Corps Center
4253 State Highway T
Puxico, MO 63960-9585
573-222-3537
Fax: 314-222-3801
http://www.mingojobcorps.com

Region Seven Main Office
U.S. Department of Labor, Employment and
Training Administration
City Center Square
1100 Main Street, Suite 1000
Kansas City, MO 64105-2112
816-426-3661
Fax: 816-426-5307
http://jobcorps.doleta.gov

St. Louis Job Corps Center
4333 Goddfellow Boulevard
St. Louis, MO 63120
314-679-6200
Fax: 314-382-9086
http://www.stlouisjobcorps.com

MONTANA
Anaconda Job Corps Center
1407 Foster Creek Road
Anaconda, MT 59711
406-563-3476
Fax: 406-563-8243
http://jobcorps.doleta.gov

Kicking Horse Job Corps Center
Rural Route Two
Ronan, MT 59864
406-644-2217
Fax: 406-644-2343

Trapper Creek Job Corps Center
5139 West Fork Road
Darby, MT 59829-5139
406-821-3286
Fax: 406-821-3290

NEBRASKA
Pine Ridge Job Corps Center
15710 Highway 385
Chadron, NE 69337
308-432-3316
Fax: 308-432-4145
http://www.pineridgejobcorps.org

NEVADA
Sierra Nevada Job Corps Center
5005 East Echo Avenue
Reno, NV 89506
702-972-5627
Fax: 702-972-7480
http://jobcorps.doleta.gov

NEW JERSEY
Edison Job Corps Center
500 Plainfield Avenue
Edison, NJ 08817-2587
908-985-4800
Fax: 908-985-8551
http://www.njjobcorps.org

NEW MEXICO
Albuquerque Job Corps Center
1500 Indian School Road, NW
Albuquerque, NM 87104
505-842-6500
Fax: 505-247-3262
www.albuquerquejobcorps.com

Roswell Job Corps Center
G Street
PO Box 597058
Roswell, NM 88201
505-347-5414
Fax: 505-347-2243
http://www.roswelljobcorps.org

NEW YORK
Brooklyn Job Corps Center
585 DeKalb Avenue
Brooklyn, NY 11205
718-623-4000
Fax: 718-623-9626
http://jobcorps.doleta.gov

Cassadaga Job Corps Center
8115 Glasgow Road
Cassadaga, NY 14718-9619
716-595-8760
Fax: 716-595-3963
http://jobcorps.doleta.gov

Delaware Valley Job Corps Center
9368 State Rt. 97
PO Box 846
Callicoon, NY 12723-0846
845-887-5400
Fax: 845-887-4762
http://jobcorps.doleta.gov

Glenmont Job Corps Academy
822 River Road
PO Box 993
Glenmont, NY 12077-0993
518-767-9341
Fax: 518-767-2106
http://jobcorps.doleta.gov

Iroquois Job Corps Center
11780 Tibbets Road
Medina, NY 14103
585-798-7000
Fax: 585-798-7046
http://jobcorps.doleta.gov

Oneonta Job Corps Center
21 Homer Folks Avenue
Oneonta, NY 13820
607-433-2111
Fax: 607-433-1629
http://jobcorps.doleta.gov

South Bronx Job Corps Center
1771 Andrews Avenue
Bronx, NY 10453
718-731-7702
Fax: 718-731-3543
http://jobcorps.doleta.gov

NORTH CAROLINA
Kittrell Job Corps Center
Kittrell College
PO Box 278
Kittrell, NC 27544

919-438-6161
Fax: 919-492-9630
http://jobcorps.doleta.gov

Lyndon Johnson Job Corps Center
466 Job Corps Drive
Franklin, NC 28734
704-524-4446
Fax: 704-369-7338
http://jobcorps.doleta.gov

Oconaluftee Job Corps Center
200 Park Circle
Cherokee, NC 28719
704-497-5411
Fax: 704-497-4417
http://jobcorps.doleta.gov

Schenck Job Corps Center
98 Schenck Drive
PO Box 98
Pisgah Forest, NC 28768
704-877-3291
http://jobcorps.doleta.gov

NORTH DAKOTA
Burdick JCC Job Corps Center
1500 University Avenue, West
Minot, ND 58703
701-838-9976
Fax: 701-838-9979
http://jobcorps.doleta.gov

OHIO
Cincinnati Job Corps Center
1409 Western Avenue
Cincinnati, OH 45214
513-651-2000
Fax: 513-651-2004
http://jobcorps.doleta.gov

Cleveland Job Corps Center
10660 Carnegie Avenue
Cleveland, OH 44106
216-795-8700
Fax: 216-795-0583
http://jobcorps.doleta.gov

Dayton Job Corps Center
3849 Germantown Road
Dayton, OH 45418
513-268-6571
Fax: 513-267-3832
http://jobcorps.doleta.gov

OKLAHOMA
Guthrie Job Corps Center
3106 West University
Guthrie, OK 73044
405-282-9930
Fax: 405-282-4977
http://jobcorps.doleta.gov

Talking Leaves Job Corps Center
PO Box 948
Tohlequah, OK 74465
918-456-9959
Fax: 918-456-1270
http://jobcorps.doleta.gov

Treasure Lake Job Corps Center
Route One, Box 30
Indianhoma, OK 73552
405-246-3203
Fax: 405-246-8222
http://jobcorps.doleta.gov

Tulsa Job Corps Center
1133 North Lewis Avenue
Tulsa, OK 74410
918-585-9111
Fax: 918-592-2430
http://jobcorps.doleta.gov

OREGON
Angell Job Corps Center
336 Northeast Blodgett Road
Yachats, OR 97498
503-547-3137
Fax: 503-547-4236
http://jobcorps.doleta.gov

Pivot Job Corps Center
2508 Northeast Everett
Portland, OR 97232
503-280-6170

Fax: 503-280-6168
http://jobcorps.doleta.gov

Springdale Job Corps Center
31224 Historic Columbia River Highway
Troutdale, OR 97060
503-695-2245
Fax: 503-695-2254
http://jobcorps.doleta.gov

Timber Lake Job Corps Center
59868 East Highway 224
Estacada, OR 97023
503-834-2291
Fax: 503-834-2333
http://jobcorps.doleta.gov

Tongue Point Job Corps Center
Highway 30
Astoria, OR 97103
503-325-2131
Fax: 503-325-5375
http://jobcorps.doleta.gov

Wolf Creek Job Corps Center
2010 Opportunity Lane
Glide, OR 97443
503-496-3507
Fax: 503-496-0015
http://jobcorps.doleta.gov

PENNSYLVANIA
Keystone Job Corps Center
PO Box 37
Drums, PA 18222
717-788-1164
Fax: 717-788-1119
http://www.jobcorpsregion2.com/Trades/Center-
Keystone.html

Philadelphia Job Corps Center
4601 Market Street
Philadelphia, PA 19139
215-471-9689
Fax: 215-747-8552
http://www.jobcorpsregion2.com/Trades/Center-
Philadelphia.html

Pittsburgh Job Corps Center
7175 Highland Drive
Pittsburgh, PA 15206
412-441-8700
Fax: 412-441-1586
www.pittsjcc.com

Red Rock Job Corps Center
PO Box 218
Lopez, PA 18628
570-477-2221
Fax: 570-447-3046
http://www.jobcorpsregion2.com/Trades/Center-
RedRock.html

SOUTH CAROLINA
Bamberg Job Corps Center
PO Box 967
Bamberg, SC 29003
803-245-5101
Fax: 803-245-5915
http://jobcorps.doleta.gov

SOUTH DAKOTA
Boxelder Job Corps Center
PO Box 110
Nemo, SD 57759
605-348-3636
Fax: 605-578-1157
http://jobcorps.doleta.gov

TENNESSEE
Jacobs Creek Job Corps Center
984 Denton Valley Road
Bristol, TN 37620-1430
423-878-4021
Fax: 423-878-7034
http://jobcorps.doleta.gov

TEXAS
David L. Carrasco Job Corps Center
11155 Gateway West
El Paso, TX 79935
915-594-0022
Fax: 915-591-0166
http://jobcorps.doleta.gov

Gary Job Corps Center
2800 Airport, Highway 21
PO Box 967
San Marcos, TX 78667-0967
512-396-6652
Fax: 512-396-6666
http://www.garyjcc.org

Laredo Job Corps Center
1701 Island Street
PO Box 1819
Laredo, TX 78041
956-727-5148
Fax: 956-727-1937
http://jobcorps.doleta.gov

North Texas Job Corps Center
1701 North Church Street
PO Box 80031501
McKinney, TX 75069
972-542-2623
Fax: 972-547-7703
http://jobcorps.doleta.gov

UTAH
Clearfield Job Corps Center
20 West 1700 South (Antelope Drive)
PO Box 160070
Clearfield, UT 84016-0070
801-774-4000
Fax: 801-773-8906
http://www.clearfieldjcc.org

Weber Basin Job Corps Center
7400 South Cornia Drive
Ogden, UT 84405-9605
801-479-9806
Fax: 801-476-5985
http://jobcorps.doleta.gov

VERMONT
Northlands Job Corps Center
100-A MacDonough Drive
Vergennes, VT 05491
802-877-2925
Fax: 802-877-2699
http://jobcorps.doleta.gov

VIRGINIA
Blue Ridge Job Corps Center
245 W. Main Street
Marion, VA 24354
276-783-7221
Fax: 276-783-1751

Flatwoods Job Corps Center
2803 Dungannon Road
Coeburn, VA 24230-5914
276-395-3384
Fax: 276-395-2043
http://www.jobcorpsregion2.com/Trades/Center-
    Flatwoods.html

Old Dominion Job Corps Center
1073 Father Judge Road
Monroe, VA 24574
434-929-4081
Fax: 434-929-3511
http://www.odjcc.com

WASHINGTON
Cascades Job Corps Center
7782 Northern State Road
PO Box 819
Sedro Woolley, WA 98284-8241
360-854-3400
Fax: 360-854-2227
http://www.cascadesjobcorps.org

Columbia Basin Job Corps Center
6739 24th Street, Building 2402
Moses Lake, WA 98837
509-762-5581
Fax: 509-762-9540
http://jobcorps.doleta.gov

Curlew Job Corps Center
Three Campus Street
Curlew, WA 99118
509-779-4611
Fax: 509-779-4328
http://jobcorps.doleta.gov

Fort Simcoe Job Corps Center
40 Abella Lane
White Swan, WA 98952

509-874-2244
Fax: 509-874-2342
http://jobcorps.doleta.gov

Region Ten Main Office
U.S. Department of Labor, Employment and Training
    Administration
Job Corps Office, Suite 960
1111 Third Avenue
Seattle, WA 98101-3212
206-553-7938
Fax: 206-553-4009
http://jobcorps.doleta.gov

WEST VIRGINIA

Charleston Job Corps Center
Virginia and Summers Streets
Charleston, WV 25301
304-344-4041
Fax: 304-345-3849
http://jobcorps.doleta.gov

Harpers Ferry Job Corps Center
PO Box 237
Harpers Ferry, WV 25425
304-725-2011
Fax: 304-728-8200
http://jobcorps.doleta.gov

WISCONSIN

Blackwell Job Corps Center
4155 County Highway H
Laona, WI 54541
715-674-2311
Fax: 715-674-4305
http://www.jobcorpschicagokc.com/aboutjc/jccenters/
    blackwell.htm

PUERTO RICO

Arecibo Job Corps Center
PO Box 544
Garrochales, PR 00652-0540
787-881-2300
Fax: 787-881-0971

Barranquitas Job Corps Center
PO Box 68
Barranquitas, PR 00794
787-857-5200
Fax: 787-857-2262

Ramey Job Corps Center
PO Box 250463
Aguadilla, PR 00604-0463
809-890-2030
Fax: 809-890-4749

JOB TRAINING PARTNERSHIP ACT (JTPA) PROGRAMS

The Job Training Partnership Act (JTPA) of 1982 established a federally funded program that provides job training and employment for economically disadvantaged individuals and others who face serious barriers to employment. The U. S. Employment Service and state employment services administer JTPA programs through local offices, usually called "Job Service Centers," which are located throughout the country.

JTPA programs are available for veterans, workers age 55 and older, youth, people with disabilities, people who have been fired or laid off ("dislocated workers"), migrant and seasonal agricultural workers, women seeking non-traditional employment, and various other groups. These programs typically feature apprenticeships, on-the-job training, classroom training, basic skills training in areas such as math and English, job search assistance, and counseling.

The JTPA program includes some features intended for specific groups of job seekers. *Title II-B* provides summer jobs and training for economically disadvantaged young people. The program offers basic and remedial education, work-experience programs, and support services, such as transportation.

Title II-C provides training and employment programs throughout the year for young people, regardless of whether they are enrolled in school. The program varies somewhat, depending on the office administering it, but in general it offers all the services the JTPA provides for adults, limited internships in the private sector, school-to-work transition services, and alternative high school services.

Title III provides employment and training for "dislocated" workers. The program is intended for people who have lost their jobs in mass layoffs, plant closings, or because of some other situation that makes it unlikely they will return to their jobs. Title III features early intervention programs, occupational skill training, job search assistance, support services, and assistance in moving to obtain employment. This JTPA program is authorized under the Economic Dislocation and Worker Adjustment Assistance Act and operates in conjunction with the Worker Adjustment and Retraining Notification Act (WARN), which requires advance notice of plant closings or mass layoffs. It allows unions, local governments, and state agencies to help these workers become employed again as quickly as possible.

Title IV authorizes services for Native Americans, migrant and seasonal farm workers, veterans of the military, the Job Corps, and other programs. JTPA programs for migrant and seasonal farm workers are intended to help workers and their families improve their job skills, obtain stable employment, and become economically self-sufficient. Participants in these programs are not required to remain employed in agricultural occupations. In fact, many of these programs feature training in fields that offer better wages, such as computer operations, medical assisting, or welding.

Jobs and training for Native Americans are also authorized under *Public Law 102-477*, the Indian Employment Training and Related Services Demonstration Act. This legislation allows Indian tribes to operate their employment and training services more efficiently by combining JTPA funds with other sources of money.

Apprenticeships and on-the-job training for veterans of military service, along with the surviving spouses and dependents of veterans killed or missing in action, are also funded through the GI Bill, which has been in effect since World War II. Veterans who undertake apprenticeship training should register with the Department of Labor's Bureau of Apprenticeship and Training to ensure that they receive the proper credentials upon completion of the program and to arrange for the GI Bill to pay part of the cost of the training. New programs are approved every month, often at the request of a veteran interested in a program that has not yet been approved. Veterans should call the nearest Veterans Administration regional office to learn whether they are entitled to benefits under the GI Bill, then locate and get hired for an apprenticeship program and have the program's director file applicable forms with the Veterans Administration. Veterans already enrolled in training programs may be eligible for back pay on educational benefits from the Veterans Administration for up to one year.

JTPA training programs are often planned by State Job Training Coordinating Councils, which are composed of business representatives, state and local government entities, and people who are unemployed. Some states have also established Human Resource Investment Councils to review and coordinate programs. Communities with populations of at least 200,000 are among the various JTPA Service Delivery Areas (SDAs) designated to receive federal job training funds. Local elected officials appoint Private Industry Councils to oversee training programs in each Service Delivery Area. These councils include representatives from business, education, organized labor, rehabilitation agencies, community-based organizations, economic development agencies, and public employment services.

This section of the directory features JTPA programs for adults, disabled workers, dislocated agricultural workers, other dislocated workers, homeless workers, Native Americans, migrant and seasonal farm workers, older workers, veterans of the military, women seeking nontraditional employment, and young people. The subsection for veterans also contains some programs that are funded under the GI Bill, not the JTPA, and programs for Native Americans that operate under Public Law 102-477.

APPRENTICESHIP SALARIES

Vary widely, depending on the trade, the geographic location, and the employer.

POSTAPPRENTICESHIP SALARIES

Vary widely, depending on the trade, the geographic location, and the employer.

PROGRAM PROFILE

Missoula Job Service Center
Job Training Partnership Act Program
539 South Third Street West
Box 5027
Missoula, MT 59801
406-728-7060
Fax: 406-721-7094

General Nature of the Program

The Job Training Partnership Act funds a great many job training programs for individuals who meet certain criteria. For instance, a program might serve migrant and seasonal farm workers, veterans of the military, older workers, people with disabilities, or women seeking nontraditional employment. The money is awarded by a competitive grant process to job centers and other orga-

nizations, meaning that these organizations may or may not have funds available in any given year.

On-the-job training is provided for workers who need to improve their skills and increase their knowledge to obtain meaningful employment. It can be applied to jobs in the public or private sector but is not meant for seasonal occupations, jobs where tips or commissions make up most of the employee's income, or jobs that have a high turnover of employees. In other words, the program is intended to help workers find permanent, dependable employment.

Supervised training is an important element of the Job Training Partnership Act. Tracy Cuplin studies books and performs hands-on work under the oversight of skilled workers at his new job. "I knew some of it from my former job," he says, "but to learn some of the processes at Borden's, I had to start from scratch."

Typical Day

Tracy reports to his job at various times of the day or night, since the chemical plant never shuts down except during maintenance periods every 90 days or so. Workers rotate shifts, putting in six or seven days at a time during the day, evening, or night and taking a couple of days off between each rotation. They usually work eight hours a day but sometimes put in 12 hours, taking breaks whenever there's a lull in the activity.

Tracy also takes time out to read books that explain the details of his trade. In addition, he sometimes studies before and after work, and he listens as more experienced workers explain certain aspects of the job. When he finishes each reading assignment, his supervisor tests him on the material.

About 25 people work at the chemical plant. Tracy is part of a four-person crew that makes formaldehyde, a chemical used in the adhesives that bind wood chips and other materials into lumber products, such as plywood, particle board, and chip board. Tracy's duties include unloading shipments of alcohol from railroad tanker cars and monitoring water softeners, water in the boilers, and the cooling tower. During the first few months of training, he was closely supervised.

"We're using a lot of heat and some water and alcohol," he explains. "We pass it through silver at a high temperature, through a catalyst, and it's converted to formaldehyde. I'm usually inside when I'm on swing shift, but I go outside to work on our running equipment. You're there, and you're serious, and you get it done according to the prescribed company method. In a chemical plant you've got to have safety procedures, eliminate spills, and produce a product that meets or exceeds the customer's expectations."

Path to Becoming an Apprentice

Although he didn't arrive at Borden Chemical Company in the way he anticipated, Tracy had a desire to work there for some time before circumstances placed him with the company. In his previous job with a lumber company, he had learned many skills that have proved useful at the chemical plant. He had also become acquainted with some people who are now his coworkers, which he says helped him land his new job. After losing his previous job, he filed an application with Borden Chemical and checked back periodically to remind them that he was available. Still, he was between jobs for two years before an opening came up at the chemical plant at about the same time that Tracy learned about the Job Training Partnership Act.

Salary Range

The Job Training Partnership Act requires that employees in training receive the same general treatment, benefits, and wages as other employees, and they must work under the same conditions. Tracy was paid a standard entry-level wage for his trade, was covered by health insurance, and received other benefits during his training period. He will continue to receive periodic raises after the completion of the training.

Advice

For anyone who has lost a job, Tracy recommends asking a Job Service caseworker about JTPA programs. "It would give them the edge over someone who was not knowledgeable about the on-the-job training program. It can only be a plus," he notes.

He also notes that workers of all ages should be willing to learn new skills, and everyone in a complex trade such as his must expect to keep learning indefinitely. "I'll probably be in training until I retire," he comments. "As new technology comes out, we're adding new instrumentation and computers and computer-controlled sensing devices and things like that to our plant. There's always something new to learn."

Future Goals

After two years with Borden Chemical, Tracy is still in training but is no longer in the Job Training Partnership Act program, which helped fund his training for the first

six months only. All new employees at Borden Chemical are in training for two to three years. Tracy is working to earn a boiler operator's license; in Montana this license is awarded after the worker has accumulated about two years of experience on low-pressure boilers. Tracy has already completed the first of three certifications required for that license for formaldehyde.

He says he expects to work at the plant until retirement: "I feel I'm lucky with this situation here. I was fifty-three years old when Borden's picked me up. Usually, companies choose younger people for their employment programs. I don't plan on leaving until they don't need me anymore."

ADULT WORKERS
ARKANSAS
Central Arkansas Planning and Development District
115 Jefferson
PO Box 187
Lonoke, AR 72086
501-676-2721
Fax: 501-676-5020

City of Little Rock
500 West Markham, Room 220, West
City Hall Annex
Little Rock, AR 72201
501-371-4488
Fax: 501-371-4873

Eastern Arkansas Private Industry Council
260 Shoppingway
PO Box 1388
West Memphis, AR 72303
870-735-6730
Fax: 870-732-4995

North Central Arkansas Development Council
1652 White Drive
PO Box 2396
Batesville, AR 72501
870-793-5233
Fax: 870-793-4035

Northeast Arkansas Employment and Training Services
2809 Forrest Home Road
Jonesboro, AR 72401

870-932-1564
Fax: 870-932-5310

Northwest Arkansas Economic Development District
818 Highway 62-65
PO Box 190
Harrison, AR 72602-0190
870-741-5404
Fax: 870-741-1905

Southeast Arkansas Economic Development District
721 Walnut
PO Box 6806
Pine Bluff, AR 71601
870-536-1971
Fax: 870-536-7718

Southwest Arkansas Planning and Development District
600 Bessie Street
PO Box 767
Magnolia, AR 71753
870-234-4030
Fax: 870-234-0135

West Central Arkansas Planning and Development District
ABT Bank Building
PO Box 1558
Hot Springs, AR 71902
501-624-1036
Fax: 501-321-5444

Western Arkansas Employment Development Agency
1500 Main Street
PO Box 1266
Van Buren, AR 72956
501-474-7061
Fax: 501-474-4321

CALIFORNIA
Proteus Inc., Bakersfield
929 Niles Street
Bakersfield, CA 93305
805-323-8053
Fax: 805-323-8096
http://www.proteusinc.org

Proteus Inc., Delano
1427 South Lexington
Delano, CA 93215
805-725-0803
Fax: 805-725-5638
http://www.proteusinc.org

Proteus Inc., Dinuba
Tulare County Private Industry Council
241 South L Street
Dinuba, CA 93618
209-591-5701
Fax: 209-591-0674
http://www.proteusinc.org

Proteus Inc., London
Tulare County Private Industry Council
Community Center, Minnesota Avenue
London, CA 93618
209-595-0723
http://www.proteusinc.org

Proteus Inc., Porterville
Tulare County Private Industry Council
54 North Main, Suite 10
Porterville, CA 93257
209-688-4963
Fax: 209-781-7989
http://www.proteusinc.org

Proteus Inc., Visalia
Tulare County Private Industry Council
900 North Dinuba Boulevard
Visalia, CA 93291
209-627-0100
Fax: 209-627-6558
http://www.proteusinc.org

Proteus Inc., Wasco
930 F Street
Wasco, CA 93280-2099
805-758-8757
Fax: 805-758-3565
http://www.proteusinc.org

DISTRICT OF COLUMBIA
U.S. Department of Labor
Office of Strategic Planning and Policy Development
Washington, DC 20210
202-219-7674

KANSAS

ANW Special Education Cooperative
710 Bridge Street
Humboldt, KS 66748
316-473-2257

Department of Human Services
City Hall
455 North Main, Second Floor
Wichita, KS 67202
316-268-4691

Fort Scott Community College
Comprehensive Education and Employment
    Training Center
2108 South Horton
Fort Scott, KS 66701
316-223-2700

Marshall County Special Services Cooperative
405 North Fourth Street
Marysville, KS 66508
785-562-2943

**SDA1, Kansas Department of Human
    Resources**
332 East Eighth Street
PO Box 398
Hays, KS 67601
913-628-1014
Fax: 913-625-0092

SDA2, Private Industry Council
117 Southwest 10th Street, Third Floor
Topeka, KS 66612
913-234-0500
Fax: 913-234-0552

SDA3, Kansas Department of Human Resources
552 State Avenue
Kansas City, KS 66101-2464
913-281-3000
Fax: 913-281-0069

SDA4, Kansas Department of Human Resources
402 East Second
PO Box 877
Wichita, KS 67201
316-266-8615
Fax: 316-266-8656

Urban League of Wichita Inc.
1802 East 13th Street, North
Wichita, KS 67214
316-683-3315

USD #259 Continuing Education
923 Cleveland
Wichita, KS 67214
316-833-3153

WYOMING

Fleming Associates
1001 West 31st Street
Cheyenne, WY 82001
307-634-6883
Fax: 307-634-9462

JETS Technology Institute Inc.
625 East Madison
PO Box 1777
Riverton, WY 82501-1777
307-856-7279
Fax: 307-856-5727

NOWCAP
851 Werner Court, Suite 275
Casper, WY 82601-1311
Fax: 307-234-1029

Platte County School District One
13th and Oak Streets
Wheatland, WY 82201-0000
307-322-5480
Fax: 307-332-2084

SAGE Technical Services
5875 West Zero Road
Casper, WY 82604-2110
307-234-0242
Fax: 307-234-0552

DISABLED WORKERS
ALABAMA
Janice Capilouto Center for the Deaf
5950 Monticello Drive
Montgomery, AL 36117
334-244-8090

Supreme Bedding
245 Martin Patton Avenue
Montgomery, AL 36116

CALIFORNIA
Intercultural Education Employment and Training
1362 Post Street
San Francisco, CA 94109
415-441-1881
Fax: 415-885-4155

COLORADO
Goodwill Community Services
17 North Spruce
Colorado Springs, CO 80901
719-634-2242

CONNECTICUT
Direct Care Workers Training
CREC-Direct Care Training
111 Charter Oak Avenue
Hartford, CT 06106
203-247-2732

Empower I and II
106 River Road
East Haddam, CT 06423
203-873-1480

Supported Education Program
Six Poquonock Avenue
Windsor, CT 06095
203-647-6130

FLORIDA
Florida Division of Vocational Rehabilitation, District Eight
4770 Biscayne Boulevard, Suite 1260
Miami, FL 33137
305-571-5666

Florida Division of Vocational Rehabilitation, District Five
3555 Maguire Boulevard
Bennington Building, #205

Orlando, FL 32803-3723
407-897-2725

Florida Division of Vocational Rehabilitation, District Four
4221 North Himes Avenue, Suite 205
Tampa, FL 33607-6209
813-871-7300

Florida Division of Vocational Rehabilitation, District One
One South A Street, Suite 106
Pensacola, FL 32501-5575
850-444-8855

Florida Division of Vocational Rehabilitation, District Seven
3745 Broadway, Suite 203
Fort Myers, FL 33901
941-278-7317

Florida Division of Vocational Rehabilitation, District Six
1901 South Congress Avenue, Suite 340
Boynton Beach, FL 33426
407-279-1905

Florida Division of Vocational Rehabilitation, District Three
Flagler Building, Suite 101
2050 Art Museum Drive
Jacksonville, FL 32207
904-348-2780

Florida Division of Vocational Rehabilitation, District Two
825 Northwest 23rd Avenue, Building Two
Gainesville, FL 32609
352-955-3256

GEORGIA
Project Jumpstart
820 North Mulberry Street
Jackson, GA 30233
706-775-8112

HAWAII
Work Hawaii
Castle Cooperative Employment Project
45-386 Kanehoe Bay Drive

Kanehoe, HI 96744
808-235-4591

Hudson, NH 03051
603-886-1237

ILLINOIS
Futures in Business
1400 American Lane
Schaumburg, IL 60196

NEW JERSEY
Twilight Skills Program
200 Hackensack Avenue
Hackensack, NJ 07601
201-343-6000

INDIANA
Workforce Development Center
10 North Senate Avenue, Third Floor
Indianapolis, IN 46214
317-233-4009

NEW MEXICO
Sandia National Laboratories Career
4401 A Lomas Boulevard
Albuquerque, NM 87110
505-265-7936

LOUISIANA
**Job Training and Placement for Students
 with Disabilities**
1309 Lake Avenue
Metairie, LA 70005
504-830-4411

Transition Services Project
725 University Boulevard, SE
Albuquerque, NM 87106-4338
505-842-3516

Office of Manpower Programs
Joseph S. Yenni Building
1221 Elmwood Parl Boulevard, Suite 403
Harahan, LA 70123
504-736-6450

NEW YORK
Gateway
Empire State Plaza
Corning Tower, 28th Floor
Albany, NY 12223
518-457-2270

MAINE
Just-A-Start Summer Program
432 Columbia Street, Suite 12
Cambridge, MA 02141
617-494-0444

NORTH CAROLINA
Job Readiness Training Program
60 Lee's Creek Road
Asheville, NC 28806
704-258-1086

MONTANA
Displaced Homemaker Program
32 South Ewing
Helena, MT 59601
406-443-0800

OHIO
Cuyahoga East Vocational Education Consortium
211 Alpha Park Road
Highland Heights, OH 44143
216-473-1444

NEW HAMPSHIRE
Project Partnerships
Alvirne High School
200 Dairy Road

OKLAHOMA
Oklahoma State Employment Service
4509 South Interstate 35,
    Service Road

Oklahoma City, OK 73129
405-670-9100

SOUTH DAKOTA
Career Learning Center
1310 Main Avenue, South
Brookings, SD 57006-3841
605-688-4370

TEXAS
Upper Rio Grande Literacy Partnership Program
1155 Westmoreland, Suite 235
El Paso, TX 79925
915-772-5627

WEST VIRGINIA
Northern Panhandle Private Industry Council
2003 Warwood Avenue
Wheeling, WV 26003-7103
304-242-0172

Project LINK, Bridges Inc.
201 Walnut Street
Morgantown, WV 26505
304-296-3092

WYOMING
Adult Learning Center
2500 College Drive
Rock Springs, WY 82902-0428
307-382-1829

Title II-B Summer Youth Program
1620 Central Avenue, Suite 300
Cheyenne, WY 82001
307-635-9291

DISLOCATED AGRICULTURAL WORKERS
CALIFORNIA
Proteus Inc., Administrative Offices
4612 West Mineral King
Visalia, CA 93291
209-733-5423
Fax: 209-738-1137
http://www.proteusinc.org

Proteus Inc., Bakersfield
929 Niles Street
Bakersfield, CA 93305
805-323-8053
Fax: 805-323-8096
http://www.proteusinc.org

Proteus Inc., Coalinga
590 East Elm
Coalinga, CA 93210
209-934-0112
Fax: 209-934-0412
http://www.proteusinc.org

Proteus Inc., Delano
1427 South Lexington
Delano, CA 93215
805-725-0803
Fax: 805-725-5638
http://www.proteusinc.org

Proteus Inc., Dinuba
241 South L Street
Dinuba, CA 93618
209-591-5701
Fax: 209-591-0674
http://www.proteusinc.org

Proteus Inc., Fresno
1803 Van Ness
Fresno, CA 93721
209-485-5600
Fax: 209-485-1832
http://www.proteusinc.org

Proteus Inc., Hanford
217 West Seventh Street
Hanford, CA 93230
209-582-9253
Fax: 209-582-1023
http://www.proteusinc.org

Proteus Inc., Kerman
5148 West Whitesbridge
Kerman, CA 93630
209-846-4242
Fax: 209-846-5378
http://www.proteusinc.org

Proteus Inc., London
Community Center
Minnesota Avenue

London, CA 93618
209-595-0723
http://www.proteusinc.org

Proteus Inc., Porterville
54 North Main, Suite 10
Porterville, CA 93257
209-688-4963
Fax: 209-781-7989
http://www.proteusinc.org

Proteus Inc., Sanger
1849 Academy Street
Sanger, CA 93757
209-875-7146
http://www.proteusinc.org

Proteus Inc., Selma
2003 First Street, Suite 128
Selma, CA 93662
209-891-0135
Fax: 209-891-0143
http://www.proteusinc.org

Proteus Inc., Visalia
900 North Dinuba Boulevard
Visalia, CA 93291
209-627-0100
Fax: 209-627-6558
http://www.proteusinc.org

Proteus Inc., Wasco
930 F Street
Wasco, CA 93280-2099
805-758-8757
Fax: 805-758-3565
http://www.proteusinc.org

DISLOCATED WORKERS
ARKANSAS
Arkansas Department of Workforce Education
Executive Building, Suite 220
2020 West Third Street
Little Rock, AR 72205
501-324-9463
Fax: 501-324-9468

Little Rock AFB Transition Assistance
314 MSSQ/MSE
Little Rock, AR 72099-5065
501-988-3830

CALIFORNIA
Adult Basic Education Program
4640 Maine Avenue
Baldwin Park, CA 91706
818-962-3311

Business Services Division
320 Campus Lane
Suisun, CA 94585
707-864-3370

NOVA Career Connection
505 West Olive Avenue, Suite 550
Sunnyvale, CA 94086
408-730-7232

CONNECTICUT
Bridgeport Jobs
350 Fairfield Avenue, Third Floor
Bridgeport, CT 06604
203-334-5627

Defense Conversion Program
Zero Emission Vehicles
Shaw's Cove Six, Suite 100
New London, CT 06320
203-440-3534

DISTRICT OF COLUMBIA
American Institute of Banking
1120 Connecticut Avenue, NW
Washington, DC 20036
202-663-5371

FLORIDA
Project Ocean
PO Drawer 311
Cedar Key, FL 32625
904-486-4311

GEORGIA
**Heating, Ventilation, Air Conditioning, and
   Refrigeration Training**
PO Box 285
Morrow, GA 30260
404-961-3575

United Parcel Service
400 Parameter Club
Terraces North
Atlanta, GA 30346
404-913-7048

ILLINOIS

Division of Student and Workforce Services
River Road
PO Box 888
Kankakee, IL 60901
815-933-0373

Industrial Training Program
1545 North Lavergne
Chicago, IL 60651-1516
312-854-4557

INDIANA

Indiana's One-Stop Career Center System
10 North Senate Avenue
Indianapolis, IN 46204-2277
317-232-7381

IOWA

Eastern Iowa Community College
306 West River Drive
Davenport, IA 52801
319-322-5015

Farm Focus II
3420 University Avenue, Suite A
Waterloo, IA 50701
319-291-2546

Iowa's One-Stop Career Center System
150 Des Moines Street
Des Moines, IA 50319
515-281-9036

KANSAS

SDA1, Kansas Department of Human Resources
485 North Chick Avenue
Colby, KS 67701
913-462-6862

SDA1, Kansas Department of Human Resources
2308 First Avenue
Dodge City, KS 67801
316-227-2149

SDA1, Kansas Department of Human Resources
107 East Spruce Street
Garden City, KS 67846
316-276-2339

SDA1, Kansas Department of Human Resources
2120 11th Street
Great Bend, KS 67530
316-793-5445

SDA1, Kansas Department of Human Resources
518 North Washington Street
Hutchinson, KS 67501
316-663-6131

SDA1, Kansas Department of Human Resources
807 South Kansas Avenue
Liberal, KS 67901
316-624-1863

SDA1, Kansas Department of Human Resources
116 East Sixth Street
Newton, KS 67114
316-283-4220

SDA1, Kansas Department of Human Resources
203 North 10th Street
Salina, KS 67401
913-827-0385

SDA2, Kansas Department of Human Resources
112 North Sixth Street
Atchison, KS 66002
913-367-0090

SDA2, Kansas Department of Human Resources
120 North Eisenhower, Suite B
Junction City, KS 66441
913-762-8870

SDA2, Kansas Department of Human Resources
910 Haskell Avenue, Suite Five
Lawrence, KS 66101
913-865-5463

SDA2, Kansas Department of Human Resources
621 Humboldt
Manhattan, KS 66502
913-539-0591

SDA2, Kansas Department of Human Resources
1017 Broadway
Marysville, KS 66508
913-562-2238

SDA2, Kansas Department of Human Resources
3601 Southwest 29th, Suite 12
Topeka, KS 66614
913-271-8787

SDA3, Kansas Department of Human Resources
1125 North Fifth Street
Kansas City, KS 66101
913-342-9675

SDA3, Kansas Department of Human Resources
215A Delaware Street
Leavenworth, KS 66048
913-682-8410

SDA3, Kansas Department of Human Resources
460 East Santa Fe
Olathe, KS 66061
913-768-0606

SDA3, Kansas Department of Human Resources
6901 Shawnee Mission Parkway
Overland Park, KS 66202
913-236-6500

SDA3, Kansas Department of Human Resources
117 Southwest 10th
Topeka, KS 66612
913-234-0500

SDA4, Kansas Department of Human Resources
221 West Chestnut Avenue
Arkansas City, KS 67005
316-442-3130

SDA4, Kansas Department of Human Resources
123 East Second Avenue
El Dorado, KS 67042
316-321-2350

SDA5, Kansas Department of Human Resources
119 North Grant Street
Chanute, KS 66720
316-431-4950

SDA5, Kansas Department of Human Resources
512 Market Street
Emporia, KS 66801
316-342-3355

SDA5, Kansas Department of Human Resources
200 Arco Place
Independence, KS 67301
316-332-1660

SDA5, Kansas Department of Human Resources
3008 North Joplin
PO Box A
Pittsburg, KS 66762
316-232-2620
Fax: 316-232-1222

SDA5, Kansas Department of Human Resources
104 South Pine Street
Pittsburg, KS 66762
316-231-4250

MAINE

Western Maine Community Action Program
PO Box 70
Auburn, ME 04210
207-795-4061

MARYLAND

Baltimore County Career Development Center
431 Eastern Boulevard
Baltimore, MD 21221
410-574-8800

Professional Outplacement Assistance Center
901 Elkridge Landing Road
Linthicum, MD 21090-2920
410-859-3499

Upper Shore Workforce Development Program
PO Box Eight
Wye Mills, MD 21679
410-822-1716

The Work Place
Old Serverna Park Plaza
579 Baltimore-Annapolis Boulevard
Serverna Park, MD 21146
410-222-6190

MASSACHUSETTS
Guest Quarters Suite Hotels Career Development
30 Rowes Wharf
Boston, MA 02110
617-330-1440

MINNESOTA
Dakota County Employment and Training Center
1300 East 145th Street
County Road 42
Rosemount, MN 55068
612-423-8777

South Minneapolis Job Service
777 East Lake Street
Minneapolis, MN 55407
612-821-4010

MISSOURI
Job Development and Training Division
2023 Saint Mary's
Jefferson City, MO 65109
314-751-7796

UMKC's Project Refocus
4743 Troost
Kansas City, MO 64100
816-235-5160
Fax: 816-235-5238

NEVADA
Rapid Response
500 East Third Street
Carson City, NV 89713
702-687-4618

NEW YORK
Homeless Veterans Reintegration Project
21-10 Borden Avenue
Long Island, NY 11101
718-784-6800

NORTH DAKOTA
Job Service North Dakota
PO Box 5507
Bismarck, ND 58506-5507
701-328-2836

OREGON
Employment, Training, and Business Services
PO Box 215
Maryhurst, OR 97036
503-635-4591

Lane Community College
Training and Development Department
4000 East 30th Avenue
Eugene, OR 97405-0640
541-726-2223

PENNSYLVANIA
Job Service Bureau
32 East Union Street
Wilkes-Barre, PA 18711
717-826-2425

SOUTH CAROLINA
Charleston Navy Shipyard
U.S. Defense Department
Outplacement Center, Building 209
Charleston, SC 29408-6100
803-737-2611

SOUTH DAKOTA
Transition Assistance Program
730 East Watertown Street
Rapid City, SD 57701
605-394-5120

TEXAS
Project Quest
301 South Frio, Suite 400
San Antonio, TX 78207
210-270-4690

Title III Program
2015 South Interstate Highway 35, Suite 300
Austin, TX 78741
512-440-7816

VERMONT
Vermont Employment and Training Department
Five Green Mountain Drive
PO Box 488
Montpelier, VT 05601-0488
802-828-4300

VIRGINIA
Virginia Employment Commission
PO Box 7106
Fredericksburg, VA 22401
540-898-3800

WASHINGTON
Columbia Gorge Career Academy
PO Box 2169
White Salmon, WA 98672
509-493-5001

Quality through Training Program
6840 Fort Dent Way, Suite 250
Tucwila, WA 98088
206-477-0001

Re-Employment Program
3049 South 36th Street, Room 213
Tacoma, WA 98409

WISCONSIN
The Educational Fund
PO Box 1939
Fond Du Lac, WI 54935
414-929-5693

Uniroyal Goodrich Project
2105 Stout Road
Menomie, WI 54751-2336
715-232-1412

HOMELESS WORKERS
ALASKA
Avail
425 C Street
Anchorage, AK 99501
907-276-2557

ALABAMA
Adult and Community Education
PO Box 302101
Montgomery, AL 36130-2101
334-242-8181

ARKANSAS
Arkansas Families First
PO Box 2981
Little Rock, AR 72203
501-682-5227

CALIFORNIA
Career Resources Development Corporation
655 Geary Street
San Francisco, CA 94102
415-775-8800

Nova Career Connection
505 West Olive Avenue, Suite 550
Sunnyvale, CA 94086
408-730-7232

DISTRICT OF COLUMBIA
So Others Might Eat Inc.
1307 First Street, NW
Washington, DC 20001
202-328-0802

FLORIDA
One-Stop Service Center
9215 North Florida Avenue, Suite 100
Tampa, FL 33612
813-930-7575

GEORGIA
Georgia Job Training Partnership
Job Training Division
148 International Boulevard, NE, Suite 650
Atlanta, GA 30303
404-656-7392

ILLINOIS
Central Illinois Workforce Network
401 South State Street, Room 624
Chicago, IL 60605
312-793-5700

INDIANA
INET
17 West Market Street, Suite 500
Indianapolis, IN 46204
317-684-2200

KENTUCKY
Employment Service
275 East Main Street
Frankfort, KY 40621
502-732-4602

Job Link
305 West Broadway, Suite 600
Louisville, KY 40202
502-574-2500

MICHIGAN
Teen Project
State Capitol
PO Box 202501
Helena, MT 59620-2501
406-444-4443

NEW JERSEY
Employment and Training Office
Jobs/Job Training Partnership Act Coordination
135 East State Street, Third Floor, CN0055
Trenton, NJ 08625-0055
609-292-8900

NEW YORK
Gateway
Empire State Plaza
Corning Tower, 28th Floor
Albany, NY 12223
518-457-2270

Homeless Veterans Reintegration Project
21-10 Borden Avenue
Long Island City, NY 11101
718-784-6800

NORTH CAROLINA
North Carolina Social Services Department
PO Box 810
Durham, NC 27702
919-560-8000

NORTH DAKOTA
North Dakota Adult Learning Centers
State Capitol Building
600 Boulevard Avenue, East, Ninth Floor
Bismarck, ND 58505-0440
701-328-2393
Fax: 701-328-4770

SOUTH CAROLINA
One Stop Service Center
PO Box 1406
Columbia, SC 29202
803-737-2617

SOUTH DAKOTA
South Dakota Department of Labor
700 Governor's Drive
Pierre, SD 57501
605-773-3101

TEXAS
Texas Employment Commission
101 East 15th Street, Room 458T
Austin, TX 78778
512-463-7750

VERMONT
Employment and Training Department
PO Box 488
Montpelier, VT 05601-0488
802-828-4301

VIRGINIA
One Stop ET Information System
Theater Row Building, Ninth Floor
730 East Broad Street
Richmond, VA 23219
804-786-2300

WYOMING
Title II-B Summer Youth
1620 Central Avenue, Suite 300
Cheyenne, WY 82001
307-635-9291

MIGRANT WORKERS
ALABAMA
Alabama Opportunity Program
224 Church Street, Suite D
Huntsville, AL 35801
205-536-8218
Fax: 205-533-2039

ARIZONA
Portable Practical Educational Preparation Inc.
806 East 46th Streeet
Tucson, AZ 85713
520-622-3553
Fax: 520-622-1480

ARKANSAS
Arkansas Human Development Corporation
300 Spring Building, Suite 800
300 South Spring Street
Little Rock, AR 72201-2424
501-374-1103
Fax: 501-374-1413

CALIFORNIA
California Job Service, Oakdale
Employment Development Department
1405 West F Street
Oakdale, CA 95361
209-848-4226
http://www.edd.cahwnet.gov

California Job Service, Turlock
Employment Development Department
125 North Broadway
Turlock, CA 95380
209-634-4927
http://www.edd.cahwnet.gov

Center for Employment Training, San Jose
701 Vine Street
San Jose, CA 95110
408-287-7924
Fax: 408-294-7849

Central Valley Opportunity Center Inc., Madera
114 South A Street
Madera, CA 93638
209-674-0971
Fax: 209-673-8556

Central Valley Opportunity Center Inc., Merced
1748 Miles Court
PO Box 2307
Merced, CA 95348
209-383-2415
Fax: 209-383-2859

Central Valley Opportunity Center Inc., Modesto
912 11th Street
Modesto, CA 95354
209-577-3210
Fax: 209-521-9954

Central Valley Opportunity Center Inc., Winton
Winton Small Business Incubator
6838 West Bridget Court
Winton, CA 95388
209-357-3716
Fax: 209-357-3719

Employers Training Resource, County of Kern
2001 28th Street
Bakersfield, CA 93301
805-861-2495
Fax: 805-631-8723

Proteus Inc., Coalinga
590 East Elm
Coalinga, CA 93210
209-934-0112
Fax: 209-934-0412
http://www.proteusinc.org

Proteus Inc., Dinuba
241 South L Street
Dinuba, CA 93618
209-591-5701
Fax: 209-591-0674
http://www.proteusinc.org

Proteus Inc., Fresno
1803 Van Ness
Fresno, CA 93721
209-485-5600
Fax: 209-485-1832
http://www.proteusinc.org

Proteus Inc., Hanford
217 West Seventh Street
Hanford, CA 93230
209-582-9253

Fax: 209-582-1023
http://www.proteusinc.org

Proteus Inc., Kerman
5148 West Whitesbridge
Kerman, CA 93630
209-846-4242
Fax: 209-846-5378
http://www.proteusinc.org

Proteus Inc., London
Community Center
Minnesota Avenue
London, CA 93618
209-595-0723
http://www.proteusinc.org

Proteus Inc., Porterville
54 North Main, Suite 10
Porterville, CA 93257
209-688-4963
Fax: 209-781-7989
http://www.proteusinc.org

Proteus Inc., Sanger
1849 Academy Street
Sanger, CA 93757
209-875-7146
Fax: 209-875-1322
http://www.proteusinc.org

Proteus Inc., Selma
2003 First Street, Suite 128
Selma, CA 93662
209-891-0135
Fax: 209-891-0143
http://www.proteusinc.org

Proteus Inc., Visalia
900 North Dinuba Boulevard
Visalia, CA 93291
209-627-0100
Fax: 209-627-6558
http://www.proteusinc.org

Proteus Inc., Visalia, Corporate Office
4612 West Mineral King Avenue
PO Box 727
Visalia, CA 93279

209-733-5423
Fax: 209-738-1137
http://www.proteusinc.org

COLORADO
Rocky Mountain SER/JOBS for Progress Inc.
4100 West 38th Avenue
PO Box 11148
Denver, CO 80211
303-480-9394
Fax: 303-480-9214

CONNECTICUT
New England Farm Workers' Council Inc., Hartford
423 Washington Street
Hartford, CT 06106
203-249-7693
Fax: 203-249-7696

DELAWARE
Telamon Corporation, Dover
State Office, DE07, Job Training Partnership Act
504 North Dupont Highway
Dover, DE 19901
302-734-1903
Fax: 302-734-0382

DISTRICT OF COLUMBIA
U.S. Department of Labor, Employment and Training Administration
200 Constitution Avenue, NW, Room N-4641
Washington, DC 20210
202-219-5500
http://www.wdsc.org/msfw

FLORIDA
Florida Department of Education
Division of Applied Technology and Adult Education
1114 Florida Education Center
Tallahassee, FL 32399
850-487-1785
Fax: 850-488-1492

GEORGIA

Telamon Corporation, Blackshear
3351 West Highway 84
PO Box 413
Blackshear, GA 31516
912-449-3016
Fax: 912-449-4579

Telamon Corporation, Douglas
613 West Baker Highway
PO Box 966
Douglas, GA 31534
912-384-8856
Fax: 912-384-8929

Telamon Corporation, Dublin
Georgia Office 03
112 East Johnson Street
Dublin, GA 31021
912-275-0127
Fax: 912-275-7545

Telamon Corporation, Kiddie Kastle I
Georgia Office 09
684 North Washington Street
Lyons, GA 30436
912-526-9556
Fax: 912-526-3424

Telamon Corporation, Kiddie Kastle II
111 Oliver Lane
PO Box 815
Glennville, GA 30427
912-654-2182
Fax: 912-654-2190

Telamon Corporation, Kiddie Kastle III
133 Serena Drive
PO Box 469
Norman Park, GA 31771
912-769-3627
Fax: 912-769-3182

Telamon Corporation, Lyons
Georgia Office 05
120 East Liberty Avenue
Lyons, GA 30436
912-526-3094
Fax: 912-526-5906

Telamon Corporation, Macon
State Office GA01
2720 Sheraton Drive, Building D,
   Suite 140
Macon, GA 31204
912-750-7134
Fax: 912-750-7375

Telamon Corporation, Statesboro
105 Elm Street
PO Box 645
Statesboro, GA 30458
912-764-6169
Fax: 912-489-6516

Telamon Corporation, Valdosta
Georgia Office 07
200 East Mary Street
Valdosta, GA 31601
912-244-4920
Fax: 912-244-0907

HAWAII

Maui Economic Opportunity Inc.
189 Kaahumanu
PO Box 2122
Kahului, HI 96732
808-871-9591
Fax: 808-871-2426

IDAHO

Idaho Migrant Council
104 North Kimball
PO Box 490
Caldwell, ID 83606-0490
208-454-1652
Fax: 208-459-0448

ILLINOIS

Illinois Migrant Council
28 East Jackson Boulevard, 16th Floor
Chicago, IL 60604
312-663-1522
Fax: 312-663-1994

INDIANA

Telamon Corporation, Transition Resources, Indianapolis
State Office IN01
2511 East 46th Street, Suite O2
Indianapolis, IN 46205
317-547-1924
Fax: 317-547-6594

Telamon Corporation, Transition Resources, Kokomo
709 South Reed Road, U.S. 31 Bypass
PO Box 307
Kokomo, IN 46903-0307
765-457-5201
Fax: 765-457-5202

Telamon Corporation, Transition Resources, Madison
Indiana Office IN03
220 Clifty Drive, Unit J, Suite 110
Madison, IN 47250
812-273-5451
Fax: 812-273-1881

Telamon Corporation, Transition Resources, Marion
Indiana Office IN04
850 North Miller Avenue
Marion, IN 46952
765-664-7275
Fax: 765-664-7260

Telamon Corporation, Transition Resources, South Bend
Indiana Office 05
2015 West Western Avenue, Suite 410
South Bend, IN 46629
219-237-9407
Fax: 219-237-9408

Telamon Corporation, Transition Resources, Vincennes
310 North Second Street
PO Box 1536
Vincennes, IN 47591
812-886-4771

IOWA

Proteus Inc., Des Moines Education Center
900 East University
Des Moines, IA 50316
800-798-5627
Fax: 515-262-3282
http://www.netins.net/showcase/proteus

Proteus Inc., Des Moines, Central Administration
175 Northwest 57th Place
PO Box 10385
Des Moines, IA 50306
800-372-6031
Fax: 515-244-4166
http://www.netins.net/showcase/proteus

Proteus Inc., Fort Dodge
1812 Central Avenue
Fort Dodge, IA 50501
800-798-8225
Fax: 515-573-5299
http://www.netins.net/showcase/proteus

Proteus Inc., Iowa Falls
620 East Country Club Road
PO Box 207
Iowa Falls, IA 50126
800-213-6177
Fax: 515-648-9195
http://www.netins.net/showcase/proteus

Proteus Inc., Muscatine
119 Sycamore, Suite 300
Muscatine, IA 52761
800-397-9675
Fax: 319-264-0882
http://www.netins.net/showcase/proteus

Proteus Inc., Sioux City
310 South Floyd Boulevard
Sioux City, IA 51101
800-383-5627
Fax: 712-258-2104
http://www.netins.net/showcase/proteus

KANSAS

SER Corporation of Kansas
SER Rural Initiative
709 East 21st
Wichita, KS 67214
316-264-5372
Fax: 316-264-0194

KENTUCKY

Kentucky Farmworker Programs Inc.
1844 Lyda Street, Suite 210
PO Box 51146
Bowling Green, KY 42102-4446
502-782-2330
Fax: 502-781-9820

LOUISIANA

Motivation, Education and Training Inc., Baton Rouge
1055 Laurel Street
Baton Rouge, LA 70802
504-343-0301
Fax: 504-343-7977

MAINE

Training and Development Corporation
18 School Street
Bucksport, ME 04416-1669
207-469-6385
Fax: 207-469-6348

MARYLAND

Telamon Corporation, Hagerstown
Maryland Office MD02
901 Pope Avenue, South Office Suite Two
Hagerstown, MD 21740
301-790-1644
Fax: 301-790-1648

Telamon Corporation, Hagerstown
68 West Church Street
Hagerstown, MD 21740
301-665-1747
Fax: 301-665-1687

Telamon Corporation, Salisbury
State Office MD01
237 Florida Avenue
Salisbury, MD 21801
410-546-4604

MASSACHUSETTS

New England Farm Workers' Council Inc., Springfield
1628 Main Street
Springfield, MA 01103

413-781-2145
Fax: 413-781-5928

MICHIGAN

Telamon Corporation, Adrian
Michigan Office MI02
562 West Maple Avenue
Adrian, MI 49221
517-263-6825
Fax: 517-263-6914

Telamon Corporation, Bay City
Michigan Office 06
511 Adams Street
Bay City, MI 31601
517-894-8941
Fax: 517-894-8944

Telamon Corporation, Benton Harbor
Michigan Office MI20
3310 Coloma Road, Coastal Building
Benton Harbor, MI 49022
616-849-2909
Fax: 616-849-0734

Telamon Corporation, Benton Harbor
Michigan Office 09
4821 North Street, Millburg Center
Benton Harbor, MI 49022
616-944-5959
Fax: 616-944-5934

Telamon Corporation, Britton
8282 East Monroe Road
PO Box Three
Britton, MI 49229
517-451-8587
Fax: 517-451-8452

Telamon Corporation, Conklin
3501 Schler Road
PO Box 71
Conklin, MI 49403
616-899-5583
Fax: 616-899-2243

Telamon Corporation, Holland
Michigan Office 03
512 South Waverly Road, Suite 210

Holland, MI 49423
616-396-5160
Fax: 616-396-6992

Telamon Corporation, Kalamazoo
Michigan Office 04
508 Axtell Street
Kalamazoo, MI 49008
616-385-2122
Fax: 616-385-2422

Telamon Corporation, Lansing
State Office MI01
6250 West Michigan Avenue, Suite C
Lansing, MI 48917
800-782-7831
Fax: 517-323-9840

Telamon Corporation, Pullman
893 55th Street
PO Box 316
Pullman, MI 49450
616-236-5226
Fax: 616-236-6401

Telamon Corporation, Sparta
Michigan Office 05
540 South State Street
Sparta, MI 49345
616-887-0180
Fax: 616-887-1098

Telamon Corporation, Standish
429 West Cedar Street
PO Box 386
Standish, MI 48658
517-846-0633
Fax: 517-846-8669

Telamon Corporation, Traverse City
Michigan Office MI17
10767 Traverse Highway, Suite A
Traverse City, MI 49684
616-941-5300
Fax: 616-941-0924

MINNESOTA
Midwest Farmworker Employment and Training Inc.
Administrative Office
1321 Second Street, North

Sauk Rapids, MN 56379
218-281-7893

MISSISSIPI
Mississippi Delta Council for Farm Workers Opportunities Inc.
1005 State Street
Clarksdale, MS 38614
601-627-1121
Fax: 601-627-5675

MISSOURI
Rural Missouri Inc.
1014 Northeast Drive
Jefferson City, MO 65109
314-635-0136
Fax: 314-635-5636

MONTANA
Rural Employment Opportunities Inc.
25 South Ewing Street, Fifth Floor
PO Box 831
Helena, MT 59624-0831
406-442-7850
Fax: 406-442-7855

NEBRASKA
Naf Multicultural Human Development Corporation
416 East Fourth Street
PO Box 1459
North Platte, NE 69103-1459
308-534-2630
Fax: 308-534-9451

NEVADA
Center for Employment Training, Reno
520 Evans Avenue
Reno, NV 89512-3301
702-348-8668
Fax: 702-348-2034

NEW HAMPSHIRE
Farmworkers' Council Inc.
44 Walnut Street
Manchester, NH 03104

603-622-8199
Fax: 603-622-8230

NEW JERSEY
New Jersey Rural Opportunities
629 Wood Street
Vineland, NJ 08360
609-696-1000
Fax: 609-696-4892

NEW MEXICO
Home Education Livelihood Program Inc.
5101 Copper, NE
Albuquerque, NM 87108
505-265-3717
Fax: 505-265-5412

NEW YORK
Rural Opportunities Inc., Rochester
339 East Avenue, Suite 401
Rochester, NY 14604
716-546-7180
Fax: 716-546-7337

NORTH CAROLINA
Telamon Corporation, Ahoskie
111 North Mitchell Street
PO Box 37
Ahoskie, NC 27910
919-332-4381
Fax: 919-332-3260

Telamon Corporation, Benson
501 South Wall Street
PO Box 1207
Benson, NC 27546
919-207-5813
Fax: 929-207-1914

Telamon Corporation, Clinton
1216 Sunset Avenue
PO Box 1668
Clinton, NC 28329
910-592-1919
Fax: 910-592-5282

Telamon Corporation, Goldsboro
139 Arrington Bridge Road
PO Box 54
Goldsboro, NC 27533-0054
919-734-2378
Fax: 919-734-6878

Telamon Corporation, Hendersonville
30 Francis Road
PO Box 2530
Hendersonville, NC 28793
704-692-0593
Fax: 704-692-0699

Telamon Corporation, Kinston
North Carolina Office NC05
400 Glenwood Avenue, Suite 15
Kinston, NC 28501
919-527-7428

Telamon Corporation, Lumberton
North Court Square
220 Wintergreen Drive, Unit F
Lumberton, NC 28358
910-671-0504
Fax: 910-671-0190

**Telamon Corporation,
    National Headquarters**
3937 Western Boulevard
PO Box 33315
Raleigh, NC 27636
919-851-7611
Fax: 919-851-1139
http://www.telamon.org

Telamon Corporation, Raleigh
State Office NC01
4917 Waters Edge Drive, Suite 220
Raleigh, NC 27606
919-851-6141
Fax: 919-851-2605

Telamon Corporation, Rockingham
801 East Broad Street
PO Box 51
Rockingham, NC 28380
910-997-5541
Fax: 910-997-5610

Telamon Corporation, Whiteville
103 East Main Street
PO Box 1626
Whiteville, NC 28472
910-642-8229
Fax: 910-642-8555

Telamon Corporation, Wilson
109 Raleigh Road
PO Box 7074
Wilson, NC 27895
919-291-1203
Fax: 919-291-7165

NORTH DAKOTA
Midwest Farmworker Employment and Training Inc.
1323 South 23rd Street, Suite I
Fargo, ND 58103
701-293-5959
Fax: 702-293-0857

OHIO
Rural Opportunities Inc., Bowling Green
320 West Gypsy Lane Road
PO Box 186
Bowling Green, OH 43402
419-354-3552
Fax: 419-354-0244

OKLAHOMA
Oro Development Corporation
5929 North May Avenue, Suite 204
Oklahoma City, OK 73112
405-840-7077
Fax: 405-848-7871

OREGON
Oregon Human Development Corporation II
9620 Southwest Barbur Boulevard, Suite 110
Portland, OR 97219
503-245-2600
Fax: 503-245-9602

PENNSYLVANIA
Rural Opportunities Inc., Camp Hill
2331 Market Street, Second Floor
Camp Hill, PA 17011

717-731-8120
Fax: 717-731-8196

SOUTH CAROLINA
Telamon Corporation, Aiken
127 Greenville Street, SW
PO Box 1553
Aiken, SC 29801-1553
803-648-9037
Fax: 803-648-9447

Telamon Corporation, Beaufort
1609 Duke Street
PO Box 1452
Beaufort, SC 29901
803-524-1688
Fax: 803-524-9485

Telamon Corporation, Charleston
1804-C Savannah Highway
PO Box 31545
Charleston, SC 29407
803-766-1545
Fax: 803-766-3260

Telamon Corporation, Columbia
1413 Calhoun Street, Second Floor
PO Box 12217
Columbia, SC 29211-2217
803-256-7411
Fax: 803-256-8528

Telamon Corporation, Florence
912 Evans Street
PO Box 1172
Florence, SC 29501
803-667-4664
Fax: 803-667-4671

Telamon Corporation, Orangeburg
350 Broughton Street, NE
PO Box 2252
Orangeburg, SC 29116-2252
803-534-6444
Fax: 803-534-6037

Telamon Corporation, Spartanburg
134 Garner Road, Suite A
PO Box 5291

Spartanburg, SC 29304
864-573-8783
Fax: 864-573-6342

SOUTH DAKOTA
Midwest Farmworker Employment and Training Inc.
420 South Pierre
PO Box 893
Pierre, SD 57501
605-224-0454
Fax: 605-224-5877

Proteus Inc., Pierre
121 West Dakota Street
Pierre, SD 57501
800-725-1273
Fax: 605-224-5877
http://www.netins.net/showcase/proteus

Proteus Inc., Rapid City
729 East Watertown, Suite One
Rapid City, SD 57701
800-728-6583
Fax: 605-341-2972
http://www.netins.net/showcase/proteus

Proteus Inc., Sioux Falls
301 South Garfield, Suite 6-A
Sioux Falls, SD 57104
800-726-9026
Fax: 605-335-8122
http://www.netins.net/showcase/proteus

Proteus Inc., Watertown
912 Eighth Street, SE
Watertown, SD 57201
800-725-9392
Fax: 605-886-4449
http://www.netins.net/showcase/proteus

TENNESSEE
Tennessee Opportunity Program for Seasonal Farmworkers Inc.
1370 Hazelwood Drive, Suite 207
PO Box 925
Smyrna, TN 37167
615-833-8754
Fax: 615-833-7346

TEXAS
Motivation, Education and Training Inc., Cleveland
307 North College
PO Box 1749
Cleveland, TX 77328-1749
713-592-6483
Fax: 713-592-1690

UTAH
Futures Through Training Inc.
Private Industry Council
2510 Washington Boulevard, Suite 238
PO Box 1309
Ogden, UT 84402
801-399-8850
Fax: 801-399-8114

VIRGINIA
Association of Farmworker Opportunity Programs
1611 North Kent Street, Suite 910
Arlington, VA 22209
703-528-4141
Fax: 703-528-4145

Telamon Corporation, Belle Haven
15421 Merry Cat Lane
Belle Haven, VA 23306
804-442-2002
Fax: 804-442-7392

Telamon Corporation, Danville
Virginia Office 02
1332-D Piney Forest Road
Danville, VA 24540
804-836-9071
Fax: 804-836-9072

Telamon Corporation, Lynchburg
Virginia Office 04
405 Bay Street
Lynchburg, VA 24501
804-486-4100
Fax: 804-528-1692

Telamon Corporation, Richmond
6964 Forest Hill Avenue
Richmond, VA 23225

804-330-7006
Fax: 804-330-3007

Telamon Corporation, South Boston
Virginia Office 05
500 North Street
South Boston, VA 24592
804-572-8993
Fax: 804-572-8613

Telamon Corporation, South Hill
Virginia Office 06
201 East Atlantic Street
South Hill, VA 23970
804-447-7627
Fax: 804-447-4629

Telamon Corporation, Winchester
Virginia Office 07
23 1/2 South Braddock Street
Winchester, VA 22601
540-722-2507
Fax: 540-722-3366

VERMONT
Central Vermont Community Action Council Inc.
36 Barre-Montpelier Road
PO Box 747
Barre, VT 05641
802-479-1053
Fax: 802-479-5353

WASHINGTON
Washington State Migrant Council
301 North First Street, Suite One
Sunnyside, WA 98944
509-882-5800
Fax: 509-882-1605

WEST VIRGINIA
Telamon Corporation
State Office VA01
4915 Radford Avenue, Suite 202
Richmond, WV 26757
304-822-4514
Fax: 304-304-4515

Telamon Corporation, Martinsburg
State Office WV01
100 Williamsport Avenue
Martinsburg, WV 25401
304-263-0916
Fax: 304-263-4809

Telamon Corporation, Romney
320 Elk Place
PO Box 953
Romney, WV 23230-3522
804-355-4676
Fax: 804-355-6407

WISCONSIN
Dilhr/Employment and Training
201 East Washington Avenue, Room 231-X
PO Box 7972
Madison, WI 53707
608-267-7273
Fax: 608-267-0330

WYOMING
**Northwestern Community Action Programs
of Wyoming Inc.**
1922 1/2 Robertson Avenue
PO Box 158
Worland, WY 82401
307-347-6185
Fax: 307-347-4008

PUERTO RICO
**Puerto Rico Department of Labor and
Human Resources**
505 Munoz Rivera Avenue, 21st Floor
Hato Rey, PR 00918
787-754-2119
Fax: 787-753-9550

NATIVE AMERICAN WORKERS
ALABAMA
Inter-Tribal Council of Alabama
669 South Lawrence Street
Montgomery, AL 36104
205-269-5270
Fax: 205-240-3408

Inter-Tribal Council of Alabama
1021 East Main Street
Prattville, AL 36066
334-361-1005
Fax: 334-361-1539

Poarch Band of Creek Indians
HCR 69A, Box 85-B
Atmore, AL 36502
205-368-9136
Fax: 205-368-4502

ALASKA
Aleutian-Pribilof Islands Association Inc.
401 East Fireweed Lane, Suite 201
Anchorage, AK 99503-2111
907-276-2700
Fax: 907-279-4351

Arctic Slope Native Association, Limited
PO Box 1232
Barrow, AK 99559
907-852-2762

Association of Village Council Presidents
Pouch 219
Bethel, AK 99559
907-543-3241
Fax: 907-543-3596

Bristol Bay Native Association
PO Box 310
Dillingham, AK 99576
907-842-5257
Fax: 907-842-5932

Central Council of Tlingit and Haida Indian Tribes
320 West Willoughby, Suite 300
Juneau, AK 99801
907-586-1432
Fax: 907-586-8970

Cook Inlet Tribal Council
670 West Fireweed Lane, Suite 200
Anchorage, AK 99503
907-265-5900
Fax: 907-265-5947

Kawerak Inc.
PO Box 948
Nome, AK 99762
907-443-5682
Fax: 907-443-3708

Kenaitze Indian Tribe
PO Box 988
Kenai, AK 99611
907-283-3633

Kodiak Area Native Association
402 Center Avenue
Kodiak, AK 99615
907-486-5725
Fax: 907-486-2763

Kuskokwim Native Association
PO Box 127
Aniak, AK 99557
907-675-4384

Maniilaq Manpower Inc.
PO Box 725
Kotzebue, AK 99752
907-636-2105
Fax: 907-442-2003

Metlakatla Indian Community
PO Box Eight
Metlakatla, AK 99926
907-886-4441
Fax: 907-886-7997

Native Village of Barrow
PO Box 1139
Barrow, AK 99926
907-852-2611

Orutsararmuit Native Council
PO Box 927
Bethel, AK 99559
907-543-2608
Fax: 907-543-2639

Tanana Chiefs Conference
122 First Avenue
Fairbanks, AK 99701
907-452-8251
Fax: 907-459-3851

ARIZONA

Affiliation of Arizona Indian Centers Inc.
2400 North Central Avenue, Suite 301
Phoenix, AZ 85004
602-252-9040
Fax: 602-252-9077

American Indian Association of Tucson
131 East Broadway, First Floor
PO Box 2307
Tucson, AZ 85705
520-884-7131
Fax: 520-884-0240

Colorado River Indian Tribes
Route One, Box 23-B
Parker, AZ 85344
520-669-9211
Fax: 520-669-5675

Gila River Indian Community
Box 97
Sacaton, AZ 85247
520-562-3387
Fax: 520-562-3590

Hopi Tribal Council
PO Box 123
Kukotsomvi, AZ 86039
520-734-2441
Fax: 520-734-2435

Indian Development District of Arizona Inc.
5150 North 16th Street, Suite A-116
Phoenix, AZ 85016-3934
602-274-6151
Fax: 602-274-7633

Native Americans for Community Action Inc.
2717 North Steves Boulevard, Suite 11
Flagstaff, AZ 86004
520-526-2968
Fax: 520-526-0708

Navajo Tribe of Indians
PO Box 1889
Window Rock, AZ 86515
520-871-4941
Fax: 520-871-7116

Pasqua Yaqui Tribe
7474 South Camino de Oeste
Tucson, AZ 84746
520-883-5000
Fax: 520-883-5014

Phoenix Indian Center Inc.
2601 North Third Street, #211
Phoenix, AZ 85004
602-263-1017
Fax: 602-263-7822

Salt River and Pima-Maricopa Indian Community
Route One, Box 216
Scottsdale, AZ 85256
602-941-7277
Fax: 602-949-2900

ARKANSAS

American Indian Center of Arkansas Inc.
1100 North University, Suite 133
Little Rock, AR 72207-6344
501-666-9032
Fax: 501-666-5875

CALIFORNIA

American Indian Center of Santa Clara Valley Inc.
919 The Alameda
San Jose, CA 95126
408-971-9673
Fax: 408-971-0357

California Indian Manpower Consortium
4153 Northgate Boulevard
Sacramento, CA 95834
916-920-0285
Fax: 916-641-6338

Candelaria American Indian Council
3203 East Main Street
Ventura, CA 93003
805-650-8352
Fax: 805-650-8954

Indian Human Resource Center Inc.
4040 30th Street, Suite A
San Diego, CA 92104

619-281-5965
Fax: 619-281-1466

Northern California Indian Development Council Inc.
241 F Street
Eureka, CA 95501
707-445-8451

Southern California Indian Center Inc.
12755 Brookhurst Street
PO Box 2550
Garden Grove, CA 92642-2550
714-663-1102
Fax: 714-636-4226

United Indian Nations Inc.
1320 Webster Street
Oakland, CA 94612
510-763-3410
Fax: 510-763-3646

Ya-Ka-Ama Indian Education and Development
6215 Eastside Road
Forestville, CA 95436
707-887-1541

COLORADO
Denver Indian Center Inc.
4407 Morrison Road
Denver, CO 80219
303-937-0401
Fax: 303-930-2699

DISTRICT OF COLUMBIA
U.S. Department of Labor, Employment and Training Administration
200 Constitution Avenue, NW, Room N-4641
Washington, DC 20210
202-219-8502
Fax: 202-219-6338

DELAWARE
Nanticoke Indian Association Inc.
Route Four, Box 107A
Millsboro, DE 19966
302-945-2475

FLORIDA
Miccosukee Corporation
Tamiami Station
PO Box 440021
Miami, FL 33144
305-223-8380
Fax: 305-223-1011

HAWAII
Alu Like Inc.
1505 Dillingham Boulevard, #218
Honolulu, HI 96819-4417
808-836-8940
Fax: 808-834-4702

IDAHO
Kootenai Tribe of Idaho
PO Box 1269
Bonners Ferry, ID 83805
208-267-3519
Fax: 208-267-2960

ILLINOIS
Native American Educational Service College
2838 West Peterson
Chicago, IL 60659
312-761-5000
Fax: 312-761-3808

INDIANA
American Indian Manpower Council
6100 North Keystone Avenue, #357
Indianapolis, IN 46220-2427
317-251-5648

KANSAS
Mid-America All Indian Center
650 North Seneca
Wichita, KS 67203
316-262-5221
Fax: 316-262-4216

LOUISIANA

Inter-Tribal Council of Louisiana Inc.
5723 Superior Drive, Suite B-1
Baton Rouge, LA 70816
504-292-2474

MAINE

Central Main Indian Association Inc.
132-144 North Main Street
PO Box 3040
Brewer, ME 04412
207-989-5971
Fax: 207-989-5975

Passamaquoddy Joint Council
136 North Street
Calais, ME 04619
207-454-0428
Fax: 204-454-0403

Tribal Governors Inc.
136 Union Street, Suite Four
Bangor, ME 04401
207-941-6568

MARYLAND

Baltimore Indian Center Inc.
113 South Broadway
Baltimore, MD 21231
410-675-3535
Fax: 410-675-1054

MASSACHUSETTS

North American Indian Center of Boston Inc.
105 South Huntington Avenue
Jamaica Plain, MA 02130
617-232-0343
Fax: 617-232-3863

MICHIGAN

Inter-Tribal Council of Michigan Inc.
405 East Easterday Avenue
Sault Ste. Marie, MI 49783
906-632-6896

Michigan Indian Employment and Training Services Inc.
2450 Delhi Commerce Drive, Suite 5
Holt, MI 48842
517-694-7800
Fax: 517-694-8808

North American Indian Association of Detroit Inc.
22720 Plymouth Road
Detroit, MI 48239-1327
313-535-2966
Fax: 313-535-8060

Southeastern Michigan Indians Inc.
26641 Lawrence Street
Centerline, MI 48015
810-756-1350

MINNESOTA

American Indian Opportunities Inc.
1845 East Franklin Avenue
Minneapolis, MN 55404
612-341-3358
Fax: 612-341-3766

Bois Forte Reservation Tribal Council
SkillsNet-Job Service Office
PO Box 16
Nett Lake, MN 55772
218-757-3462

Fond du Lac Reservation Business Committee
SkillsNet-Job Service Office
105 University Road
Cloquet, MN 55720
218-879-1759

Grand Portage Reservation Tribal Council
SkillsNet-Job Service Office
PO Box 428
Grand Portage, MN 55605
218-475-2239

Leech Lake Reservation Tribal Council
SkillsNet-Job Service Office
Route Three, Box 100
Cass Lake, MN 56633
218-335-2531

Lower Sioux Indian Community
SkillsNet-Job Service Office
PO Box 308
Morton, MN 56270
507-697-6185

Mille Lacs Band of Chippewa Indians
SkillsNet-Job Service Office
HCR 67, PO Box 194
Onamia, MN 56359
320-532-4181

Prairie Island Tribal Council
SkillsNet-Job Service Office
1158 Island Boulevard
Welch, MN 55089
612-385-2554

Shakopee Mdewakanton Sioux Community
SkillsNet-Job Service Office
2330 Sioux Trail
Prior Lake, MN 55372
612-445-8900
Fax: 612-445-8906

Upper Sioux Community Board of Trustees
SkillsNet-Job Service Office
PO Box 147
Granite Falls, MN 56241
320-564-2360

White Earth Tribal Council
SkillsNet-Job Service Office
PO Box 418
White Earth, MN 56591
218-983-3285

MISSISSIPPI
Mississippi Band of Choctaw Indians
Choctaw Branch
PO Box 6010
Philadelphia, MS 39350
601-656-5251

MISSOURI
American Indian Council Inc.
310 Armour Road, #205
Kansas City, MO 64116
816-471-4898

MONTANA
Assiniboine and Sioux Tribes
Fort Peck Indian Reservation
PO Box 1027
Poplar, MT 59255
406-768-5155
Fax: 406-768-5478

B.C. of the Chippewa Cree Tribe
Rocky Boy Route
PO Box 578
Box Elder, MT 59521
406-295-4210

Blackfeet Tribal Business Council
PO Box 1090
Browning, MT 59417
406-338-2111
Fax: 406-338-5540

Confederated Salish and Kootenai Tribes
PO Box 278
Pablo, MT 59855
406-675-2600
Fax: 406-765-2806

Montana United Indian Association
PO Box 6043
Helena, MT 59604
406-443-5350
Fax: 406-443-5351

NEBRASKA
Indian Center Inc.
1100 Military Road
Lincoln, NE 68508
402-438-5231

**Nebraska Indian Inter-Tribal Development
    Corporation**
Route One, Box 66-A
Winnebago, NE 68071
402-878-2242

NEVADA
Inter-Tribal Council of Nevada Inc.
680 Greenbrae, Suite 280
Sparks, NV 89431

702-355-0600
Fax: 702-355-0648

Las Vegas Indian Center Inc.
2300 West Bonanza Road
Las Vegas, NV 89106
702-647-5842

NEW JERSEY
Powhatan Renape Nation
Rankokus Reservation
PO Box 225
Rankokus, NJ 08073
609-261-4747
Fax: 609-261-7313

NEW MEXICO
Alamo Navajo School Board Inc.
PO Box 907
Magdalena, NM 87825
505-854-2543
Fax: 505-854-2545

All Indian Pueblo Council Inc.
3939 San Pedro, NE, Suite D
PO Box 3256
Albuquerque, NM 87190
515-881-1992
Fax: 505-883-7682

Eight Northern Indian Pueblos Council
PO Box 969
San Juan Pueblo, NM 87566
505-852-4265
Fax: 505-852-4835

Five Sandoval Indian Pueblos
1043 Highway 313
PO Box 580
Bernalillo, NM 87004
515-867-3351

National Indian Youth Council
318 Elm Street, SE
Albuquerque, NM 87102
505-247-2251
Fax: 505-247-4251

Ramah Navajo School Board Inc.
Drawer 10
Pine Hill, NM 87357
505-775-3257
Fax: 505-775-3240

NEW YORK
American Indian Community House Inc.
404 Lafayette Street, Second Floor
New York, NY 10003
212-598-0100
Fax: 212-598-4909

Community Services of Erie and Niagara Counties Inc.
1047 Grant Street
PO Box 0086
Buffalo, NY 14207-0086

Native American Cultural Center Inc.
1475 Winton Road, North, Suite 12
Rochester, NY 14609
716-482-1100

NORTH CAROLINA
Cumberland County Association for Indian People
102 Indian Drive
Fayetteville, NC 28301
910-483-8442

Guildord Native American Association
400 Prescott Street
PO Box 5623
Greensboro, NC 27435
910-273-8686
Fax: 910-272-2925

Lumbee Regional Development Association
PO Box 68
Pembroke, NC 28372
910-521-9761
Fax: 910-521-7525

Metrolina Native American Association
2601-A East Seventh Street
Charlotte, NC 28204
704-331-4818
Fax: 704-331-9501

North Carolina Commission of Indian Affairs
217 West Jones Street
Raleigh, NC 27603-1336
919-733-5998

NORTH DAKOTA

Devils Lake Sioux Tribe
PO Box 359
Fort Totten, ND 58335
701-766-4221
Fax: 701-766-4126

Standing Rock Sioux Tribe
Box D
Fort Yates, ND 58538
701-854-7569
Fax: 701-854-7299

Three Affiliated Tribes
Fort Berthold Reservation
PO Box 597
New Town, ND 58763
701-627-4781
Fax: 701-627-3805

United Tribes Technical College
3315 University Drive
Bismarck, ND 58511
701-255-3285
Fax: 701-255-2207

OHIO

North American Indian Cultural Center
1062 Triplett Boulevard
Akron, OH 44306
216-724-1280
Fax: 216-724-9298

OKLAHOMA

Inter-Tribal Council of Northeast Oklahoma
PO Box 1308
Miami, OK 74355
918-542-4486
Fax: 918-540-2500

Oklahoma Tribal Assistance Program Inc.
PO Box 2841
Tulsa, OK 74101-2841

918-744-8866
Fax: 918-744-5635

United Urban Indian Council Inc.
1501 Classen Boulevard, #200
Oklahoma City, OK 73106-5435
405-521-9047
Fax: 405-521-9067

OREGON

Confederated Tribes of Siletz Indians
1718 Northeast 82nd Avenue
Portland, OR 97220
503-255-3510

Organization of Forgotten Americans Inc.
4509 South Sixth Street, #206
PO Box 1257
Klamath Falls, OR 97601-0276
503-882-4441
Fax: 503-882-4442

PENNSYLVANIA

Council of Three Rivers
200 Charles Street
Pittsburgh, PA 15238
412-782-4457
Fax: 412-767-4808

United American Indians of the Delaware Valley
225 Chestnut Street
Philadelphia, PA 19106
215-574-9020
Fax: 215-574-9024

RHODE ISLAND

Rhode Island Indian Council
444 Friendship Street
Providence, RI 02907
401-331-4440
Fax: 402-454-4280

SOUTH CAROLINA

South Carolina Indian Development Council Inc.
PO Box 957
Rock Hill, SC 29731
803-324-0259

SOUTH DAKOTA

Cheyenne River Sioux Tribe
PO Box 837
Eagle Butte, SD 57625
605-964-6415
Fax: 605-964-4151

Lower Brule Sioux Tribe
Box 187
Lower Brule, SD 57548
605-473-5561
Fax: 605-473-5491

Oglala Sioux Tribe
PO Box G
Pine Ridge, SD 57770
605-867-5821
Fax: 605-867-5659

United Sioux Tribal Development Corporation
PO Box 1193
Pierre, SD 57501
605-224-8865
Fax: 605-224-0069

TENNESSEE

Native American Indian Association
211 Union Street, #932
Stahlman Building
Nashville, TN 37201
615-726-0806
Fax: 615-726-0810

TEXAS

Dallas Inter-Tribal Center
209 East Jefferson Boulevard
Dallas, TX 75203-2690
214-941-1050
Fax: 214-941-1668

Ysleta Del Sur Pueblo
119 South Old Pueblo Road
PO Box 17579
El Paso, TX 79917
915-858-0271
Fax: 915-859-2988

UTAH

Indian Training and Education Center
1865 South Main, Suite One
Salt Lake City, UT 84115
801-484-4447
Fax: 801-484-4473

VERMONT

Abenaki Self-Help Association
New Hampshire Indian Council
PO Box 276
Swanton, VT 05488
802-868-2559
Fax: 802-868-5118

VIRGINIA

Mattaponi, Pamunkey, Monacan Consortium
Route Two, Box 360
King William, VA 23086
804-769-4767
Fax: 804-769-0742

WASHINGTON

American Indian Community Center
East 905 Third Avenue
Spokane, WA 99202
509-535-0886

Lummi Indian Business Council
2616 Kwina Road
Bellingham, WA 98225
360-734-8180

Seattle Indian Center Inc.
611 12th Avenue, South, #300
Seattle, WA 98144
206-329-8700
Fax: 206-328-5983

**Western Washington Indian Employment
and Training Program**
4505 Pacific Highway, East, Suite C-1
Tacoma, WA 98424
206-593-2656
Fax: 206-926-0630

WISCONSIN

Milwaukee Area American Indian Manpower Council Inc.
1711 South 11th Street, Second Floor
Milwaukee, WI 53204
414-643-8300
Fax: 414-643-1012

Stockbridge-Munsee Community
Route One
Bowler, WI 54416
715-793-4111
Fax: 715-793-1303

Wisconsin Indian Consortium
PO Box 181
Odanah, WI 54861
715-682-5308

WYOMING

Shoshone-Arapahoe Tribes
PO Box 920
Fort Washakie, WY 82514
307-332-6320
Fax: 307-332-9207

OLDER WORKERS

ALASKA

Older Alaskans Commission
Administration Department
Box C
Juneau, AK 99811-0209
907-465-3250

ARKANSAS

Arkansas Abilities Based on Long Experience (ABLE)
200 South University, Suite 205
Little Rock, AR 72205
501-660-4110

Human Services Department
1417 Donaghey Plaza South
PO Box 1437
Little Rock, AR 72203-1437
501-682-8525

CALIFORNIA

Asociacion Nacional Pro Personas Mayores
3325 Wilshire Boulevard, Suite 800
Los Angeles, CA 90010
213-487-1922

California Department of Aging
1600 K Street
Sacramento, CA 95814
916-322-3576

Intercultural Education Employment and Training
1362 Post Street
San Francisco, CA 94109
415-441-1881
Fax: 415-885-4155

COLORADO

Services for the Aging
Colorado Department of Social Services
1575 Sherman Street
Denver, CO 80203-1714
303-866-5911

CONNECTICUT

Bridgeport Jobs
350 Fairfield Avenue, Third Floor
Bridgeport, CT 06604
203-334-5627

Elderly Services Division
Social Services Department
175 Main Street
Hartford, CT 06106
203-424-5249

DELAWARE

Division of Aging
Health and Social Services Department
1901 North Dupont Highway
New Castle, DE 19720
302-577-4791

DISTRICT OF COLUMBIA

American Association of Retired Persons
PO Box 51040-GPCD
Washington, DC 20091
202-434-2277

Employment Services Department
500 C Street, NW, Room 600
Washington, DC 20001
202-724-7073

National Center on Black Aged Inc.
1424 K Street, NW, Suite 500
Washington, DC 20005
202-637-8400

National Council of Senior Citizens
Senior Aides Program
1331 F Street, NW
Washington, DC 20004
202-347-8800

Senior Community Service Project
National Council on the Aging
409 Third Street, SW, Second Floor
Washington, DC 20024
202-479-6331

State Unit Agency on Aging, Republic of Palau
444 North Capitol Street, NW, Suite 308
PO Box 100
Washington, DC 20001
202-624-7793

GEORGIA

Office of Aging
Human Resources Department
Two Peachtree Street, Suite 18-310
Atlanta, GA 30303
404-657-5329

HAWAII

Labor and Industrial Relations Department
830 Punchbowl Street, Room 316
Honolulu, HI 96813
808-548-6924

IDAHO

Idaho Office on Aging
Statehouse, Room 114
Boise, ID 83720
208-334-3833

ILLINOIS

Illinois Department on Aging
421 East Capitol Avenue
Springfield, IL 62706
217-785-0117

INDIANA

Aging and Community Services Department
251 North Illinois Street
PO Box 7083
Indianapolis, IN 46207-7083
317-232-7146

Indiana's One-Stop Career Center System
10 North Senate Avenue
Indianapolis, IN 46204-2277
317-232-7381

IOWA

Iowa Department of Elder Affairs
236 Jewett Building
914 Grand Avenue
Des Moines, IA 50319
515-281-5187

Iowa's One-Stop Career Center System
150 Des Moines Street
Des Moines, IA 50319
515-281-9036

KANSAS

American Red Cross-Midway, Kansas Chapter
707 North Main
Wichita, KS 67203

Kansas Department of Human Resources
401 Topeka Boulevard
Topeka, KS 66603
913-296-7474
Fax: 913-296-0179

Kansas Department on Aging
Docking State Office Building, 122-S
915 Southwest Harrison
Topeka, KS 66612-1500
913-296-4986

Kansas Green Thumb Inc.
715 North Main
Newton, KS 67114
316-283-7473

Let's Help Inc.
302 Van Buren
PO Box 2492
Topeka, KS 66601
785-232-4357

National Association for Hispanic Elderly
1333 South 27th Street
PO Box 6148
Kansas City, KS 66106
913-722-1155
Fax: 913-722-6646

National Indian Council on the Aging Inc.
636 Minnesota Avenue, Suite B
Kansas City, KS 66101
913-371-6357
Fax: 913-371-7866

North Central/Flint Hills Area Agency on Aging, Manhattan
437 Houston Street
Manhattan, KS 66502
785-776-9294
Fax: 785-776-9479

North Central/Flint Hills Area Agency on Aging, Salina
245 North Ninth Street
Salina, KS 67401-2111
785-827-4857

Senior Services Inc., of Wichita
Kansas Elks Training Center for the Handicapped
200 South Walnut
Wichita, KS 67213-4777
316-267-0302
Fax: 316-267-0805

SER Corporation
709 East 21st Street
Wichita, KS 67214
316-264-0194
Fax: 316-264-0194

Southeast Kansas AAA
811 West Main
PO Box 269
Chanute, KS 66720
800-794-2440
Fax: 316-431-1602

KENTUCKY

Aging Services Division
Cabinet for Human Resources
275 East Main Street, Sixth Floor, West
Frankfort, KY 40621
502-564-6930

LOUISIANA

Elderly Affairs Office
4528 Bennington Avenue
PO Box 80374
Baton Rouge, LA 70898-0374
504-925-4390

MAINE

Bureau of Maine's Elderly
Human Services Department
State of Maine
Augusta, ME 04333
207-626-5335

Training Resource Center
185 Lancaster Street
PO Box 738
Portland, ME 04104-0738
207-775-5891

MARYLAND

Job Training Partnership Act Employment Training Program
1100 North Eutaw Street, Room 310
Baltimore, MD 21201

410-767-2800
Fax: 410-767-2842

Maryland Office on Aging
1004 State Office Building
301 West Preston Street
Baltimore, MD 21201
410-225-1113

Maryland's CareerNet System
1414 Key Highway, Second Floor
Baltimore, MD 21230
410-333-4454

MASSACHUSETTS
Computer Training Center
119 Beach Street, Fourth Floor
Boston, MA 02111-2511
617-542-4180

Elder Affairs Department
Commonwealth of Massachusetts
One Ashburton Place
Boston, MA 02108
617-727-7750

MICHIGAN
Office of Services to the Aging
101 North Pine Street
PO Box 30026
Lansing, MI 48909
517-373-4068

MINNESOTA
Jobs and Training Department
390 North Robert Street
St. Paul, MN 55101
612-297-1054

MISSISSIPPI
Adult Services, Division of Aging
Human Services Department
PO Box 352
Jackson, MS 39205-0352
601-359-4929

MISSOURI
Division of Aging, Social Services Department
2701 West Main
Box 1337
Jefferson City, MO 65102
314-751-3082

NEBRASKA
Nebraska Department on Aging
State Office Building
PO Box 95044
Lincoln, NE 68509-5044
402-471-4619

NEVADA
Nevada Division for Aging Services
Human Resources Department
340 North 11th, State Mailroom Complex
Las Vegas, NV 89158
702-486-3545

NEW HAMPSHIRE
New Hampshire Governor's Office
Human Resources Division
57 Regional Drive
Concord, NH 03301
603-271-2611

NEW JERSEY
New Jersey Community Affairs Department
Division on Aging
South Broad and Front Street, CN 807
Trenton, NJ 08625-0807
609-588-3354

NEW MEXICO
National Indian Council on Aging Inc.
City Centre, Suite 510-W
6400 Uptown Boulevard, NE
Albuquerque, NM 87100
505-888-3302

New Mexico Agency on Aging
La Villa Rivera Building
224 East Palace Avenue, Fourth Floor

Santa Fe, NM 87501
505-827-7640

NEW YORK
National Urban League Inc.
Seniors in Community Service Program
500 East 62nd Street
New York, NY 10021
212-310-9120

New York Office for the Aging
Title V Unit, Agency Building Two
Empire State Plaza
Albany, NY 12223
518-473-5108

NORTH CAROLINA
Capital Area Ready Older Workers Program
PO Box 550
Raleigh, NC 27602
919-856-6040

Division of Aging, Human Resources Department
Taylor Building, Room 216
693 Palmer Drive
Raleigh, NC 27603
919-733-8399

NORTH DAKOTA
Job Service
1000 East Divide Avenue
PO Box 5507
Bismarck, ND 58502
701-224-2843

OHIO
Ohio Department on Aging
50 West Broad Street, Ninth Floor
Columbus, OH 43266-0501
614-466-7083

OKLAHOMA
Oklahoma Governor's Office
Will Rogers Building, Room 408
2401 North Lincoln

Oklahoma City, OK 73105
405-557-5373

OREGON
Employment, Training, and Business Services
PO Box 215
Maryhurst, OR 97036
503-635-4591

Senior and Disabled Division
313 Public Service Building
Salem, OR 97310
503-945-6413

PENNSYLVANIA
Bureau of Job Service
32 East Union Street
Wilkes-Barre, PA 18711
717-826-2425

Pennsylvania Department of Aging
Market Street Station Office Building, Sixth Floor
400 Market Street
Harrisburg, PA 17101-2307
717-783-6007

RHODE ISLAND
Rhode Island Department of Elderly Affairs
160 Pine Street
Providence, RI 02903
401-277-2819

SOUTH CAROLINA
South Carolina Governor's Office
Division on Aging
202 Arbor Lake Drive, Suite B 301
Columbia, SC 29223
803-735-0210

SOUTH DAKOTA
Turning Point's Career Learning Center
908 North West Avenue
Sioux Falls, SD 57104-5722
605-367-4293

TENNESSEE
Tennessee Commission on Aging
706 Church Street, Suite 201
Nashville, TN 37219-5573
615-741-2056

TEXAS
Goodwill Industries of Central Texas
300 North Lamar Boulevard
Austin, TX 78703-4697
512-476-5335
Fax: 512-472-6521

Texas Department on Aging
1949 Interstate Highway 35, South
Austin, TX 78741
512-444-2727

Texas One-Stop Career Center System
101 East 15th Street
Austin, TX 78778
512-463-2652

UTAH
Utah Division of Aging and Adult Services
120 North 200 West
PO Box 4550
Salt Lake City, UT 84145-0500
801-538-3910

VIRGINIA
Green Thumb Inc. Headquarters
2000 North 14th Street, Suite 800
Arlington, VA 22201
703-522-7272

U.S. Forest Service
Human Resources Programs
1621 North Kent Street, Room 1010, RP-E
Rosslyn, VA 22209
703-235-8834

**Virginia Governor's Employment and Training
    Department**
Commonwealth Building, Third Floor
4615 West Broad Street
Richmond, VA 23230

804-367-9818
Fax: 804-367-6172

VERMONT
**Vermont Department of Rehabilitation
    and Aging**
103 South Main Street
Waterbury, VT 05676
802-241-2127

WASHINGTON
National Asian Pacific Center on Aging
Melbourne Tower
1511 Third Avenue, Suite 914
Seattle, WA 98101
206-624-1221
Fax: 206-624-1023

Washington State Office on Aging
Social and Health Services Department
4413 Woodview Drive, SE, QG-16
Olympia, WA 98504
206-493-2557

WISCONSIN
Wisconsin Bureau on Aging
Health and Social Services Department
PO Box 7850
Madison, WI 53707-7850
608-266-4448

Wisconsin's One-Stop Career Center System
201 East Washington Avenue
Madison, WI 53707
608-266-2439

WEST VIRGINIA
West Virginia Commission on Aging
Holly Grove Boulevard
Charleston, WV 25305-0160
304-558-3317

WYOMING
Five Percent Older Worker Program
1130 Major Avenue
PO Box BD

Riverton, WY 82501
307-856-6880

Wyoming Division on Aging
139 Hathaway Building
Cheyenne, WY 82002-0710
307-777-7986

AMERICAN SAMOA
American Samoa, Government of
Territorial Administration on Aging
Pago Pago, AS 96799
684-633-1251

GUAM
Labor Department
PO Box 9970
Tamuning, GU 96931-9970
FTS 556-3165

PUERTO RICO
Social Services Department
Assistant Secretariat of Family Services
Box 11398
Santurce, PR 00910
809-723-3401

VETERANS
ALABAMA
**Veterans' Employment and Training Service,
U.S. Department of Labor**
649 Monroe Street, Room 543
Montgomery, AL 36131-6300
334-223-7677
Fax: 334-242-8927

ALASKA
**Veterans' Employment and Training Service,
U.S. Department of Labor**
1111 West Eighth Street
PO Box 25509
Juneau, AK 99802-5509
907-465-2723
Fax: 907-465-5528

ARIZONA
**Veterans' Employment and Training Service,
U.S. Department of Labor**
1400 West Washington
PO Box 6123-SC760E
Phoenix, AZ 85005
602-379-4961

ARKANSAS
Arkansas Department of Workforce Education
Executive Building, Suite 220
2020 West Third Street
Little Rock, AR 72205
501-324-9473
http://www.state.ar.us/worked/index.html

**Veterans' Employment and Training Service,
U.S. Department of Labor**
State Capitol Mall, Room G-12
PO Box 128
Little Rock, AR 72203
501-682-3786
Fax: 501-682-3752

CALIFORNIA
**Veterans' Employment and Training Service,
U.S. Department of Labor**
2550 Mariposa Mall, Room 1080
Fresno, CA 93721-2296
209-445-5193
Fax: 209-445-5023

**Veterans' Employment and Training Service,
U.S. Department of Labor**
1511 East Holt Boulevard
Ontario, CA 91761-2106
909-460-7631
Fax: 909-460-7659

**Veterans' Employment and Training Service,
U.S. Department of Labor**
363 Civic Drive
Pleasant Hills, CA 94523-1987
510-602-1541
Fax: 510-602-5023

**Veterans' Employment and Training Service,
U.S. Department of Labor**
814 West Colton Avenue
Redlands, CA 92374-2930

909-335-6763
Fax: 909-798-6857

**Veterans' Employment and Training Service,
U.S. Department of Labor**
800 Capitol Mall, Room W1142
PO Box 826880
Sacramento, CA 94280-0001
916-654-8178
Fax: 916-654-9469

**Veterans' Employment and Training Service,
U.S. Department of Labor**
8977 Activity Road
San Diego, CA 92126-4427
619-689-6008
Fax: 619-689-6012

**Veterans' Employment and Training Service,
U.S. Department of Labor**
1520 San Fernando Road
San Fernando, CA 91340-3193
818-898-4126
Fax: 818-361-3417

**Veterans' Employment and Training Service,
U.S. Department of Labor**
71 Stevenson Street, Suite 705
San Francisco, CA 94105
415-975-4702
Fax: 415-975-4704

**Veterans' Employment and Training Service,
U.S. Department of Labor**
745 Franklin Street, Room 218
San Francisco, CA 94102-3287
415-749-7479
Fax: 415-749-7476

**Veterans' Employment and Training Service,
U.S. Department of Labor**
932 Broadway
Santa Monica, CA 90401-2383
310-576-6444
Fax: 310-395-4819

COLORADO
**Veterans' Employment and Training Service,
U.S. Department of Labor**
2555 Airport Road
Colorado Springs, CO 80910-3176

719-475-3750
Fax: 719-633-4227

**Veterans' Employment and Training Service,
U.S. Department of Labor**
Two Park Central, Suite 400
1515 Arapahoe Street
Denver, CO 80202-2117
303-844-2151
Fax: 303-620-4257

**Veterans' Employment and Training Service,
U.S. Department of Labor**
1801 California Street, Suite 910
Denver, CO 80202-2614
303-844-1175
Fax: 303-844-1179

CONNECTICUT
**Veterans' Employment and Training Service,
U.S. Department of Labor**
Connecticut Job Service
500 State Street
Bridgeport, CT 06604
203-579-6262

**Veterans' Employment and Training Service,
U.S. Department of Labor**
Connecticut Department of Labor Building
200 Folly Brook Boulevard
Wethersfield, CT 06109
860-566-3326
Fax: 860-566-3733

DELAWARE
**Veterans' Employment and Training Service,
U.S. Department of Labor**
4425 North Market Street, Room 420
Wilmington, DE 19809-0828
302-761-8138
Fax: 302-761-6621

DISTRICT OF COLUMBIA
**Veterans' Employment and Training Service,
U.S. Department of Labor**
200 Constitution Avenue, NW, Room S-1316
Washington, DC 20210

202-219-9116
Fax: 202-219-4773

**Veterans' Employment and Training Service,
U.S. Department of Labor**
500 C Street, NW, Room 108
Washington, DC 20001
202-724-7004
Fax: 202-724-7006

FLORIDA
**Veterans' Employment and Training Service,
U.S. Department of Labor**
1001 Executive Drive, Second Floor,
Room 26
PO Box 149123
Orlando, FL 32803-2999
407-897-2888

**Veterans' Employment and Training Service,
U.S. Department of Labor**
3160 Fifth Avenue, North, Room 101
PO Box 84
St. Petersburg, FL 33731-0084
813-893-2415

**Veterans' Employment and Training Service,
U.S. Department of Labor**
Marathon Building, Suite 205
PO Box 1527
Tallahassee, FL 32302-1527
904-942-8800
Fax: 904-922-2690

GEORGIA
**Veterans' Employment and Training Service,
U.S. Department of Labor**
Atlanta Federal Center
61 Forsyth Street, SW, Room 6-T85
Atlanta, GA 30303
404-562-2305
Fax: 404-562-2313

**Veterans' Employment and Training Service,
U.S. Department of Labor**
Sussex Place, Suite 504
148 International Boulevard, NE
Atlanta, GA 30303-1751

404-656-3127
Fax: 404-657-7403

HAWAII
**Veterans' Employment and Training Service,
U.S. Department of Labor**
830 Punchbowl Street, Room 315
PO Box 3680
Honolulu, HI 96813
808-522-8216
Fax: 808-586-9258

IDAHO
**Veterans' Employment and Training Service,
U.S. Department of Labor**
317 Main Street, Room 303
PO Box 2697
Boise, ID 83701
208-334-6163
Fax: 208-334-6389

ILLINOIS
**Veterans' Employment and Training Service,
U.S. Department of Labor**
230 South Dearborn, Room 1064
Chicago, IL 60604
312-353-4942
Fax: 312-353-4943

**Veterans' Employment and Training Service,
U.S. Department of Labor**
401 South State Street, Two North
Chicago, IL 60605
312-793-3433
Fax: 312-793-4795

**Veterans' Employment and Training Service,
U.S. Department of Labor**
555 South Pasfield
Springfield, IL 62704
217-524-7769
Fax: 217-785-9715

**Veterans' Employment and Training Service,
U.S. Department of Labor**
221 North Genesee Street
Waukegan, IL 60085
847-336-0415

INDIANA
Veterans' Employment and Training Service, U.S. Department of Labor
2425 Coliseum Boulevard, South
Fort Wayne, IN 46803
219-426-8081
Fax: 219-424-4705

Veterans' Employment and Training Service, U.S. Department of Labor
10 North Senate Avenue, Room SE 103
Indianapolis, IN 46204
317-232-6804
Fax: 317-233-5720

IOWA
Veterans' Employment and Training Service, U.S. Department of Labor
150 Des Moines Street
Des Moines, IA 50309-5563
515-281-9061
Fax: 515-281-9063

KANSAS
Veterans' Employment and Training Service, U.S. Department of Labor
401 Topeka Boulevard
Topeka, KS 66603-3182
913-296-5032
Fax: 913-296-0264

KENTUCKY
Veterans' Employment and Training Service, U.S. Department of Labor
320 Garrard Street
Covington, KY 41011
606-292-6666

Veterans' Employment and Training Service
U.S. Department of Labor
CHR Building, Second Floor, West
275 East Main Street
Frankfort, KY 40621-2339
502-564-7062
Fax: 502-564-1476

LOUISIANA
Veterans' Employment and Training Service, U.S. Department of Labor
Administration Building, Room 184
PO Box 94094
Baton Rouge, LA 70804-9094
504-389-0339
Fax: 504-342-3152

MAINE
Veterans' Employment and Training Service, U.S. Department of Labor
522 Lisbon Street
PO Box 3106
Lewiston, ME 04243
207-783-5352
Fax: 207-783-5304

MARYLAND
Job Service
Office of Veterans' Employment
67 Thomas Johnson Drive
Frederick, MD 21702
301-694-2185

Veterans' Employment and Training Service, U.S. Department of Labor
1100 North Eutaw Street, Room 210
Baltimore, MD 21201
410-767-2110
Fax: 410-767-2112

Veterans' Employment and Training Service, U.S. Department of Labor
201 Baptist Street
Salisbury, MD 21801
410-543-6667

Veterans' Employment and Training Service, U.S. Department of Labor
PO Box 1317
Wheaton, MD 20915
301-929-4379
Fax: 301-929-4383

MASSACHUSETTS

Veterans' Employment and Training Service,
U.S. Department of Labor
J. F. Kennedy Federal Building, Room E-315
Government Center
Boston, MA 02203
617-565-2080
Fax: 617-565-2082

Veterans' Employment and Training Service,
U.S. Department of Labor
C. F. Hurley Building, Second Floor
19 Staniford Street
Boston, MA 02114-2502
617-626-6690
Fax: 617-727-2330

Veterans' Employment and Training Service,
U.S. Department of Labor
Division of Employment Security
618 Achusnet Avenue
New Bedford, MA 02740
508-999-2361
Fax: 617-727-4325

MICHIGAN

Veterans' Employment and Training Service,
U.S. Department of Labor
7310 Woodward Avenue
Detroit, MI 48202
313-876-5613
Fax: 313-876-5365

Veterans' Employment and Training Service,
U.S. Department of Labor
3391 Plainfield, NE
Grand Rapids, MI 49505
616-361-3200

Veterans' Employment and Training Service ,
U.S. Department of Labor
911 Spring
PO Box 328
Petoskey, MI 49770
616-347-5150
Fax: 616-347-2220

MINNESOTA

Veterans' Employment and Training Service,
U.S. Department of Labor
320 West Second Street, Room 205
Duluth, MN 55802
218-723-4766

Veterans' Employment and Training Service,
U.S. Department of Labor
610 Piper Jaffray Plaza
444 Cedar Street
St. Paul, MN 55101
612-296-3665
Fax: 612-282-2711

MISSISSIPPI

Veterans' Employment and Training Service,
U.S. Department of Labor
1520 West Capitol Street
PO Box 1699
Jackson, MS 39215-1699
601-965-4204
Fax: 601-961-7717

MISSOURI

Veterans' Employment and Training Service,
U.S. Department of Labor
310 Northwest Englewood Road, Suite 200
PO Box 28040
Gladstone, MO 64118-0040
816-467-7987
Fax: 816-467-7999

Veterans' Employment and Training Service,
U.S. Department of Labor
421 East Dunklin Street
PO Box 59
Jefferson City, MO 65104-0059
573-751-3921
Fax: 573-751-6710

Veterans' Employment and Training Service,
U.S. Department of Labor
1100 Main Street, Suite 850
Kansas City, MO 64105-2112
816-426-7151
Fax: 816-426-7259

MONTANA
**Veterans' Employment and Training Service,
    U.S. Department of Labor**
1215 Eighth Avenue
Helena, MT 59601
406-449-5431
Fax: 406-444-3365

NEBRASKA
**Veterans' Employment and Training Service,
    U.S. Department of Labor**
550 South 16th Street
PO Box 94600
Lincoln, NE 68509-4600
402-437-5289
Fax: 402-471-2318

NEVADA
U.S. Veterans Employment Service
500 East Third Street
Carson City, NV 89701-4762
702-687-4632

**Veterans' Employment and Training Service,
    U.S. Department of Labor**
1923 North Carson Street, Room 205
Carson City, NV 89702
702-687-4632
Fax: 702-687-3976

NEW HAMPSHIRE
**Veterans' Employment and Training Service,
    U.S. Department of Labor**
143 North Main Street, Room 208
Concord, NH 03301
603-225-1424
Fax: 603-225-1545

NEW JERSEY
**Veterans' Employment and Training Service,
    U.S. Department of Labor**
517 Federal Street
Camden, NJ 08103-1147
609-757-2576

**Veterans' Employment and Training Service,
    U.S. Department of Labor**
Labor Building, 11th Floor, CN-058
Trenton, NJ 08625
609-292-2930
Fax: 609-292-9070

NEW MEXICO
**Veterans' Employment and Training Service,
    U.S. Department of Labor**
401 Broadway, NE
PO Box 25085
Albuquerque, NM 87125-5085
505-766-2113
Fax: 505-841-9025

NEW YORK
Homeless Veterans Reintegration Project
21-10 Borden Avenue
Long Island City, NY 11101
718-784-6800

**Veterans' Employment and Training Service,
    U.S. Department of Labor**
Leo O'Brien Federal Building, Room 819
Albany, NY 12207
518-472-3691

**Veterans' Employment and Training Service,
    U.S. Department of Labor**
Harriman State Campus Building 12, Room 518
Albany, NY 12240-0099
518-457-7465

**Veterans' Employment and Training Service,
    U.S. Department of Labor**
290 Main Street, Room 231
Buffalo, NY 14202-4076
716-851-2748
Fax: 716-851-2792

**Veterans' Employment and Training Service,
    U.S. Department of Labor**
345 Hudson Street, Room 7315
PO Box 682, Mail Stop 7E
New York, NY 10014-0682
212-352-6183
Fax: 212-352-6185

Veterans' Employment and Training Service, U.S. Department of Labor
201 Varick Street, Room 766
New York, NY 10014
212-337-2211
Fax: 212-337-2634

Veterans' Employment and Training Service, U.S. Department of Labor
450 South Salina Street, Second Floor, Room 200
Syracuse, NY 13202-2402
315-479-3381
Fax: 315-479-3421

Veterans' Employment and Training Service, U.S. Department of Labor
State Office Building, Room 702
207 Genesee Street
Utica, NY 13501
315-793-2323
Fax: 315-793-2303

NORTH CAROLINA

Veterans' Employment and Training Service, U.S. Department of Labor
700 Wade Avenue, Building M
PO Box 27625
Raleigh, NC 27611-1154
919-856-4792

NORTH DAKOTA

Veterans' Employment and Training Service, U.S. Department of Labor
1000 East Divide Avenue
PO Box 1632
Bismarck, ND 58502-1632
701-250-4337
Fax: 701-328-4000

OHIO

Veterans' Employment and Training Service, U.S. Department of Labor
1841 Prospect Avenue
Cleveland, OH 44115
216-787-5660

Veterans' Employment and Training Service, U.S. Department of Labor
145 South Front Street, Room 523
PO Box 1618
Columbus, OH 43216
614-466-2768
Fax: 614-752-5007

Veterans' Employment and Training Service, U.S. Department of Labor
684 North Park Avenue
PO Box 1188
Warren, OH 44482-1188
216-399-8114
Fax: 216-399-1957

OKLAHOMA

Veterans' Employment and Training Service, U.S. Department of Labor
400 Will Rogers Memorial Office Building
PO Box 52003
Oklahoma City, OK 73152-2003
405-231-5088
Fax: 405-557-7123

OREGON

Veterans' Employment and Training Service, U.S. Department of Labor
1433 Southwest Sixth Avenue
Portland, OR 97201
503-731-3478

Veterans' Employment and Training Service, U.S. Department of Labor
Employment Division Building, Room 108
875 Union Street, NE
Salem, OR 97311-0100
503-378-3338

PENNSYLVANIA

Veterans' Employment and Training Service, U.S. Department of Labor
640 Hamilton Street, 10th Floor
Allentown, PA 18103
610-821-6571

**Veterans' Employment and Training Service,
U.S. Department of Labor**
Labor and Industry Building, Room 1108
Seventh and Forster Streets
Harrisburg, PA 17121
717-787-5834

**Veterans' Employment and Training Service,
U.S. Department of Labor**
71 South Union Avenue
Lansdowne, PA 19050
610-284-7588

**Veterans' Employment and Training Service,
U.S. Department of Labor**
U.S. Customs House, Room 802
Second and Chester Streets
Philadelphia, PA 19106
215-597-1664

**Veterans' Employment and Training Service,
U.S. Department of Labor**
State Office Building
300 Liberty Avenue, Room 1307
Pittsburgh, PA 15222
412-565-2469
Fax: 412-565-2518

**Veterans' Employment and Training Service,
U.S. Department of Labor**
Job Service Office
135 Franklin Avenue
Scranton, PA 18503
717-963-4735

RHODE ISLAND
**Veterans' Employment and Training Service,
U.S. Department of Labor**
Rhode Island Department of Employment and Training
507 U.S. Courthouse and Federal Building
Providence, RI 02903
401-528-5134
Fax: 401-528-5106

SOUTH CAROLINA
**Veterans' Employment and Training Service,
U.S. Department of Labor**
631 Hampton Street, Suite 140
PO Box 1755
Columbia, SC 29202-1755

803-765-5195
Fax: 803-253-4153

SOUTH DAKOTA
**Veterans' Employment and Training Service,
U.S. Department of Labor**
420 South Roosevelt Street
PO Box 4730
Aberdeen, SD 57402-4730
605-626-2325

TENNESSEE
**Veterans' Employment and Training Service,
U.S. Department of Labor**
1309 Poplar Avenue
Memphis, TN 38104-2006
901-543-7853
Fax: 901-543-7882

**Veterans' Employment and Training Service,
U.S. Department of Labor**
915 Eighth Avenue, North
PO Box 198587
Nashville, TN 37208
615-736-7680
Fax: 615-741-4241

TEXAS
**Veterans' Employment and Training Service,
U.S. Department of Labor**
1117 Trinity Street
PO Box 1468
Austin, TX 78767
512-463-2207
Fax: 512-475-2999

**Veterans' Employment and Training Service,
U.S. Department of Labor**
3649 Leopard Street, Suite 600
PO Box 748
Corpus Christi, TX 78403
512-882-3994
Fax: 512-882-1621

**Veterans' Employment and Training Service,
U.S. Department of Labor**
525 Griffin Street, Room 205
Dallas, TX 75202

214-767-4987
Fax: 214-767-2734

**Veterans' Employment and Training Service,
U.S. Department of Labor**
301 West 13th Street, Room 407
PO Box 591
Fort Worth, TX 76101-0591
817-335-5111
Fax: 817-336-8723

**Veterans' Employment and Training Service,
U.S. Department of Labor**
2040 North Loop, West, #300
PO Box 922024
Houston, TX 77292
713-956-4170
Fax: 713-956-5938

**Veterans' Employment and Training Service,
U.S. Department of Labor**
412 South High Street
PO Box 2152
Longview, TX 75606-2152
903-758-1783
Fax: 903-757-7835

**Veterans' Employment and Training Service,
U.S. Department of Labor**
1602 16th Street
PO Box 2858
Lubbock, TX 79408-2858
806-763-6416
Fax: 806-747-8629

**Veterans' Employment and Training Service,
U.S. Department of Labor**
330 Dwyer
PO Box 830277
San Antonio, TX 78283-0277
210-222-8484
Fax: 210-227-0632

UTAH
**Veterans' Employment and Training Service,
U.S. Department of Labor**
140 East 300 South
Salt Lake City, UT 84111-2333

801-524-5703
Fax: 801-536-7420

VERMONT
**Veterans' Employment and Training Service,
U.S. Department of Labor**
87 State Street, Room 303
PO Box 603
Montpelier, VT 05602
802-828-4441

VIRGINIA
**Veterans' Employment and Training Service,
U.S. Department of Labor**
703 East Main Street, Room 118
Richmond, VA 23219
804-786-7270
Fax: 804-786-4548

**Veterans' Employment and Training Service,
U.S. Department of Labor**
5060 Valleyview Boulevard, NW
PO Box 40008
Roanoke, VA 24022
540-561-7494
Fax: 540-561-7510

WASHINGTON
Job Service
4908 112th Street, SW
Tacoma, WA 98499-5143
206-589-7345

Job Service
9600 Veterans Drive, SW
Tacoma, WA 98498
206-582-8440

Job Service and Veterans Service
Fort Lewis, WA 98433
206-967-2790

**Veterans' Employment and Training Service,
U.S. Department of Labor**
605 Woodview Square Loop, SE, Third Floor
PO Box 165
Lacey, WA 98503-1040
360-438-4600
Fax: 360-438-3160

**Veterans' Employment and Training Service,
U.S. Department of Labor**
1111 Third Avenue, Suite 800
Seattle, WA 98101-3212
206-553-4831
Fax: 206-553-6853

WEST VIRGINIA
**Veterans' Employment and Training Service,
U.S. Department of Labor**
Capitol Complex, Room 205
112 California Avenue
Charleston, WV 25305-0112
304-558-4001
Fax: 304-344-4591

WISCONSIN
**Veterans' Employment and Training Service,
U.S. Department of Labor**
201 East Washington Avenue,
Room 250
PO Box 8310
Madison, WI 53708-8310
608-266-3110
Fax: 608-261-6710

WYOMING
**Veterans' Employment and Training Service,
U.S. Department of Labor**
100 West Midwest Avenue
PO Box 2760
Casper, WY 82602-2760
307-261-5454
Fax: 307-473-2642

PUERTO RICO
Veterans' Employment and Training Service
Puerto Rico Department of Labor and Human
Resources
#198 Calle Guayama
Hato Rey, PR 00917
787-754-5391
Fax: 787-754-2983

WOMEN
CALIFORNIA
Women in Non-Traditional Employment Roles
PO Box 90511
Long Beach, CA 90809
310-590-2266
Fax: 310-430-9181

DISTRICT OF COLUMBIA
Home Builders Institute
1090 Vermont Avenue, NW
Washington, DC 20005
202-371-0600

International Masonry Institute
823 15th Street, NW
Washington, DC 20005
202-383-3911
Fax: 202-783-0433

National Council of La Raza
1111 19th Street, NW
Washington, DC 20036
202-776-1742
Fax: 202-776-1792

Wider Opportunities for Women
National Workforce Network
815 15th Street, NW
Washington, DC 20005
202-638-3143
Fax: 202-638-4885

ILLINOIS
Chicago Women in Trades
220 South Ashland Avenue, Suite 101
Chicago, IL 60667
312-942-1444
Fax: 312-942-0802

MAINE
Michigan Women's Resource Center
25 Sheldon, SE, Suite 220
Grand Rapids, MI 49503
616-458-5443
Fax: 616-458-9933

Women Unlimited
280 State Street
Augusta, ME 04330
207-623-7576
Fax: 207-623-7299

MINNESOTA

Employment and Training
2000 Plymouth Avenue, North
Minneapolis, MN 55445
612-521-0342
Fax: 612-521-8513

MONTANA

Displaced Homemaker Program
32 South Ewing
Helena, MT 59601
406-443-0800

OHIO

PREP Inc.
2261 Francis Lane
Cincinnatti, OH 45206
513-221-4700
Fax: 513-221-3403

PENNSYLVANIA

TOP/WIN
2300 Alter Street
Philadelphia, PA 19147
215-545-3700
Fax: 215-545-3700

TENNESSEE

YWCA, Greater Memphis
1044 Mississippi Boulevard
Memphis, TN 38126
901-948-0493
Fax: 901-942-9383

WASHINGTON

Columbia Industries
900 South Dayton
PO Box 7346

Kennewick, WA 99336
509-582-4142

Community Colleges of Spokane
Institute for Extended Learning
West 3305 Fort George Wright Drive
Spokane, WA 99204
509-533-3131
Fax: 509-533-3226

Renton Technical College
3000 Northeast Fourth, Building L
PO Box 2490
Renton, WA 98056
206-235-2212
Fax: 206-235-7864

YOUTH

ARKANSAS

Arkansas Department of Workforce Education
Executive Building, Suite 220
2020 West Third Street
Little Rock, AR 72205
501-324-9463
Fax: 501-324-9468
http://www.state.ar.us/worked/index.html

KANSAS

Field Kindley Memorial High School
Seventh and Ellis
Coffeyville, KS 67337
316-252-6819

Hutchinson Community College
1300 North Plum
Hutchinson, KS 67501
316-665-3551

Smoky Hill Education Service Center
1648 West Magnolia
Salina, KS 67401
785-825-9185

Southwest Plains Regional Service Center
PO Drawer 1010
Sublette, KS 67877-1010
785-628-1014

USD 446 Independence HS
1301 North 10th Street
Independence, KS 67301
316-332-1815

USD 501 Topeka Public Schools
624 Southwest 24th Street
Topeka, KS 66711
785-232-0551

WYOMING

Title II-B Summer Youth Program
1620 Central Avenue, Suite 300
Cheyenne, WY 82001
307-635-9291

SCHOOLS, JOB CENTERS, AND ADMINISTRATIVE OFFICES

U.S. OFFICES OF APPRENTICESHIP TRAINING, EMPLOYER AND LABOR SERVICES

The United States apprenticeship system is managed by the Office of Apprenticeship Training, Employer and Labor Services (OATELS), which is a consolidation of the former Bureau of Apprenticeship and Training (BAT) with employer and labor liaison responsibilities. OATELS engages in partnership activities, ensuring quality service and customer satisfaction. Its national, regional, and state offices are listed below.

NATIONAL OFFICE

Office of Apprenticeship Training, Employer and Labor Services
Bureau of Apprenticeship and Training
Frances Perkins Building
200 Constitution Avenue, NW
Washington, DC 20210

Office of the Administrator
Room N4671
202-693-2796
Fax: 202-693-2808 or 202-693-2761

REGIONAL OFFICES

Region I (Connecticut, Maine, Massachusetts, New Hampshire, New Jersey, New York, Rhode Island, Puerto Rico, Vermont, Virgin Islands)
U.S. Department of Labor
Employment and Training Administration
Office of Apprenticeship Training, Employer and Labor Services
JFK Federal Building, Room E-370
Boston, MA 02203
617-788-0177
Fax: 617-788-0304
Griffin.John@dol.gov

Region II (Delaware, District of Columbia, Maryland, Pennsylvania, Virginia, West Virginia)
U.S. Department of Labor
Employment and Training Administration
Office of Apprenticeship Training, Employer and Labor Services
170 South Independence Mall, West, Suite 820-East
Philadelphia, PA 19106-3315

215-861-4830
Fax: 215-861-4833
Hersh.Joseph@dol.gov

Region III (Alabama, Florida, Georgia, Kentucky, Mississippi, North Carolina, South Carolina, Tennessee)
U.S. Department of Labor
Employment and Training Administration
Office of Apprenticeship Training, Employer and Labor Services
61 Forsyth Street
Atlanta, GA 30303
404-562-2335
Fax: 404-652-2329
Garner.Garfield@dol.gov

Region IV (Arkansas, Colorado, Louisiana, Montana, New Mexico, North Dakota, Oklahoma, South Dakota, Texas, Utah, Wyoming)
U.S. Department of Labor
Employment and Training Administration
Office of Apprenticeship Training, Employer and Labor Services
Federal Building
525 Griffin Street, Room 311
Dallas, TX 75202
214-767-4993
Fax: 214-767-4995
Opitz.Steve@dol.gov

Region V (Illinois, Indiana, Iowa, Kansas, Michigan, Minnesota, Missouri, Nebraska, Ohio, Wisconsin)
U.S. Department of Labor
Employment and Training Administration

Office of Apprenticeship Training, Employer
    and Labor Services
230 South Dearborn Street, Room 656
Chicago, IL 60604
312-596-5500
Fax: 312-596-5501
Benewich.Terrence@dol.gov

**Region VI (Alaska, Arizona, California, Hawaii,
    Idaho, Nevada, Oregon, Washington)**
71 Stevenson Street, Suite 815
San Francisco, CA 94105
415-975-4007
Fax: 415-975-4010
Longeuay.Michael@dol.gov

STATE OFFICES
Alabama
USDOL/ETA/OATELS-BAT
Medical Forum Building. - Room 648
950 22nd Street North
Birmingham, AL 35203
205-731-1308
collins.gregory@dol.gov

Alaska
USDOL/ETA/OATELS-BAT
Room G-30
605 W. 4th Avenue
Anchorage, AK 99501
907-271-5035
hakala.john@dol.gov

Arizona
USDOL/ETA/OATELS-BAT
230 North 1st Avenue
Suite 510
Phoenix, AZ 85025
602-514-7007
henry.colleen@dol.gov

Arkansas
USDOL/ETA/OATELS-BAT
Federal Building - Room 3507
700 West Capitol Street
Little Rock, AR 72201
501-324-5415
lamkin.kenneth@dol.gov

California
USDOL/ETA/OATELS-BAT
Suite 1090-N
1301 Clay Street
Oakland, CA 94612-5217
510-637-2951
kober.william@dol.gov

Colorado
USDOL/ETA/OATELS-BAT
U.S. Custom House
721 19th Street - Room 465
Denver, CO 80202
303-844-4794
nagel.louis@dol.gov

Connecticut
USDOL/ETA/OATELS-BAT
Federal Building
135 High Street - Room 367
Hartford, CT 06103
860240-4311
grandmaison.richard@dol.gov

Delaware
Temporarily closed
For more information call:
215-861-4830

Florida
USDOL/ETA/OATELS-BAT
550 Water Street, Room 1228
Federal Building
PO Box 14
Jacksonville, FL 32202
904-232-2596
melton.james@dol.gov

Georgia
USDOL/ETA/OATELS-BAT
Room 6T80
61 Forsyth Street, SW
Atlanta, GA 30303
404-562-2323
davison.john@dol.gov

Hawaii
USDOL/ETA/OATELS-BAT
Room 5-117

300 Ala Moana Boulevard
Honolulu, HI 96850
808-541-2519
valles.alfred@dol.gov

Idaho
USDOL/ETA/OATELS-BAT
Suite 204
1150 North Curtis Rd.
Boise, ID 83706-1234
208-321-2972
adolay.barbara@dol.gov

Illinois
USDOL/ETA/OATELS-BAT
Room 656
230 South Dearborn Street
Chicago, IL 60604
312-596-5508
wyatt.david@dol.gov

Indiana
USDOL/ETA/OATELS-BAT
Federal Building and U.S. Courthouse
46 East Ohio Street - Room 528
Indianapolis, IN 46204
317-226-7001
delgado.john@dol.gov

Iowa
USDOL/ETA/OATELS-BAT
210 Walnut Street - Room 715
Des Moines, IA 50309
515-284-4190
sisson.greer@dol.gov

Kansas
USDOL/ETA/OATELS-BAT
444 SE Quincy Street - Room 247
Topeka, KS 66683-3571
785-295-2624
engel.dolores@dol.gov

Kentucky
USDOL/ETA/OATELS-BAT
Federal Building - Room 168
600 Martin Luther King Place
Louisville, KY 40202

502-582-5223
delgado.john@dol.gov

Louisiana
Temporarily closed
For more information, call:
214-767-4993

Maine
Temporarily closed
For more information call:
617-788-0177

Maryland
USDOL/ETA/OATELS-BAT
Federal Building - Room 430-B
31 Hopkins Plaza
Baltimore, MD 21201
410-962-2676
laudeman.robert@dol.gov

Massachusetts
USDOL/ETA/OATELS-BAT
Room E-370
JFK Federal Building
Boston, MA 02203
617-788-0177
houser.jill@dol.gov

Michigan
USDOL/ETA/OAELS-BAT
315 W. Allegan – Room 209
Lansing, MI 48933
517-377-1746
bivins.glenn@dol.gov

Minnesota
USDOL/ETA/OATELS-BAT
316 N. Robert Street - Room 144
St. Paul, MN 55101
651-290-3951
guido.dean@dol.gov

Mississippi
USDOL/ETA/OATELS-BAT
Federal Building - Suite 515
100 West Capitol Street
Jackson, MS 39269
601-965-4346
westcott.fred@dol.gov

Missouri
USDOL/ETA/OATELS-BAT
1222 Spruce Street-Room 9.102E
Robert A. Young Federal Building
St. Louis, MO 63103
314-539-2522
perry.neil@dol.gov

Montana
USDOL/ETA/OATELS-BAT
Federal Building
10 West 15th Street, Suite 1300
Helena, MT 59626
406-441-1076
gillespie.john@dol.gov

Nebraska
USDOL/ETA/OATELS-BAT
111 South 18th Plaza, Suite C-49
Omaha, NE 68102-1322
402-221-3281
guido.dean@dol.gov

Nevada
USDOL/ETA/OATELS-BAT
600 S. Las Vegas Boulevard, Suite 520
Las Vegas, NV 89101
702-388-6396
henry.colleen@dol.gov

New Hampshire
USDOL/ETA/OATELS-BAT
Cleveland Building - Room 3703
55 Pleasant Street
Concord, NH 03301
603-225-1444
grandmaison.richard@dol.gov

New Jersey
USDOL/ETA/OATELS-BAT
485 Route 1 South
Building E, 3rd Floor
Iselin, NJ 08830
732-750-9191
fitzgerald.dennis@dol.gov

New Mexico
USDOL/ETA/OATELS-BAT
500 4th Street NW, Suite 401
Albuquerque, NM 87102

505-245-2155
lamkin.kenneth@dol.gov

New York
USDOL/ETA/OATELS-BAT
Leo O'Brien Federal Building, Room 809
North Pearl & Clinton Avenue
Albany, NY 12207
518-431-4008
houser.jill@dol.gov

North Carolina
USDOL/ETA/OATELS-BAT
Terry Sanford Federal Building
310 New Bern Avenue, Suite 260
Raleigh, NC 27601
919-856-4062
nugent.james@dol.gov

North Dakota
USDOL/ETA/OATELS-BAT
304 East Broadway, Room 332
Bismarck, ND 58501
701-250-4700
polk.dan@dol.gov

Ohio
USDOL/ETA/OATELS-BAT
200 North High Street, Room 605
Columbus, OH 43215
614-469-7375
dayspring.maryann@dol.gov

Oklahoma
USDOL/ETA/OATELS-BAT
1500 South Midwest Boulevard, Suite 202
Midwest City, OK 73110
405-732-4338
mclain.cynthia@dol.gov

Oregon
USDOL/ETA/OATELS-BAT
256 Warner-Milne Road, Room 3
Oregon City, OR 97045
503-557-8257
kober.william@dol.gov

Pennsylvania
USDOL/ETA/OATELS-BAT
Federal Building

228 Walnut Street, Room 356
Harrisburg, PA 17108
717-221-3496
bydlon.thomas@dol.gov

Rhode Island

USDOL/ETA/OATELS-BAT
Federal Building
100 Hartford Avenue
Providence, RI 02909
401-528-5198
carney.howard@dol.gov

South Carolina

USDOL/ETA/OATELS-BAT
Strom Thurmond Federal Building
1835 Assembly Street - Room 838
Columbia, SC 29201
803-765-5547
lee.james@dol.gov

South Dakota

USDOL/ETA/OATELS-BAT
Room 204
2500 West 49th Street
Sioux Falls, SD 57105
605-330-2566
reese.donald@dol.gov

Tennessee

USDOL/ETA/OATELS-BAT
Airport Executive Plaza
1321 Murfreesboro Road Suite 541
Nashville, TN 37210
615-781-5318
brown.nat@dol.gov

Texas

USDOL/ETA/OATELS-BAT
300 East 8th Street, Suite 914
Austin, TX 78701
512-916-5435
goodson.dennis@dol.gov

Utah

USDOL/ETA/OATELS-BAT
1600 West 2200 South, Suite 101
Salt Lake City, UT 84119
801-975-3650
pelaez-gary.juan@dol.gov

Virginia

USDOL/ETA/OATELS-BAT
400 North 8th Street
Federal Building, Suite 404
Richmond, VA 23219-23240
804-771-2488
walker.james@dol.gov

Washington

USDOL/ETA/OATELS-BAT
1111 Third Avenue, Suite 815
Seattle, WA 98101-3212
206-553-0076
wetmore.anne@dol.gov

West Virginia

USDOL/ETA/OATELS-BAT
One Bridge Place, 2nd Floor
No. 10 Hale Street
Charleston, WV 25301
304-347-5794
milnes.kenneth@dol.gov

Wisconsin

USDOL/ETA/OATELS-BAT
740 Regent Street, Suite 104
Madison, WI 53715-1233
608-441-5377
guido.dean@dol.gov

Wyoming

USDOL/ETA/OATELS-BAT
American National Bank Building
1912 Capitol Avenue, Room 508
Cheyenne, WY 82001-3661
307-772-2448
nagel.louis@dol.gov

COMMUNITY COLLEGES, VOCATIONAL-TECHNICAL CENTERS, AND TRADE SCHOOLS

ARIZONA

Maricopa Community College, Mesa
Technology Department
1833 West Southern Avenue
Mesa, AZ 85202
602-461-7137
http://www.mc.maricopa.edu

Maricopa Community College, Paradise Valley
18401 North 32nd Street
Phoenix, AZ 85032
602-493-2600
http://www.pvc.maricopa.edu

Maricopa Community College, Phoenix
1202 West Thomas Road
Phoenix, AZ 85013-4234
602-264-2492
Fax: 602-285-7700
http://www.pc.maricopa.edu

Maricopa Community Colleges
District Support Services Center
2411 West 14th Street
Tempe, AZ 84281
602-731-8000
http://www.maricopa.edu

Maricopa Community Colleges, Chandler-Gilbert
2626 East Pecos Road
Chandler, AZ 85225
602-732-7000
Fax: 602-732-7090
http://www.cgc.maricopa.edu

Maricopa Community Colleges, Estrella Mountain
3000 North Dysart Road
Avondale, AZ 85323-1000
602-935-8000
http://www.emc.maricopa.edu

Maricopa Community Colleges, Gateway
108 North 40th Street
Phoenix, AZ 85034-1795
602-392-5000
http://www.gatewaycc.edu

Maricopa Community Colleges, Glendale
6000 West Olive Avenue
Glendale, AZ 85302
602-435-3000
http://www.gc.maricopa.edu

Maricopa Community Colleges, Scottsdale
9000 East Chaparral Road
Scottsdale, AZ 85250-2699
602-423-6000
http://www.sc.maricopa.edu

Maricopa Community Colleges, South Mountain
7050 South 24th Street
Phoenix, AZ 85040-5806
602-243-8123
http://www.southmountaincc.edu

Pima Community College
4905 East Broadway Boulevard
Tucson, AZ 85709
520-884-6725
http://www.pima.edu

CALIFORNIA

City College of San Francisco
50 Phelan Avenue
San Francisco, CA 94112-1821
415-239-3000
Fax: 415-239-3936
http://www.ccsf.edu

Foothill College
12345 El Monte Road
Los Altos, CA 94022

650-949-7777
http://www.foothill.fhda.edu

DISTRICT OF COLUMBIA
Career College Association
10 G Street, NE, Suite 750
Washington, DC 20002-4213
202-336-6700
Fax: 202-336-6828
http://www.career.org

DC Apprenticeship School
704 26th Street, NE, #205
Washington, DC 20002-3266
202-724-3747

FLORIDA
Seminole Community College
Division of Applied Technologies
100 Weldon Boulevard
Sanford, FL 32773-6199
407-328-2376
Fax: 407-328-2139
http://www.seminole.cc.fl.us

University of Florida
Physical Plant Division, Building 700
Gainesville, FL 32611
904-462-1016

HAWAII
Honolulu Community College
874 Dillingham Boulevard
Honolulu, HI 96817-4505
808-845-9245
http://honolulu.hawaii.edu

INDIANA
Indiana University
Apprenticeship Program
2931 East Tenth Street
Bloomington, IN 47418
812-855-6296
Fax: 812-855-9549
http://www.indiana.edu/~phyplant/html/body_
    bm_-_iu_apprentship_program.html

Ivy Tech State College, Anderson
104 West 53rd Street
Anderson, IN 46013
800-644-4882
Fax: 765-643-3294
http://www.ivytech.edu/eastcentral

Ivy Tech State College, Columbus
4475 Central Avenue
Columbus, IN 47203-1868
800-922-4838
http://www.ivytech.edu/columbus

Ivy Tech State College, East Chicago
410 Columbus Drive
East Chicago, IN 46312-2714
219-392-3600
http://www.gary.ivytech.edu

Ivy Tech State College, Elkhart
2421 Industrial Parkway
Elkhart, IN 46516-5430
219-293-4657
http://www.ivytech.edu/elkhart

Ivy Tech State College, Evansville
3501 North First Avenue
Evansville, IN 47710-3319
812-426-2865
Fax: 812-429-1483
http://www.ivytech.edu/evansville

Ivy Tech State College, Fort Wayne
3800 North Anthony Boulevard
Fort Wayne, IN 46805-1489
219-482-9171
http://www.ivytech.edu/fortwayne

Ivy Tech State College, Gary
1440 East 35th Avenue
Gary, IN 46409-1499
219-981-1111
http://www.gary.ivytech.edu

Ivy Tech State College, Indianapolis
1 West 26th Street
PO Box 1763
Indianapolis, IN 46206
317-921-4772

Fax: 317-921-4348
http://www.ivytech.edu/indianapolis

Ivy Tech State College, Kokomo
1815 East Morgan Street
Kokomo, IN 46901-2548
765-459-0561
Fax: 765-454-5111
http://www.ivytech.edu/kokomo

Ivy Tech State College, Lafayette
3101 South Creasy Lane
Lafayette, IN 447903
765-477-9100
http://www.laf.ivytech.edu

Ivy Tech State College, Lawrenceburg
575 Main Street
Lawrenceburg, IN 47025-1661
800-403-2190
http://www.ivytech.edu/lawrenceburg

Ivy Tech State College, Logansport
2815 East Market Street
Logansport, IN 46947-2548
219-753-5101
Fax: 219-753-5103
http://www.ivytech.edu/logansport

Ivy Tech State College, Madison
590 Ivy Tech Drive
Madison, IN 47250-1883
812-265-2580
http://www.ivytech.edu/madison

Ivy Tech State College, Marion
1015 East Third Street
Marion, IN 46952-4005
765-662-9843
http://www.ivytech.edu/eastcentral

Ivy Tech State College, Muncie
4301 South Cowan Road
Muncie, IN 47303
765-289-2291
http://www.ivytech.edu/eastcentral

Ivy Tech State College, Richmond
2325 Chester Boulevard
Richmond, IN 47374-1298

800-659-4562
Fax: 317-962-8741
http://www.ivytech.edu/richmond

Ivy Tech State College, Sellersburg
8204 Highway 311
Sellersburg, IN 47172-1829
800-321-9021
http://www.ivytech.edu/sellersburg

Ivy Tech State College, South Bend
1534 West Sample Street
South Bend, IN 46619-3837
219-289-7001
http://www.ivytech.edu/southbend

Ivy Tech State College, Terre Haute
7999 U.S. Highway 41, South
Terre Haute, IN 47802-4845
812-877-6316
Fax: 812-299-5723
http://ivytech7.cc.in.us

Ivy Tech State College, Valparaiso
2401 Valley Drive
Valparaiso, IN 46383-2520
219-464-8514
http://www.gary.ivytech.edu

Ivy Tech State College, Warsaw
850 East Smith Street
Warsaw, IN 46580-4543
219-267-5428
http://www.ivytech.edu/warsaw

Tucker Area Vocational Technical Center
107 South Pennsylvania Avenue
Marion, IN 46952
317-664-9091
Fax: 317-651-2048
http://stats.ind.net/traffic/mnc/tucker-voc-k12-2-
    t1.html

KANSAS
Allen County Community College
1801 North Cottonwood
Iola, KS 66749

316-365-5116
http://www.allencc.edu/web/index.htm

Dodge City Community College
Center for Business and Industry
2501 North 14th
Dodge City, KS 67801
316-225-1321
http://www.dccc.cc.ks.us

Donnelly College
608 North 18th Street
Kansas City, KS 66102
913-621-6070
http://www.donnelly.edu

Johnson County Community College
12345 College Boulevard
Overland Park, KS 66210-1299
913-469-8500
http://www.jccc.net/home/index.php

Kansas City Vocational-Technical School
2220 North 59th Street
Kansas City, KS 66104
913-596-5500
http://www.kckats.com

MICHIGAN
Delta College
1961 Delta Road
University Center, MI 48710
989-686-9000
http://www.delta.edu

Henry Ford Community College
115-B Patterson Technical Building
5101 Evergreen Road
Dearborn, MI 48128
313-845-9609
http://www.henryford.cc.mi.us

MISSISSIPPI
Mississippi Gulf Coast Community College
Box 100
Gautier, MS 39553

601-497-9602
http://www.mgccc.edu

MISSOURI
Crowder Community College
601 Laclede Avenue
Neosho, MO 64850
417-451-3223
http://www.crowder.edu

East Central College
Highway 50, West, and Prairie Dell Road
PO Box 529
Union, MO 63084
314-583-5193
http://www.eastcentral.edu

Metropolitan Community College
3200 Broadway
Kansas City, MO 64111
816-482-5270
http://kcmetro.edu

Mineral Area College
PO Box 1000
Flat River, MO 63601
314-431-1307
http://www.mac.cc.mo.us

Moberly Area Community College
101 College Avenue
Moberly, MO 65270
816-263-4110
info@macc.edu
http://www.macc.cc.mo.us

North Central Missouri College
1301 Main Street
Trenton, MO 64683
816-359-3213
http://www.ncmc.cc.mo.us

Ozarks Technical Community College
1417 North Jefferson
Springfield, MO 65802
417-895-7102
http://www.otc.cc.mo.us

State Fair Community College
3201 West 16th Street
Sedalia, MO 65301
816-530-5800
http://sfcc.cc.mo.us/pages/1.asp

St. Charles County Community College
4601 Mid River Mall Drive
St. Peters, MO 63376
314-922-8000
http://www.stchas.edu

St. Louis Community College
Center for Business Industry and Labor
300 South Broadway
St. Louis, MO 63102
314-539-5310
http://www.stlcc.cc.mo.us

Three Rivers Community College
2080 Three Rivers Boulevard
Poplar Bluffs, MO 63901
314-840-9689
http://www.trcc.commnet.edu

NEW HAMPSHIRE
New Hampshire Community Technical College, Laconia
379 Belmont Road
Laconia, NH 03246-8528
603-524-3207
Fax: 603-524-8084
http://www.laconia.nhctc.edu

NEW MEXICO
Albuquerque Technical Vocational Institute
Trades and Service Occupations
525 Buena Vista, SE
Albuquerque, NM 87106
505-224-4667
Fax: 505-224-4684
http://www.tvi.cc.nm.us

NEW YORK
Clarkson University
Pipeline for Educational Programs
Box 5512

Potsdam, NY 13699-5512
315-268-3785
Fax: 315-268-7615
http://www.clarkson.edu

Onondaga Community College
4941 Onondaga Road
Syracuse, NY 13215-2099
315-463-9265
http://www.sunyocc.edu

Southampton College
Long Island University
239 Montauk Highway
Southampton, NY 11968-4198
516-283-4000
Fax: 516-283-4081
http://www.southampton.liunet.edu

NORTH CAROLINA
North Carolina State University
Box 7004
Raleigh, NC 27695-7132
919-515-2011
http://www.ncsu.edu

U.S. Army
HQ XVIII Abn Corps and Fort Bragg
Fort Bragg, NC 28307
910-396-4534

OHIO
Cuyahoga Community College
700 Carnegie Avenue
Cleveland, OH 44115-2878
800-207-8742
http://www.tri-c.edu

OREGON
Blue Mountain Community College
2411 Northwest Carden Avenue
PO Box 100
Pendleton, OR 97801
541-276-1260
http://www.bmcc.cc.or.us

Chemeketa Community College
Building 17
PO Box 14007
Salem, OR 97309
503-399-6932
http://www.chemeketa.edu

Clackamas Community College
19600 South Molalla Avenue
Oregon City, OR 97045
503-657-6958
http://www.clackamas.cc.or.us

Clatsop Community College
85 West Marine Drive
Astoria, OR 97103
503-325-8103
http://www.clatsopcollege.com

Lane Community College
Apprenticeship Building, Room 205A
4000 East 30th Avenue
Eugene, OR 97405
541-747-4501
http://lanecc.edu

Linn-Benton Community College
6500 Pacific Boulevard, SW
Albany, OR 97321-3779
541-917-4870
http://www.linnbenton.edu

Mount Hood Community College
14030 Northeast Sacramento
Portland, OR 97230
503-256-0432
http://www.mhcc.edu

Rogue Community College
3345 Redwood Highway
Grants Pass, OR 97527-9298
541-471-3500
Fax: 541-471-3588
http://www.roguecc.edu

Umpqua Community College
PO Box 967
Roseburg, OR 97470

541-440-4668
http://www.umpqua.cc.or.us

TEXAS
Houston Community College
7615 Athlowe
Houston, TX 77088
713-630-7227

UTAH
College of Eastern Utah
451 East 400 North
Price, UT 84501-2699
801-637-2120
http://www.ceu.edu

Delta Technical Center
305 East 200 North
Delta, UT 84624-8405
801-864-4020
http://www.dtc.millard.k12.ut.us

Ogden-Weber Applied Technology College
559 AVC Lane
Ogden, UT 84404-6704
801-621-2373
http://www.owatc.com

Salt Lake Community College
4600 South Redwood Road
PO Box 30808
Salt Lake City, UT 84130-0808
801-957-4066
Fax: 801-957-4895

Snow College
150 East College Avenue
Ephraim, UT 84627-1299
801-283-4021
http://www.snow.edu

Utah Valley State College
800 West 1200 South
Orem, UT 84058-0001
801-785-8700
http://www.uvsc.edu

VIRGINIA

Central Virginia Community College
3506 Wards Road
Lynchburg, VA 24502
804-386-4500
Fax: 804-386-4681
http://www.cvcc.vccs.edu

Charlottesville-Albemarle Technical Education Center
100 East Rio Road
Charlottesville, VA 22901
804-973-8012
Fax: 804-973-4876
http://catec.org

Danville Community College
1008 South Main Street
Danville, VA 24541
804-797-2222
Fax: 804-797-8455
http://www.dcc.vccs.edu

Fairfax County Schools
Centreville Adult Center
5775 Spindle Court
Centreville, VA 20121
703-227-2300
Fax: 703-227-2327

Jackson River Technical Center
105 East Country Club Lane
Covington, VA 24426
540-862-1308
Fax: 540-862-3592
http://www.jrtc.info

Lord Fairfax Community College
PO Box 47
Middletown, VA 22645
540-869-1120
Fax: 540-869-7881
http://www.lf.vccs.edu

Massanutten Technical Center
325 Pleasant Valley Road
Harrisonburg, VA 22801
540-434-5961
Fax: 540-434-1402
http://www.rockingham.k12.va.us/mtc/MTC.html

New Horizons Regional Education Center
520 Butler Farm Road
Hampton, VA 23666
804-766-1101
Fax: 804-766-2458
http://www.nhgs.tec.va.us

Norfolk Technical Vocational Center
1330 North Military Highway
Norfolk, VA 23502
804-441-5625
Fax: 804-441-5713
http://www.nps.k12.va.us/schools/ntvc

Patrick Henry Community College
PO Drawer 5311
Martinsville, VA 24115
540-638-8777
Fax: 540-638-6469
http://www.ph.vccs.edu

Richmond Technical Center
2020 Westwood Avenue
Richmond, VA 23230
804-780-6018
Fax: 804-780-6061
http://richmond.k12.va.us/schools/rtc

Roanoke Regional Apprenticeship Center
2200 Grandin Road, SW
Roanoke, VA 24015
540-853-1061
Fax: 540-981-1062

Southside Virginia Community College
Christiana Campus
Route 1, Box 60
Alberta, VA 23821
804-949-1000
Fax: 804-949-7863
http://www.sv.vccs.edu

Southside Virginia Community College
John H. Daniel Campus
Route 1, Box 60
Keysville, VA 23947
804-736-2033
Fax: 804-736-2082
http://www.sv.vccs.edu

Spotsylvania Career and Technical Center
6703 Smith Street Road
Spotsylvania, VA 22553
540-898-2655
Fax: 540-891-1784
http://www.spotsylvania.k12.va.us/sctc/

Valley Vocational Technical Center
49 Hornet Road
Fishersville, VA 22939
540-245-5009
Fax: 540-885-0407
http://www.vvtc.tec.va.us/vvtc.htm

Virginia Community College System
Academic Services and Research
101 North 14th Street
Richmond, VA 23219
804-692-0360
Fax: 804-786-3787
http://www.so.cc.va.us

Wytheville Community College
1000 East Main Street
Wytheville, VA 24382
800-468-1195
Fax: 540-223-4778
http://www.wcc.vccs.edu

WASHINGTON
Community Colleges of Spokane
Institute for Extended Learning
West 3305 Fort George Wright Drive
Spokane, WA 99204
509-533-3131
Fax: 509-533-3226
http://ccs.spokane.cc.wa.us

Renton Technical College
3000 Northeast Fourth, Building L
PO Box 2490
Renton, WA 98056
205-235-2212
Fax: 206-235-7864
http://www.renton-tc.ctc.edu

Seattle Vocational Institute
2120 South Jackson Street
Seattle, WA 98144

206-587-4940
Fax: 206-587-4949
http://sviweb.sccd.ctc.edu

Skagit Valley College, Mount Vernon Campus
Vocational Education
2405 East College Way
Mount Vernon, WA 98273-5899
360-416-7736
http://www.skagit.edu

Skagit Valley College, San Juan Center Campus
Vocational Education
PO Box 1432
Friday Harbor, WA 98250
360-378-3220
http://www.skagit.edu

Skagit Valley College, South Whidbey Center Campus
Vocational Education
4141 Highway 525, Suite B-15
Clinton, WA 98260
360-341-2324
http://www.skagit.edu

Skagit Valley College, Whidbey Campus
Vocational Education
1900 Southeast Pioneer Way
Oak Harbor, WA 98277-3099
360-679-5330
http://www.skagit.edu

South Seattle Community College
6000 16th Avenue, SW
Seattle, WA 98106-1499
206-764-5350
http://www.southseattle.edu

WISCONSIN
Blackhawk Technical College
6004 Prairie Road
PO Box 5009
Janesville, WI 53547
608-757-7627
Fax: 608-757-7740
http://www.blackhawk.edu

Chippewa Valley Technical College
620 West Clairemont Avenue
Eau Claire, WI 54701
715-833-6344
Fax: 715-833-6470
http://www.cvtc.edu

Fox Valley Technical College
1825 North Bluemound Drive
PO Box 2277
Appleton, WI 54913-2277
414-735-5778
Fax: 414-735-2582
http://www.fvtc.edu

Gateway Technical College
1001 South Main Street, Room M 204
Racine, WI 53403
414-631-7404
Fax: 414-656-6986
http://www.gateway.tec.wi.us

Indianhead Technical College
505 Pine Ridge Drive
PO Box 10B
Shell Lake, WI 54871
800-243-WITC
http://www.witc.edu

Indianhead Technical College
1290 North Avenue
Cleveland, WI 53015-1414
414-458-4183
Fax: 414-457-6211
http://www.witc.edu/

Madison Area Technical College
2125 Commercial Avenue
Madison, WI 53704
608-757-7729
Fax: 608-246-6880
http://matcmadison.edu/matc

Mid-State Technical College
500 32nd Street, North
Wisconsin Rapids, WI 54494
715-423-5650
Fax: 715-422-5345
http://www.mstc.edu

Milwaukee Area Technical College
700 West State Street
Milwaukee, WI 53233-1443
414-297-6720
Fax: 414-297-7764
http://www.milwaukee.tec.wi.us

Moraine Park Technical College
236 North National Avenue
PO Box 1940
Fond du Lac, WI 54936-1940
414-929-2111
Fax: 414-924-3421
http://www.moraine.tec.wi.us

Nicolet College
PO Box 518
Rhinelander, WI 54501
715-369-4425
Fax: 715-365-4445
http://www.nicoletcollege.edu

Northcentral Technical College
1000 West Campus Drive
Wausau, WI 54401
715-675-3331
Fax: 715-675-9776
http://www.northcentral.tec.wi.us

Northeast Wisconsin Technical College
2740 West Mason Street
PO Box 19042
Green Bay, WI 54307-9042
414-498-5462
Fax: 414-498-6260
http://www.nwtc.edu

Waukesha County Technical College
Center for Business and Industry Services
892 Main Street
Pewaukee, WI 53072
414-695-7828
Fax: 414-691-5593
http://www.wctc.edu

Western Wisconsin Technical College
304 North Sixth Street
PO Box 908
La Crosse, WI 54602-0908

608-785-9175
Fax: 608-785-9205
http://www.western.tec.wi.us

Wisconsin Technical College System

310 Price Place
PO Box 7874
Madison, WI 53707-7874
608-267-9066
Fax: 608-266-1285
http://www.witechcolleges.com

WYOMING

Laramie County Community College

1400 College Drive
Cheyenne, WY 82007-3204
307-778-1348
Fax: 307-778-1344
http://www.lccc.cc.wy.us

Western Wyoming Community College

2500 College Drive
PO Box 428
Rock Springs, WY 82902-0428
307-382-1600
Fax: 307-382-7665
http://www.wwcc.wy.edu

JOB CENTERS AND STATE LIAISONS

ALABAMA

Alabama Department of Economic and Community Affairs
401 Adams Avenue
PO Box 5690
Montgomery, AL 36103-5690
334-242-5300
Fax: 334-242-5855

Alabama Department of Industrial Relations
Industrial Relations Building
Room 2813
649 Monroe Street
Montgomery, Alabama 36131-0001
334-242-8003
Fax: 334-242-8012

ALASKA

Alaska Department of Community and Regional Affairs
Division of Community and Rural Development
333 West Fourth Avenue, Suite 220
Anchorage, AK 99501-2341
907-269-4607
Fax: 907-269-4520

Job Service
3301 Eagle Street
Anchorage, AK 99503
907-269-4746

Job Service
877 Commercial Drive
Wasilla, AK 99654
907-352-2500

ARIZONA

Division of Employment and Rehabilitation Services
1789 West Jefferson, Suite 901A
PO Box 6123
Phoenix, AZ 85005
602-542-4910
Fax: 602-542-2273

Job Service
277 West Fourth Street
Benson, AZ 85602
520-586-2513

Job Service
207 Bisbee Road
Bisbee, AZ 85603
520-338-1628

Job Service
829 Hancock Road
Bullhead City, AZ 86442
520-763-4154

Job Service
401 North Marshall Street
Casa Grande, AZ 85222
520-426-3529

Job Service
PO Box 2600
Chinle, AZ 86503-2600
520-674-5798

Job Service
1155 North Arizona Boulevard
Coolidge, AZ 85228
520-723-5351

Job Service
1645 East Cottonwood Street, #E
Cottonwood, AZ 86326
520-634-3337

Job Service
1140 F Avenue
Douglas, AZ 85607
520-364-4446

Job Service
1900 McCulloch Boulevard, North, #104
Lake Havasu City, AZ 86403
520-680-6005

Job Service
480 North Grand Avenue
Nogales, AZ 85621
520-287-4635

Job Service
337 North Navajo Drive
Page, AZ 86040
520-645-5201

Job Service
1032 South Hope Avenue
Parker, AZ 86413
520-669-6755

Job Service
122 East State Highway 260
Payson, AZ 85541
520-474-4521

Job Service
9801 North Seventh Street
Phoenix, AZ 85020
602-997-2681

Job Service
4635 South Central Avenue
Phoenix, AZ 85040
602-276-5587

Job Service
40 South 11th Street
Show Low, AZ 85901
520-537-2948

Job Service
2981 East Tacoma
Sierra Vista, AZ 85635
520-458-4005

Job Service
205 West First Street
St. Johns, AZ 85936
520-337-2663

Job Service
Main Street
Tuba City, AZ 86045
520-283-4510

Job Service
195 West Irvington Road
Tucson, AZ 85714
520-741-7188

Job Service
7750 East Broadway Boulevard
Tucson, AZ 85710
520-886-2145

Job Service
316 West Fort Lowell Road
Tucson, AZ 85705
520-293-1919

Job Service
104 South Arizona Avenue
Willcox, AZ 85643
520-384-3583

Job Service
319 East Third Street
Winslow, AZ 86047
520-289-4644

Job Service
201 South Third Avenue
Yuma, AZ 85364
520-783-1221

ARKANSAS
Arkansas Employment Security Department
Office of Employment and Rehabilitation Services
PO Box 2981
Little Rock, AR 72203
501-682-5227
Fax: 501-682-3144

Job Service
1223 West Seventh Street
Little Rock, AR 72201
601-682-2127

CALIFORNIA
Broadcast Employment Services
PO Box 4116
Oceanside, CA 92052

Fax: 619-754-2115
http://www.tvjobs.com

California Job Service, Modesto, Employment Development Department
629 12th Street
Modesto, CA 95354
209-576-6001
http://www.edd.cahwnet.gov

California Job Service, Oakdale, Employment Development Department
1405 West F Street
Oakdale, CA 95361
209-848-4226
http://www.edd.cahwnet.gov

California Job Service, Turlock, Employment Development Department
125 North Broadway
Turlock, CA 95380
209-634-4927
http://www.edd.cahwnet.gov

Employment Development Department
800 Capitol Mall
PO Box 826880, MIC 83
Sacramento, CA 94280-0001
916-654-8210
Fax: 916-657-5294

Job Service
900 East Gene Autry Way
Anaheim, CA 92805
714-978-7421

Job Service
201 East 18th Street
Antioch, CA 94509
510-777-2124

Job Service
150 Harrison Avenue
Auburn, CA 95603
916-823-4130

Job Service
2450 South Bascom Avenue
Campbell, CA 95008
408-369-3611

Job Service
21010 Vanowen Street
Canoga Park, CA 91303
818-596-4444

Job Service
2045 40th Avenue, #B
Capitola, CA 95010
408-464-6260

Job Service
23820 Avalon Boulevard
Carson, CA 90745
310-834-3481

Job Service
1045 Tierra Del Rey
Chula Vista, CA 91910
619-482-6096

Job Service
7105 South Center Drive, Building 420
Clearlake, CA 95422
707-994-4825

Job Service
1940 North Bullis Road
Compton, CA 90221
310-639-8180

Job Service
363 Civic Drive
Concord, CA 94523
510-602-1520

Job Service
237 River Road
Corona, CA 91720
909-734-4160

Job Service
933 South Glendora Avenue
Covina, CA 91790
818-962-7011

Job Service
433 Front Street
Danville, CA 94526-3403
510-820-2614

Job Service
2216 East El Monte Way
Dinuba, CA 93618
209-591-2581

Job Service
1360 North Magnolia Avenue
El Cajon, CA 92020
619-441-2300

Job Service
550 West Main Street
El Centro, CA 92243
619-352-1801

Job Service
10404 Valley Boulevard
El Monte, CA 91731
818-350-6500

Job Service
1301 Simpson Way
Escondido, CA 92029
619-745-6211

Job Service
3060 Travis Boulevard
Fairfield, CA 94533
707-428-2005

Job Service
306 East Redwood Avenue
Fort Bragg, CA 95437
707-964-4081

Job Service
39155 Liberty Street, #116
Fremont, CA 94538
510-794-3669

Job Service
233 East Commonwealth Avenue
Fullerton, CA 92632
714-680-7800

Job Service
12661 Hoover Street
Garden Grove, CA 92641
714-890-4300

Job Service
190 Leavesley Road
Gilroy, CA 95020
408-842-2164

Job Service
1255 South Central Avenue
Glendale, CA 91204
818-247-1321

Job Service
124 North Irwin Street
Hanford, CA 93230
209-584-9261

Job Service
12100 Aviation Boulevard
Hawthorne, CA 90250
310-725-2103

Job Service
24790 Amador Street
Hayward, CA 94544
510-293-1771

Job Service
151 North Lyon Avenue
Hemet, CA 92543
909-652-7831

Job Service
11049 Magnolia Boulevard
Hollywood, CA 91601
818-509-5600

Job Service
47110 Calhoun Street
Indio, CA 92201
619-347-0761

Job Service
571 Crane Street
Lake Elsinore, CA 92530
909-245-0516

Job Service
991 Parallel Drive
Lakeport, CA 95453
707-262-3100

Job Service
631 East Oak Street
Lodi, CA 95240
209-333-5319

Job Service
1313 Pine Avenue
Long Beach, CA 90813
562-599-5871

Job Service
10829 Venice Boulevard
Los Angeles, CA 90034
310-280-2830

Job Service
1405 South Broadway
Los Angeles, CA 90015
213-744-2244

Job Service
5401 Crenshaw Boulevard
Los Angeles, CA 90043
213-744-2018

Job Service
1231 South Gerhart Avenue
Los Angeles, CA 90022
213-887-3970

Job Service
12700 Avalon Boulevard
Los Angeles, CA 90061
213-418-7170

Job Service
1116 North McCadden Place
Los Angeles, CA 90038
213-993-4600

Job Service
1918 North Broadway
Los Angeles, CA 90031
213-221-4195

Job Service
1204 East Street
Marysville, CA 95901-4843
916-741-4216

Job Service
23456 Madero
Mission Viejo, CA 92691
714-588-3900

Job Service
12715 Pioneer Boulevard
Norwalk, CA 90650
562-868-3713

Job Service
2027 Mission Avenue
Oceanside, CA 92054
619-754-5080

Job Service
1511 East Holt Boulevard
Ontario, CA 91761
909-983-5821

Job Service
635 South Ventura Road
Oxnard, CA 93030
805-382-8650

Job Service
1207 East Green Street
Pasadena, CA 91106
818-304-7900

Job Service
835 Park Street
Paso Robles, CA 03446
805-238-4842

Job Service
715 Southpoint Boulevard, #G
Petaluma, CA 94954
707-769-5650

Job Service
4535 Missouri Flat Road
Placerville, CA 95667
916-622-2525

Job Service
2248 Sunrise Boulevard
Rancho Cordova, CA 95670
916-464-2520

Job Service
1325 Pine Street
Redding, CA 96001
916-225-2180

Job Service
480 North Mountain View Avenue
San Bernardino, CA 92401
909-383-4064

Job Service
1520 San Fernando Road
San Fernando, CA 91340
818-365-4637

Job Service
3196 South Higuera Street
San Luis Obispo, CA 93401
805-544-9050

Job Service
3301 Kerner Boulevard
San Rafael, CA 94901
415-454-0355

Job Service
1001 South Grand Avenue
Santa Ana, CA 92705
714-558-4294

Job Service
130 East Ortega Street
Santa Barbara, CA 93101
805-568-1278

Job Service
21515 Soledad Canyon Road
Santa Clarita, CA 91350
805-255-8546

Job Service
304 Carmen Lane
Santa Maria, CA 93454
805-922-8373

Job Service
606 Healdsburg Avenue
Santa Rosa, CA 95401
707-576-2090

Job Service
980 Enchanted Way
Simi Valley, CA 93065
805-582-8721

Job Service
197 Mono Way
Sonora, CA 95370
209-532-6941

Job Service
3215 Tweedy Boulevard
South Gate, CA 90280
213-566-8993

Job Service
1286 Kyburz Avenue
South Lake Tahoe, CA 96150
916-542-5441

Job Service
135 West Fremont Street
Stockton, CA 95202
209-948-7278

Job Service
420 South Pastoria Avenue
Sunnyvale, CA 94086
408-736-9031

Job Service
40880 County Center Drive
Temecula, CA 92591
909-308-2750

Job Service
1220 Engracia Avenue
Torrance, CA 90501
310-782-2100

Job Service
213 West 11th Street
Tracy, CA 95376
209-833-1015

Job Service
625 Kings Court
Ukiah, CA 95482
707-463-4703

Job Service
2523 South Mooney Boulevard
Visalia, CA 93277
209-636-7300

Job Service
567 Arthur Road
Watsonville, CA 95076
408-761-7420

Job Service
7240 Greenleaf Avenue
Whittier, CA 90602
562-945-3041

Merced College
1743 Ashby Road
Mercer, CA 95348
209-383-0360

Merced County Private Industry Training Department, Los Banos
848 Sixth Street
Los Banos, CA 93635
209-826-0636
http://www.co.merced.ca.us/pitd/pitdhome.htm

Merced County Private Industry Training Department, Merced
1020 West Main Street
Merced, CA 95340
209-385-7326
http://www.co.merced.ca.us/pitd/pitdhome.htm

COLORADO
Colorado Governor's Job Training Office
720 South Colorado Boulevard, Suite 550
Denver, CO 80222
303-758-5020
Fax: 303-758-5578
http://www.colorado.gov

Job Service Center, Aurora
11059 East Bethany Drive
Aurora, CO 80014-2617
303-695-1660

Job Service Center, Boulder
2905 Center Green Court
Boulder, CO 80301-2274
303-449-6643

Job Service Center, Broomfield
5139 West 120th Avenue
Broomfield, CO 80020-5608
303-439-8161

Job Service Center, Canon City
410 Macon Avenue
Canon City, CO 81212-3225
719-275-7408

Job Service Center, Cortez
103 North Chestnut Street
Cortez, CO 81321-3103
970-565-3759

Job Service Center, Delta
107 West 11th Street
Delta, CO 81416-1824
970-874-5781

Job Service Center, Edwards
57 Edwards Access Road 19
Edwards, CO 81632-3103
970-926-4440

Job Service Center, Fort Morgan
411 Main Street
Fort Morgan, CO 80701-2136
303-867-9401

Job Service Center, Glenwood Springs
107 Village Plaza
Glenwood Springs, CO 81601-3103
970-945-8638

Job Service Center, Grand Junction
222 South Sixth Street
Grand Junction, CO 81501-2768
970-248-7350

Job Service Center, Greeley
1551 North 17th Avenue
Greeley, CO 80631
303-353-3800

Job Service Center, Gunnison
109 East Georgia Avenue
Gunnison, CO 81230-2211
970-641-0031

Job Service Center, Limon
820 Limon
Limon, CO 80828-2136
719-775-2387

Job Service Center, Loveland
418 East Fourth Street
Loveland, CO 80537-5637
970-667-4261

Job Service Center, Montrose
2233 East Main Street
Montrose, CO 81401-3831
970-249-7783

Job Service Center, Pueblo
701 Court Street
Pueblo, CO 81003-3010
719-546-5627

Job Service Center, Sterling
201 South Fourth
Sterling, CO 80751-2136
719-522-9342

Job Service Center, Thornton
550 East Thornton Parkway
Denver, CO 80234-3831
303-452-2304

CONNECTICUT

Ansonia Job Center
555 Main Street
Ansonia, CT 06401
203-734-3367
Fax: 203-734-0030

Bridgeport Job Center
500 State Street
Bridgeport, CT 06604
203-579-6062
Fax: 203-579-6374

Bristol Connecticut Works Career Center
55 South Street
Bristol, CT 06010
860-582-7421
Fax: 860-584-4798
http://www.ctdol.state.ct.us

Connecticut Department of Labor
200 Folly Brook Boulevard
Wethersfield, CT 06109
203-566-4280
Fax: 203-566-1520
http://www.ctdol.state.ct.us

Danbury Job Center
152 West Street
Danbury, CT 06813
203-731-2893
Fax: 203-731-2854

Danielson Job Center
95 Westcott Road
Danielson, CT 06239
860-779-5846
Fax: 860-779-5853

Enfield Connecticut Works Career Center
620 Enfield Street
Enfield, CT 06239
860-741-2139
Fax: 860-741-4290
http://www.ctdol.state.ct.us/enfield/enifacts.htm

Hamden Connecticut Works Career Center
37 Marne Street
Hamden, CT 06514
203-789-7734
Fax: 203-288-0788
http://www.ctdol.state.ct.us/hamden/hamdfacts.htm

Hartford Connecticut Works Career Center
3580 Main Street
Hartford, CT 06120
860-566-5790
Fax: 860-566-8417
http://www.ctdol.state.ct.us/hartford/htfdfacts.htm

Meriden Connecticut Works Career Center
290 Pratt Street
Meriden, CT 06450

203-238-6100
Fax: 203-238-6696
http://www.ctdol.state.ct.us/meriden/merifacts.htm

Middletown Job Center
170B Main Street
Middletown, CT 06457
860-344-2993
Fax: 860-754-5090
http://www.ctdol.state.ct.us/mddltwn/middlefacts.
htm

New Britain Connecticut Works Career Center
260 Lafayette Street
New Britain, CT 06053
860-827-7775
Fax: 860-827-7065
http://www.ctdol.state.ct.us/newbritn/nbritfacts.htm

New Haven Connecticut Works Career Center
560 Ella Grasso Boulevard, Building Three
New Haven, CT 06519
203-624-1493
Fax: 203-562-1106
http://www.ctdol.state.ct.us/ctworks/newhavenfacts.
htm

New London Connecticut Works Career Center
Shaws Cove Six
New London, CT 06320
860-443-2041
Fax: 860-447-6218
http://www.ctdol.state.ct.us/newlondn/newlfacts.htm

Norwich Job Center
Six Cliff Street
Norwich, CT 06360
860-887-3587
Fax: 860-892-2263
http://www.ctdol.state.ct.us/norwich/norfacts.htm

Stamford Job Center
111 High Ridge Road
Stamford, CT 06905
860-348-2696
Fax: 203-348-4531

Torrington Job Center
286 Winsted Road
Torrington, CT 06790

860-842-5581
Fax: 860-626-6223

Waterbury Connecticut Works Career Center
249 Thomaston Avenue
Waterbury, CT 06702
203-596-4140
Fax: 203-596-4133
http://www.ctdol.state.ct.us/waterbry/wtbyfacts.htm

Willimantic Connecticut Works Career Center
1320 Main Street
Willimantic, CT 06226
860-423-2521
Fax: 860-450-7527
http://www.ctdol.state.ct.us/williman/willifacts.htm

DELAWARE
Delaware Department of Labor
Division of Employment Training
PO Box 9828
Newark, DE 19809
302-761-8110
Fax: 302-761-6221
http://www.delawareworks.com

Employment and Training Division, DOL
211 Carroll's Plaza, #104
Dover, DE 19903-0616
302-739-5473
Fax: 302-739-6485

Employment and Training Division, DOL
600 North Dupont Highway, #207
Georgetown, DE 19947-0548
302-856-5230
Fax: 302-856-5772

Employment and Training Division, DOL
Pencador Corporate Plaza
Building 225, Suite 211
Newark, DE 19702
302-453-4350
Fax: 302-368-6599

Employment and Training Division, DOL
4425 North Market Street, First Floor
PO Box 9828
Wilmington, DE 19809-0828

302-761-8075
Fax: 302-761-6634

DISTRICT OF COLUMBIA
**District of Columbia Department of Employment
    Services**
500 C Street, NW, Suite 600
Washington, DC 20001
202-724-7185
Fax: 202-724-7112

FLORIDA
Department of Labor and Employment Security
Hartman Building
2012 Capital Circle, SE, Suite 303
Tallahassee, FL 32399-2152
904-922-7021
Fax: 904-488-8930

Job Service
58 Market Street
Apalachicola, FL 32320
904-653-9790

Job Service
256 Apollo Beach Boulevard
Apollo Beach, FL 33572
813-671-5015

Job Service
106 East Byrd Avenue
Bonifay, FL 32425
904-547-5961

Job Service
205 South Moon Avenue
Brandon, FL 33511
813-744-6000

Job Service
620 South Broad Street
Brooksville, FL 34601
352-796-1466

Job Service
206 East Moody Boulevard
Bunnell, FL 32137
904-437-7581

Job Service
105 Live Oaks Gardens
Casselberry, FL 32707
407-262-7422

Job Service
104 North Fifth Street
Chipley, FL 32428
904-638-6287

Job Service
1099 Ferdon Boulevard, South
Crestview, FL 32536-4509
904-689-7823

Job Service
829 U.S. 98 Bypass, South
Dade City, FL 33857
352-521-1485

Job Service
1040 Southeast Fifth Avenue
Delray Beach, FL 33060
561-279-1660

Job Service
2142 Sadler Road
Fernandina Beach, FL 32034
904-277-7272

Job Service
2660 West Oakland Park Boulevard
Fort Lauderdale, FL 33311
954-730-2600

Job Service
3475 North Hiatus Road
Fort Lauderdale, FL 33351
954-746-7900

Job Service
939 Pondella Road
Fort Myers, FL 33903
941-772-1776

Job Service
130 Staff Drive, NE
Fort Walton Beach, FL 32548
904-833-9106

Job Service
4205 Hollywood Boulevard
Hollywood, FL 33021
954-985-4750

Job Service
381 North Krome Avenue
Homestead, FL 33030
305-246-6368

Job Service
212 South First Street
Immokalee, FL 33934
941-657-3128

Job Service
597 North Bermuda Avenue
Kissimmee, FL 34741
407-846-5255

Job Service
248 Hickopochee Avenue
La Belle, FL 33935
941-675-1248

Job Service
343 West Central Avenue
Lake Wales, FL 33853
941-678-4155

Job Service
633 Northeast 167th Street
Miami, FL 33162
305-654-7175

Job Service
701 Southwest 27th Avenue
Miami, FL 33135
305-643-7600

Job Service
401 Northwest Second Avenue
Miami, FL 33128
305-377-7255

Job Service
7430 Southwest 97th Avenue
Miami, FL 33173
305-252-4440

Job Service
8300 Northwest 53rd Street
Miami, FL 33166
305-470-5620

Job Service
3050 Horseshoe Drive, North, #198
Naples, FL 33942
941-434-5006

Job Service
16405 Northwest 25th Avenue
Opa Locka, FL 33054
305-628-7215

Job Service
3113 West Colonial Drive
Orlando, FL 32808
407-297-2044

Job Service
5449 South Semoran Boulevard, #17
Orlando, FL 32822
407-249-6586

Job Service
1001 Executive Center Drive
Orlando, FL 32803
407-897-2880

Job Service
9953 Pines Boulevard
Pembroke Pines, FL 33024
954-433-7823

Job Service
3670 North L Street, #A
Pensacola, FL 32505
904-444-8925

Job Service
3491 Gandy Boulevard, #100
Pinellas Park, FL 34665
813-547-7707

Job Service
1301 West Copans Road
Pompano Beach, FL 33064
954-969-3541

Job Service
12372 U.S. Highway 19
Port Richey, FL 34667
813-862-8541

Job Service
9326 South Federal Highway
Port St. Lucie, FL 34952-4213
561-335-0603

Job Service
1205 Elizabeth Street
Punta Gorda, FL 33950
941-637-6981

Job Service
2139 Main Street
Sarasota, FL 34237
941-361-6100

Job Service
2451 U.S. Highway One, South
St. Augustine, FL 32086
904-825-5044

Job Service
525 Mirror Lake Drive, North
St. Petersburg, FL 33701
813-893-2255

Job Service
1111 South Federal Highway
Stuart, FL 34994
561-221-4020

Job Service
9215 North Florida Avenue, #101
Tampa, FL 33612
813-930-7400

Job Service
915 15th Street
Vero Beach, FL 32960
561-778-5072

Job Service
301 Broadway
West Palm Beach, FL 33404
561-840-3109

Job Service
80 East 30th Street
West Palm Beach, FL 33404
561-863-1711

Job Service
2221 Lee Road
Winter Park, FL 32789
407-623-1045

Job Service of Florida
9300 North Century Boulevard
Century, FL 32535
904-256-4166

Job Service of Florida
1040 South Federal Highway
Delray Beach, FL 33483
561-737-4925

Job Service of Florida
805 Virginia Avenue, #1
Fort Pierce, FL 32701
561-468-4060

Job Service of Florida
215 North Market Street
Jacksonville, FL 32202
904-798-4780

Job Service of Florida
430 South First Street
Lake City, FL 32025
904-758-0433

Job Service of Florida
4469 South Congress Avenue
Lake Worth, FL 33461
561-433-3658

Job Service of Florida
114 East Ninth Street
Panama City, FL 32401
904-872-4340

Job Service of Florida
224 North Jefferson Street
Perry, FL 32347
850-584-7604

Job Service of Florida
385 East Jefferson Street, #A
Quincy, FL 32351
904-627-9544

Job Service of Florida
80 East 30th Street
Riviera Beach, FL 33404-2314
561-840-3109

Job Service of Florida
1307 North Monroe Street, #30B
Tallahassee, FL 32303
904-488-8701

Job Service of Florida
2810 Sharer Road
Tallahassee, FL 32312
904-488-8701

Job Service of Florida
3111 South Dixie Highway
West Palm Beach, FL 33405
561-837-5680

Job Service of Florida
5601 Corporate Way
West Palm Beach, FL 33407
561-640-6199

Job Service of Florida
242 Royal Palm Beach Boulevard
West Palm Beach, FL 33411
561-793-5061

GEORGIA
Georgia Department of Labor Office, Albany
1608 South Slappey Boulevard
Albany, GA 31706-3450
912-430-5010
Fax: 912-430-5078
http://www.dol.state.ga.us

Georgia Department of Labor Office, Americus
120 West Church Street
Americus, GA 31709
912-931-2520
http://www.dol.state.ga.us

Georgia Department of Labor Office, Athens
788 Prince Avenue
Athens, GA 30603
706-542-8500
Fax: 706-369-5895
http://www.dol.state.ga.us

Georgia Department of Labor Office, Augusta
601 Greene Street
Augusta, GA 30903
706-721-3131
http://www.dol.state.ga.us

Georgia Department of Labor Office, Bainbridge
310 South Scott Street
Bainbridge, GA 31717-1017
912-248-2618
Fax: 912-248-2681
http://www.dol.state.ga.us

Georgia Department of Labor Office, Blairsville
Haralson Memorial Center
185 Wellborne Street
Blairsville, GA 30512-4531
706-745-6959
Fax: 706-745-6453
http://www.dol.state.ga.us

Georgia Department of Labor Office, Blue Ridge
East Second Street
Blue Ridge, GA 30513-0488
706-632-2133
Fax: 706-632-7316
http://www.dol.state.ga.us

Georgia Department of Labor Office, Brunswick
2517 Tara Lane
Brunswick, GA 31520
912-264-7244
Fax: 912-262-3334
http://www.dol.state.ga.us

Georgia Department of Labor Office, Cairo
101 Martin Luther King Avenue
Cairo, GA 31728-0685
912-377-6526
Fax: 912-377-8013
http://www.dol.state.ga.us

Georgia Department of Labor Office, Camilla
35 South Street
Camilla, GA 31730
912-336-7845
Fax: 912-336-9772
http://www.dol.state.ga.us

Georgia Department of Labor Office, Carrollton
275 Northside Drive
Carrollton, GA 30117-0509
770-836-6668
Fax: 770-836-6770
http://www.dol.state.ga.us

Georgia Department of Labor Office, Cartersville
19 Felton Place
Cartersville, GA 32137
770-387-3760
http://www.dol.state.ga.us

Georgia Department of Labor Office, Cedartown
1108 North Main Street
Cedartown, GA 30125-1019
770-749-2213
http://www.dol.state.ga.us

Georgia Department of Labor Office, Clayton County
1193 Forest Parkway
Lake City, GA 30260
404-363-7643
Fax: 404-362-2547
http://www.dol.state.ga.us

Georgia Department of Labor Office, Cobb-Cherokee
465 Big Shanty Road
Marietta, GA 30066-3303
770-528-6100
Fax: 770-528-6139
http://www.dol.state.ga.us

Georgia Department of Labor Office, Columbus
700 Veterans Parkway
Columbus, GA 31902
706-649-7423
Fax: 706-649-1049
http://www.dol.state.ga.us

Georgia Department of Labor Office, Cordele
1205 South Seventh Street
Cordele, GA 31010-1136
912-276-2355
Fax: 912-276-2706
http://www.dol.state.ga.us

Georgia Department of Labor Office, Covington
7249 Industrial Boulevard
Covington, GA 30210
770-784-2455
Fax: 770-784-2459
http://www.dol.state.ga.us

Georgia Department of Labor Office, Dalton
1406 Chattanooga Avenue
Dalton, GA 30720
706-272-2301
Fax: 706-272-2318
http://www.dol.state.ga.us

Georgia Department of Labor Office, Dekalb County
3879 Covington Highway
Decatur, GA 30032
404-298-3970
Fax: 404-298-3995
http://www.dol.state.ga.us

Georgia Department of Labor Office, Douglas
310 West Bryan Street
Douglas, GA 31533-1363
912-389-4254
Fax: 912-389-4307
http://www.dol.state.ga.us

Georgia Department of Labor Office, Dublin
910 North Jefferson Street
Dublin, GA 31021
912-275-6525
Fax: 912-275-6599
http://www.dol.state.ga.us

Georgia Department of Labor Office, Eastman
207 Fifth Avenue
Eastman, GA 31023-1649
912-374-6994
Fax: 912-374-6996
http://www.dol.state.ga.us

Georgia Department of Labor Office, Elberton
Five Seaboard Street
Elberton, GA 30635
706-213-2028
Fax: 706-213-2036
http://www.dol.state.ga.us

Georgia Department of Labor Office, Gainesville
2419 Corporate Drive, SW
Gainesville, GA 30504-6056
770-535-5484
Fax: 770-531-5699
http://www.dol.state.ga.us

Georgia Department of Labor Office, Griffin
1514 Highway 16, West
Griffin, GA 30224
770-228-7226
Fax: 770-229-3287
http://www.dol.state.ga.us

Georgia Department of Labor Office, Gwinnett County
1535 Atkinson Road
Lawrenceville, GA 30243-5601
770-995-6913
Fax: 770-995-6912
http://www.dol.state.ga.us

Georgia Department of Labor Office, Habersham Area
215 Hodges Street
Cornelia, GA 30531
706-776-0811
http://www.dol.state.ga.us

Georgia Department of Labor Office, Hinesville
137 South Main Street
Hinesville, GA 31313-3217
912-370-2595
Fax: 912-370-2598
http://www.dol.state.ga.us

Georgia Department of Labor Office, Jesup
189 North Brunswick Street
Jesup, GA 31598-0833
912-427-5842
Fax: 912-427-5881
http://www.dol.state.ga.us

Georgia Department of Labor Office, Kings Bay
1712 Osborne Road, Suite L
St. Marys, GA 31558-2632
912-673-6942
Fax: 912-673-7077
http://www.dol.state.ga.us

Georgia Department of Labor Office, LaFayette
200 West Villanow Street
LaFayette, GA 30728
706-738-5525
Fax: 706-638-5529
http://www.dol.state.ga.us

Georgia Department of Labor Office, LaGrange
1002 Longley Place
LaGrange, GA 30240-5733
706-845-4000
Fax: 706-845-4005
http://www.dol.state.ga.us

Georgia Department of Labor Office, Macon
3090 Mercer University
Macon, GA 31213-2899
912-751-6164
Fax: 912-751-6639
http://www.dol.state.ga.us

Georgia Department of Labor Office, Milledgeville
156 Roberson Mill Road
Milledgeville, GA 31061-0730
912-445-5465
http://www.dol.state.ga.us

Georgia Department of Labor Office, Monroe
226 Alcova Street
Monroe, GA 30655
770-207-4111
Fax: 770-207-4114
http://www.dol.state.ga.us

Georgia Department of Labor Office, Moultrie
115 Fifth Street, SE
Moultrie, GA 31776-1050
912-891-7147
Fax: 912-891-7149
http://www.dol.state.ga.us

Georgia Department of Labor Office, Newnan
30 Bledsoe Road
Newnan, GA 30265
770-254-7220
Fax: 770-254-7277
http://www.dol.state.ga.us

Georgia Department of Labor Office,
North Metro
2943 North Druid Hills Road
Atlanta, GA 30329-3909
404-679-5200
Fax: 404-679-4929
http://www.dol.state.ga.us

Georgia Department of Labor Office,
Northwest Georgia
759 Battfield Parkway
Fort Oglethorpe, GA 30742
706-861-1990
Fax: 706-861-0062
http://www.dol.state.ga.us

Georgia Department of Labor Office, Perry
741-A Main Street
Perry, GA 31069-1781
912-987-5051
Fax: 912-987-3770
http://www.dol.state.ga.us

Georgia Department of Labor Office, Rome
462 Riverside Parkway
Rome, GA 30162-5107
706-295-6051
http://www.dol.state.ga.us

Georgia Department of Labor Office,
Savannah
5520 White Bluff Road
Savannah, GA 31403-2069
912-356-2773
http://www.dol.state.ga.us

Georgia Department of Labor Office,
South Metro
2636-14 Martin Luther King
Atlanta, GA 30311
404-699-6900
http://www.dol.state.ga.us

Georgia Department of Labor Office,
Statesboro
62 Packinghouse Road
Statesboro, GA 30459-0558
912-681-5156
Fax: 912-681-5228
http://www.dol.state.ga.us

Georgia Department of Labor Office, Sylvester
204 East Franklin Street
Sylvester, GA 31791
912-777-2120
Fax: 912-777-2121
http://www.dol.state.ga.us

Georgia Department of Labor Office, T
homasville
120 North Crawford Street
Thomasville, GA 31799-1340
912-225-4033
http://www.dol.state.ga.us

Georgia Department of Labor Office, Thomson
230 Main Street
Thomson, GA 30824
706-595-3665
Fax: 706-595-7209
http://www.dol.state.ga.us

Georgia Department of Labor Office, Tifton
902 South Main Street
Tifton, GA 31793-0067
912-386-3322
Fax: 912-386-7188
http://www.dol.state.ga.us

Georgia Department of Labor Office, Toccoa
112 North Alexander Street
Toccoa, GA 30577
706-282-4514
Fax: 706-282-4513
http://www.dol.state.ga.us

Georgia Department of Labor Office, Valdosta
2808 North Oak Street
Valdosta, GA 31602
912-333-5211
Fax: 912-333-5301
http://www.dol.state.ga.us

Georgia Department of Labor Office, Vidalia
16 Carter Center
Vidalia, GA 30474
912-537-9847
Fax: 912-537-6238
http://www.dol.state.ga.us

Georgia Department of Labor Office, Waycross
600 Plant Avenue
Waycross, GA 31502-1609
912-285-6105
Fax: 912-287-6550
http://www.dol.state.ga.us

HAWAII

Jobs Administration
Human Service Department
677 Queen Street, #400A
Honolulu, HI 96813
808-587-5250

Jobs Works
Human Services Department
677 Ala Moana Boulevard, #720
Honolulu, HI 96813
808-587-3850

IDAHO

Blackfoot Job Service
155 North Maple
Blackfoot, ID 83221-0009
208-785-2200
Fax: 208-785-5036

Blaine County Job Service
513 North Main, Suite One
Hailey, ID 83333-3000
208-788-3526
Fax: 208-788-3041

Boise Job Service
219 Main
Boise, ID 83735-0030
208-334-6225

Bonners Ferry Job Service
6541 Main Street
Bonners Ferry, ID 83805-9779

208-267-5581
Fax: 208-267-3797

Burley Job Service
127 West Fifth Street, North
Burley, ID 83318-0158
208-678-5518
Fax: 208-678-1765

Canyon County Job Service
5909 Graye Lane
Caldwell, ID 83606-0220
208-459-4617
Fax: 208-454-7720

Coeur d'Alene Job Service
1221 West Ironwood Drive, #200
Coeur d'Alene, ID 83814-2668
208-769-1558
Fax: 208-769-1574

Emmett Job Service
2030 South Washington
Emmett, ID 83617-0127
208-365-5316
Fax: 208-365-6599

Grangeville Job Service
102 North College
Grangeville, ID 83530-0550
208-983-0440
Fax: 208-983-0302

Idaho Department of Employment
317 Maine Street
Boise, ID 83735-0001
208-334-6110
Fax: 208-334-6430

Idaho Falls Job Service
150 Shoup Avenue, #12
Idaho Falls, ID 83402-3653
208-785-2200

Kellogg Job Service
120 West Cameron
Kellogg, ID 83837-2392
208-783-1202
Fax: 208-783-5561

Lewiston Job Service
1158 Idaho Street
Lewiston, ID 83501-1147
208-799-5000
Fax: 208-799-5007

Magic Valley Job Service
771 North College Road
Twin Falls, ID 83303-0529
208-736-3000
Fax: 208-736-3007

McCall Job Service
Village Square
McCall, ID 83638-0966
208-634-7102
Fax: 208-634-2965

Meridian Job Service
205 East Watertower Lane
Meridian, ID 83642-6282
208-895-6640
Fax: 208-895-8441

Moscow Job Service
221 East Second Street
Moscow, ID 83843-1628
208-882-7571
Fax: 208-882-8324

Mountain Home Job Service
575 North Third, East
Mountain Home, ID 83647-0160
208-587-7911
Fax: 208-587-2964

Orofino Job Service
153 Johnson Avenue
Orofino, ID 83544-0391
208-476-5506
Fax: 208-476-3471

Payette Job Service
175 North 16th Street
Payette, ID 83661-0179
208-642-3375
Fax: 208-642-7150

Pocatello Job Service
460 North Fifth Avenue
Pocatello, ID 83205-4087
208-236-6214

Rexburg Job Service
316 North Third, East
Rexburg, ID 83440-0158
208-356-4451
Fax: 208-356-0042

Salmon Job Service
1301 Main Street, Suite 1
Salmon, ID 83467-0990
208-756-2234
Fax: 208-756-4672

Sandpoint Job Service
2101 West Pine Street
Sandpoint, ID 83864-9399
208-263-7544
Fax: 208-265-0193

St. Maries Job Service
105 North Eighth Street
St. Maries, ID 83861-1845
208-245-2518
Fax: 208-245-2012

ILLINOIS
Department of Commerce and Community Affairs
620 East Adams, Sixth Floor
Springfield, IL 62701
217-785-6006
Fax: 217-785-6454

Job Service
729 Interstate One, Route 83
Bensenville, IL 60106-1256
630-595-8866

Job Service
1007 Washington Avenue
Cairo, IL 62914
618-734-1498

Job Service
441 East Willow Street
Carbondale, IL 62901
618-459-7306

Job Service
4931 West Diversey Avenue
Chicago, IL 60639
773-889-6820

Job Service
8750 South Stony Island Avenue
Chicago, IL 60617
773-221-3737

Job Service
1515 East 71st Street
Chicago, IL 60619
773-947-2500

Job Service
1657 South Blue Island Avenue
Chicago, IL 60608
312-243-5100

Job Service
2444 West Lawrence Avenue
Chicago, IL 60625
773-334-6646

Job Service
3500 West Grand Avenue
Chicago, IL 60651
773-227-7117

Job Service
4544 West Carroll Avenue
Chicago, IL 60624
773-626-0180

Job Service
5101 South Cicero Avenue
Chicago, IL 60632
773-838-3100

Job Service
657 West Lake Street
Chicago, IL 60661
312-332-1278

Job Service
837 West 119th Street
Chicago, IL 60643
773-821-4100

Job Service
407 North Franklin Street
Danville, IL 61832
217-442-3044

Job Service
1701 East Lincoln Highway
De Kalb, IL 60115
815-756-6356

Job Service
2311 Hoffman Drive
Effingham, IL 62401
217-342-4149

Job Service
50 Kriege Farm Road
Glen Carbon, IL 62025
618-656-6100

Job Service
Five American Village
Granite City, IL 62040
618-656-6100

Job Service
14829 Dixie Highway
Harvey, IL 60426
708-596-2354

Job Service
1121 South Park Avenue
Herrin, IL 62948
618-942-2137

Job Service
City Building
Hoopeston, IL 60942
217-283-6519

Job Service
502 East Edwards Street
Litchfield, IL 62056
217-324-2138

Job Service
837 South Westmore Avenue
Lombard, IL 60148-3724
630-495-4345

Job Service
115 North 15th Street
Mattoon, IL 61938
217-235-0327

Job Service
54 East Crownview
Mount Vernon, IL 62864
618-244-1700

Job Service
223 South 13th Street
Murphysboro, IL 62966
618-6887-2341

Job Service
406 Elm Street
Peoria, IL 61605
309-671-3113

INDIANA
Department of Workforce Development
10 North Senate Avenue, Room 302
Indianapolis, IN 46204
317-233-5661
Fax: 317-233-4793

Department of Workforce Development
10 North Senate, Room E204
Indianapolis, IN 46204
317-232-1832
http://www.dwd.state.in.us

East Central Private Industry Council
201 East Charles Street
PO Box 1081
Muncie, IN 47308-1081
765-741-5863

Indianapolis Private Industry Council
17 West Market Street, #500
Indianapolis, IN 46204
317-684-2220

Interlocal Association
143 Green Meadows Drive, #2
PO Box 69
Greenfield, IN 46140-0069
317-467-0248

JobSource
1106 Meridian Plaza, #325
PO Box 149

Anderson, IN 46015-0149
765-641-6518

JobWorks
201 East Rudisill Boulevard
Fort Wayne, IN 46806
219-745-2000

**Kankakee Valley Workforce Development
Services**
150 Lincoln Square, #2001
PO Box 450
Valparaiso, IN 46384
219-464-4861

Richmond-Wayne County Chamber of Commerce
33 South Seventh Street, Suite Two
Richmond, IN 47374
765-962-1511
Fax: 765-966-0882
http://www.infocom.com/rwcchamber/education.htm

River Valley Resources Inc.
1315 Clifty Drive
Madison, IN 47250
812-265-2652

Western Indiana Private Industry Council
30 North Eighth Street
Terre Haute, IN 47808
812-234-6602

IOWA
Iowa Department of Economic Development
100 East Grand Avenue
Des Moines, IA 50319
515-281-5365
Fax: 515-281-5144

Job Service
508 Poplar Street
Atlantic, IA 50022
712-243-2351

Job Service
619 North Carroll Street
Carroll, IA 51401
712-792-2685

Job Service
800 Seventh Street, SE
Cedar Rapids, IA 52401
319-365-9474

Job Service
201 North 13th Street
Centerville, IA 52544
515-856-6371

Job Service
126 South Grand Street
Chariton, IA 50049
515-774-4816

Job Service
1200 West Cedar Street
Cherokee, IA 51012
712-225-2274

Job Service
712 Davis Avenue
Corning, IA 50841
515-322-4707

Job Service
902 West Kimberly Road
Davenport, IA 52806
319-386-4770

Job Service
1413 Broadway
Denison, IA 51442
712-263-6102

Job Service
7600 University Avenue
Des Moines, IA 50325
515-281-4799

Job Service
590 Iowa Street
Dubuque, IA 52001
319-556-5800

Job Service
51 West Washington Avenue
Fairfield, IA 52556
515-472-5466

Job Service
130 North Clark Street
Forest City, IA 50436-1643
515-582-2976

Job Service
2700 First Avenue, South
Fort Dodge, IA 50501
515-576-0242

Job Service
610 Eighth Street
Fort Madison, IA 52627
319-372-4412

Job Service
354 Public Square
Greenfield, IA 50849
515-743-2433

Job Service
907 Chatburn Avenue, Suite A
Harlan, IA 51537
712-755-3777

Job Service
203 Second Avenue, NE
Independence, IA 50644
319-334-2653

Job Service
106 Washington Street
Keokuk, IA 52632
319-524-1862

Job Service
105 West Main Street
Knoxville, IA 50138
515-842-3972

Job Service
115 Plymouth Street, NW
Le Mars, IA 51031
712-546-8178

Job Service
223 West Main Street
Manchester, IA 52057
319-927-4447

Job Service
1427 Fourth Street, SW
Mason City, IA 50401
515-423-1133

Job Service
213 South Cedar Street
Monticello, IA 52310
319-465-4044

Job Service
101 North Locust Avenue
New Hampton, IA 50659
515-394-3825

Job Service
115 North Third Avenue, West
Newton, IA 50208
515-792-5131

Job Service
1000 North Broadway Street
Red Oak, IA 51566
712-623-2569

Job Service
1201 Second Avenue
Sheldon, IA 51201
712-324-4152

Job Service
500 North Broad Street
Shenandoah, IA 51601
712-246-4470

Job Service
2508 Fourth Street
Sioux City, IA 51101
712-277-8540

Job Service
925 East Fourth Street
Waterloo, IA 50703
319-235-9864

KANSAS
Workforce Development Center, Arkansas City
221 West Chestnut Avenue
PO Box 858

Arkansas City, KS 67005-0858
316-442-3130
Fax: 316-442-6740

Workforce Development Center, Atchison
818 Kansas Avenue
Atchison, KS 66002-2396
913-367-4814
Fax: 913-367-3980

Workforce Development Center, Chanute
119 North Grant Street
PO Box 778
Chanute, KS 66720-0778
316-431-4950
Fax: 316-431-2375

Workforce Development Center, Colby
485 North Chick Avenue
PO Box E
Colby, KS 67701-0984
913-462-6862
Fax: 913-462-8371

Workforce Development Center, Dodge City
2308 First Avenue
PO Box 1029
Dodge City, KS 67801-1029
316-227-2149
Fax: 316-227-9667

Workforce Development Center, El Dorado
123 East Second Avenue
PO Box 350
El Dorado, KS 67042-0350
316-321-2350
Fax: 316-321-7653

Workforce Development Center, Emporia
512 Market Street
PO Box 707
Emporia, KS 66801-0707
316-342-3355
Fax: 316-342-2806

Workforce Development Center, Garden City
107 East Spruce Street
PO Box 994
Garden City, KS 67846-0994
316-276-2339
Fax: 316-276-7306

Workforce Development Center, Great Bend
2120 11th Street
PO Box 969
Great Bend, KS 67530-0969
316-793-5445
Fax: 316-793-3188

Workforce Development Center, Hays
332 East Eighth Street
PO Box 659
Hays, KS 67601-0659
913-625-5654
Fax: 913-625-0092

Workforce Development Center, Hutchinson
518 North Washington Street
PO Box 1799
Hutchinson, KS 67504-1799
316-663-6131
Fax: 316-669-0738

Workforce Development Center, Independence
200 Arco Place
Independence, KS 67301-3312
316-332-1660
Fax: 316-332-1668

Workforce Development Center, Kansas City
552 State Avenue
Kansas City, KS 66101-2462
913-281-3000
Fax: 913-281-0069

Workforce Development Center, Lawrence
833 Ohio Street
PO Box 589
Lawrence, KS 66044-0589
913-843-0531

Workforce Development Center, Leavenworth
600 South Fifth Street
PO Box 646
Leavenworth, KS 66048-1098
913-682-4152
Fax: 913-682-1804

Workforce Development Center, Liberal
807 South Kansas Avenue
Liberal, KS 67901-4193

316-624-1863
Fax: 316-624-3355

Workforce Development Center, Manhattan
621 Humboldt Street
PO Box 940
Manhattan, KS 66502-0009
913-776-8884
Fax: 913-776-0568

Workforce Development Center, Newton
116 East Sixth Street
PO Box 406
Newton, KS 67114-0406
316-283-4220
Fax: 316-283-4201

Workforce Development Center, Overland Park
8417 Santa Fe Drive
Overland Park, KS 66212-2799
913-642-8484
Fax: 913-642-7260

Workforce Development Center, Pittsburg
104 South Pine Street
PO Box A
Pittsburg, KS 66762-0605
316-231-4250
Fax: 316-231-6448

Workforce Development Center, Salina
203 North 10th Street
PO Box 1817
Salina, KS 67402-1817
913-827-0385
Fax: 913-827-2307

Workforce Development Center, Topeka
1430 Southwest Topeka Boulevard
Topeka, KS 66612-1897
913-296-1715
Fax: 913-296-1984

Workforce Development Center, Wichita
402 East Second Street
PO Box 877
Wichita, KS 67201-0877
316-266-8600
Fax: 316-266-8656

KENTUCKY
Workforce Development Cabinet
Office of Training and Reemployment
209 St. Clair Street, Fourth Floor
Frankfort, KY 40601
502-564-5360
Fax: 502-564-7452

LOUISIANA
Baton Rouge Job Service
1991 Wooddale Boulevard
Baton Rouge, LA 70806
504-925-4311

Baton Rouge Workforce Development Center
2155 Fuqua Street
Baton Rouge, LA 70804
504-342-1659
Fax: 504-342-2349

Job Service
1991 Wooddale Boulevard
Baton Rouge, LA 70806
504-925-4311

Job Service
2331 Airline Drive
Bossier City, LA 71111
318-741-7360

Job Service
301 North Stewart Street
Deridder, LA 70634
318-462-2482

Job Service
219 Louisiana Avenue
Ferriday, LA 71334
318-747-8648

Job Service
1827 South Burnside Avenue, #D
Gonzales, LA 70737
504-644-5666

Job Service
706 East Vermilion Street
Lafayette, LA 70501
318-262-5511

Job Service
7710 Highway 90, East
Morgan City, LA 70380
504-380-2448

Job Service
107 South 12th Street
Oakdale, LA 71463
318-335-4335

Job Service
262 West Bellevue Street
Opelousas, LA 70570
318-948-0246

Job Service
2900 Dowdell Street
Shreveport, LA 71103
318-676-7746

One-Stop Career Centers
PO Box 94094
Baton Rouge, LA 70804
504-342-3076

MAINE
Job Service
20 Union Street
Augusta, ME 04330
207-287-3431

Job Service
Two Anthony Avenue
Augusta, ME 04330
207-624-5120

Job Service
45 Oak Street
Bangor, ME 04401
207-561-4600

Job Service
39 Bangor Street
Houlton, ME 04730
207-532-9416

Job Service
522 Lisbon Street
Lewiston, ME 04240
207-783-5310

Job Service
63 Main Street
Sanford, ME 04073
207-324-5460

Job Service
140 North Avenue
Skowhegan, ME 04976-1942
207-474-4950

Job Service
30 Airport Road
Waterville, ME 04901
207-872-5516

Maine Department of Labor
20 Union Street
PO Box 309
Augusta, ME 04330
207-287-3788
Fax: 207-287-5292

MARYLAND
Department of Labor, Licensing and Regulation
217 East Redwood Street
Baltimore, MD 21202
410-333-6901
Fax: 410-333-8628

Job Service
2016 Industrial Drive
Annapolis, MD 21401
410-794-7920

Job Service
1228 East Joppa Road
Baltimore, MD 21286
410-321-4066

Job Service
6321 Greenbelt Road
College Park, MD 20740
301-441-2137

Job Service
7060 Oakland Mills Road, #L12
Columbia, MD 21046
410-312-5762

Job Service
67 Thomas Johnson Drive, #26
Frederick, MD 21702
301-694-2180

Job Service
7500 Ritchie Highway
Glen Burnie, MD 21061
410-424-1300

Job Service
2121 Brightseat Road
Landover, MD 20785
301-386-0701

Job Service
614 Main Street
Laurel, MD 20707
301-206-2020

Job Service
Route 245, Washington Street
Leonardtown, MD 20650
301-475-8300

Job Service
216 East Alder Street
Oakland, MD 21550
301-334-3972

Job Service
200 Duke Street, #1400
Prince Frederick, MD 20678
410-535-8815

Job Service, Employment Services
South Office Building
Wheaton Plaza
Kensington, MD 20895
301-929-4386

MASSACHUSETTS
Corporation for Business Work and Learning
Schrafft Center
529 Main Street, Suite 400
Boston, MA 02129
617-242-3072
Fax: 617-727-8158

MICHIGAN

Eastern Upper Peninsula Employment and Training Consortium
2901 Interstate 75 Business Spur, Building One
Sault Ste. Marie, MI 49783
906-635-1752

Ingham Intermediate School District
611 Hagadorn Road
Mason, MI 48854
517-244-1338
Fax: 517-676-3399
http://mois.org

Job Service
1401 Cleaver Road
Caro, MI 48723
517-673-7787

Job Service
36209 South Gratiot Avenue
Clinton Township, MI 48035
810-791-2930

Job Service
555 West Woodlawn Avenue
Hastings, MI 49058
616-948-8087

Job Service
33523 Eight Mile Road
Livonia, MI 48152-4104
810-476-5980

Job Service
5880 West U.S. Highway 10
Ludington, MI 49431
616-845-7361

Job Service
102 West Munising Avenue
Munising, MI 49862
906-387-2091

Job Service
8221 Fruit Ridge Avenue, NW
Sparta, MI 49345
616-887-8370

Job Service
37250 Van Dyke Avenue
Sterling Heights, MI 48312
810-939-9650

Job Service
1288 28th Street, SW
Wyoming, MI 49509-2702
616-531-5360

Job Service
214 East Michigan Avenue
Ypsilanti, MI 48198
313-482-5202

Michigan Jobs Commission
201 North Washington Square
Lansing, MI 48913
517-373-6227
Fax: 517-373-0314
http://www.michigan.gov/mdcd

Six County Employment Alliance
2831 North Lincoln Road
Escanaba, MI 49829
906-789-9732

Western Upper Peninsula Manpower Consortium
100 Marquette Street
Ironwood, MI 49938
906-932-4059

MINNESOTA

Albert Lea Workforce Center
1649 West Main Street
Skyline Mall
Albert Lea, MN 56007-1868
507-379-3409
Fax: 507-379-3413

Alexandria Workforce Center
701 Broadway Street, #101
First Bank Building
Alexandria, MN 56308-1811
320-762-7800
Fax: 320-762-7530

Anoka County Community Action
SkillsNet-Job Service Office
1201 89th Avenue, NE, #345
Blaine, MN 55434
612-783-4747
Fax: 612-783-4700

Arrowhead Economic Opportunity Agency
SkillsNet-Job Service Office
703 Third Avenue, South
Virginia, MN 55792-2797
218-749-2912

Austin Job Service
1900 Eighth Avenue, NW
Riverland Community College
Austin, MN 55912-1473
507-433-0555

Bemidji Job Service
1819 Bemidji Avenue
PO Box 6007
Bemidji, MN 56601
218-755-2936
Fax: 218-755-3841

Bi-County CAP
SkillsNet-Job Service Office
2715 15th Street
Bemidji, MN 56601-0579
218-751-4631

Brainerd Job Service
1919 South Sixth Street
PO Box 767
Brainerd, MN 56401-0767
218-828-2450
Fax: 218-828-2664
http://www.brainerd.com

Cambridge Workforce Center
1575 East Highway 95, Suite C
Cambridge, MN 55008-1756
612-689-7136
Fax: 612-689-7140

Cloquet Workforce Center
715 Cloquet Avenue
Cloquet, MN 55720-1629
218-879-5201
Fax: 218-879-7180

Community Action for Sub. Hennepin
SkillsNet-Job Service Office
33 10th Avenue, South, #150
Hopkins, MN 55343
612-933-9180
Fax: 612-933-6147

Community Action of Minneapolis
SkillsNet-Job Service Office
401 Second Avenue, South
Minneapolis, MN 55401
612-348-8858
Fax: 612-348-9834

Crookston Job Service
721 South Minnesota Street
PO Box 604
Crookston, MN 56716-0604
218-281-6020
Fax: 218-281-6025

Dakota County Workforce Services
33 East Wentworth Avenue
St. Paul, MN 55188
612-450-2633
Fax: 612-450-2709

Dakotas County Workforce Center
60 East Marie, #209
Southview Office Plaza
St. Paul, MN 55118-5900
612-552-5000

Detroit Lakes Workforce Center
801 Roosevelt
Moorhead, Clay County Family Services Center
Detroit Lakes, MN 56501-3703
218-846-7379
Fax: 218-846-0773

Duluth Community Action Program
SkillsNet-Job Service Office
1305 London Road
Duluth, MN 55805
218-724-8538

Duluth Job Service
320 West Second Street, Suite 205
Government Services Center
Duluth, MN 55802-1494

218-723-4730
Fax: 218-723-4745

Duluth Job Training Program
332 City Hall
Duluth, MN 55802
218-723-3771
Fax: 218-723-3636

East Grand Forks Job Service
1616 Central Avenue, NE
PO Box 666
Grand Forks, MN 56721-0666
218-773-9841
Fax: 218-773-0425

Fairmont Workforce Center
923 North State Street, #110
PO Box 767
Fairmont, MN 56031-0767
507-235-5518
http://www.fairmont.org

Faribault Job Service
201 South Lyndale Avenue, Suite One
Faribo Town Square
Faribault, MN 55021-5758
507-332-3220
Fax: 507-332-5487

Fergus Falls Workforce Center
125 West Lincoln Avenue, #1
PO Box 418
Fergus Falls, MN 56538-0418
218-739-7560
Fax: 218-739-7496

Freeborn County Community Action Agency
SkillsNet-Job Service Office
411 South Broadway
Albert Lea, MN 56007
507-377-5199

Grand Rapids Workforce Center
1215 Southeast Second Avenue
Itasca Resource Center
Grand Rapids, MN 55744-0678
218-327-4480
Fax: 218-327-4179

Heartland Community Action Agency
SkillsNet-Job Service Office
310 South First Street
Willmar, MN 56201
320-235-0850

Hennepin County Training and Employment Assistance
300 South Sixth Street
Minneapolis, MN 55487-0001
612-348-5203
Fax: 612-348-3932

Hibbing Workforce Center
3920 13th Avenue, East
Hibbing, MN 55746-0068
218-262-6777
Fax: 218-262-7316

Hutchinson Job Service
Two Century Avenue
PO Box 550
Hutchinson, MN 55350-0550
320-587-4740
Fax: 320-234-7769

Inter-County Community Council
SkillsNet-Job Service Office
PO Box 189
Oklee, MN 56742
218-796-5144

International Falls Workforce Center
407 Fourth Street
International Falls, MN 56649-2413
218-283-9427
Fax: 218-283-4042

Koochiching-Itasca Action Council
SkillsNet-Job Service Office
413 13th Street, SE
Grand Rapids, MN 55744
218-327-4480

Lakes and Pines Community Action Council
SkillsNet-Job Service Office
1700 Maple Avenue, East
Mora, MN 55051
320-679-1800

Litchfield Workforce Center
114 North Holcombe Avenue, #170
Meeker County Family Services Building
Litchfield, MN 55355-2273
320-693-2859
Fax: 320-693-9146

Little Falls Workforce Center
315 12th Street, NE
Coborns Complex
Little Falls, MN 56345-2910
320-632-2356
Fax: 320-632-6824

Mahube Community Council
SkillsNet-Job Service Office
Highway 59, South
Detroit Lakes, MN 56502-0747
218-847-1385

Mankato Job Service
1650 Madison Avenue
PO Box 1210
Mankato, MN 56002-1210
507-389-6723
Fax: 507-389-2708

Marshall Workforce Center
1424 East College Drive, Suite 200
Market Street Complex
Marshall, MN 56256-5005
507-537-6236
Fax: 507-537-6362

Midwest Farmworker Employment and Training
SkillsNet-Job Service Office
1311 Second Street, North
St. Cloud, MN 56302-1231

Minneapolis Employment and Training Program
310 1/2 City Hall
Minneapolis, MN 55415
612-673-5700
Fax: 612-673-2108

Minnesota Community Action Association
SkillsNet-Job Service Office
1997 Sloan Place, #30
Maplewood, MN 55117
612-222-5337
Fax: 612-222-5362

Minnesota Valley Action Council
SkillsNet-Job Service Office
410 Jackson Street
Mankato, MN 56001
507-345-6822

Minnesota Workforce Center, Anoka County
1201 89th Avenue, NE, Suite 235
Blaine, MN 55434
612-783-4800
Fax: 612-783-4844

Minnetonka Workforce Center
6121 Baker Road, Suite 111
Baker Technology Plaza
Minnetonka, MN 55345-5952
612-945-3600
Fax: 612-945-3601

Montevideo Workforce Center
129 West Nichols
Montevideo, MN 56265-0636
320-269-8819
Fax: 320-269-5696

Moorhead Workforce Center
715 11th Street, North, Suite 201
Clay County Family Service Center
Moorhead, MN 56560-2086
218-236-2191
Fax: 218-299-5871

Mora Job Service
130 South Park Street
Mora, MN 55051-1431
320-679-3611
Fax: 320-679-3692

New Ulm Workforce Center
1618 South Broadway
New Ulm, MN 56073-3756
507-354-3138
Fax: 507-354-6997

North Minneapolis Workforce Center
1200 Plymouth Avenue, North
Minneapolis, MN 55411-4085
612-520-3500
Fax: 612-520-3530

Northeast Minnesota Office of Job Training
820 North Ninth Street, Suite 240
Virginia, MN 55792-1028
218-749-1274
Fax: 218-749-1274

North St. Paul Workforce Center
2098 East 11th Avenue
McKnight 36 Plaza
St. Paul, MN 55109-5100
612-779-5666
Fax: 612-779-5646

Northwest Community Action
SkillsNet-Job Service Office
PO Box 195
Badger, MN 56714

Northwest Private Industry Council
721 South Minnesota Street
Crookston, MN 56716
218-281-6020
Fax: 218-281-6025

Olmsted Community Action Program
SkillsNet-Job Service Office
1421 Third Avenue, SE
Rochester, MN 55904
507-285-8785

Opportunities Industrialization Centers
Piper Jaffray Plaza, Suite 610
444 Cedar Street
St. Paul, MN 55101
612-296-6174
Fax: 612-215-1988

Otter Tail-Wadena Community Action Council
SkillsNet-Job Service Office
PO Box L
New York Mills, MN 56567
218-385-2900

Owatonna Workforce Center
110 West Fremont Street
Owatonna, MN 55060
507-455-5850
Fax: 507-444-2408
http://www.ic.owatonna.mn.us/cityow.html

Park Rapids Job Service
1011 East First Street
Park Rapids, MN 56470-1712
218-732-3396
Fax: 218-732-0929

Prairie Five Community Action Council
SkillsNet-Job Service Office
Seventh and Washington Street
Montevideo, MN 56265-0695
320-269-6578

Private Industry Workforce Council #5
500 Elm Street, East
Annandale, MN 55302-0579
320-274-2650
Fax: 320-274-3516

Ramsey Action Programs
SkillsNet-Job Service Office
450 North Syndicate Street, Bigelow Building
St. Paul, MN 55104
612-645-6445

Ramsey County Job Training Program
1945 Manton Street
Maplewood, MN 55109-4444
612-770-8900
Fax: 612-770-6890

Red Lake Community Action Agency
SkillsNet-Job Service Office
PO Box 550
Red Lake, MN 56671

Red Wing Workforce Center
1606 West Third Street
Red Wing, MN 55066-0033
612-385-6480
Fax: 612-385-6484

Rochester Job Service
300 11th Avenue, NW, #112
PO Box 9130
Rochester, MN 55903-9130
507-285-7315
Fax: 507-280-5523

Rural Minnesota CEP
803 Roosevelt Avenue
Detroit Lakes, MN 56501

218-846-7400
Fax: 218-846-7404

Scott-Carver-Dakota CAP Agency
SkillsNet-Job Service Office
1257 Marshall Road
Shakopee, MN 55379
612-496-2125

Semcac
SkillsNet-Job Service Office
204 South Elm Street
Rushford, MN 55971-0549

Shakopee Job Service
1136-A Shakopee Town Square
Shakopee, MN 55379-2812
612-496-4160
Fax: 612-496-7682

South Central Workforce Center
410 Jackson Street, Third Floor
Mankato, MN 56001
507-345-1837
Fax: 507-345-2414

Southeastern Minnesota Private Industry Council
300 11th Avenue, NW, #110
Rochester, MN 55901-2739
507-281-4670
Fax: 507-252-2495

South Minneapolis Workforce Center
777 Lake Street
Minneapolis, MN 55407-1546
612-821-4000

Southwest Minnesota Private Industry Council
1424 East College Drive, #100
Marshall, MN 56258-5097
507-537-6987
Fax: 507-537-6997

St. Cloud Workforce Center
3333 West Division Street, #212
PO Box 67
St. Cloud, MN 56302-0067
320-255-3266
Fax: 320-654-5173

Stearns-Benton Employment and Training Council
3333 West Division, #210
St. Cloud, MN 56302-0615
320-202-2100
Fax: 320-202-2199

Stillwater Workforce Center
14900 61st Street, North, #20
PO Box Six
Stillwater, MN 55082-0006
612-297-2440
Fax: 612-430-6864

St. Paul-Midway Job Service
2455 West University Avenue
St. Paul, MN 55114-1528
612-642-0363
Fax: 612-649-5707

St. Paul Workforce Center
494 Sibley Street
St. Paul, MN 55101-2310
612-228-3283
Fax: 612-228-3299

Thief River Falls Workforce Center
1301 Highway One, East
PO Box 679
Thief River Falls, MN 56701-0679
218-681-0909
Fax: 218-681-0913

Three Rivers Community Action
SkillsNet-Job Service Office
1414 Northstar Drive
Zumbrota, MN 55992
507-732-7391

Tri-County Action Programs
SkillsNet-Job Service Office
700 West Saint Germain Street
St. Cloud, MN 56302
320-251-1612

Tri-County Community Action Program
SkillsNet-Job Service Office
501 LeMieur Street
Little Falls, MN 56345-2799
320-632-3691

Tri-Valley Opportunity Council
SkillsNet-Job Service Office
102 North Broadway
Crookston, MN 56716
218-281-5832

Virginia Job Service
830 North Ninth Street, #200
Olcott Plaza
Virginia, MN 55792-2345
218-749-7704
Fax: 218-749-9680

Wadena Job Service
311 Jefferson Street, North
PO Box 643
Wadena, MN 56482-0643
218-631-3240
Fax: 218-631-3241

Waseca Workforce Center
105 Third Avenue, NE
East Annex Building
Waseca, MN 56093-2911
507-835-8240

Washington County Workforce Center
14900 North 61st Street
Stillwater, MN 55082-0006
612-430-6850
Fax: 612-430-6864

West Central Minnesota Community Action
SkillsNet-Job Service Office
307 Eighth Avenue, West
Alexandria, MN 56308
320-762-3010

Western Community Action
SkillsNet-Job Service Office
203 West Main Street
Marshall, MN 56258-1339
507-537-1416

Willmar Workforce Center
1900 Highway 294, NE, #2040
Kandiyohi County Health and Human Services Building
Willmar, MN 56201-9423
320-231-5174
Fax: 320-231-6054

Winona Job Service
52 East Fifth Street
Winona, MN 55987-0739
507-453-2920
Fax: 507-453-2960

Winona Workforce Center
1250 Homer Road, #200
Winona Technical College
Winona, MN 55987-4897
507-453-2920
Fax: 507-453-2960

Worthington Workforce Center
511 10th Street
Worthington, MN 56187-2342
507-376-3116
Fax: 507-376-3630

Wright County Community Action
SkillsNet-Job Service Office
130 West Division Street
Maple Lake, MN 55358
320-963-6500

MISSISSIPPI

Job Service
4100 Mamie Street
Hattiesburg, MS 39402
601-264-0502

Job Service
5959 Interstate 55, North
Jackson, MS 39213-9722
601-961-7931

Mississippi Department of Economic and Community Development
Employment Training Division
301 West Pearl Street
Jackson, MS 39203-3089
601-949-2234
Fax: 601-949-2291

Mississippi Employment Service, Bruce
City Hall
Bruce, MS 38915
601-983-2453

Mississippi Employment Service, Calhoun City
City Hall
Calhoun City, MS 38916
601-628-8346

Mississippi Employment Service, Cleveland
119 North Commerce Avenue
Cleveland, MS 38732-2735
601-843-2704

Mississippi Employment Service, Corinth
714 Taylor Street
Corinth, MS 38834
601-286-3308
Fax: 601-286-3300

Mississippi Employment Service, Greenwood
313 Lamar Street
Greenwood, MS 38930
601-453-7141
Fax: 601-455-4206

Mississippi Employment Service, Houston
665 North Jefferson Street
Houston, MS 38851
601-456-3563

Mississippi Employment Service, Kosciusko
222 West Washington Street
Kosciusko, MS 39090
601-289-2621

Mississippi Employment Service, McComb
416 Marion Avenue
McComb, MS 39648
601-684-4421
Fax: 601-684-4423

Mississippi Employment Service, Natchez
310 Briarwood Road
Natchez, MS 39120
601-442-0243

Mississippi Employment Service, Oxford
2603 West Oxford Loop
Oxford, MS 38655
601-234-5411

MISSOURI

Central Ozarks Private Industry Council
Forum Shopping Center
1202 Forum Drive
Rolla, MO 65401
314-364-7030

Department of Economic Development
2023 St. Mary's Boulevard
PO Box 1087
Jefferson City, MO 65109-1087
573-526-8229

Employment and Training Center
2020 Parkway Drive
St. Peters, MO 63301
314-447-6464

Full Employment Council
Service Delivery Area 12
3675 South Noland Road, Suite 301
Independence, MO 64055
816-254-3297

Full Employment Council
1740 Paseo, Suite D
Kansas City, MO 64108
816-471-2330

Jefferson-Franklin Counties Inc.
4630 Yeager Road
Hillsboro, MO 63050
314-789-3502

Job Council of the Ozarks
1514 South Glenstone
Springfield, MO 65804
417-887-4343

Job Service
908 North Second Street
Clinton, MO 64735
816-885-5541

Job Service
203 North Sixth Street
Hannibal, MO 63401
573-248-2520

Job Service
511 South Kyler Street
Monett, MO 65708
417-235-7877

Job Service
505 East Walnut Street
Springfield, MO 65806
417-895-6899

Office of Employment and Training
Department of Human Resources
121 South Meramec Avenue
Clayton, MO 63105
314-889-3453

Ozark Action Inc.
710 East Main
PO Box 588
West Plains, MO 65775
417-256-6147

Private Industry Council Inc.
Service Delivery Area Five
1411 Southwest Boulevard
Jefferson City, MO 65109
573-634-8048

Private Industry Council Inc.
Service Delivery Area Seven
PO Box 1351
Joplin, MO 64802
417-782-5872

Private Industry Council Inc.
120 West Monroe
Paris, MO 65275
816-327-5125

Southeast Missouri Private Industry Council
760 South Kings Highway, Suite F
Cape Girardeau, MO 63703
800-451-0990

St. Louis Agency on Training and Employment
317 North 11th Street, Suite 400
St. Louis, MO 63101
314-589-8000
Fax: 314-231-7923

Western Missouri Private Industry Council Inc.
515 South Kentucky
PO Box 701
Sedalia, MO 65302-0701
816-827-3722

MONTANA

Anaconda Job Service Center
307 East Park
Anaconda, MT 59711
406-563-3444
Fax: 406-563-7827

Billings Job Service Center
2121-B Rosebud Drive
Billings, MT 59102
406-652-3080
Fax: 406-652-0444

Bitterroot Job Service Center
333 Main Street
Hamilton, MT 59840
406-363-1822
Fax: 406-363-1823

Bozeman Job Service Center
121 North Willson
Bozeman, MT 59715
406-586-5455
Fax: 406-585-9023

Butte Job Service Center
206 West Granite
Box 309
Butte, MT 59703
406-782-0417
Fax: 406-782-1416

Cut Bank Job Service Center
20 South Central
Cut Bank, MT 59427
406-873-2191
Fax: 406-837-5393

Dillon Job Service Center
730 North Montana
Box 1300
Dillon, MT 59725

406-683-4259
Fax: 406-683-2903

Flathead Job Service Center
527 First Avenue, East
Kalispell, MT 59901
406-758-6200
Fax: 406-758-6290

Glasgow Job Service Center
238 Second Avenue, South
Glasgow, MT 59230
406-228-9369
Fax: 406-228-8793

Glendive Job Service Center
211 South Kendrick
Glendive, MT 59330
406-365-3314
Fax: 406-365-5831

Great Falls Job Service Center
1018 Seventh Street, South
Great Falls, MT 59405
406-791-5800
Fax: 406-791-5889

Havre Job Service Center
416 First Street
Havre, MT 59501
406-265-5847
Fax: 406-265-1386

Helena Job Service Center
715 Front Street
Helena, MT 59601
406-447-3200
Fax: 406-447-3224

Lewistown Job Service Center
300 First Avenue, North
Lewistown, MT 59457
406-538-8701
Fax: 406-538-7249

Libby Job Service Center
120 West Fifth Street
Libby, MT 59923
406-293-6282
Fax: 406-293-5134

Livingston Job Service Center
228 South Main
Box 1199
Livingston, MT 59047
406-222-0520
Fax: 406-222-1593

Miles City Job Service Center
12 North 10th Street
Box 1786
Miles City, MT 59301
406-232-1316

Missoula Job Service Center
539 South Third Street, West
Box 5027
Missoula, MT 59806
406-728-7060
Fax: 406-721-7094

Montana Department of Labor and Industry
State Job Training Bureau
PO Box 1728
Helena, MT 59624
406-444-2416
Fax: 406-444-3037

Polson Job Service Center
417-B Main Street
Box 970
Polson, MT 59860
406-883-5261
Fax: 406-883-4564

Shelby Job Service Center
402 First Street, South
Shelby, MT 59474
406-434-5161
Fax: 406-434-2351

Sidney Job Service Center
211 North Central
Sidney, MT 59270
406-482-1204
Fax: 406-482-7453

Thompson Falls Job Service Center
608 Main Street
Box 669
Thompson Falls, MT 59873

406-827-3472
Fax: 406-827-3327

Wolf Point Job Service Center
217 Third Avenue, South
Wolf Point, MT 59201
406-653-1720
Fax: 406-653-1196

NEBRASKA

Alliance Job Service Center
302 Box Butte Avenue
Alliance, NE 69301-3342
308-763-2935

Beatrice Job Service Center
1801 North Sixth Street
Beatrice, NE 68310-1408
402-223-6060

Chadron Job Service Center
250 Main Street
Chadron, NE 69337-2121
308-432-6121

Columbus Job Service Center
2809 13th Street
Columbus, NE 68601-4918
402-564-7160

Falls City Job Service Center
1423 Harlan Street
Falls City, NE 68355-2653
402-245-4401

Fremont Job Service Center
406 East Sixth Street
Fremont, NE 68025
402-727-3250

Grand Island Job Service Center
724 West Koenig
Grand Island, NE 68802
308-385-6300

Hastings Job Service Center
Landmark Center, #338
2727 West Second Street

Hastings, NE 68901-4663
402-462-2191

Holdrege Job Service Center
502 East Avenue, Second Floor
Holdrege, NE 68949-2217
308-995-5627

Job Training of Greater Lincoln
129 North 10th Street
Lincoln, NE 68508
402-441-7111
Fax: 402-441-6038

Job Training of Greater Nebraska, Region Five
119 Norfolk Avenue, Box 706
Norfolk, NE 68702
402-370-3445
Fax: 402-370-3435

Job Training of Greater Nebraska, Region Four
941 O Street, Eighth Floor
Lincoln, NE 68501
402-471-3181
Fax: 402-471-3482

Job Training of Greater Nebraska, Region Three
211 West Third Street, #B
Grand Island, NE 68801
308-385-6331
Fax: 308-385-6330

Job Training of Greater Nebraska, Region Two
Craft State Office Building
200 South Silber Street
North Platte, NE 69101
308-535-8189
Fax: 308-535-8189

Job Training of Greater Omaha
2421 North 24th Street
Omaha, NE 68110
402-444-4700
Fax: 402-444-3755

Kearney Job Service Center
Woodridge Plaza, Suite 106
124 West 46th Street
Kearney, NE 68848
308-865-5404

Lincoln Job Service Center
110 N Street
Lincoln, NE 68509
402-471-2275

McCook Job Service Center
220 West First Street
McCook, NE 69001-3601
308-345-8470

Nebraska City Job Service Center
905 Third Corso
Nebraska City, NE 68410
402-873-3384

North Platte Job Service Center
114 South Chestnut
North Platte, NE 69103
308-535-8021

Omaha Job Service Center
5404 Cedar Street
Omaha, NE 68106-2365
402-595-3000

Omaha Job Service Center
5036 Ames Avenue
Omaha, NE 68104-2318
402-595-3123

Scottsbluff Job Service Center
1717 Avenue C
Scottsbluff, NE 69361-2332
308-635-3191

Sidney Job Service Center
927 23rd Avenue
Sidney, NE 69162-1418
308-254-6937

York Job Service Center
510 Lincoln Avenue
York, NE 68467-2997
402-362-5891

NEVADA

Community Employment and Training Center, Henderson
119 Water Street
Henderson, NV 89015-7290
702-486-6710

Community Employment and Training Center, Las Vegas
Nevada Department of Employment, Training and Rehabilitation
902 West Owens Avenue
Las Vegas, NV 89106-2516
702-486-5290

Employment Security Department
301 Brougher Avenue
Tonopah, NV 89049
702-482-9722

Employment Security Division, Carson City
1929 North Carson Street
Carson City, NV 89701-1218
702-687-4560

Employment Security Division, Ely
480 Campton Street
Ely, NV 89301-1908
702-289-1616

Employment Security Division, Fallon
121 Industrial Way
Fallon, NV 89406-3116
702-423-5115

Employment Security Division, North Las Vegas
2827 Las Vegas Boulevard, North
Las Vegas, NV 89030-5703
702-486-5600

Employment Security Division, Sparks
2010 Oddie Boulevard
Sparks, NV 89431-3598
702-688-1145

Employment Security Division, Winnemucca
475 West Haskell Street, #1
Winnemucca, NV 89445-6702
702-623-6520

HELP of Southern Nevada
953 East Sahara Avenue, #23B
Las Vegas, NV 89104-3005
702-369-4357
Fax: 702-369-0247

Job Opportunities in Nevada
Employment Security Division, Elko
172 Sixth Street
Elko, NV 89801-3708
702-738-8095
Fax: 702-738-4900

Job Opportunities in Nevada
768 Aultman Street
Ely, NV 89301-1557
702-289-3061
Fax: 702-289-3062

Job Opportunities in Nevada
143 Keddie Street
Fallon, NV 89406-2820
702-423-6162
Fax: 702-423-0762

Job Opportunities in Nevada
890 Fifth Street
Hawthorne, NV 89415
702-945-5900
Fax: 702-945-5900

Job Opportunities in Nevada
215 Bridge Street, #12
Yerington, NV 89447-2544
702-463-2230
Fax: 702-463-5990

**Nevada Department of Employment,
   Training and Rehabilitation**
Nevada Career Information System
500 East Third Street
Carson City, NV 89713-0021
702-687-4577
Fax: 702-687-4119

Reno Employment Service Office
70 West Taylor Street, #200
Reno, NV 89509-1700
702-688-1392

**Truckee Meadows Community
   College**
7000 Dandini Boulevard
Reno, NV 89512-3901
702-829-9041
Fax: 702-829-9032

U.S. Job Training Partnership
300 Booth Street
Reno, NV 89509-1316
702-784-5290

Western Nevada Community College
17 Gibson Avenue
Carson City, NV 89701
702-887-3163
Fax: 702-887-3175

Western Nevada Community College
160 Campus Way
Fallon, NV 89406-2661
702-423-7565

Workforce Network
4385 Neil Road, Suite 118
Reno, NV 89502-5100
702-688-1710

NEW HAMPSHIRE

Berlin Job Service Center
New Hampshire Department of Employment Security
151 Pleasant Street
Berlin, NH 03570
603-752-5500

Claremont Job Service Center
New Hampshire Department of Employment Security
17 Water Street
Claremont, NH 03743
603-543-3111

Concord Job Service Center
New Hampshire Department of Employment Security
10 West Street
Concord, NH 03301-3548
603-228-4100

Dover Job Service Center
New Hampshire Department of Employment Security
Three Plaza Drive
Dover, NH 03820
603-742-3600

Keene Job Service Center
New Hampshire Department of Employment Security
109 Key Road
Keene, NH 03431-3926
603-352-1904

Laconia Job Service Center
New Hampshire Department of Employment
    Security
426 Union Avenue
Laconia, NH 03246
603-524-3960

Lebanon Job Service Center
New Hampshire Department of Employment
    Security
85 Mechanic Street
Lebanon, NH 03766
603-448-6340

Littleton Job Service Center
New Hampshire Department of Employment
    Security
Lisbon Road
Littleton, NH 03561
603-444-2971

Manchester Job Service Center
New Hampshire Department of Employment Security
317 Lincoln Street
Manchester, NH 03103
603-627-7841

Nashua Job Service Center
New Hampshire Department of Employment Security
33 Pine Street
Nashua, NH 03060
603-882-5177

New Hampshire Job Training Coordinating Council
64B Old Suncook Road
Concord, NH 03301
603-228-9500
Fax: 603-228-8557

**New Hampshire Job Training Council,
    Claremont District**
One College Drive
Claremont, NH 03743-9707
603-542-0935

**New Hampshire Job Training Council,
    Manchester District**
1066 Front Street
Manchester, NH 03102-8528
603-626-6337

**New Hampshire Job Training Council,
    Nashua District**
600 State Street
Portsmouth, NH 03801-4370
603-431-5962

**New Hampshire Job Training Council,
    Rochester District**
22 South Main Street
Rochester, NH 03867-2702
603-335-3936

Portsmouth Job Service Center
New Hampshire Department of Employment Security
2000 Lafayette Road
Portsmouth, NH 03801
603-436-3702

Salem Job Service Center
New Hampshire Department of Employment Security
29 South Broadway
Salem, NH 03079
603-893-9185

U.S. Job Training Partnership
55 Pleasant Street
Concord, NH 03303-1619
603-225-14444

NEW JERSEY

Job Service
797 Broadway
Bayonne, NJ 07002
201-858-3037

Job Service
57 Park
Bloomfield, NJ 07003
201-680-5550

Job Service
40 Broad Street, East
Bridgeton, NJ 08302
609-453-3900

Job Service
220 West Broad Street
Burlington, NJ 08016
609-386-0224

Job Service
186 South Clinton Street
East Orange, NJ 07018
201-266-1985

Job Service
40 Bennett Road
Englewood, NJ 07631
201-568-9840

Job Service
Highway Nine and Pond Road
Freehold, NJ 07728
908-780-3272

Job Service
370 West Broadway
Haledon, NJ 07508
201-977-4350

Job Service
U.S. Highway 30 and Elvins Avenue
Hammonton, NJ 08037
609-561-8800

Job Service
14 Howe Avenue
Passaic, NJ 07055
201-916-2643

Job Service
339 Maple Street
Perth Amboy, NJ 08861
908-293-5016

Job Service
111 West Water Street
Toms River, NJ 08753
908-341-6330

Job Service, Employment Services
60 State Street
Hackensack, NJ 07601
201-996-8950

Job Service, Employment Services
Five Sussex Avenue
Morristown, NJ 07960
201-631-6321

New Jersey Department of Labor
CN055
Trenton, NJ 08629-0055
609-292-2323
Fax: 609-633-9271

NEW MEXICO

Job Service
319 Onate Street
Espanola, NM 87532
505-753-2285

Labor Service
501 Mountain Road, NE
Albuquerque, NM 87102
505-841-9352

NEW YORK

Fort Green Youth Job Service
154 Lawrence Street
Brooklyn, NY 11201
718-330-0978

Job Service
115 Ontario Street
Albany, NY 12206
518-465-0797

Job Service
25 Harrison Street
Jamestown, NY 14701
716-664-2041

Job Service
231 West Main Street
Malone, NY 12953
518-483-2260

Job Service
50 North Street
Monticello, NY 12701-1711
914-794-3340

Job Service
24 South Third Avenue
Mount Vernon, NY 10550
914-664-7900

Job Service
105 North Main Street
Newark, NY 14513
315-331-2011

Job Service
1141 Hylan Boulevard
Staten Island, NY 10305
718-447-2931

Job Service
1801 Sixth Avenue
Troy, NY 12180

Job Service
4175 Transit Road
Williamsville, NY 14221-7206
716-634-9081

NORTH CAROLINA

Job Service
48 Grove Street
Asheville, NC 28801
704-251-6200

Job Service
803 Wilson Street
Whiteville, NC 28472
910-642-0146

North Carolina Department of Commerce
301 North Wilmington Street
Raleigh, NC 27626-0571
919-733-7979
Fax: 919-733-8356

NORTH DAKOTA

Job Service
19 East Main
Beulah, ND 58523
701-873-5607

Job Service
1000 East Divide Avenue
Bismarck, ND 58501
701-328-2825

Job Service
216 North Second Street
Bismarck, ND 58501
701-328-5021

Job Service
301 College Drive, South
Devils Lake, ND 58301
701-662-9300

Job Service
66 Osborn Drive
Dickinson, ND 58601
701-227-3100

Job Service
1350 32nd Street, SW
Fargo, ND 58103-3433
701-329-7300

Job Service
Fort Yates, ND 58538
701-854-5607

Job Service
927 West 12th Street
Grafton, ND 58237
701-352-4450

Job Service
2016 South Washington Street
Grand Forks, ND 58201
701-795-3700

Job Service
119 Ninth Street, West
Harvey, ND 58341
701-324-4552

Job Service
429 Second Street, SW
Jamestown, ND 58401
701-251-2256

Job Service
501 First Street, NW
Mandan, ND 58554
701-663-6461

Job Service
3416 North Broadway
Minot, ND 58703
701-857-7500

Job Service
PO Box 477
New Town, ND 58763-0477
701-627-4390

Job Service
517 Main Avenue
Oakes, ND 58474
701-742-2546

Job Service
103 Main Avenue, East
Rolla, ND 58367-7104
701-477-5631

Job Service
250 Central Avenue, South
Valley City, ND 58072
701-845-7261

Job Service
524 Second Avenue, North
Wahpeton, ND 58075
701-671-2711

Job Service
422 First Avenue, West
Williston, ND 58801
701-774-4370

Job Service North Dakota
1000 East Divide Avenue
PO Box 5507
Bismarck, ND 58506-5507
701-328-2836
Fax: 701-328-4000

OHIO
Athens Job Training Partnership Office
11100 State Route 550
Athens, OH 45701
614-592-6601

Batavia Clermont 2001 Clergy
4400 State Route 222
Batavia, OH 45103
513-230-6077

Batavia Clermont Department of Human Services
Employment Services Division
2400 Clermont Center Drive
Batavia, OH 45103
513-732-7492

Bucyrus Crawford Job Training Center
334 North Sandusky Avenue
Bucyrus, OH 44820
419-562-0100

Bureau of Employment Services
400 East Poe Road
Bowling Green, OH 43402
419-353-5321
Fax: 419-353-3016
http://jfs.ohio.gov

Bureau of Employment Services
228 South Main Street
Bryan, OH 43506
419-636-9077
Fax: 419-636-7306
http://jfs.ohio.gov

Bureau of Employment Services
1935 East Second Street
Defiance, OH 43512
419-782-6050
Fax: 419-782-4755
http://jfs.ohio.gov

Bureau of Employment Services
799 North Main Street
Lima, OH 45801
419-222-3128
Fax: 419-228-6347
http://jfs.ohio.gov

Bureau of Employment Services
347 North Main Street
Marion, OH 43302
614-382-1115
Fax: 614-382-8845
http://jfs.ohio.gov

Bureau of Employment Services
103 North Washington
Tiffin, OH 44883
419-447-6812
Fax: 419-447-1872
http://jfs.ohio.gov

Bureau of Employment Services
5454 Airport Highway
Toledo, OH 43615
419-865-7248
Fax: 419-865-7648
http://jfs.ohio.gov

Bureau of Employment Services
1810-1814 Madison Avenue
Toledo, OH 43624
419-245-2956
Fax: 419-245-2462
http://jfs.ohio.gov

Coshocton County Services Building
1724 South Seventh Street
Coshocton, OH 43812
614-623-0900

Georgetown Job Training Partnership Office
200 South Green Street
Georgetown, OH 45121
800-233-7891

Greenville Job Training Partnership Office
104 West Third Street
Greenville, OH 45331
937-548-0090

Lima Job Training Partnership Office
610 North Main Street
Lima, OH 45801
419-229-5872
Fax: 419-222-2785

Ohio Bureau of Employment Services
145 South Front Street, Fourth Floor
Columbus, OH 43216
614-466-3817

One-Stop Career Center
119-A South Court Street
PO Box 230

Circleville, OH 43113
614-474-7518

One-Stop Career Center
62 East Sugartree Street
Wilmington, OH 45160
513-382-7762
Fax: 513-383-2657

U.S. Job Training Partnership
201 Cleveland Avenue, SW
Canton, OH 44702-1929
330-489-4483

Wapakoneta Job Training Partnership Office
Six East Main Street
Wapakoneta, OH 45895
419-738-7864

Winchester Job Training Partnership Office
19211 Main Street
Winchester, OH 45697
937-695-0316

OKLAHOMA
Oklahoma Employment Security Commission
Will Rogers Memorial Office Building
2401 North Lincoln
Oklahoma City, OK 73105
405-557-5329
Fax: 405-557-1478

OREGON
Central Oregon Intergovernmental Council
PO Box 575
Redmond, OR 97756
541-548-8163

Emerald Job Center
Southern Willamette Private Industry Council
78 B Centennial Loop
Eugene, OR 97401
541-687-3826

Employment Training and Business Services
PO Box 215
Maryhurst, OR 97036
503-635-4591

Job Council
673 Market Street
Medford, OR 97504
541-776-5100

Klamath-Lake Employment Training Council Inc.
220 Pine Street
Klamath Falls, OR 97601
541-882-5691

Mid-Columbia Employment and Training
1113 Kelly Avenue
Dalles, OR 97058-2767
541-298-4101

Oregon Department of Human Resources
Adult and Family Services Division
500 Summer Street, NE
Salem, OR 97310-1013
503-945-5601
Fax: 503-378-2897

Oregon Economic Development Department
255 Capitol Street, NE, Suite 399
Salem, OR 97310-1600
503-373-1995
Fax: 503-581-5115

Oregon Employment Department, Albany
139 Southeast Fourth Avenue
PO Box 70
Albany, OR 97321
541-967-2171
Fax: 541-967-2137
http://www.oregon.gov/EMPLOY

Oregon Employment Department, Ashland
1250 Siskiyou Boulevard
Ashland, OR 97520
541-552-6852
Fax: 541-552-6855
http://www.oregon.gov/EMPLOY

Oregon Employment Department, Astoria
818 Commercial
PO Box 805
Astoria, OR 97103
503-325-4821
http://www.oregon.gov/EMPLOY

Oregon Employment Department, Baker City
1575 Dewey Avenue
Baker City, OR 97814
541-523-6331
http://www.oregon.gov/EMPLOY

Oregon Employment Department, Beaverton
12901 Southwest Jenkins, #C
PO Box 768
Beaverton, OR 97075
503-644-1229
http://www.oregon.gov/EMPLOY

Oregon Employment Department, Bend
1007 Southwest Emkay Drive
Bend, OR 97702
541-388-6070
http://www.oregon.gov/EMPLOY

Oregon Employment Department, Brookings
16399 Lower Harbor Road
Brookings, OR 97415
541-469-9836
http://www.oregon.gov/EMPLOY

Oregon Employment Department, Burns
809 West Jackson Street, #400
Burns, OR 97720
541-573-5251
Fax: 541-573-3628
http://www.oregon.gov/EMPLOY

Oregon Employment Department, Coos Bay
2075 Sheridan Avenue
PO Box 986
North Bend, OR 97459
541-756-8459
Fax: 541-756-3900
http://www.oregon.gov/EMPLOY

Oregon Employment Department, Corvallis
545 Southwest Second Street, Suite C
Corvallis, OR 97333
541-757-4261
Fax: 541-757-4264
http://www.oregon.gov/EMPLOY

Oregon Employment Department, Dallas
580 Main Street, Suite B
PO Box 279

Dallas, OR 97338
503-831-1950
Fax: 503-831-1950
http://www.oregon.gov/EMPLOY

Oregon Employment Department, Enterprise
116 South River Street
Enterprise, OR 97828
541-426-4972
Fax: 541-426-6224
http://www.oregon.gov/EMPLOY

Oregon Employment Department, Eugene
2510 Oakmont Way
Eugene, OR 97401
541-686-7601
Fax: 541-686-7954
http://www.oregon.gov/EMPLOY

Oregon Employment Department, Florence
1234 Rhododendron Drive
PO Box 1178
Florence, OR 97439
541-997-1913
Fax: 541-997-1448
http://www.oregon.gov/EMPLOY

Oregon Employment Department, Gold Beach
94145 Fifth Place
PO Box D
Gold Beach, OR 97444
541-247-7043
Fax: 541-247-7855
http://www.oregon.gov/EMPLOY

Oregon Employment Department, Grants Pass
201 Northeast Eighth Street
PO Box 609
Grants Pass, OR 97526
541-474-3161
Fax: 541-474-3195
http://www.oregon.gov/EMPLOY

Oregon Employment Department, Hermiston
950 Southeast Columbia Drive, Suite B
Hermiston, OR 97838
541-567-3381
Fax: 541-567-2306
http://www.oregon.gov/EMPLOY

Oregon Employment Department, Hillsboro
265 Southeast Oak Street, Suite A
PO Box 240
Hillsboro, OR 97123
503-681-0219
Fax: 503-693-0623
http://www.oregon.gov/EMPLOY

Oregon Employment Department, Hood River
1100 East Marina Way, Suite 120
Hood River, OR 97031
541-386-6020
Fax: 541-386-6065
http://www.oregon.gov/EMPLOY

Oregon Employment Department, John Day
725 West Main, Suite B
John Day, OR 97845
541-575-0744
Fax: 541-575-2344
http://www.oregon.gov/EMPLOY

Oregon Employment Department, Klamath Falls
801 Oak Avenue
PO Box 68
Klamath Falls, OR 97601
541-883-5630
Fax: 541-883-5540
http://www.oregon.gov/EMPLOY

Oregon Employment Department, LaGrande
1901 Adams Avenue
LaGrande, OR 97850
541-963-7111
Fax: 541-963-5515
http://www.oregon.gov/EMPLOY

Oregon Employment Department, Lakeview
18 South G Street, Suite 207
PO Box 1230
Lakeview, OR 97630
541-947-3501
Fax: 541-947-4823
http://www.oregon.gov/EMPLOY

Oregon Employment Department, Lebanon
380 Market Street
Lebanon, OR 97355
541-451-1934

Fax: 541-451-1936
http://www.oregon.gov/EMPLOY

Oregon Employment Department, Lincoln City
4422 West Devils Lake Boulevard, Suite 1A
Lincoln City, OR 97367
541-994-6992
Fax: 541-994-6502
http://www.oregon.gov/EMPLOY

Oregon Employment Department, Madras
257 Southwest Third Street
Madras, OR 97741
541-475-2382
Fax: 541-475-9384
http://www.oregon.gov/EMPLOY

Oregon Employment Department, McMinnville
310 Kirby Street
PO Box Seven
McMinnville, OR 97128
503-472-5118
Fax: 503-434-5408
http://www.oregon.gov/EMPLOY

Oregon Employment Department, Medford
119 North Oakdale Street
PO Box 1068
Medford, OR 97501
541-776-6081
Fax: 541-776-6093
http://www.oregon.gov/EMPLOY

Oregon Employment Department, Milton-Freewater
299 North Columbia
Milton-Freewater, OR 97862
541-938-3371
Fax: 541-938-4729
http://www.oregon.gov/EMPLOY

Oregon Employment Department, Newberg
301 North Elliott, Suite Four
Newberg, OR 97132
503-538-2368
Fax: 503-538-3482
http://www.oregon.gov/EMPLOY

Oregon Employment Department, Newport
120 Northeast Avery Street
PO Box 10
Newport, OR 97365

541-265-8891
Fax: 541-265-5975
http://www.oregon.gov/EMPLOY

Oregon Employment Department, Ontario
375 Southwest Second Avenue
PO Box 40
Ontario, OR 97914
541-889-5394
http://www.oregon.gov/EMPLOY

Oregon Employment Department, Oregon City
506 High Street
PO Box 71
Oregon City, OR 97045
503-657-2071
Fax: 503-657-6830
http://www.oregon.gov/EMPLOY

Oregon Employment Department, Pendelton
408 Southeast Seventh Street
Pendelton, OR 97801
541-276-9050
Fax: 541-278-2068
http://www.oregon.gov/EMPLOY

Oregon Employment Department, Portland Downtown
1433 Southwest Sixth
PO Box 159
Portland, OR 97207
503-731-4139
Fax: 503-229-5761
http://www.oregon.gov/EMPLOY

Oregon Employment Department, Portland Gresham
19421 Southeast Stark
PO Box 2070
Portland, OR 97030
503-669-7112
Fax: 503-666-8973
http://www.oregon.gov/EMPLOY

Oregon Employment Department, Portland North
30 North Webster, Suite E
Portland, OR 97217
503-280-6046
Fax: 503-280-6015
http://www.oregon.gov/EMPLOY

Oregon Employment Department, Prineville
934 North Madras Highway
PO Box 26
Prineville, OR 97754
541-447-8076
Fax: 541-447-3423
http://www.oregon.gov/EMPLOY

Oregon Employment Department, Redmond
541 South Seventh
PO Box 1196
Redmond, OR 97756
541-548-8196
Fax: 541-548-6379
http://www.oregon.gov/EMPLOY

Oregon Employment Department, Roseburg
846 Southeast Pine Street
PO Box 100
Roseburg, OR 97470
541-440-3344
Fax: 541-440-3498
http://www.oregon.gov/EMPLOY

Oregon Employment Department, Salem
605 Cottage Street, NE
PO Box 751
Salem, OR 97308
503-378-4846
Fax: 503-378-6480
http://www.oregon.gov/EMPLOY

Oregon Employment Department, Santiam Center
11656 Sublimity Road
Sublimity, OR 97385
503-769-7439
Fax: 503-316-3210
http://www.oregon.gov/EMPLOY

Oregon Employment Department, Springfield
210 Sixth Street
Springfield, OR 97477
541-726-3570
Fax: 541-726-2534
http://www.oregon.gov/EMPLOY

Oregon Employment Department, St. Helens
500 North Highway 30, Suite 320
St. Helens, OR 97051
503-397-4995

Fax: 503-397-7154
http://www.oregon.gov/EMPLOY

Oregon Employment Department, Tillamook
3600 East Third Street
Tillamook, OR 97141
503-842-4488
Fax: 503-842-8857
http://www.oregon.gov/EMPLOY

Oregon Employment Department, Woodburn
120 East Lincoln, Suite 101
Woodburn, OR 97071
503-982-2817
Fax: 503-982-1839
http://www.oregon.gov/EMPLOY

Oregon Tilth Placement Services
PO Box 218
Tualatin, OR 97062
503-929-6742
Fax: 503-692-4877

South Coast Business
PO Box 1118
Coos Bay, OR 97420
541-269-2013

Training and Employment Consortium
PO Box 2979
LaGrande, OR 97850
541-963-7942

Training and Employment Consortium
368 Southwest Fifth Avenue
Ontario, OR 97914
541-889-7864

PENNSYLVANIA
Job Service
160 West Hamilton Street
Allentown, PA 18101-1939
610-821-6735

Job Service
1101 Green Avenue
Altoona, PA 16601
814-946-7185

Job Service
120 Merchant Street
Ambridge, PA 15003
412-266-4455

Job Service
107 South Richard Street
Bedford, PA 15522
814-623-6107

Job Service
118 East Third Street
Berwick, PA 18603
717-752-4531

Job Service
61 West Walnut Street
Bethlehem, PA 18018
610-861-2035

Job Service
40 Davis Street
Bradford, PA 16701
814-368-6195

Job Service
701 Crosby Street, #B
Chester, PA 19013
610-447-3350

Job Service
209 East Locust Street
Clearfield, PA 16830
814-765-0567

Job Service
250 Harmony Street
Coatesville, PA 19320
610-384-9393

Job Service
1051 Morrell Avenue
Connellsville, PA 15425
412-628-5000

Job Service
10 West Second Street
Coudersport, PA 16915
814-274-9330

Job Service
207 Beaver Drive
Du Bois, PA 15801
814-371-0250

Job Service
220 Ferry Street
Easton, PA 18042
610-250-1708

Job Service
1316 State Street
Erie, PA 16501
814-871-4321

Job Service
108 North Stratton Street
Gettysburg, PA 17325
717-334-1173

Job Service
599 Sells Lane
Greensburg, PA 15601
412-832-5300

Job Service
19 Barnhart Drive
Hanover, PA 17331
717-637-0207

Job Service
2971 North Seventh Street
Harrisburg, PA 17110
717-783-3270

Job Service
Route 191, South
Honesdale, PA 18431
717-253-7135

Job Service
54 Pennsylvania Avenue
Huntingdon, PA 16652
814-643-1530

Job Service
350 North Fourth Street
Indiana, PA 15701
412-357-3030

Job Service
200 Lincoln Street
Johnstown, PA 15901
814-533-2493

Job Service
71 South Union Avenue
Lansdowne, PA 19050
610-284-6870

Job Service
324 McKinley Avenue
Latrobe, PA 15650
412-537-7777

Job Service
35 East Cumberland Street
Lebanon, PA 17042
717-274-2554

Job Service
21 South Brown Street
Lewistown, PA 17044
717-248-7897

Job Service
225 East Church Street
Lock Haven, PA 17745
717-893-2410

Job Service
5627 North Fifth Street
Philadelphia, PA 19120
215-560-4200

Job Service
930 Washington Avenue
Philadelphia, PA 19147
215-952-1137

Job Service
5501 Chestnut Street
Philadelphia, PA 19139
215-560-3900

Job Service
444 North Third Street, #C3
Philadelphia, PA 19123
215-560-1982

Job Service
2901 Grant Avenue
Philadelphia, PA 19114
215-560-4512

Job Service
235 West Chelten Avenue
Philadelphia, PA 19144
215-560-5188

Job Service
1300 Fairmount Avenue
Philadelphia, PA 19123
215-560-5333

Job Service
300 Liberty Avenue
Pittsburgh, PA 15222
412-565-5337

Job Service
122 Western Avenue
Pittsburgh, PA 15215
412-565-2631

Job Service
320 Bilmar Drive
Pittsburgh, PA 15205
412-429-2809

Job Service
6206 Broad Street
Pittsburgh, PA 15206
412-645-7024

Job Service
120 North Charlotte Street
Pottstown, PA 19464
610-323-2920

RHODE ISLAND
Department of Employment and Training
Oliver Stedman Government Center
4808 Tower Hill Road
Wakefield, RI 02879
401-277-2090
Fax: 401-277-1476

**Greater Rhode Island Regional Employment and
    Training Board Inc.**
35 Belver Avenue, Suite 227
North Kingstown, RI 02852
401-295-7114
Fax: 401-295-5081

Job Service
73 Valley Road
Middletown, RI 02842
401-847-3680

Job Service
219 Pond Street
Woonsocket, RI 02895
401-762-9010

SOUTH CAROLINA
Job Service
2214 Wall Street
Barnwell, SC 29812
803-245-3015

Job Service
One Sheridan Circle
Bluffton, SC 29910
803-681-4372

Job Service
Wilson Extension
Chester, SC 29706
803-377-8147

Job Service
700 Taylor Street
Columbia, SC 29201
803-737-9935

Job Service
519 Monument Street
Greenwood, SC 29646
864-223-1681

Job Service
13 Middleton Way
Greer, SC 29651
864-877-9614

Job Service
Highway 76
Marion, SC 29571
803-423-6900

Job Service
Gold Mine Street
McCormick, SC 29835
864-465-2888

Job Service
555 Middleton Street, NE
Orangeburg, SC 29115-4729
803-534-3336

Job Service
120 South Main Street
Saluda, SC 29138
864-445-2047

Job Service
101 Mabel T. Willis Boulevard
Walterboro, SC 29488
803-538-8980

SOUTH DAKOTA
Job Service
120 Fifth Avenue, SE
Aberdeen, SD 57401
605-626-2340

Job Service
909 South Main Street
Britton, SD 57430
605-448-2533

Job Service
1310 Main Avenue, South
Brookings, SD 57006
605-688-4350

Job Service
238 South Chicago Street
Hot Springs, SD 57747
605-745-5101

Job Service
PO Box 242
Hot Springs, SD 57747-0242
605-673-4488

Job Service
258 Third Street, SW
Huron, SD 57350
605-353-7155

Job Service
801 West Main Street
Lead, SD 57754
605-584-1361

Job Service
120 Southwest Second Street
Madison, SD 57042
605-256-5300

Job Service
104 South Grant Street
Milbank, SD 57252
605-432-9595

Job Service
120 West Second Street
Miller, SD 57362
605-853-3117

Job Service
321 North Main Street
Mitchell, SD 57301
605-995-3211

Job Service
318 First Avenue, East
Mobridge, SD 57601
605-845-2971

Job Service
301 Military Road
North Sioux City, SD 57049
605-232-9545

Job Service
116 West Missouri Avenue
Pierre, SD 57501
605-773-3372

Job Service
PO Box 400
Pine Ridge, SD 57770-0400
605-867-5843

Job Service
111 New York Street
Rapid City, SD 57701
605-394-2296

Job Service
638 East Boulevard, North
Rapid City, SD 57701-1501
605-394-2307

Job Service
Courthouse
Redfield, SD 57469
605-472-0435

Job Service
807 West Russell Street
Sioux Falls, SD 57104
605-367-5350

Job Service
205 Oak Street, East
Sisseton, SD 57262
605-698-3964

Job Service
PO Box 322
Springfield, SD 57062-0322
605-369-5424

Job Service
913 Main Street
Sturgis, SD 57785
605-347-6253

Job Service
1024 Cherry
Vermillion, SD 57212
605-677-6900

Job Service
715 South Maple
Watertown, SD 57201
605-882-5131

Job Service
230 11th Street, NE
Watertown, SD 57201
605-882-5165

Job Service
710 West First Street
Webster, SD 57274
605-345-4781

Job Service
115 Wallace Avenue, North
Wessington Springs, SD 57382
605-539-1293

Job Service
102 East Second Street
Winner, SD 57580
605-842-0474

Job Service
113 East Third Street
Yankton, SD 57078
605-668-2900

South Dakota Department of Labor
Kneip Building
700 Governor's Drive
Pierre, SD 57501-2277
605-773-3101
Fax: 605-773-4211

TENNESSEE

Job Service
119 Cole Avenue
Camden, TN 38320
901-584-6058

Job Service
139 East Lake Avenue
Celina, TN 38551
615-243-2652

Job Service
311 East Martin Luther King Boulevard
Chattanooga, TN 37403-4108
423-634-3046

Job Service
224 South Second Street
Clarksville, TN 37040
615-648-5530

Job Service
204 West Fourth Street
Columbia, TN 38401
615-380-2500

Job Service
Highway 127, North
Crossville, TN 38555
615-484-4651

Job Service
1054 Highway 92, South
Dandridge, TN 37725
423-397-9461

Job Service
North Main Street
Erwin, TN 37650
423-743-4146

Job Service
650 Nashville Pike
Gallatin, TN 37066-3194
615-451-5800

Job Service
1481 West Mullins Street
Humboldt, TN 38343
901-784-3552

Job Service
416 East Lafayette Street
Jackson, TN 38301
901-423-5860

Job Service
629 North Main Street
Jamestown, TN 38556
615-879-9594

Job Service
PO Box 1181
La Follette, TN 37766-1181
423-566-9618

Job Service
241 East Taylor Street
Lawrenceburg, TN 38464
615-766-1405

Job Service
780 Highway 321, North
Lenoir City, TN 37771
423-986-5506

Job Service
67 West Church Street
Lexington, TN 38351
901-968-8159

Job Service
University Street
Livingston, TN 38570
615-823-1827

Job Service
909 Eighth Avenue, North
Nashville, TN 37203
615-741-3626

Job Service
475 Oak Ridge Turnpike
Oak Ridge, TN 37830
423-483-7474

Job Service
923 East College Street
Pulaski, TN 38478
615-424-4006

Job Service
955 East McKinney Avenue
Rogersville, TN 37857
423-272-2661

Job Service
2113 Wayne Road
Savannah, TN 38372
901-925-5095

Job Service
2308 Memorial Boulevard, #A
Springfield, TN 37172
615-382-2418

Job Service
111 East Lincoln Street
Tullahoma, TN 37388
615-454-1905

Job Service
1418 Stad Avenue
Union City, TN 38261
901-884-2621

Job Service
101 South Church Street
Waverly, TN 37185
615-296-2393

TEXAS

Job Service
1117 Trinity Street, #404
Austin, TX 78701
512-463-2222

Job Service
6404 Callaghan Road
San Antonio, TX 78229
210-344-3444

Texas Workforce Commission
101 East 15th Street
Austin, TX 78778
512-463-2654
Fax: 512-463-2799

UTAH

Job Service
150 North Main Street
Beaver, UT 84713
801-438-2288

Job Service
196 East Center Street
Blanding, UT 84511
801-678-2244

Job Service
138 West 990 South
Brigham City, UT 84302-3195
801-723-5261

Job Service
680 East Main Street
Castle Dale, UT 84513
801-381-2301

Job Service
703 West 600 South
Cedar City, UT 84720-3016
801-586-6527

Job Service
176 East 200 North
Cedar City, UT 84720-2619
801-586-6585

Job Service
North Valley Square Shopping Center, #90
Heber City, UT 84032
801-654-0360

Job Service
345 West 100 South
Hurricane, UT 84737-1927
801-635-3705

Job Service
59 East Red Shadow
Kanab, UT 84741
801-644-2909

Job Service
310 South 100 East, #12
Kanab, UT 84741-3652
801-644-5888

Job Service
446 North 100 West
Logan, UT 84321-3919
801-752-5381

Job Service
62 North 300 West
Milford, UT 84751
801-387-2643

Job Service
91 Uranium Avenue
Moab, UT 84532
801-259-7124

Job Service
480 21st Street
Ogden, UT 84401
801-626-0450

Job Service
214 24th Street
Ogden, UT 84401
801-399-2181

Job Service
480 27th Street
Ogden, UT 84401
801-626-0300

Job Service
565 North Main Street
Panguitch, UT 84759
801-676-8893

Job Service
1846 Prospector Avenue
Park City, UT 84060
801-649-8451

Job Service
1550 North 200 West
Provo, UT 84604-2573
801-373-7500

Job Service
115 East 100 South
Richfield, UT 84701-2647
801-896-6491

Job Service
510 West 200 North
Roosevelt, UT 84066-2652
801-722-2283

Job Service
2861 South 900 West
Salt Lake City, UT 84119-2419
801-269-4800

Job Service
5735 South Redwood Road
Salt Lake City, UT 84123
801-269-4700

Job Service
140 East 300 South
Salt Lake City, UT 84111-2333
801-536-7400

Job Service
720 South 200 East
Salt Lake City, UT 84111-3804
801-536-7000

Job Service
750 North 2850 East
St. George, UT 84770
801-628-5026

Job Service
40 South 200 East
St. George, UT 84770-3431
801-673-3588

Job Service
Seven South Main Street
Tooele, UT 84074
801-882-7700

Job Service
1050 Market Drive
Vernal, UT 84078
801-789-1211

Job Service
25 East Telegraph Street
Washington, UT 84780
801-628-4664

VERMONT

One-Stop Career Center, Barre District Office
Barre-Montpelier Road
PO Box 308
Montpelier, VT 05601-0308
802-828-3860
Fax: 802-828-3824

One-Stop Career Center, Bennington District Office
State Office Building
One Veterans Memorial Drive, Box Two
Bennington, VT 05201-1998
802-442-6376
Fax: 802-447-2726

One-Stop Career Center, Brattleboro District Office
State Office Building
PO Box 920
Brattleboro, VT 05302-0920

802-254-4555
Fax: 802-257-2896

One-Stop Career Center, Burlington District Office
59 Pearl Street
PO Box 310
Burlington, VT 05402-0310
802-658-1120

One-Stop Career Center, Middlebury District Office
86 Exchange Street
Middlebury, VT 05753-1157
802-388-4921

One-Stop Career Center, Morrisville District Office
Pleasant Street
PO Box 429
Morrisville, VT 05661-0429
802-888-4545

One-Stop Career Center, Newport District Office
20 Farrant Street
PO Box 665
Newport, VT 05855-0665
802-334-6545
Fax: 802-334-3351

One-Stop Career Center, Rutland District Office
200 Asa Bloomer Building
Rutland, VT 05701-9413
802-786-5837
Fax: 802-786-5896

One-Stop Career Center, Springfield District Office
Department of Employment and Training
25 Main Street
Springfield, VT 05156-2914
802-885-2167
Fax: 802-885-2728

One-Stop Career Center, St. Albans District Office
20 Houghton Street, #101
St. Albans, VT 05478-2246
802-524-6585
Fax: 802-524-7933

**One-Stop Career Center, St. Johnsbury
    District Office**
38 Main Street
PO Box 129

St. Johnsbury, VT 05819-0129
802-748-3177
Fax: 802-748-6620

One-Stop Career Center, White River Junction
    District Office
Three Gilman Office Center
PO Box 797
White River Junction, VT 05001-0797
802-295-8805

VIRGINIA

Governor's Employment and Training
    Department
Theater Row Building, Ninth Floor
701 East Broad Street
Richmond, VA 23219
804-786-2315
Fax: 804-786-2340

Job Service
Rural Route One, Box 39C
Buena Vista, VA 24416-9702
540-261-2188

Job Service
504 Cedar Road
Chesapeake, VA 23320
757-547-9717

Job Service
105 North Maple Avenue
Covington, VA 24426
540-962-0983

Job Service
165 Deer Run Road
Danville, VA 24134
804-791-5291

Job Service
3501 Lafayette Boulevard
Fredericksburg, VA 22408
540-898-3800

Job Service
1320 Lasalle Avenue
Hampton, VA 23669
757-727-4884

Job Service
1590 North Main Street
Marion, VA 24354
540-783-7293

Job Service
5145 East Virginia Beach Boulevard
Norfolk, VA 23502
757-455-3900

Job Service
10 North Jefferson Street
Petersburg, VA 23803
804-862-6420

Job Service
3116 South Street
Portsmouth, VA 23707-4116
757-396-6865

Job Service
206 Third Avenue
Radford, VA 24141
540-831-5985

Job Service
719 Church Street
Richlands, VA 24641
540-964-4008

Job Service
5211 West Broad Street
Richmond, VA 23230
804-662-9596

Job Service
6707 Warwick Road
Richmond, VA 23225
804-674-3649

Job Service
3751 Nine Mile Road, #A
Richmond, VA 23223-4813
804-236-3500

Job Service
1438 Seymour Drive
South Boston, VA 24592
804-572-8674

Job Service
2019 Meade Parkway
Suffolk, VA 23434
757-925-2376

Job Service
502 Viking Drive
Virginia Beach, VA 23452
757-431-4978

Job Service
PO Box 673
Wytheville, VA 24382-0673
540-228-8468

Virginia Tech
205 West Roanoke Street
Blacksburg, VA 24061-0527
540-231-7571
http://vaview.vavu.vt.edu

WASHINGTON
ANEW (Apprenticeship and Nontraditional Employment for Women)
Renton Technical College
PO Box 2490
Renton, WA 98056
425-235-2212
Fax: 206-235-7864

Center for Career Alternatives
901 Rainier Avenue, South
Seattle, WA 98144
206-322-9080

Edmonds School District and Employment Security Department
Scriber Lake High School
19400 56th Avenue, West
Lynnwood, WA 98036
425-670-7281

Employment Security Department
Employment and Training Division
PO Box 9046
Olympia, WA 98507-9046
360-438-4611
Fax: 360-438-3224

Job Service
301 Valley Mall Way, Suite 110
Mount Vernon, WA 98273
360-675-3403

Job Service
1601 East Front Street
Port Angeles, WA 98362-4628
360-457-9407

Job Service
2106 Second Avenue
Seattle, WA 98121
206-464-6449

Job Service
1313 Tacoma Avenue, South
Tacoma, WA 98402
206-593-7310

Job Service
South Camas
Wapato, WA 98951
509-877-3166

Job Service
215 Bridge Street
Wenatchee, WA 98801
509-662-0413

Job Service, Employment Service
2707 I Street, NE
Auburn, WA 98002
206-931-3900

Office of Port Jobs
2512 Second Avenue, Suite 208
Seattle, WA 98121
206-728-5706

Seattle Indian Center
611 12th Avenue, South, Suite 300
Seattle, WA 98144
206-329-8700

Seattle Public Schools
Department of Vocational/Technical Education
13720 Roosevelt Way, North
Seattle, WA 98133
206-281-6008

Washington Tilth Placement Services
PO Box 85885
Seattle, WA 98145
206-853-8449

WEST VIRGINIA

Beckley Job Service
2871 Robert C. Byrd Drive
Beckley, WV 25802
304-256-6792
Fax: 304-256-6798

Bluefield Job Service
Five Mercer Plaza
Bluefield, WV 24701
304-327-7155
Fax: 304-325-8695

Charleston Job Service
1321 Plaza East
Charleston, WV 25325
304-558-0342
Fax: 304-558-0349

Clarksburg Job Service
153 West Main Street
Clarksburg, WV 26302
304-627-2125
Fax: 304-627-2129

Elkins Job Service
11 Randolph Avenue
Elkins, WV 26241
304-637-0255
Fax: 304-637-0263

Fairmont Job Service
109 Adams Street
Fairmont, WV 26555
304-363-5550
Fax: 304-363-4956

Huntington Job Service
914 Fifth Avenue
Huntington, WV 25713
304-528-5525
Fax: 304-528-5529

Logan Job Service
214 Dingess Street
Logan, WV 25601

304-792-7010
Fax: 304-792-7013

Martinsburg Job Service
Berkely Plaza Center
Martinsburg, WV 25401
304-267-0030
Fax: 304-267-0033

Moorefield Job Service
608 C North Main Street
Moorefield, WV 26836
304-538-7741
Fax: 304-538-2614

Morgantown Job Service
304 Scott Avenue
Morgantown, WV 26505
304-285-3120

New Martinsville Job Service
249 Clark Street
New Martinsville, WV 26155
304-455-0902
Fax: 304-455-0904

Parkersburg Job Service
300 Lakeview Center
36th Street at Murdoch
Parkersburg, WV 26102
304-420-4525
Fax: 304-420-4521

Point Pleasant Job Service
225 Sixth Street
Point Pleasant, WV 25550
304-675-0857
Fax: 304-675-0859

Ronceverte Job Service
299 East Edgar Avenue
Ronceverte, WV 24970
304-647-7415
Fax: 304-647-7412

Summersville Job Service
806 Broad Street
Summersville, WV 26651
304-872-0820

Weirton Job Service
203 Three Springs Drive
Weirton, WV 26062
304-723-5752
Fax: 304-723-5982

Welch Job Service
20 McDowell Street
Welch, WV 24801
304-436-3131
Fax: 304-436-4400

Wheeling Job Service
Central Union Building
Wheeling, WV 26003
304-238-1045
Fax: 304-238-1049

Williamson Job Service
120 West First Avenue
Williamson, WV 25661
304-236-6012

Winfield Job Service
4237 D State Route 34
Hurricane, WV 25526
304-757-7270
Fax: 304-757-7984

WISCONSIN

Adams County Job Center
139 South Main Street
PO Box 158
Adams, WI 53910
608-339-9559
Fax: 608-339-6170

Appleton Regional Job Center
426 West College Avenue
Appleton, WI 54911
414-832-5657
Fax: 414-832-1542

Ashland Job Center
220 Third Avenue, West
Ashland, WI 54806
715-682-7228
Fax: 715-682-7220

Baraboo Job Service
1000 Log Lodge Court
Baraboo, WI 53913
608-355-3140
Fax: 608-355-3144

Barron County Job Center
113 North Main Street
Rice Lake, WI 54868
715-234-6826
Fax: 715-234-7821

Bayfield County Jobs
117 East Fifth Street
Washburn, WI 54891
715-373-6180
Fax: 715-373-6130

Beaver Dam Job Service
138 Front Street
Beaver Dam, WI 53916
414-887-4260
Fax: 414-887-4278

Beloit Job Center
1146 Grant Avenue
Beloit, WI 53511
608-364-3740
Fax: 608-364-3761

Black River Falls Jobs
720 Red Iron Road
Black River Falls, WI 54615-5456
715-284-7117
Fax: 715-284-2946

Brown County Job Center
1145 Pine Street
Green Bay, WI 54301
414-448-5033
Fax: 414-448-5046

Burnett County Jobs
7410 County Road K, #125
Siren, WI 54872
715-349-2131
Fax: 715-349-2145

Calumet County Job Center
206 Court Street
Chilton, WI 53014

414-849-9336
Fax: 414-849-1431

Central City Initiative
429 West North Avenue
Milwaukee, WI 53212
414-263-8720
Fax: 414-263-8765

Chippewa County Job Center
13 East Spruce Street
Chippewa Falls, WI 54729
715-726-2552

Clark County Job Center
501 Hewett Street
Neillsville, WI 54456
716-743-2101

Clintonville Job Service
57 South Main Street
Clintonville, WI 54929
715-823-6576
Fax: 715-823-1307

Crawford County Job Center
200 East Blackhawk Avenue
Prairie du Chien, WI 53821-1531
608-326-5545
Fax: 608-326-2464

Dane County Job Center
1819 Aberg Avenue, Suite C
Madison, WI 53704
608-242-4900
Fax: 608-242-4917

Dunn County Jobs
1603 Stout Road
Menomonie, WI 54751
715-232-4024

Eau Claire Job Center
418 Wisconsin Street
Eau Claire, WI 54703
715-836-2901
Fax: 715-836-2989

Elkhorn Job Service
1000 East Centralia Street
Elkhorn, WI 53121
414-723-5371

Florence County Job Center
425 Lake Avenue
Florence, WI 54121
715-528-4251
Fax: 715-528-5071

Fond du Lac Job Center
349 North Peters Avenue
Fond du Lac, WI 54936-1217
414-929-3900
Fax: 414-929-3924

Fort Atkinson Job Service
41 South Water Street, East
Fort Atkinson, WI 53538
414-563-7841
Fax: 414-563-7849

Grant County Job Center
8820 State Highway 35
Lancaster, WI 53813
608-723-2153
Fax: 608-723-7564

Green Bay Job Service
330 South Jefferson Street
Green Bay, WI 54301
414-448-5000
Fax: 414-448-5013

Green County Job Center
1518 11th Street, Second Floor
Monroe, WI 53566
608-325-7611
Fax: 608-329-6815

Green Lake County Job Center
742 Greentree Mall
Berlin, WI 54923
414-361-3400
Fax: 414-361-1164

Hartford Job Center
666 Grand Avenue
Hartford, WI 53027
414-673-2324
Fax: 414-673-5543
http://www.wfdc.org/

Hayward Job Center
15618 U.S. Highway 63, Suite 108
Hayward, WI 54843
715-634-4845

Iowa County Job Center
319 Elaine Court
Route Two, Box 14
Dodgeville, WI 53533
608-935-3996
Fax: 608-935-5072

Iron County Jobs
300 Taconite Street, Highway 51
Hurley, WI 54534
715-561-2928
Fax: 715-561-2822

Janesville Job Service
17 South River Drive
Janesville, WI 53545
608-758-6000
Fax: 608-758-6009

Kenosha County Job Center
8600 Sheridan Road
Kenosha, WI 53143
414-697-2500

Kewaunee County Job Center
613 Dodge Street
Kewaunee, WI 54216
414-388-4410

La Crosse Training Center
304 North Sixth Street
La Crosse, WI 54601-3330
608-785-9440

La Crosse Job Service
402 North Eighth Street
La Crosse, WI 54601
608-785-9341
Fax: 608-785-9327

Lac du Flambeau Job Service
418 Little Pine Road
Lac du Flambeau, WI 54538
715-588-7371

Lafayette County Job Center
324 Main Street
Darlington, WI 53530
608-776-4577
Fax: 608-776-2375

Langlade County Employment and Training Center
312 Forrest Avenue
Antigo, WI 54409
715-623-4257

Lincoln County Job Center
607 North Sales Street
Merrill, WI 54452
715-536-8499

Manitowoc Job Center
Two North Eighth Street
Manitowoc, WI 54220
414-683-4675
Fax: 414-683-4358

Marinette Job Service
903 1/2 Pierce Avenue
PO Box 457
Marinette, WI 54143
715-732-7840
Fax: 715-732-7844

Marquette Job Center
15 West Street
PO Box 99
Montello, WI 53949
608-297-7550

Marshfield Job Service
300 South Peach Avenue, #3
Marshfield, WI 54449
715-387-6386
Fax: 715-387-6388

Mauston Job Center
WWTC Career Center
211 Hickory Street
Mauston, WI 53948-1377
608-847-4899

Menasha Job Center
1313 Midway Road
Menasha, WI 54952

414-832-5300
Fax: 414-832-5297

Milwaukee District Job Service
6087 North Teutonia Street
Milwaukee, WI 53209
414-227-4309
Fax: 414-227-4298

Milwaukee Job Center North
2800 West Capitol Drive
Milwaukee, WI 53216
414-873-6400
Fax: 414-449-5740

Milwaukee Job Center South
611 West National Avenue
Milwaukee, WI 53204
414-384-4000
Fax: 414-384-5558

Milwaukee South Job Service
6817 West Morgan Avenue
Milwaukee, WI 53220
414-546-6800
Fax: 414-546-6803

Milwaukee South Jobs
3023 West Greenfield
Milwaukee, WI 53215
414-382-7555
Fax: 414-382-7581

Oconto County Employment Resource Opportunity Center
Newcap Inc.
1201 Main Street
Oconto, WI 54153
414-834-4621

Oshkosh Job Center
315 Algoma Road, #108
Oshkosh, WI 54901
414-424-2000
Fax: 414-424-2058

Ozaukee County Job Center
7269 Highway 60
Cedarburg, WI 53012
414-376-4120

Fax: 414-376-4135
http://www.wfdc.org

Pepin County Job Center
317 West Main Street
Durand, WI 54736
715-672-8801

Pierce County Job Center
388 West Main Street
Ellsworth, WI 54011
715-273-6788
Fax: 715-273-6787

Polk County Job Center
404 Main Street
Balsam Lake, WI 54810
715-485-3115

Portage Job Center
311 East Wisconsin
Portage, WI 53901
608-742-4598

Racine Employment Administration
1717 Taylor Avenue
Racine, WI 53403
414-638-7200
Fax: 414-638-7210

Rhinelander Job Service
130 South Stevens
Rhinelander, WI 54501
715-365-2686
Fax: 715-365-2646

Richland County Job Center
373 West Sixth Street
Richland Center, WI 53581
608-647-2992
Fax: 608-647-3276

Rusk County Jobs
311 East Miner Avenue
Ladysmith, WI 54848
715-532-2125

Shawano County Job Center
707 East Elizabeth Street
Shawano, WI 54166

715-524-2511
Fax: 715-524-4508

Sheboygan Job Service
934 Michigan Avenue
Sheboygan, WI 53081
414-459-3840
Fax: 414-459-3845

Southwest Technical College Job Center
1800 Bronson Boulevard
Fennimore, WI 53809
608-822-3262
Fax: 608-822-6019

Sparta Jobs Center
Community Service Building B
Route Two
Sparta, WI 54656-9602
608-269-8903
Fax: 608-269-8908

St. Croix County Job Center
516 Second Street
Hudson, WI 54016
715-381-5100

St. Croix County Job Center
New Richmond Enterprise Center
240 Wisconsin Avenue, #110
New Richmond, WI 54017
715-246-7770

Stevens Point Job Service
1001 Maple Bluff Road, #1
Stevens Point, WI 54481
715-345-5330
Fax: 715-345-5221

Sturgeon Bay Job Service
229 North 14th Avenue
Sturgeon Bay, WI 54235
414-743-8859

Superior Job Service
1616 Tower Avenue
Superior, WI 54880
715-392-7800
Fax: 715-392-7891

Taylor County Jobs
153 South Second Street, Suite B
Medford, WI 54451
715-748-3143

Tomah Job Center
WWTC Career Center
1310 TownLine Road
Tomah, WI 54660-1360
608-374-7745
Fax: 608-374-7741

Viroqua Job Service
WWTC Career Center
220 Main Street
Viroqua, WI 54665-1650
608-637-2996

Washburn County Jobs
Ed Elliott Building
PO Box 147
Shell Lake, WI 54871
715-468-7155
Fax: 715-468-7145

Washington County Job Center
333 East Washington Street, Suite 2200
West Bend, WI 53095
414-335-5300
Fax: 414-335-5321
http://www.wfdc.org

Watertown Job Service
115 South Fourth Street
Watertown, WI 53094
414-262-6960
Fax: 414-262-6976

**Waukesha County Workforce Development
   Center**
892 Main Street
Pewaukee, WI 53072
414-695-7800
Fax: 414-695-7777
http://www.wfdc.org

Waupaca Area Job Center
120 West Badger Street
Waupaca, WI 54981
715-258-9338
Fax: 715-258-6997

Wausau Jobs
210 River Drive
Wausau, WI 54403
715-843-0131

Wausau Job Service
364 Grand Avenue
Wausau, WI 54403
715-843-0100
Fax: 715-845-3183

Waushara Job Center
118 North Saint Marie
PO Box 530
Wautoma, WI 54982
414-787-3338
Fax: 414-787-4310

West Bend CareerNet
120 North Main Street
West Bend, WI 53095
414-338-3860
Fax: 414-338-1771
http://www.careernet.org

Wisconsin Dells Job Service
620 Elm Street
Wisconsin Dells, WI 53964
608-254-6353

Wisconsin Department of Workforce Development
700 West State Street
Milwaukee, WI 53233-1419
414-297-7100
http://www.dwd.state.wi.us

Wisconsin Rapids Job Center
2821 Eighth Street, South
Wisconsin Rapids, WI 54494
715-422-5000
Fax: 715-422-5026

WYOMING

Casper Employment Resources
851 Werner Court, Suite 120
Casper, WY 82601-1308
800-730-9725

Cheyenne Employment Resources
6101 North Yellowstone Road, #186C
Cheyenne, WY 82003-7002
307-777-3700
Fax: 307-777-5870

Cody Employment Resources
1026 Blackburn Avenue, Suite One
Cody, WY 82414-8464
800-730-3654
Fax: 307-587-8247

Evanston Employment Resources
98 Independence Drive
PO Box 3210
Evanston, WY 82931-3210
800-730-3741
Fax: 307-789-5625

Gillette Employment Resources
310 Miller Avenue
PO Box 1448
Gillette, WY 82717-1448
800-927-6574
Fax: 307-686-2975

Jackson Employment Resources/Job Service
155 West Gill Avenue
PO Box 1003
Jackson, WY 83001-1003
800-927-5496
Fax: 307-739-8570

Laramie Employment Resources
112 South Fifth Street
PO Box 948
Laramie, WY 82070-0948
307-742-2153
Fax: 307-742-4464

Rawlins Employment Resources
1703 Edinburgh
PO Box 70
Rawlins, WY 82301-0070
307-324-3485
Fax: 307-324-8863

Riverton Employment Resources/Job Service
422 East Freemont
PO Box 1610

Riverton, WY 82501-1610
800-730-3651
Fax: 307-856-3468

Rock Springs Employment Resources/Job Service

79 Winston Drive, Suite 229
Rock Springs, WY 82901-5770
307-382-2747
Fax: 307-362-3177

Sheridan Employment Resources

2266 North Main
Sheridan, WY 82801-9225
307-672-9775
Fax: 307-674-9874

Torrington Employment Resources

2017 East A Street
PO Box Z
Torrington, WY 82240
307-532-4171
Fax: 307-532-7649

GUAM

Government of Guam

304 East Sunset Boulevard
PO Box CQ
Tiyan (NAS), GU 96910
671-475-0750
Fax: 671-477-5022

PUERTO RICO

Council for Occupational Development and Human Resources

431 Ponce de Leon, 17th Floor
Hato Rey, PR 00918
809-754-5633
Fax: 809-763-0195

VIRGIN ISLANDS

Department of Labor

2131 Hospital Street
Christiansted
St. Croix, VI 00820
809-773-1994
Fax: 809-773-0094

OCCUPATIONAL INFORMATION COORDINATING COMMITTEES (OICCs)

The National Occupational Information Coordinating Committee (NOICC) is a federal interagency committee that promotes the development and use of occupational and labor market information. Its goals are (1) to improve coordination and communication among developers and users of occupational information, (2) to help states meet the occupational information needs of vocational education and employment and training program managers, and (3) to help individuals make career decisions. The committee works with a network of State Occupational Information Coordinating Committees (SOICC), whose members represent state producers and users of occupational information. Many coordinating committee members also include representatives from higher education.

The basic NOICC/SOICC systems include the following:

- Occupational Information Systems (OIS): These state computerized databases contain mechanisms for combining multiple-source occupation and education data so that it can be understood and analyzed by a variety of audiences.
- Career Information Delivery Systems (CIDS): These computer-based systems provide information about occupations and training opportunities. The systems help individuals match personal characteristics with compatible occupations. CIDS are located at almost 19,000 sites nationwide.

NOICC also sponsors the following programs, which focus on career guidance and counseling:

- The National Career Development Guidelines: These guidelines, a competency-based approach to career development, help school staff provide quality career guidance and counseling programs to students.
- NOICC's Improved Career Decision Making (ICDM): Counselors can increase their knowledge and use of labor market information in career counseling using this training program.
- The Career Development Portfolio: This sequential career planning is good for use with students

in grades 5 through 12 to link work-based skills to academic preparation. The guide, developed by NOICC, the American School Counselor Association, and the Maine SOICC, is being tested in five states.

NATIONAL OFFICE

Occupational Information Coordinating Committee, National Office
2100 M Street, NW, Suite 156
Washington, DC 20037
202-653-5665
Fax: 202-653-2123
noicc@digex.net

STATE OFFICES

Occupational Information Coordinating Committee, Alabama
Center for Commerce, Room 424
401 Adams Avenue
PO Box 5690
Montgomery, AL 36103-5690
205-242-2990
Fax: 205-353-1816
soiccal@huntingdon.edu

Occupational Information Coordinating Committee, Alaska
Alaska Department of Labor
Research and Analysis
PO Box 25501
Juneau, AK 99802
907-465-4518
Fax: 907-465-2101
brynn_keith@labor.state.ak.us

Occupational Information Coordinating Committee, Arizona
1789 West Jefferson, First Floor, North
PO Box 6123, Site Code 897J
Phoenix, AZ 85005-6123

602-542-3871
Fax: 602-542-6474

Occupational Information Coordinating Committee, Arkansas
Employment and Training Services
PO Box 2981
Little Rock, AR 72203
501-682-3159
Fax: 501-682-3713
ccozart@flash.net

Occupational Information Coordinating Committee, California
1116 Ninth Street, Lower Level Seven
PO Box 944222
Sacramento, CA 94244-2220
916-323-6544
Fax: 916-322-0842
corcoran@cwo.com

Occupational Information Coordinating Committee, Colorado
State Board Community College
1391 Speer Boulevard, Suite 600
Denver, CO 80204-2554
303-866-4488
cosoicc@indra.com

Occupational Information Coordinating Committee, Connecticut
Connecticut Department of Education
25 Industrial Park Road
Middletown, CT 06457
203-638-4042
Fax: 203-638-4062

Occupational Information Coordinating Committee, Delaware
University Office Plaza
PO Box 9029
Newark, DE 19714-9029
302-368-6963
Fax: 302-368-6748
jmcfadden@state.de.us

Occupational Information Coordinating Committee, District of Columbia
500 C Street NW, Suite 215
Washington, DC 20001

202-724-7237
Fax: 202-724-7236

Occupational Information Coordinating Committee, Florida
Hartman Building, Suite 200
2012 Capitol Circle, SE
Tallahassee, FL 32399-06673
904-488-1048
Fax: 904-488-2558
rebecca_rust@jb.fdles.state.fl.us

Occupational Information Coordinating Committee, Georgia
148 International Boulevard, Sussex Place
Atlanta, GA 30303
404-656-9639
Fax: 404-651-9568

Occupational Information Coordinating Committee, Hawaii
830 Punchbowl Street, Room 315
Honolulu, HI 96813
808-586-8750
Fax: 808-586-9099
hsoicc@pixi.com

Occupational Information Coordinating Committee, Idaho
Len B. Jordan Building, Room 301
650 West State Street
PO Box 83720
Boise, ID 83720-0095
208-334-3705
Fax: 208-334-2365
cmolleru@cis.state.id.us

Occupational Information Coordinating Committee, Illinois
217 East Monroe, Suite 203
Springfield, IL 62706
217-785-0789
Fax: 217-785-6184
jstaggs@pop.state.il.us

Occupational Information Coordinating Committee, Indiana
10 North Senate Avenue, Second Floor
Indianapolis, IN 46204-2277
317-232-8528

Fax: 317-233-4824
admin@ima.isd.state.in.us

Occupational Information Coordinating Committee, Iowa

200 East Grand Avenue
Des Moines, IA 50319
515-242-4889
Fax: 515-281-7528
pshenk@netins.net

Occupational Information Coordinating Committee, Kansas

401 Topeka Avenue
Topeka, KS 66603
913-296-2387
Fax: 913-296-2119

Occupational Information Coordinating Committee, Kentucky

2031 Capital Plaza Tower
Frankfort, KY 40601
502-564-4258
Fax: 502-564-3044

Occupational Information Coordinating Committee, Louisiana

PO Box 94094
Baton Rouge, LA 70804
504-342-5149
Fax: 504-342-5115

Occupational Information Coordinating Committee, Maine

State House Station 71
Augusta, ME 04333
207-624-6200
Fax: 207-624-6206
denis.fortier@state.me.us

Occupational Information Coordinating Committee, Maryland

1100 North Eutaw Street, Room 205
Baltimore, MD 21201
410-333-7780
Fax: 410-333-7438
jd0023@mail.pratt.lib.md.us
http://www.careernet.state.md.us/moicc.htm

Occupational Information Coordinating Committee, Massachusetts

C. F. Hurley Building, Second Floor
Government Center
Boston, MA 02114
617-626-5718
Fax: 617-626-5742

Occupational Information Coordinating Committee, Michigan

Victor Office Center, Third Floor
201 North Washington Square, Box 30015
Lansing, MI 48909
517-373-0363
Fax: 517-373-0363

Occupational Information Coordinating Committee, Minnesota

390 North Robert Street
St. Paul, MN 55101
612-296-2072
Fax: 612-296-5429
carole.fuller@state.mn.us

Occupational Information Coordinating Committee, Mississippi

301 West Pearl Street
Jackson, MS 39203-3089
601-949-2240
Fax: 601-949-2291

Occupational Information Coordinating Committee, Missouri

400 Dix Road
Jefferson City, MO 65109
314-751-3800
Fax: 314-751-2149
kraithel@services.dese.state.mo.us

Occupational Information Coordinating Committee, Montana

1301 Lockey Street, Second Floor
PO Box 1728
Helena, MT 59624-1728
406-444-2741
Fax: 406-444-2638

Occupational Information Coordinating Committee, Nebraska

State House Station
PO Box 94600

Lincoln, NE 68509-4600
402-471-9953

Occupational Information Coordinating Committee, Nevada

1923 North Carson Street, Suite 211
Carson City, NV 89710
702-687-4577
Fax: 702-687-4119
oiccnv@aol.com

Occupational Information Coordinating Committee, New Hampshire

64B Old Suncook Road
Concord, NH 03301-7317
603-228-3349
Fax: 603-228-3209
soiccnh@aol.com

Occupational Information Coordinating Committee, New Jersey

609 Labor & Industry Building, CN 056
Trenton, NJ 08625-0056
609-292-2682
Fax: 609-292-6692

Occupational Information Coordinating Committee, New Mexico

401 Broadway, NE, Tiwa Building
PO Box 1928
Albuquerque, NM 87103
505-841-8455
Fax: 505-841-8421
http://www.state.nm.us/soicc.htm

Occupational Information Coordinating Committee, New York

State Campus, Building 12, Room 488
Albany, NY 12240
518-457-6182
Fax: 518-457-0620
david.trzaskos@dol.mailnet.state.ny.us

Occupational Information Coordinating Committee, North Carolina

700 Wade Avenue
PO Box 25903
Raleigh, NC 27611
919-733-6700
Fax: 919-733-8662

maccormac.nancy@esc.state.nc.us
http://www.ncesc.com/

Occupational Information Coordinating Committee, North Dakota

1720 Burnt Boat Drive
PO Box 5507
Bismarck, ND 58506-5507
701-328-9733
Fax: 701-328-9731
marrs@prairie.nodak.edu

Occupational Information Coordinating Committee, Ohio

145 South Front Street
Columbus, OH 43215
614-466-1109
Fax: 614-752-9621
lmi@odnvms.ohio.gov

Occupational Information Coordinating Committee, Oklahoma

1500 West Seventh Avenue
Stillwater, OK 74074
405-743-5198
Fax: 405-743-6808
curtis_shumaker@okvotech.org

Occupational Information Coordinating Committee, Oregon

875 Union Street, NE
Salem, OR 97311
503-378-5747
Fax: 503-373-7515

Occupational Information Coordinating Committee, Pennsylvania

Department of Labor and Industry
300 Capitol Associates Building
Harrisburg, PA 17120-0034
717-772-1330
Fax: 717-772-2168

Occupational Information Coordinating Committee, Rhode Island

22 Hayes Street, Room 133
Providence, RI 02908
401-272-0830
Fax: 401-351-9081
http://www.det.state.ri.us/rioicchm.html

Occupational Information Coordinating Committee, South Dakota
420 South Roosevelt Street
PO Box 4730
Aberdeen, SD 57402-4730
605-626-2314
Fax: 605-626-2322
philg@dol-abr.state.sd.us

Occupational Information Coordinating Committee, Tennessee
Volunteer Plaza, 11th Floor
500 James Robertson Parkway
Nashville, TN 37245-1600
615-741-6451
Fax: 615-532-9434
soicctn.bird@juno.com

Occupational Information Coordinating Committee, Texas
Travis Building, Suite 205
3520 Executive Center Drive
Austin, TX 78731
512-502-3750
Fax: 512-502-3763
richard.froeschle@access.texas.gov

Occupational Information Coordinating Committee, Utah
140 East 300 South
PO Box 45249
Salt Lake City, UT 84147
801-536-7806
Fax: 801-536-7420
tstewar@email.state.ut.us

Occupational Information Coordinating Committee, Vermont
Five Green Mountain Drive
PO Box 488
Montpelier, VT 05601-0488
802-229-0311
Fax: 802-828-4022
http://www.det.state.vt.us

Occupational Information Coordinating Committee, Virginia
703 East Main Street
PO Box 1358
Richmond, VA 23211
804-786-7496
Fax: 804-786-7844

Occupational Information Coordinating Committee, Washington
PO Box 9046
Olympia, WA 98507-9046
360-438-4803
Fax: 360-438-3215
mparis@wln.com

Occupational Information Coordinating Committee, West Virginia
PO Box 487
Institute, WV 25112-0487
304-759-0724
Fax: 304-759-0726
gmcguire@cbplanet.net

Occupational Information Coordinating Committee, Wisconsin
201 East Washington Avenue
PO Box 7944
Madison, WI 53707-7944
608-267-9613
Fax: 608-267-0330
phillam@mail.state.wi.us

Occupational Information Coordinating Committee, Wyoming
100 West Midwest
PO Box 2760
Casper, WY 82602
307-265-5715
Fax: 307-473-3806
gallaghe@cerberus.state.wy.us

Occupational Information Coordinating Committee, American Samoa
American Samoa Government
Pago Pago, AS 96799
684-633-4485
Fax: 684-633-1139

Occupational Information Coordinating Committee, Guam
Human Resource Development Agency
PO Box 2817
Agana, GU 96910

671-649-9341
Fax: 671-649-9344

**Occupational Information Coordinating Committee,
    Northern Mariana Islands**
Northern Mariana College
Building N, Room N-1
PO Box 149
Saipan, CM 96950
670-234-7394
Fax: 670-231-0915
bruceb@nmcnet.edu

**Occupational Information Coordinating Committee,
    Puerto Rico**
PO Box 366212
San Juan, PR 00936-6212
787-723-7110
Fax: 787-724-6374

**Occupational Information Coordinating Committee,
    Virgin Islands**
PO Box 303359
St. Thomas, VI 00803-3359
809-776-3700
Fax: 809-774-5908
soiccvi@teacher.uvi.edu

STATE APPRENTICESHIP COUNCILS

ARIZONA
Arizona Department of Commerce
1700 West Washington, Suite 220
Phoenix, AZ 85007
602-771-1181
Fax: 602-771-1205
paulab@azcommerce.com

CALIFORNIA
Department of Industrial Relations
455 Golden Gate Avenue, 8th Floor
San Francisco, CA 94102
415-703-4916
Fax: 415-703-5477
lacosta@hq.dir.ca.gov

CONNECTICUT
Apprenticeship Program Manager
Connecticut Labor Department
Apprenticeship & Training Division
200 Folly Brook Boulevard
Wethersfield, CT 06109-1114
860-263-6085
Fax: 860-263-6323
jack.guerrera@po.state.ct.us

DELAWARE
Apprenticeship and Training Section
Division of Employment and Training
Delaware Department of Labor
4425 North Market Street
PO Box 9828
Wilmington, DE 19809
302-761-8118
Fax: 302-761-6657
kevin.calio@state.de.us

DISTRICT OF COLUMBIA
D.C. Apprenticeship Council
609 H Street, NE
4th Floor, Room 401
Washington, DC 20002
202-698-5099

Fax: 202-698-5721
lewis.brown@dc.gov

FLORIDA
Director of Apprenticeship
Florida Department of Education
325 West Gaines Street, #754
Tallahassee, FL 32399-0400
850-245-0454
Fax: 850-245-9010
steve.campora@fldoe.org

HAWAII
Workforce Development Division
Department of Labor and Industrial Relations
830 Punchbowl Street, Room 329
Honolulu, HI 96813
808-586-8837
Fax: 808-586-8876
eyoung@dlir.state.hi.us

KANSAS
**Kansas Department of Commerce, Apprenticeship
Program**
1000 Southwest Jackson Street, Suite 100
Topeka, KS 66612-1354
785-296-4161
Fax: 785-291-3512
lashelle@kanasacommerce.com

KENTUCKY
Commissioner, Kentucky Department of Labor
1047 U.S. 127 South, Suite 4
Frankfort, KY 40601
502-564-2784
Fax: 502-564-2248
jim.zimmerman@ky.gov

LOUISIANA
Director, Louisiana Department of Labor
Apprenticeship Division
PO Box 94094

Baton Rouge, LA 70804-9094
225-342-7820
Fax: 225-342-2717
prodriguez@ldol.state.la.us

MAINE
Director of Apprenticeship Standards
Department of Labor
Bureau of Employment & Training Programs
55 State House Station
Augusta, ME 04333-0055
207-624-6390
Fax: 207-624-6499
gene.a.ellis@maine.gov

MARYLAND
Maryland Apprenticeship & Training Program
Division of Workforce Development
1100 North Eutaw Street, Room 606
Baltimore, MD 21201
410-767-2968
Fax: 410-767-2220
smiddleton@dllr.state.md.us

MASSACHUSETTS
Division of Apprentice Training
Department of Workforce Development
PO Box 146759
19 Staniford Street
Boston, MA 02114
617-626-5407
Fax: 617-626-5427
jrich@detma.org

MINNESOTA
Minnesota Department of Labor and Industry
Apprenticeship Unit
443 Lafayette Road
St. Paul, MN 55155-4303
651-284-5194
Fax: 651-284-5740
jerry.briggs@state.mn.us

MONTANA
Apprenticeship and Training Program
Montana Department of Labor & Industries
PO Box 1728

Helena, MT 59624-1728
406-444-3556
Fax: 406-444-3037
mmaki@state.mt.us

NEVADA
Apprenticeship Training Representative
State Apprenticeship Council
c/o Office of the Nevada Labor Commissioner
555 E. Washington Avenue, Suite 4100
Las Vegas, NV 89101
702-486-2738
Fax: 702-486-2660
lbrown@laborcommissioner.com

Labor Commissioner
675 Fairview Drive, Room 226
Carson City, NV 89701
775-687-4850
mail@LaborCommissioner.com

NEW HAMPSHIRE
Apprenticeship Consultant NH Department of Education
21 South Fruit Street, Suite 20
Concord, NH 03301
603-271-3893
Fax: 603-271-4079
mmorgan@ed.state.nh.us

NEW MEXICO
State Director of Apprenticeship
Labor and Industrial Division
New Mexico Department of Labor
501 Mountain Road, NE
Albuquerque, NM 87102
505-841-8990
Fax: 505-841-8739
cbrewington@state.nm.us

NEW YORK
Apprenticeship Training Unit
New York State Department of Labor
State Campus Building #12, Room 436
Albany, NY 12240
518-457-6820

Fax: 518-457-7154
christine.timber@labor.state.ny.us

NORTH CAROLINA
Apprenticeship and Training Bureau
North Carolina Department of Labor
4 West Edenton Street
Raleigh, NC 27601
614-644-2242
Fax: 614-728-8366
bsaunders@mail.dol.state.nc.us

OHIO
Ohio State Apprenticeship Council
Ohio Department of Jobs & Family Services
145 South Front Street
Columbus, OH 43215
614-644-2242
Fax: 614-728-8366
SICKLJ@odjfs.state.oh.us

OREGON
Apprenticeship and Training Division
Oregon State Bureau of Labor and Industries
800 Northeast Oregon Street, Room 32
Portland, OR 97232
503-731-4891
Fax: 503-731-4623
steve.simms@state.or.us

PENNSYLVANIA
Bureau of Labor Law Compliance
PA Department of Labor and Industry
1301 Labor and Industry Building
7th and Forster Street
Harrisburg, PA 17120
800-932-0665
Fax: 717-787-0517
robeobrien@state.pa.us

RHODE ISLAND
Supervisor of Apprenticeship Training Programs
RI Department of Labor and Training
Division of Professional Regulation

1511 Pontiac Avenue, Building 70
Post Office Box 20247
Cranston, RI 02920-0943
401-462-8580
Fax: 401-462-8528
bekno@dlt.state.ri.us

VERMONT
Department of Employment & Training
Apprenticeship Division
5 Green Mountain Drive
PO Box 488
Montpelier, VT 05601-0488
802-828-5082
Fax: 802-828-4374
pnagy@det.state.vt.us

VIRGINIA
Apprenticeship Program
Virginia Department of Labor and Industry
13 South Thirteenth Street
Richmond, VA 23219
804-786-2382
Fax: 804-786-8418
bev.donati@doli.virginia.gov

WASHINGTON
Apprenticeship Program Manager
Department of Labor and Industries
PO Box 44530
Olympia, WA 98504-4530
360-902-5320
Fax: 360-902-4248
maso235@lni.wa.gov

WISCONSIN
State of Wisconsin Department of Workforce Development
Bureau of Apprenticeship Standards
PO Box 7972
Madison, WI 53707
608-266-3133
Fax: 608-266-0766
Karen.morgan@dwd.state.wi.us

PUERTO RICO

**Employment, Training and Services
to Participants Area**

Right to Employment Administration
PO Box 364452
San Juan, PR 00936-4452
787-765-7383
Fax: 787-764-4856 or 787-751-4858
mmunoz@adt.gobierno.pr

VIRGIN ISLANDS

Virgin Islands Department of Labor

2162 King Cross Street
Christiansted, St. Croix, VI 00820-4660
340-773-1440 ext.244
Fax: 340-773-1515
htgeorge@vidol.gov

STATE APPRENTICESHIP WEB SITES

Please be advised that some states do not have an apprenticeship web site. In those cases, links are provided to the state's Department of Labor Web site to aid you in contacting the state for more information about apprenticeship programs.

ALABAMA
Alabama Department of Industrial Relations
http://dir.alabama.gov

ALASKA
Alaska Job Center Network
Apprenticeship Opportunities in Alaska
http://www.ajcn.state.ak.us/apprentice

ARIZONA
Arizona Department of Commerce
Arizona Apprenticeship System
http://www.commerce.state.az.us/workforce/cover.asp

ARKANSAS
Arkansas Department of Workforce Education
http://dwe.arkansas.gov

CALIFORNIA
Department of Industrial Relations
http://www.dir.ca.gov/apprenticeship.html

COLORADO
Colorado Department of Labor and Employment
http://www.coworkforce.com/lmi/lmidir/eta.htm

CONNECTICUT
Connecticut Apprenticeship System
http://www.ctdol.state.ct.us/progsupt/appren/appren.htm

DELAWARE
Apprenticeship & Technical Training
http://www.k12.de.us/adulted/ate.html

DISTRICT OF COLUMBIA
Department of Employment Services
Apprenticeship Program
http://does.dc.gov/does/cwp/view,a,1232,q,537407.asp

FLORIDA
Florida Department of Education
http://www.firn.edu/doe/apprenticeship/index.html

GEORGIA
Georgia Department of Labor
http://www.dol.state.ga.us

HAWAII
Hawaii Department of Labor & Industrial Relations
http://hawaii.gov/labor

IDAHO
Idaho Works
http://www.idahoworks.org

ILLINOIS
Illinois Department of Employment Security
http://www.ides.state.il.us

INDIANA
Indiana Department of Workforce Development
Skilled Trades Apprenticeship
http://www.in.gov/dwd/employer/advanceindiana/
    program/sta_info.html

IOWA
Iowa Workforce Development Apprenticeship
Opportunities
http://www.iowaworkforce.org/region9/apprenticeship.htm

KANSAS
Kansas Department of Labor
http://www.dol.ks.gov

KENTUCKY
Kentucky Department of Labor
http://www.labor.ky.gov/esat/appren.htm

LOUISIANA
Louisiana Department of Labor
Louisiana Works
Apprenticeship Program Search
http://www.ldol.state.la.us/job_websponsorsearch.
   asp?Portal=JOB

MAINE
Maine.gov
Maine Apprenticeship Program
http://www.mainecareercenter.com/business/MAPlink.
   htm

MARYLAND
Maryland Division of Workforce Development
Apprenticeship and Training
http://www.dllr.state.md.us/labor/appr.html

MASSACHUSETTS
Commonwealth of Massachusetts Department of
Labor and Workforce Development
Division of Apprenticeship Training
http://www.mass.gov/dat

MICHIGAN
Michigan Department of Labor & Economic Growth
School-to-Registered Apprenticeship Program
and Tax Credit
http://www.michigan.gov/mdcd/0,1607,7-122-1680_
   2788_2792---,00.html

MINNESOTA
Minnesota Department of Labor & Industry
Apprenticeship
http://www.doli.state.mn.us/appr.html

MISSISSIPPI
Mississippi Department of Employment Security
http://mdes.ms.gov/wps/portal/index.html

MISSOURI
Missouri Department of Labor & Industrial Relations
Division of Labor Standards
http://www.dolir.state.mo.us/ls/prevailingwage/
   employees.htm

MONTANA
Montana Department of Labor & Industry
Workforce Services Division
Apprenticeship and Training Program
http://jsd.dli.state.mt.us/service/apprentice.asp

NEBRASKA
United States Department of Labor Bureau of
Apprenticeship and Training
Nebraska Office
http://www.workforce.state.ne.us/bat/default.htm

NEVADA
Nevada Department of Employment, Training &
Rehabilitation
http://detr.state.nv.us

NEW HAMPSHIRE
New Hampshire Department of Labor
Apprenticeships
http://www.labor.state.nh.us/apprenticeships.asp

NEW JERSEY
State of New Jersey Employment Information
Apprenticeship Training in New Jersey
http://wnjpin.state.nj.us/stc/apprentice1.html

NEW MEXICO
New Mexico Workforce Connection
New Mexico Department of Labor
Apprenticeship Program
http://www.dol.state.nm.us/WIA_PartnerA3.html

NEW YORK
New York State Department of Labor
http://www.labor.state.ny.us

NORTH CAROLINA
North Carolina Department of Labor
  Apprenticeship & Training Bureau
http://www.dol.state.nc.us/appren/appindex.htm

NORTH DAKOTA
Job Service North Dakota
http://www.jobsnd.com/seekers/train_wia_ojt.html

OHIO
Ohio State Apprenticeship Council
http://jfs.ohio.gov/apprenticeship

OKLAHOMA
Oklahoma Employment Security Commission
http://www.oesc.state.ok.us

OREGON
Bureau of Labor and Industries
  Apprenticeship and Training Division
http://www.boli.state.or.us/BOLI/ATD/index.shtml

PENNSYLVANIA
Pennsylvania Apprentice Coordinators Association
http://www.apprentice.org

RHODE ISLAND
Rhode Island Department of Labor and Training
  Division of Professional Regulation
http://www.det.state.ri.us/webdev/appren/appren.htm

SOUTH CAROLINA
South Carolina Employment Security Commission
http://www.sces.org

SOUTH DAKOTA
South Dakota Department of Labor
http://www.state.sd.us/dol

TENNESSEE
Tennessee Department of Labor & Workforce
  Development
http://www.state.tn.us/labor-wfd

TEXAS
Texas Workforce
  Apprenticeship in Texas
http://www.twc.state.tx.us/svcs/apprentice.html

VERMONT
Vermont Department of Employment & Training
  Apprenticeship Training Division
http://www.det.state.vt.us/jt/apprentice.cfm

VIRGINIA
Virginia Department of Labor & Industry
  Registered Apprenticeship
http://www.dli.state.va.us/whatwedo/apprenticeship/
  apprenticeship_p1.html

UTAH
Utah Department of Workforce Services
  Job Seekers
http://jobs.utah.gov/jobseeker/dwsdefault.asp

WASHINGTON
Washington State Department of Labor & Industries
  Apprenticeship
http://www.lni.wa.gov/TradesLicensing/Apprenticeship

WEST VIRGINIA
West Virginia Bureau of Employment Programs
http://www.wvbep.org/bep

WISCONSIN
Wisconsin Department of Workforce Development
  Apprenticeship Standards
http://www.dwd.state.wi.us/dws/appr

WYOMING
Wyoming Department of Workforce Services
http://www.wyomingworkforce.org

VIRGIN ISLANDS
Department of Labor
http://www.usvi.org/labor/index.html

PART IV
FURTHER RESOURCES

GLOSSARY OF U.S. APPRENTICESHIP TERMS

ABC Associated Builders and Contractors.

AFL-CIO American Federation of Labor and Congress of Industrial Organizations. The largest federation of labor unions in the United States, comprising national and international unions in various occupations and industries.

AGC Associated General Contractors of America.

apprentice An individual who is employed to learn an apprenticeable occupation and is registered with a sponsor in an approved apprenticeship program or in an independent program.

apprenticeable occupation A skilled trade(s) or craft(s), which has been recognized by the United States Department of Labor, Office of Apprenticeship, Training, Employer, and Labor Services or a state apprenticeship training office.

apprenticeship agreement A written agreement between an apprentice and either the apprentice's employer(s), or an apprenticeship committee acting as agent for employer(s), containing the terms and conditions of the employment and training of the apprentice.

Apprenticeship and Training Division (ATD) The division of the Bureau of Labor and Industries that provides technical assistance to apprenticeship committees, works with industry to develop new programs, registers new apprentices, and ensures compliance with state and federal regulations and policies. ATD also issues nationally recognized journey worker certificates to individuals who successfully complete an apprenticeship program.

apprenticeship committee A quasi-public entity approved by the WSATC to perform apprenticeship and training services for employers and employees.

apprenticeship committees Made up of employer and employee representatives of the industry, the committees operate individual apprenticeship programs. They decide how apprentices are selected, what apprentices learn in the program, how apprentices progress through the program, apprentice wage rates, and the supervision ratios. Committees select appren-

tices, approve advancements, discipline apprentices, and approve apprentices' completion of the program based on program standards and committee policies. In doing this, committees must follow state and federal regulations and policies for operating a program. Other names for Apprenticeship committees are Joint Apprenticeship and Training Committees (JATC), Trades Apprenticeship and Training Committees (TATC), and Joint or Trade Apprenticeship Committees (JAC) or (TAC), and sometimes apprenticeship committees.

apprenticeship program A plan for administering an apprenticeship agreement(s). The plan must contain all terms and conditions for the qualification, recruitment, selection, employment, and training of apprentices, including such matters as the requirement for a written apprenticeship agreement.

Apprenticeship Training, Employer and Labor Services (ATELS) Federal apprenticeship agency that oversees federal apprenticeship program registration and standard changes and approvals.

AWCI Association of the Wall and Ceiling Industries International.

BAC International Union of Bricklayers and Allied Craftworkers.

BAT Bureau of Apprenticeship and Training; the division of the U.S. Department of Labor that regulates apprenticeship on the federal level.

certificate of completion A certificate awarded upon completion of an apprenticeship program.

CFR The Code of Federal Regulations.

DINAP Division of Indian and Native American Programs, administered by the U.S. Department of Labor's Employment and Training Administration.

DOT code The nine-digit code number for an occupation found in the Dictionary of Occupational Titles. Together, the nine digits provide a unique identification code for a particular occupation, which differentiates it from all others.

ETA Employment and Training Administration.

GATB General Aptitude Test Battery. A written test covering mathematics, sciences, word usage, or other subjects that may be important for the apprentice to know. This is only one of several tests an applicant may encounter. Other tests are more specific to a particular trade and may test such skills as mechanical comprehension and visualization as well as math skills.

GED General Equivalency Diploma. A diploma equivalent to the high school diploma, earned by passing a standardized test.

HVAC Heating, ventilation, and air conditioning.

IABSOI International Association of Bridge, Structural, and Ornamental Ironworkers.

IATSE International Alliance of Theatrical Stage Employees, Moving Picture Technicians, Artists and Allied Crafts of the United States and Canada, AFL-CIO, CLC.

IBEW International Brotherhood of Electrical Workers.

IBPAT International Brotherhood of Painters and Allied Trades.

IUEC International Union of Elevator Constructors.

IUOE International Union of Operating Engineers.

JAC Joint Apprenticeship Committee (Council). The administrative body of the apprenticeship program, which sets the rules and requirements, determines the need for new apprentices, and interviews applicants. In programs cosponsored by a labor union or unions and a company or association of companies, the JAC usually consists of representatives from labor and management.

JAP Joint Apprenticeship Program. (See JAC.)

JAT Joint Apprenticeship Training. (See JAC.)

JATC Joint Apprenticeship Training Council (or Committee). (See JAC.)

JATTF Joint Apprenticeship Training Trust Fund. (See JAC.)

Journeyman A skilled craftsman or craftswoman who has completed a number of years of training in a particular craft or trade.

JTPA Job Training Partnership Act.

jurisdiction The geographical area covered by a particular local union or JAC.

letter of intent An employer's guarantee (normally in the form of a letter) to the apprenticeship sponsor that he or she (1) intends to hire the apprentice and (2) has sufficient work lined up for the apprentice to carry him of her through the term of the apprenticeship.

LIUNA Laborers' International Union of North America.

nonjoin Indicates a program where there is no labor organization or collective bargaining agreement. It is sponsored by employer association(s) and administered by an apprenticeship committee composed equally from employer and employee representatives.

Office of Apprenticeship Training, Employer and Labor Services (OATELS) Federal apprenticeship agency that oversees federal apprenticeship program registration and standard changes and approvals.

oral interview As part of the application process, one person or a small group of people will ask the apprenticeship applicant questions regarding his or her physical health, interest in the trade, and attitude toward the type of work that would be performed. Personal traits, such as aggressiveness and sincerity, are also noted. The oral interview helps the sponsor determine whether applicants would commit themselves to the work and whether they would be persistent enough to finish the program.

preapprenticeship training Training offered at some vocational and technical schools and high schools to help potential apprentices acquire the basic skills necessary to qualify for an apprenticeship program.

prevailing wage The hourly wage, usual benefits and overtime, paid in the largest city in each county to the majority of workers, laborers, and mechanics. Prevailing wages are established by the Department of Labor and Industries for each trade and occupation employed in the performance of public work. They are established separately for each county and are reflective of local wage conditions.

probationary period Period of time at the beginning of an apprenticeship, during which either the apprentice or the program sponsor can choose to terminate the apprenticeship.

residency requirement Some apprenticeship programs require that participants live within a certain area (the program's jurisdiction) for a period of time (usually a year or less) before applying to the program, and, once accepted, while participating in it.

SAC State Apprenticeship Council. A state organization similar to the BAT.

SMACNA Sheet Metal and Air Conditioning Contractors' National Association.

SMWIA Sheet Metal Workers International Association.

trade Any apprenticeable occupation defined by the apprenticeship, training, employer, and labor services section of the United States Department of Labor and these rules.

training agent Employer of registered apprentices approved by the program sponsor to furnish on-the-job training to satisfy the approved apprenticeship program standards who agrees to employ registered apprentices in that work process. The training agent shall use only registered apprentices to perform the work processes of the approved program standards.

training agreement A written agreement between a training agent and a program sponsor that contains the provisions of the apprenticeship program applicable to the training agent and the duties of the training agent in providing on-the-job training.

UA United Association of Journeymen and Apprentices of the Plumbing and Pipefitting Industry of the United States and Canada.

UAW United Auto Workers.

UBC United Brotherhood of Carpenters and Joiners of America.

USDOL U.S. Department of Labor.

Veteran's DD-214 The basic military discharge form issued to those who have successfully completed their military service.

GLOSSARY OF CANADIAN APPRENTICESHIP TERMS

apprentice on-the-job training standards/record book (log book) A booklet issued to registered apprentices in which acquired skills, knowledge, and time worked at a trade or occupation are recorded. The booklet becomes the apprentice's achievement record. The name given to the booklet may differ between provinces and territories. For example, it is sometimes referred to as a Log Book or as a Progress Record book.

apprenticeship accreditation A process by which an agency or association grants public recognition to a training establishment, program of study, or service which meets certain pre-determined standards.

apprenticeship program outline A list of topics and performance objectives to be learned during each period of an apprenticeship program's in-school or off-the-job technical training.

apprenticeship registration A formal process requiring an individual to meet all the requirements for apprenticeship, including having signed an apprenticeship contract, agreement, or memorandum of understanding with an employer and the provincial/territorial agency responsible for apprenticeship. The term "registered" is now being regularly substituted for indentured. For specific information respecting the requirements for registering an apprentice, please contact the provincial/territorial offices listed on the Red Seal Web site at the following address: http://www.red-seal.ca.

apprenticeship technical training A period of training/instruction provided to apprentices in a classroom setting away from the job site. It usually takes place in a vocational school, community college, technical institute, or private training institute but could be delivered in-house by an employer. The emphasis is on teaching the theory component of the trade or occupation, reinforced where appropriate, with shop/lab training. This training is intended to supplement the on-the-job training.

apprenticeship term The normal length of time required for a person to attain journeyperson status from the time of registration as an apprentice and is usually a combination of both formal training and work experience. The length of time is generally expressed in years and hours per year or in hours.

Canadian Council of Directors of Apprenticeship (CCDA) A national body comprised of the provincial and territorial government officials responsible for managing and directing apprenticeship programs within the provinces and territories and two federal government representatives. The mission of the council is to facilitate the mobility of apprentices and journeypersons in Canada through the establishment of uniform standards of training and examinations as confirmed by a Red Seal endorsement.

curriculum resources Resource materials developed to set the standards for and facilitate the training of apprentices and journeypersons. Resource materials include, but are not limited to, skill profile charts, occupational analyses, apprenticeship program outlines, journeyperson upgrading and updating course outlines, trade/occupation manuals and modularized learning resource materials. Refer also to the definitions herein for each of these examples of curriculum resources.

day release training Technical training for apprentices whereby their employers release them from work for one day at a time, usually one day of each week.

delivery of technical training The process of providing formal apprenticeship course instruction in the theory and practical subjects set out in a provincial/territorial apprenticeship program outline. Courses may be delivered using block release or individualized methods.

Designated Red Seal Trade A trade or occupation that has been designated by the Canadian Council of Directors of Apprenticeship (CCDA) for inclusion in the Interprovincial Standards "Red Seal" Program. The training and certification is based on a national occupational standard, and provinces and territories participating in the program for that trade or occupation are permitted to affix a Red Seal to the certificates of candidates who meet the standard. Refer also to the definition herein for Interprovincial (IP) Examination.

education/entrance requirements The level of formal education or other criteria such as an examination or assessment process that is established within a province or territory that an individual must possess/pass prior to becoming an apprentice or attending technical training. While these requirements may vary from trade to trade and province to province, CCDA advises that most employers require prospective apprentices to have a grade 12 education.

fixed entry/open exit training A system of training based on specific performance criteria where progress in learning is measured in terms of demonstrated skills and knowledge and where an apprentice or other learner is allowed to progress through and exit a course of instruction at a rate determined by his or her own capabilities. This training system is also referred to as the Modified Block Release training system. Learning is usually supported by the use of modularized learning resource materials and the services of a facilitator/instructor. Refer also to the definition herein for "Modularized Learning Resource Materials".

flexible/distance education Formal training delivery methods that enable registered apprentices and other learners to complete a course of study utilizing current communications technologies and may include some traditional classroom-based instruction. Some examples of current communications technologies being utilized to reduce the periods of formal classroom instruction include the Internet, interactive computer-based training, and video teleconferencing.

hour release training Technical training for apprentices whereby they are released from work by their employers to attend technical training for a number of hours per day, usually one day a week.

Human Resources and Skills Development Canada (HRSDC) This is the Federal Department that has responsibility for providing the secretariat services for the Interprovincial Standards "Red Seal" Program, including the translation, printing, and distribution of interprovincial examinations. The department is also responsible for the development and distribution of National Occupational Analyses.

Industry Trade Advisory Committee Individuals appointed to represent the interests of employers and labor on a committee officially designated by a provincial or territorial agency to offer advice and make recommendations regarding apprenticeship and journeyperson training and certification standards. Committees are normally comprised of an equal number of employee and employer representatives knowledgeable in the trade or occupation and are seen as the primary vehicle for ensuring industry has a voice in the development and delivery of apprenticeship training.

Interprovincial (IP) Examination An examination used to determine whether completing apprentices and experienced journeypersons meet the national standard in a designated "Red Seal" trade or occupation. Examinations are based on the national occupational analysis for that trade or occupation. Refer also to the definition herein for Designated Red Seal Trade.

journeyperson certification—compulsory A prevailing provincial/territorial legislation requirement in which persons entering or working in a designated trade or occupation must possess a Certificate of Qualification or be registered as apprentices, in order to work or practice in that trade or occupation. Those working in the trade or occupation prior to the compulsory requirement may be eligible for exemption from this requirement by the provincial/territorial authorities. In some jurisdictions, the Certification Program is referred to as the "Trades Qualification (TQ) Program".

journeyperson certification only A provision of prevailing provincial/territorial legislation that provides for the certification of persons at the journeyperson level only but makes no provision for the registration and training of persons as apprentices. This provision is often incorporated to reduce barriers to the mobility of qualified workers.

journeyperson certification—voluntary A provision of prevailing provincial/territorial legislation that provides a voluntary opportunity for eligible journeypersons working in a specific designated trade or occupation to become certified. In some jurisdictions, the certification program is referred to as the "Trades Qualification (TQ) Program".

modularized learning resource materials Educational packages which include learning objectives, learning activities, and self-assessment procedures designed to guide the learning of apprentices and journeypersons for a specific unit of training. Packages may be developed for use in individualized and/or instructor/facilitator driven settings and for apprentice training and/or journeyperson upgrading/updating.

National Occupational Classification (NOC) code An alpha-numeric indicator identifying a trade or occupation in the National Occupational Classification publication. This code replaces the previously used Canadian Classification and Dictionary of Occupations (CCDO) Code.

occupational analysis—national (NOA) A document that lists the blocks, tasks, and sub-tasks performed by workers in a designated trade or occupation in jurisdictions across Canada. The NOA for Red Seal designated trades are prepared by industry experts under the guidance of the federal government and the assistance of the provincial/territorial jurisdictions in which the trade or occupation is designated. It is used as the base document in the development of an interprovincial "Red Seal" examination or examination item bank.

occupational analysis—province/territory A document that lists the blocks, tasks, sub-tasks, activities, and functions that are performed by journeypersons in a designated trade or occupation within a specific province/territory.

period Is an interval of work experience and formal training, usually established in hours and set by regulation that forms a portion of the term of an apprenticeship (usually of one year duration).

pre-employment training A training course that provides intensive instruction designed to prepare an individual for entry into employment in a specific trade or occupation and which may articulate with an apprenticeship program. The course may include educational upgrading and/or the first period of formal training for a specific apprenticeship program.

pre-employment training—compulsory A compulsory pre-employment training course that must be completed prior to participating in an apprenticeship program for a specific designated trade or occupation.

pre-employment training—voluntary A pre-employment training course that can be taken on a voluntary basis and is not a pre-requisite to entering into an apprenticeship program in a specific designated trade or occupation.

prior learning assessment and recognition (PLAR) A process under which recognition is extended towards completion of an apprenticeship for skills, knowledge, or competencies that have been acquired experientially through work experience, previous education and training, or self studies. The prior learning should articulate with the formal technical training or on-the-job training requirements for the trade or occupation in which the apprenticeship is to be served.

province/territory in-school level practical examination Performance tests developed by a Province/Territory to determine whether an apprentice has successfully mastered the practical skills required to complete the apprenticeship period or level of technical training.

province/territory journeyperson (TQ) examination An examination developed to determine whether an eligible journeyperson meets the prevailing industry standards for provincial/territorial certification in a designated trade or occupation. The examination may include a written and/or practical component.

Province/Territory Journeyperson Course Outline— UPDATING A curriculum outline which identifies the training content required to bring a journeyperson's skill or set of skills up to date with new methods, technology and procedures required in the trade or occupation in which the person is currently employed or certified.

Province/Territory Journeyperson Course Outline— UPGRADING A refresher program curriculum outline, which reviews the training content necessary to meet current journeyperson certification requirements.

province/territory level written examination A written examination developed by a Province/Territory to determine whether an apprentice has successfully completed a period or level of formal apprenticeship technical training. The written examination may also be used as a means of determining if credit for prior training and/or work experience should be granted to a registered apprentice.

province/territory skill profile chart A comprehensive portrayal of the major trade areas and associated tasks for a trade or occupation that an individual must successfully perform to meet job requirements. The profile may be presented in a graphical format, e.g. DACUM chart or a narrative format.

ratio - journeyperson/apprentice The number of qualified/certified journeypersons that an employer must employ in a designated trade or occupation in order to be eligible to register an apprentice as determined by prevailing provincial/territorial legislation, regulation, policy directive, or bylaw issued by the authority or agency responsible. Ratio may be fixed for all employers or variable and can be adjusted by the authority responsible to take into account an employer's ability to train. Generally in the absence of an established ratio, a ratio of one apprentice to one journeyperson is used.

training delivery method—block release Refers to a training delivery method by which apprentices are released from work by their employers to attend prescribed full-time in-school technical training for a specified period (usually three to 10 weeks) usually once each year.

training delivery method—individualized A single learner focused (as opposed to a group of learners) method of providing apprenticeship technical training instruction utilizing current communications technologies and/or a facilitator/instructor in a classroom, shop, or lab. Jurisdictions that are moving to an individualized course base method of instruction will show only the total hours of training as opposed to a number of periods and total weeks of instruction. Modularized learning resource materials are often used to support this type of training delivery. Refer also to the definition herein for "Modularized Learning Resource Materials".

train-the-trainer program A program designed to provide training and coaching skills to journeypersons responsible for the workplace training and supervision of apprentices.

CAREER RESOURCES ON THE INTERNET

The following sites contain information primarily for jobs in the United States, although some of the sites are broader in scope. At the end of the chapter, there is a short list of career sites that pertain solely to Canada.

Alabama Job Bank
http://www.ajb.org/al

Alaska Job Bank
http://www.jobs.state.ak.us

American Jobs
http://www.americanjobs.com

America's Employers
http://www.americasemployers.com

America's Job Bank
http://www.jobsearch.org

Ansir For One
http://www.ansir.com/ansirforone

Arizona Job Bank
http://www.jobsearch.org/AZ

Arkansas Democrat Gazette
http://www.ardemgaz.com

Arkansas Job Bank
http://www.state.ar.us

Best Jobs in the USA Today
http://www.bestjobsusa.com

California Job Bank
http://www.caljobs.ca.gov

Career Builder
http://www.careerbuilder.com

Career City
http://www.careercity.com

Career Connection
http://www.connectme.com

Career Magazine
http://www.careermag.com

Career Net
http://www.careers.org

Colorado Job Bank
http://www.ajb.org/co/

Connecticut Job Bank
http://www.ctdol.state.ct.us

Delaware Department of Labor
http://www.delawareworks.com

District of Columbia Job Bank
http://www.ajb.org/dc/

Educational Resources Information Center (ERIC)
http://www.eric.ed.gov/

Employment Guide
http://www.employmentguide.com

Federal Job Databases
http://www.fedworld.gov/jobs/jobsearch.html

First Steps in the Hunt for a New Job
http://www.interbiznet.com/hunt

Florida Job Bank
http://www.floridajobs.org

Georgia Job Bank
http://www.dol.state.ga.us

Get A Job
http://www.getajob.com

Guam Job Bank
http://www.ajb.org/gu

Guide to Resumes and Interviews
http://www.jobweb.com/Resumes_Interviews

HEART
http://www.career.com

Help Wanted
http://www.helpwanted.com

Idaho Job Bank
http://cl.idaho.gov/idjsmain.htm

Illinois Job Bank
http://www.ajb.org/il/

Indiana College Placement and Assessment Center
http://icpac.indiana.edu/future.html

Indiana Job Bank
http://www.in.gov/jobs/stateemployment/jobbank.html

Iowa Job Bank
http://www.iowajobs.org/

Job Hunt
http://www.job-hunt.org

Job Listings Within the Hotel Industry
http://www.hoteljobs.com

JobSmart, Resumes & Cover Letters Index
http://www.jobsmart.org/tools/resume/index.cfm

Jobweb
http://www.jobweb.org

Journal/Sentinal Employment Ads
http://www.adquest.com

Kansas Job Bank
http://www.ajb.org/ks

Kentucky Job Bank
http://www.jobsearch.org/KY

Louisiana Job Bank
http://www.ldol.state.la.us

Louisiana Technical Education Training Locator
http://www.techtrainingdirectory.com/location/
   locationid/25.htm

Maine Job Bank
http://www.maine.gov/portal/working/jobs.html

Maryland Job Bank
http://www.ajb.org/md

Massachusetts Job Bank
http://www.ajb.org/ma

Michigan Job Bank
http://www.michworks.org/mtb/pages/seeker/
   Jobseeker.jsp

Minnesota Job Bank
http://www.mnworks.org

Minnesota Workforce Center
http://www.mnwfc.org

Mississippi Job Bank
http://www.ajb.org/ms/

Missouri Works
http://www.greathires.org/

Monster Board
http://www.monster.com

Montana Job Bank
http://www.ajb.org/mt/

Montana Workforce Services
http://wsd.dli.mt.gov

NationJob Kansas Jobs
http://www.nationjob.com/wichita

Nebraska Job Bank
http://www.ajb.org/ne

Nevada Job Bank
http://www.ajb.org/nv/

New Hampshire Job Bank
http://www.nhworks.org

New Jersey Job Bank
http://www.ajb.org/nj

New Mexico Job Bank
http://www.ajb.org/nm

New York Job Bank
http://www.labor.state.ny.us

North Carolina Employment Security
http://www.ncesc.com

North Dakota Job Service
http://www.jobsnd.com

Occupational Outlook Handbook
http://www.bls.gov/oco

Ohio Job List
http://www.state.oh.us/emprec.html

Ohio Job Services
http://jfs.ohio.gov

Oklahoma Job Bank
http://www.oesc.state.ok.us/default.htm

Opportunity Knocks
http://www.opportunitynocs.org

Oregon Employment Services
http://www.employment.oregon.gov/EMPLOY/ES/JOB/
    index.shtml

Pennsylvania Job Center
http://www.pennsylvaniajobs.com

Quintessential Careers
http://www.quintcareers.com

Rhode Island Job Bank
http://www.det.state.ri.us

The Riley Guide
http://www.rileyguide.com/

South Carolina Job Bank
http://www.jobsearch.org/SC

South Dakota Job Bank
http://www.ajb.org/sd/

Tennessee Job Bank
http://www.state.tn.us/labor-wfd/jobsearch.htm

Texas Job Bank
http://www.twc.state.tx.us/twc.html

TOPjobs USA
http://www.topjobsusa.com

Top Ten Technical Resume Writing Tips
http://www.taos.com/resumetips.html

Utah Job Bank
http://dwsa.state.ut.us

Vermont Job Bank
http://www.ajb.org/vt/

Virginia Job Bank
http://www.jobsearch.org/VA

Washington Job Bank
http://access.wa.gov/employment/getajob.aspx /

WE CAN of Eastern Arkansas
http://www.onestop.org

West Georgia JobNet
http://www.westga.edu/~coop

West Virginia Job Bank
http://www.ajb.org/wv

Wisconsin Job Net
http://www.dwd.state.wi.us/jobnet

Wyoming Job Bank
http://www.ajb.org/wy/

CANADIAN CAREER RESOURCES ON THE INTERNET

Alberta Apprenticeship and Industry Training
http://www.learning.gov.ab.ca

Apprenticeship and Interprovincial Standards
http://www.red-seal.ca

Canada Apprenticeship Forum
http://www.caf-fca.org

CareerKey.com
http://www.careerkey.com

Manitoba—Apprenticeship
http://www.edu.gov.mb.ca/aet/apprent/

**New Brunswick—Apprenticeship and Occupational
    Certification**
http://www.aoc-acp.gnb.ca/

**Northwest Territories—Apprenticeship and
    Occupational Certification**
http://siksik.learnnet.nt.ca

Nova Scotia—Apprenticeship Training
http://apprenticeship.ednet.ns.ca

Ontario—Apprenticeship
http://www.edu.gov.on.ca

Prince Edward Island—Apprenticeship Section
http://www.gov.pe.ca

**Quebec's Vocational and Technical Training
    Network**
http://www.inforoutefpt.org

Yukon-Department of Education
http://www.education.gov.yk.ca

DICTIONARY OF OCCUPATIONAL TITLES (DOT) LIST

This list of job titles and occupational classification numbers is provided so users can explore the occupational description further. The classified numbers refer to those used in the *Dictionary of Occupational Titles* (Government Printing Office, U.S. Department of Labor). The *Dictionary of Occupational Titles* lists occupations by their DOT number and is a standard reference tool found in the collections of most public libraries.

637.261-014	air conditioning and refrigeration mechanic
621.281-014	aircraft maintenance technician
869.684-082	asbestos worker
865.684-010	auto glass installer
620.261-010	automotive mechanic
845.381-014	automotive painter
313.381-010	baker
142.081-010	bank note designer
330.371-010	barber
312.474-010	bartender
610.381.014	blacksmith
805.261-014	boilermaker
977.381-010	bookbinder
041.061-014	breeder
861.381-014	bricklayer
899.381-010	building maintenance repairer
660.280-010	cabinet maker
829.361-010	cable splicer
520.685-050	candymaker
860.381-022	carpenter
864.381-010	carpet layer
844.364-014	cement finisher
844.364-010	cement mason
008.261-010	chemical technician
313.361-014	child care worker
819.384-010	combination welder
971.382-018	composer
973.381-010	compositor
869.664-014	construction laborer
313.361-014	cook
764.684-022	cooper
372.137-010	corrections officer
332.271-010	cosmetologist
921.663.010	crane operator
142.051-014	decorator
601.280-010	die maker
625.281-010	diesel mechanic
299.474-010	dispensing optician
007.261-010	drafter
842.664-010	drywall finisher
842.381-010	drywaller
729.281-026	electrical instrument repairer
824.261-010	electrician
828.261-022	electronics mechanic
003.161-014	electronics technician
825.361-010	elevator constructor
338.371-014	embalmer
079.374-010	emergency medical technician
029.261-014	environmental service technician
638.261-014	erection machinist (millwright)
899.261-014	facilities custodial service technician (maintenance mechanic)
418.381-010	farrier
373.364-010	firefighter
805.361-014	fitter
864.481-014	floor covering installer
040.061-034	forester
504.382-018	forger (heat treater)
011.061-010	foundry worker
620.281-038	front end/back end mechanic
187.167-030	funeral director
343.467-018	gaming dealer
953.364-010	gasfitter
865.381-010	glazier
141.161-018	graphic designer
632.281-010	gunsmith
860.381-022	hardwood floor layer
620.261-022	heavy equipment mechanic

859.683-010	heavy equipment operator	841.381-010	paperhanger
419.224-010	horse trainer	600.280-050	pattern maker
637.261-014	hvac mechanic	661.281-022	pattern setter
952.362-018	hydroelectric power plant operator	730.361-010	piano tuner
710.281-026	instrument mechanic	859.682-018	piledriver
003.261-010	instrumentation technician	863.381-014	pipecoverer
863.364-010	insulation worker	862.381-018	pipefitter
801.361-018	ironworker	842.361-018	plasterer
693.281-030	jig and fixture builder	862.381-030	plumber
601.281-026	jig and fixture tool maker	375.263-018	police officer
860.381-050	joiner	952.382-018	power plant operator
869.664-014	laborer	313.361-014	preschool worker
761.381-018	last model maker	972.381-026	press operator/platemaker
842.361-010	lather	611.482-010	pressman
783.684-026	leatherworker	979.382-018	printer
165.017-010	legislative lobbyist	221.167-018	production controller
962.362-014	lighting and sound technician	822.361-018	protective signal installer
821.361-018	line installer	188.167-010	real estate appraiser
821.261-014	lineworker	862.281-026	refrigeration mechanic
661.281-010	loftsperson	921.664-014	rigger
638.281-014	machine repairer	806.261-014	rigger (marine)
600.280-022	machinist	866.381-010	roofer
209.587-026	mailroom worker	503.687-010	sandblaster
829.261-018	maintenance electrician	604.280-014	screw machine operator and setter
828.261-022	maintenance engineer	189.167-034	security officer
600.280-042	maintenance machinist	804.281-010	sheetmetal worker
638.281-014	maintenance mechanic	806.381-050	shipfitter
861.381-030	marble mason	860.381-062	shipwright
861.381-030	marble setter	365.361-014	shoe repairer
826.381-034	marine electrician	861.381-034	soft floor layer
316.684-108	meatcutter	829.281-022	sound and communication
805.361-010	mechanic		technician
007.161-026	mechanical engineering technician	829.281-022	sound technician
078.381-014	medical laboratoy technician	862.281-022	sprinkler fitter
203.582-058	medical transcriptionist	962.261-014	stage technician
011.261-010	metallurgical technician	950.382-026	stationary engineer
638.281-018	millwright	862.381-018	steamfitter
518.664-010	mold maker	862.684-022	steamfitter helper
518.361-010	molder	771.381-010	stone cutter
960.362-010	motion picture machine operator	861.381-038	stone mason
102.017-010	museum curator and administrator	861.381-042	stone setter
011.261-018	nondestructive tester	842.664-010	taper
355.674-014	nursing assistant	219.362-070	tax return preparer
713.261-014	ocularist	861.381-046	terrazzo worker
869.683-010	operating engineer	861.664-018	tile finisher
712.381-034	orthotics technician	861.381-054	tile setter
623.281-030	outside machinist	804.281-010	tinsmith
144.061-010	painter	601.280-046	tool and die maker
840.381-014	painter (marine)	007.061-026	tool designer

601.280-042	tool maker	955.362-010	waste water treatment plant operator
601.281-022	tooling inspector		
905.663-014	truck driver	869.664-014	waterproofer
869.664-014	tuckpointer	805.381-010	welder
639.281-014	vending machine mechanic		

GUIDE FOR OCCUPATIONAL EXPLORATION (GOE) LIST

The *Guide for Occupational Exploration* was developed n the 1970s by the U.S. Department of Labor to help people explore occupations that matched their interests. The U.S. Employment Services developed an interest inventory (USES inventory) that yields results in terms of GOE interest areas. The GOE classification system organizes occupations into 14 interest areas and more than 300 subgroups. GOE codes are six digits long. The GOE is only available in book form: *Guide for Occupational Exploration* (Indianapolis, Ind.: JIST Works, 2001).

02.03.04	agricultural workers
03.01.01	agricultural workers
02.07.04	aircraft and avionics mechanics and service technicians, elevator constructors, shipbuilding and ship maintenance industry workers
01.02.01	artists and artisans
05.03.01	auto body workers, laborers, millwrights, railroad workers, truck drivers
01.04.02	book arts workers
06.02.01	bricklayers, masons, tile setters
02.06.01	business workers
09.01.01	business workers
06.02.02	carpenters, construction laborers
02.05.01	chemical technicians, geological technicians, laboratory testing technicians, nuclear reactor operators and technicians
12.03.03	child care workers and educators
11.05.01	cooks, chefs, and kitchen workers
08.03.02	cooks, chefs, and kitchen workers
11.04.01	cosmetologists and barbers
01.05.01	crafts and trades workers at living historical sites and farms
05.03.03	dispensing opticians
05.02.01	electricians and line workers
01.08.01	electronics technicians
04.04.01	emergency services technicians
04.04.02	emergency sevices technicians
02.02.01	engineers and engineering technicians
02.07.02	engineers and engineering technicians, operating and stationary engineers
11.08.01	funeral directors and embalmers
14.01.01	health care workers
02.05.02	health care workers, medical laboratory technicians
02.03.02	herbalists
14.04.01	herbalists, midwives
06.02.03	insulators and asbestos workers, ironworkers, laborers
08.03.03	ironworkers, welders
04.03.01	law enforcement officers, private investigators, and security guards
08.04.01	machinists and tool programmers, metalworkers
08.02.01	machinists and tool programmers; tool, die, mold, and pattern makers
14.05.01	medical laboratory technicians
12.03.04	museum and gallery workers
08.03.05	printing industry workers
07.0.01	railroad conductors
07.06.01	railroad workers
12.03.01	social activists and human services workers
14.07.01	social activists and human services workers
07.05.01	truck drivers

NATIONAL OCCUPATIONAL CLASSIFICATION (NOC) LIST

The National Occupational Classification is a system for describing the occupations in Canada. It gives individual job seekers, statisticians, career counsellors, employers, and labor market analysts a standardized way of describing and understanding the nature of work. The system includes a series of publications that help people to analyze and use various statistics on the labor market in Canada. The index of job titles is a basic index for cataloging and referencing information on all the different jobs held by Canadians.

7441	air conditioner installer, residential
7441	air conditioner installer, window
7332	air conditioner repairer—window unit
7313	air conditioning and heating mechanic
7216	air conditioning and refrigeration contractor
7313	air conditioning and refrigeration mechanic
4131	air conditioning course teacher—community college
7441	air conditioning installer, window
7612	air conditioning mechanic helper
7216	air conditioning mechanics foreman/woman
2244	aircraft avionics technician
7315	aircraft body repairer
2244	aircraft electrical equipment inspector and tester
2244	aircraft electrical mechanic
2244	aircraft electrical system mechanic
2244	aircraft electrical technician
2244	aircraft electrician
2244	aircraft electronic equipment inspector and tester
2244	aircraft electronic equipment installer
2244	aircraft electronic system mechanic
7315	aircraft engine mechanic
7315	aircraft engine mechanical systems technician
2244	aircraft maintenance engineer (AME)—avionics
7216	aircraft maintenance engineer (AME) chief
7315	aircraft maintenance engineer (AME), mechanical systems
7315	aircraft maintenance engineer (AME), rotorcraft
7315	aircraft maintenance engineer (AME), structures
7315	aircraft maintenance engineer (except avionics)
7216	aircraft maintenance engineers (AME) supervisor
7315	aircraft maintenance mechanic apprentice
7315	aircraft maintenance technician
7315	aircraft mechanic
7315	apprentice aircraft mechanic, mechanical systems
7315	apprentice aircraft mechanical systems mechanic
7315	apprentice AME (aircraft maintenance engineer)
7332	apprentice appliance service technician
7231	apprentice automotive machinist
2244	apprentice avionics technician
7322	auto glass installer
7322	auto body mechanic
7322	auto body repairer
7322	auto body technician
7322	auto body technician—collision
7322	auto body technician—refinishing
7322	auto body worker
2244	avionics maintenance technician
2244	avionics mechanic
2244	avionics technician
6252	baker
7262	boiler repairer
7262	boilermaker
7262	boilermaker apprentice
9473	bookbinder—printing
7281	brick and stone mason
9414	brick maker—clay products

9414	brick-moulding machine operator—clay products
7281	bricklayer
7219	building maintenance supervisor
7244	cableman/woman—electric power systems
7215	carpentry contractor
7295	carpet layer
7282	cement finisher
7282	cement mason
6241	chef
2211	chemical technician
4212	child-care worker (except day care)
4214	child-care worker, day care
7282	concrete mason
7611	construction laborer
6242	cook
6242	cook, apprentice
6482	cosmetologist
7371	crane operator
7371	crane operator apprentice
7232	die cutter
3231	dispensing optician
7284	drywall finisher
7284	drywall finisher apprentice
7284	drywall hanger
7332	electrical appliance repairer
7241	electrician
2242	electronic service technician apprentice
2241	electronics technician
7318	elevator constructor
7318	elevator constructor and mechanic apprentice
3234	emergency medical technician (EMT)
7383	farrier
6262	firefighter
7295	floor and wall covering installer, residential
6272	funeral director
7292	glazier
5241	graphic designer
7312	heavy equipment mechanic
7313	HVAC (heating, ventilation, and air conditioning) mechanic
2244	instrument technician, aircraft
2243	instrument technician, industrial
7219	insulating contractor
7293	insulation installer
7293	insulator
7293	insulator apprentice
7264	ironworker
7264	ironworker apprentice

7264	ironworker generalist
7264	ironworker—ornamental
7264	ironworker—reinforcing rebar
7611	joiner helper - construction
7262	journeyman/woman boilermaker
7281	journeyman/woman bricklayer
7281	journeyman/woman brickmason
7272	journeyman/woman cabinetmaker
7271	journeyman/woman carpenter
7282	journeyman/woman cement finisher
7241	journeyman/woman construction electrician
6242	journeyman/woman cook
7284	journeyman/woman drywall installer
7318	journeyman/woman elevator constructor
7318	journeyman/woman elevator mechanic
7295	journeyman/woman floor covering installer
7295	journeyman/woman floor mechanic
7253	journeyman/woman gas fitter
7292	journeyman/woman glazier
7312	journeyman/woman heavy-duty equipment mechanic
7242	journeyman/woman industrial electrician
7311	journeyman/woman industrial mechanic
7293	journeyman/woman insulator
7264	journeyman/woman ironworker
7284	journeyman/woman lather
7245	journeyman/woman lineman/woman - telecommunications
7231	journeyman/woman machinist
7281	journeyman/woman mason
7322	journeyman/woman motor vehicle body repairer
7294	journeyman/woman painter and decorator
7252	journeyman/woman pipefitter
7284	journeyman/woman plasterer
7251	journeyman/woman plumber
7313	journeyman/woman refrigeration and air conditioning mechanic
7264	journeyman/woman reinforcing-iron worker
7291	journeyman/woman roofer
7261	journeyman/woman sheet metal worker
7252	journeyman/woman sprinkler system installer
7252	journeyman/woman steamfitter-pipefitter
7281	journeyman/woman stonemason
7283	journeyman/woman tilesetter
7232	journeyman/woman tool and die maker
7373	journeyman/woman water well driller
7265	journeyman/woman welder
3414	laboratory technician, optical - retail

9617	laborer—food and beverage processing
9613	laborer—gas utility
7452	laborer—material handling
9612	laborer—metal fabrication
9611	laborer—metallurgy
9611	laborer—mineral and metal processing
9619	laborer—packaging
9619	laborer—packaging company
9615	laborer—plastic products manufacturing
9611	laborer—primary metal and mineral products processing
9619	laborer—printing
9614	laborer—pulp and paper
9615	laborer—rubber products manufacturing
7621	laborer—sanitary service
9618	laborer—shellfish processing
9619	laborer—shoe manufacturing
9619	laborer—tannery
9616	laborer—textile processing
7452	laborer—warehousing and storage
9614	laborer—wood processing
9511	lathe machining operator
7284	lather
7284	lather apprentice
7218	letterpress foreman/woman—printing
7381	letterpress operator—printing
7381	letterpress proof press operator—printing
7381	letterpress proof puller—printing
7218	letterpress room foreman/woman
7411	line-haul driver
7245	line installer—telecommunications
7245	lineman-technician/linewoman-technician—telecommunications
7244	lineman/woman—electric power systems
7244	lineman/woman—electric streetcar
7621	line-painting machine operator—highways and roads
7245	line technician, telecommunications
9482	line-up adjuster—motor vehicle manufacturing
7245	lineman-technician/linewoman-technician—telecommunications
7244	lineman/woman—electric power systems
7244	lineman/woman—electric streetcar
7231	machinist
7219	marble and terrazzo contractor-setter
7219	marble setters foreman/woman
7219	marble setting foreman/woman
7283	marble tilesetter
7281	mason, brick and stone
7282	mason, cement
7282	mason, concrete
7283	mason, marble
6241	master chef
7321	mechanic—motor vehicle manufacturing
3212	medical laboratory aide
3212	medical laboratory assistant
3234	medical technician
2212	metallurgical engineering technician
3232	midwife
7311	millwright
7311	millwright apprentice
5112	museum curator
5124	museum educator
0511	museum manager
5133	musician
3232	nurse-midwife
3413	nursery aide - hospital
8254	nursery farmer
8432	nursery worker
3413	nursing assistant (non-registered)
3233	nursing assistant (registered - Québec)
1463	office messenger
1414	office reception clerk
1414	office receptionist
5133	opera singer
7421	operating engineer, heavy equipment
3231	ophthalmic dispenser
3235	ophthalmic technician (except retail)
3414	optical laboratory assistant
3414	optical laboratory technician
3414	optical technician
7294	painter
7294	paperhanger
3234	paramedic
3234	paramedic worker
7421	pile driver winch operator
7371	pile driving crane operator
7611	pile driving ground worker
7252	pipefitter
7284	plasterer
7284	plasterer apprentice
7381	press operator - printing
7218	printers foreman/woman
5136	printmaker—visual arts
6462	prison guard
6462	prison officer
7291	roofer and waterproofer
5136	sculptor
1241	secretary

7214	sheet metal contractor		7283	terrazzo, tile and marble setter
7261	sheet metal installer		7283	terrazzo worker
7261	sheet metal mechanic		7219	tile and marble contractor
7261	sheet metal mechanic apprentice		7283	tile layer
7261	sheet metal worker		7283	tilesetter
7263	shipfitter		7283	tilesetter, apprentice
7263	shipfitter apprentice		7232	tool and die maker
9612	shipfitter helper		7232	tool and die maker apprentice
7214	shipfitters foreman/woman		7411	truck driver
9612	shipwright helper		3216	ultrasonography technician
7263	shipwright, metal		3216	ultrasonography technologist
7271	shipwright, wood		7284	wallboard installer
4164	social services planner		7611	wallboard sander
4212	social welfare officer		7284	wallboard taper
7351	stationary engineer		7611	water pipe installer
7252	steam pipefitter		7265	welder
7252	steamfitter		7265	welder apprentice
7281	stonecutter		5121	writer
7281	stonemason		3215	X-ray (radiology) technician

OCCUPATIONAL INFORMATION NETWORK (O*NET)-STANDARD OCCUPATIONAL CLASSIFICATION (SOC) SYSTEM LIST

The Occupational Information Network (O*NET)-Standard Occupational Classification System (SOC) index is the Bureau of Labor Statistics' career classification system.

13-2021.02	appraisers, real estate
51-2011.01	aircraft structure assemblers, precision
51-2011.00	aircraft structure, surfaces, rigging, and systems assemblers
17-1011.00	architects, except landscape and naval
17-3011.01	architectural drafters
25-4011.00	archivists
43-3021.02	billing, cost, and rate clerks
43-3021.03	billing, posting, and calculating machine operators
43-3031.00	bookkeeping, accounting, and auditing clerks
43-5011.00	cargo and freight agents
49-2022.01	central office and PBX installers and repairers
19-4061.01	city planning aides
17-3022.00	civil engineering technicians
17-2051.00	civil engineers
13-1072.00	compensation, benefits, and job analysis specialists
15-1011.00	computer and information scientists, research
15-1021.00	computer programmers
15-1031.00	computer software engineers, applications
15-1032.00	computer software engineers, systems software
15-1041.00	computer support specialists
15-1051.00	computer systems analysts
47-4011.00	construction and building inspectors
11-9021.00	construction managers
25-4012.00	curators
15-1061.00	database administrators
29-2032.00	diagnostic medical sonographers
29-1031.00	dietitians and nutritionists
27-3041.00	editors
11-9032.00	education administrators, elementary and secondary school
11-9033.00	education administrators, postsecondary
11-9031.00	education administrators, preschool and child care center/program
51-9061.04	electrical and electronic inspectors and testers
49-2095.00	electrical and electronics repairers, powerhouse, substation, and relay
17-2071.00	electrical engineers
47-2111.00	electricians
17-2072.00	electronics engineers, except computer
47-4021.00	elevator installers and repairers
25-1032.00	engineering teachers, postsecondary
13-1041.01	environmental compliance inspectors
19-2041.00	environmental scientists and specialists, including health
43-4071.00	file clerks
27-4032.00	film and video editors
27-1013.00	fine artists, including painters, sculptors, and illustrators

33-2021.01	fire inspectors
33-2021.02	fire investigators
43-1011.02	first-line supervisors, administrative support
45-4011.00	forest and conservation workers
51-4033.01	grinding, honing, lapping, and deburring machine set-up operators
49-9041.00	industrial machinery mechanics
43-4199.99	information and record clerks, all other
25-9031.00	instructional coordinators
43-9041.01	insurance claims clerks
27-3091.00	interpreters and translators
43-4111.00	interviewers, except eligibility and loan
51-6011.03	laundry and drycleaning machine operators and tenders, except pressing
25-4021.00	librarians
43-4121.00	library assistants, clerical
25-1082.00	library science teachers, postsecondary
25-4031.00	library technicians
43-4031.03	license clerks
17-3031.02	mapping technicians
17-2121.02	marine architects
15-2099.99	mathematical science occupations, all other
15-2021.00	mathematicians
49-9011.00	mechanical door repairers
31-9092.00	medical assistants
29-2071.00	medical records and health information technicians
31-9094.00	medical transcriptionists
49-9044.00	millwrights
51-7031.00	model makers, wood
43-4031.02	municipal clerks
33-2011.01	municipal firefighters
33-1021.01	municipal firefighting and prevention supervisors
25-4013.00	museum technicians and conservators
15-1081.00	network systems and data communications analysts
51-4011.01	numerical control machine tool operators and tenders, metal and plastic
43-9061.00	office clerks, general
43-4151.00	order clerks
23-2011.00	paralegals and legal assistants
33-3041.00	parking enforcement workers
51-7032.00	pattern makers, wood
13-1071.02	personnel recruiters
47-2152.02	plumbers
43-5053.00	postal service mail sorters, processors, and processing machine operators
51-9199.99	production workers, all other
11-9141.00	property, real estate, and community association managers
27-4013.00	radio operators
43-4181.02	reservation and transportation ticket agents
49-2098.00	security and fire alarm systems installers
47-2211.00	sheet metal workers
27-1013.02	sketch artists
19-4061.00	social science research assistants
51-8021.00	stationary engineers and boiler operators
43-9111.00	statistical assistants
13-2081.00	tax examiners, collectors, and revenue agents
49-2022.00	telecommunications equipment installers and repairers, except line installers
53-6041.00	traffic technicians
19-3051.00	urban and regional planners
13-1022.00	wholesale and retail buyers, except farm products

JOB TITLE INDEX

Page numbers in **bold** indicate
major treatment of a topic

A

accountant. *See* bookkeeper; hospitality
   accountant
acoustical carpenter 1:157, 1:244–1:245,
   2:158
acoustical ceiling installer 1:247
activist, agricultural 1:60, 1:64, 1:68,
   1:69
actor 1:98–1:99, 1:106, 1:108, 1:109
administrator. *See specific type of
   administrator, e.g.: health facility
   administrator*
advanced emergency medical
   technician 1:312
advanced-defibrillator medic 1:312
advanced-epinephrine medic 1:312
advertising copy writer 1:197
advertising executive 1:147, 1:152, 1:198
aerospace engineer 1:318
aerospace worker 1:449, 1:455–1:456,
   1:458–1:459
agricultural genetics researcher 1:57
agricultural interpreter 1:57
agricultural researcher 1:51–1:52
agricultural worker **1:43–1:80**. *See also*
   herbalist
agroecologist 1:52, 1:55, 1:72, 1:74
agro-forester 1:48
air and hydronic balancing technician
   2:115, 2:200
air conditioning technician 1:475,
   2:125, 2:207
airbrush artist 1:99
aircraft machinist 1:457
aircraft mechanic/service technician
   1:81–1:97
airframe mechanic 1:81
airline motion picture worker 2:231
alarm/communications electrician
   1:260

alternative energy specialist 1:44, 1:47,
   2:222
alternative/green builder 1:47, 1:49,
   1:59, 1:74, 1:80
amusement area employees 2:231
animal caretaker 1:43
animation, video 1:321
animator 1:99, 2:236
anthropologist 1:58
appropriate agricultural technology
   specialist 1:69
aquaculturalist 1:76
aquatic resource specialist 1:69
archaeologist 1:58, 2:63
archaeology interpreter 1:231
architect 1:173
architectural glazier 1:357–1:362, 1:364,
   1:365
architectural metalworker 1:361–1:363,
   2:37–2:38, 2:98, 2:100
architectural woodworker 1:162, 1:184
archives technician 2:59
archivist 2:59
armored car guard 1:434
art conservator 2:63, 2:64
art director 1:99, 1:102, 2:231
art gallery conservator 2:62–2:64
artist/artisan **1:98–1:112**, 2:63
art restorer 2:63
arts administrator 1:108
art specialist, television studio 1:201
asbestos worker **1:401–1:413**
asphalt paver 1:468
assembly technician, printing 2:165
assistant engineer, marine 2:210
assistant engineer, railroad 2:172
athletic trainer 1:365, 1:375–1:378, 1:380
audio installer 1:256
automatic sprinkler system repairer. *See*
   sprinkler system repairer
auto body painter 2:97, 2:100
auto body worker **1:113–1:118**
auto glass installer 1:116, 1:356,
   1:361–1:362

automotive machinist 1:449, 1:453,
   1:455–1:459
automotive mechanic 1:116–1:118,
   1:473–1:480
automotive painter and refinisher
   1:115, 1:116, 1:118, 2:103
auto upholsterer 1:116
avionics technician 1:83–1:84. *See also*
   aircraft mechanic/service technician

B

baby-sitter 1:189
baker 1:203, 1:205–1:209, 1:212–1:217
bank note designer 1:103
barber **1:218–1:221, 1:223–1:225**
bartender 1:203
basic emergency medical technician
   1:304–1:309, 1:311–1:317
basket weaver 1:230, 1:231
beautician 1:218. *See also* cosmetologist
bed and breakfast manager 1:53
beekeeper 1:75
bindery worker 1:130, 2:162, 2:165–
   2:167, 2:169
biographer 1:197
biologist 1:58, 1:69, 1:202
blacksmith 1:104, 1:119–1:120, 1:124,
   1:230–1:233, 2:27, 2:29–2:38
bladesmith 2:27, 2:36
blank book binding worker 1:130
blueprint reader 1:420
boatbuilder 2:212, 2:214
body and fender repairer. *See* auto body
   worker
bodyguard 1:434
body piercer 1:110
boiler maker **1:119–1:129**, 2:281
boiler mechanics 1:119
book arts worker **1:130–1:135**
book binder 1:130, 1:132–1:135, 2:162,
   2:166–2:167, 2:169
book conservator 1:108, 1:130,
   1:133–1:135

489

STATE INDEX

A